AUTOMECHANICS

Second Edition

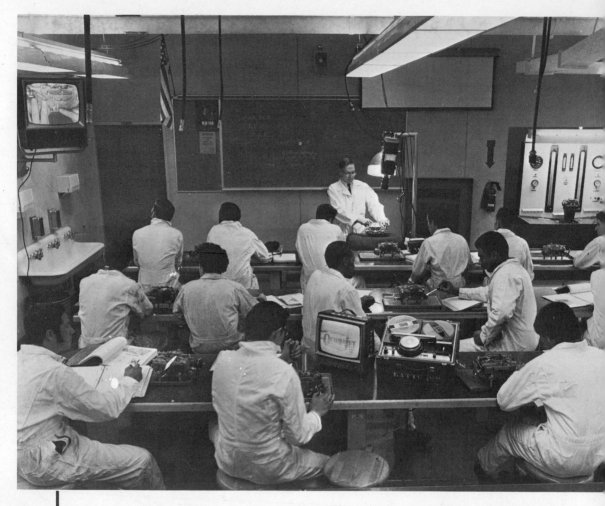

An instructor of a fuel system class in Los Angeles Trade-Technical College uses closed-circuit television to facilitate instruction. The monitor is at the upper left. While the class is studying one type of carburetor, the student in the center rear of the class is using a tape-recorded program of instructions on another type. The student standing (top right) is flow-testing a rebuilt carburetor to see if it measures up to the manufacturer's specifications.

Race driver Dan Gurney checks out a prototype of a 429 cu.in. V-8 racing engine. This engine has aluminum heads with a canted valve arrangement and a crescent-shaped combustion chamber. The street version is rated at 370 Hp.

AUTO ME CHAN ICS

Second Edition

HAROLD T. GLENN
Long Beach, California

Author of automotive manuals, troubleshooting guides, and books on safety and driver education

Chas. A. Bennett Co., Inc.
Peoria, Illinois 61614

ACKNOWLEDGMENTS

The author wishes to acknowledge his indebtedness to the following firms for their cooperation in furnishing information and photographs:

AC Spark Plug Division, General Motors Corporation
Albertson & Company, Sioux Tools
Allen Electric and Equipment Company
American Motors Corporation
Ammco Tools, Inc.
The Atlantic Refining Company
John Bean Division, Food Machinery and Chemical Corporation
Bear Manufacturing Company
Bendix Products Division, Bendix Aviation Corporation
Bennett-Feragen
The Black & Decker Mfg. Co.
Bohn Aluminum & Brass Corporation
Briggs & Stratton Corporation
Buick Motor Division, General Motors Corporation
Cadillac Motor Car Division, General Motors Corporation
Carter Carburetor Division, ACF Industries
Champion Spark Plug Company
Chevrolet Motor Division, General Motors Corporation
Chrysler Division, Chrysler Corporation
Delco-Remy Division, General Motors Corporation
DeSoto Division, Chrysler Corporation
Dodge Division, Chrysler Corporation
The Dole Valve Company
E. I. du Pont de Nemours & Company

The Electric Auto-Lite Company
Federal-Mogul Service Division, Federal-Mogul Corporation
Ford Division, Ford Motor Company
Fram Corporation
The B. F. Goodrich Company
The Goodyear Tire & Rubber Company
Harrison Radiator Division, General Motors Corporation
Hercules Motors Corporation
International Harvester Company
The Jam Handy Organization
Johnson Motors Division, Outboard Marine Corporation
Lambretta Division, Innocenti Corporation
Los Angeles Times, Home Magazine
Lawn Boy Division, Outboard Marine Corporation
Marvel-Schebler Products Division, Borg-Warner Corporation
Mack Trucks, Inc.
Mercury Division, Ford Motor Company
National Safety Council
New Departure Division, General Motors Corporation
Oldsmobile Division, General Motors Corporation
Plomb Tool Company
Plymouth Division, Chrysler Corporation

Pontiac Motor Division, General
    Motors Corporation
Pratt & Whitney Aircraft Division,
    United Aircraft Corporation
Purolator Products, Inc.
    Raybestos Division,
    Raybestos-Manhattan, Inc.
Reo Motors, Inc.
The Rubber Manufacturers Association
    Inc.
The L. S. Starrett Company
Stewart-Warner Corporation

Sun Electric Corporation
Sunnen Products Company
The Texas Company
United States Rubber Company
Van Norman Automotive Equipment
    Company
Warner Gear Division, Borg-Warner
    Corporation
Weaver Manufacturing Company
Weidenhoff Corporation
Wisconsin Motor Corporation

Special thanks are due to my wife Anna for her assistance and proofreading of
the text.

PREFACE

AUTOMECHANICS — and its companion small-engine textbook, EX-PLORING POWER MECHANICS — contain a complete program of instruction and a definite working plan. Each text is comprehensive enough so that the teacher can select the units and/or projects which fit into his situation to best advantage.

The "why's" are explained, for understanding, and are followed by the "how's." Simple, descriptive language is used to assist the student. Service jobs, related to and following each section, provide opportunity for reinforcing knowledge gained from the reading matter. They also provide the teacher with definite project sequence based on learning-difficulty order. Such jobs elevate student interest and provide the practice necessary to develop elementary vocational skills.

Two series of questions follow each chapter. The Check Your Knowledge questions are keyed to the text so that they can be used as a workbook. The Self-Check tests are included for grading purposes.

Applied science is emphasized in theory-of-operation sections. The project length has been adjusted to fit a 45-minute class period.

WORKBOOKS. The correlated workbooks are "interlocked" with the textbooks and contain related mathematics and science assignments. Each series of problems is graded in complexity, and those which are more difficult are headed by the caption, **Technician Level.**

PROGRESS CHARTS. Correlated progress charts are available for each main unit.

Table of Contents

General Safety Practices

Attitudes

The practice of safety in the shop goes beyond the knowledge of the proper use of hand tools and equipment. A most important consideration is your attitude. You must understand the hazards of the

Look before you leap. Courtesy Los Angeles Times, Home Magazine.

SAFETY FIRST
LAST
AND ALWAYS

Carelessness can result in hurt "feelings."

job you are about to undertake and must appreciate the need for applying safety practices that will protect you from injury. Awareness of personal safety comes only through an understanding of the dangers which are present. Most accidents are caused by thoughtlessness, so you must be on guard at all times.

It is most important to give the job your undivided attention. "Visiting" is not permitted because it distracts you and may lead to an accident.

You don't have to be crazy to take chances, but it helps! Courtesy National Safety Council.

the athletic field where it is an approved activity.

Walk—avoid running! A running person cannot always keep from slipping with the possibility of serious injury. Bumping the operator of a machine might cause him to have an accident which would be your fault. Cultivate personal caution at all times. A cautious person is one who knows and observes safe procedures. Learn that caution and foresight pay off. A person who has learned to cultivate personal caution has trained himself to visualize the results of his actions.

Make it a habit to remove any article lying on the floor before someone trips over it. Learn to recognize unsafe conditions. In doing so you are protecting yourself and fellow workers.

• Get into the habit of removing sharp pointed tools from bench edges where you, or someone else going by, may get hurt—this is an application of personal caution.

There's always a safe way for every job. Courtesy National Safety Council.

Horseplay, scuffling, punching, or playing pranks is dangerous. Some boys cannot pass by without striking a classmate, and the immediate response is to strike back. In no time at all both boys are scuffling. This childish action may result in a fall or possible injury from sharp tools, steel benches, and heavy equipment which are always present in a shop. Keep such physical activity for

• Store sharp-edged tools in racks and not in drawers where someone could cut himself when picking up other implements.

• When stacking stock, make sure that it is arranged with the large boxes on the bottom of the pile.

• Round stock should be secured with chocks to prevent the pile from rolling.

• Keep stock out of aisles or passageways because someone may fall over it.

• A protruding nail is an invitation to a first-aid station; either hammer it down or pull it out.

• Remove any splinters from boxes or pieces of wood which could puncture your skin.

• Scraps of sharp metal on the floor could pierce someone's shoe, causing a serious wound. Pick them up and place them in the scrap box.

• Wipe spilled oil or grease off the floor—*even though you did not spill it.* Preventable falls send far too many people to the hospital.

Let's become safety conscious!

Personal Safety

• Report any injury to your instructor immediately. No matter how small the injury—report it! It is far better to waste antiseptic than to ignore one small wound which may later become infected. There must never be a letdown in the battle against infection.

• If something gets into your eye, it is dangerous to rub it. Instead report to your instructor immediately. You may press the particle into the eyeball and scratch its surface. Or, if you use an unsterile cloth, you may cause serious eye infection and possible blindness.

• Be sure to wash your hands after handling caustics, acids, or batteries to

Always expect the unexpected. Courtesy National Safety Council.

avoid getting chemicals on your skin and into your eyes.

• Wash your hands thoroughly before eating and always after using the lavatory. The need for personal cleanliness cannot be overstressed. Many skin conditions can be traced to improper cleanup after work. A good soap, thoroughly applied, removes dirt and grime as well as acids and caustics.

• Asking for help when lifting a heavy object is a sign of mental strength, not weakness. Many serious injuries are caused by lifting improperly, lifting objects too heavy for one man, or lifting unwieldy shapes. More than 25 percent of all disabilities are caused by the improper handling of materials. This is the largest single cause of disability from all accidents. Sprains, strains, and hernias—the results of improper lifting—are painful and disabling.

13

Get help for heavy or awkward loads. Courtesy National Safety Council.

• When lifting a heavy object, place your feet close to the object for proper balance. Keep your elbows as straight as possible and bend the knees while gripping. Use your large leg muscles to lift—not the back muscles. Keep your back straight. When lifting a heavy object with the help of others, be sure that a signal is given by one of the team so that excess strain is not placed on any one member of the group. Teamwork accomplishes much more than individual effort.

• Carry all objects in such a manner that you can see clearly where you are going. Long objects should be carried by two people to protect others. If a long object has to be carried by one person, make sure that the dangerous front end is held low so it can be seen. The rear end will be high enough to pass over people's heads as you make turns.

• Power tools are provided with guards to prevent accidents. They are placed there for your protection. Be sure to call the instructor's attention to any loose or missing guard.

Protective Clothing

Wearing the proper clothing is very important when working in the shop.

Each shop requires a specialized protective garment, depending on the nature of the work. Some shopwork demands additional temporary protection when doing special jobs. This may take the form of goggles and gloves when welding; goggles or face shield for grinding; or a rubber mat when working around live electrical circuits.

In general, coveralls are necessary in the auto shop to protect you from dirt and grime. White coveralls are the ones

You can always use a world of protection. Courtesy National Safety Council.

most commonly used in the trade. Dark ones are sometimes worn because they do not show the dirt; however, dirty coveralls of any color stain car upholstery and are not pleasant to look at. It is good practice to develop a habit of cleanliness by changing your coveralls at least once a week.

Gloves should be worn when handling hot objects, especially when welding. They are also good protection when working with shattered glass in automotive work. **Caution:** *They must not be used when buffing or working around machinery as there is danger of the gloves being caught and pulling your hand into the machine.*

Safety shoes with extra strong toe

When the tool's not right, the guy's not bright. Courtesy National Safety Council.

Tool misuse is tool abuse. Courtesy General Motors Corporation.

supports protect your feet from falling objects. They are also good protection against burns when welding and are especially desirable for the protection afforded the ankles against bruises and scuffs when working under a car.

Safety in the Use of Hand Tools

The hand tool is still very important, despite the development of complex machine tools. Everyone has need for hand tools, but not everyone knows how to use or care for them properly. A recent study of shop accidents showed that 66 percent of all injuries in one year were caused by misuse of the common hand tool. Most hand tool accidents are caused by (1) improper storage, (2) failure to keep the tool in good condition, (3) using the tool improperly, and (4) failure to use the right tool for the job.

15

You can't always make a hit by flying off the handle. Courtesy General Motors Corporation.

Hand tools should be stored in a tool rack which has a place for each tool; they should not be stored in drawers or boxes. Tools should be cleaned frequently and stored in a dry place to prevent rusting. A light coating of oil will keep them bright under adverse conditions. Knowledge gained in this section of the book will assist you in learning how to use each hand tool properly so that undue strain will not be placed on it, causing it to slip— which could result in injury. You will also learn how to select the tool which is designed for the job at hand so that it will not be subjected to unnecessary stress.

Peen Hammers

The *peen hammer* is a very commonly used tool in power mechanics. The flat end of the head is called the *face*, and the other end the *peen*. If the peen is ball shaped, it is known as a *ball-peen hammer*. The hole for the handle is called the *eye*.

There are right and wrong ways to hold a hammer. The beginner usually "chokes" the handle by gripping it too near the head. When you want to strike

a heavy blow, grip the handle near the end. This increases the length of the *lever arm* and makes the blow more effective.

It is dangerous to use a hammer with a loose head, as it may fly off. The eye of the hammer head is tapered both ways from the center. After the handle is inserted, a steel wedge is driven into the end to expand the handle and hold it firmly. If the wedge starts to loosen, drive it in again; if it is missing, replace it.

When you use a hammer on a machined surface, protect the surface with a piece of soft brass or wood. Special soft hammers of plastic and lead faces are frequently used to prevent damaging finely machined surfaces. If the work is hardened steel, there is additional danger from flying particles. A hard steel hammer face, striking a hard steel object, is likely to fracture. The fractured piece may fly off with the speed of a bullet and can create a serious puncture wound.

Using a hammer handle for bumping purposes is likely to split it which can cause splinter wounds.

Hold it! Get a chisel before you wreck that screwdriver. Courtesy General Motors Corporation.

A screwdriver is not meant to be used as a pry. Courtesy General Motors Corporation.

Oh, come now! Let's use the proper-sized tool. Courtesy General Motors Corporation.

Screwdrivers

Every mechanic uses a screwdriver. Most screwdriver handles are made of plastic or wood. The steel portion extending from the handle is called the *shank,* and the flattened end which fits into the slot of the screw is called the *blade.*

A screwdriver is designed to withstand considerable twisting force but not to be used as a pry or chisel. The blade is hardened to keep it from wearing; it may snap if too much bending strain is applied.

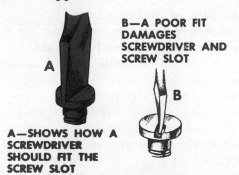

B—A POOR FIT DAMAGES SCREWDRIVER AND SCREW SLOT

A—SHOWS HOW A SCREWDRIVER SHOULD FIT THE SCREW SLOT

A screwdriver tip must fit the slot properly; otherwise, it will slip. Courtesy General Motors Corporation.

Using a screwdriver as a cold chisel will split the handle. However, most screwdrivers made for automotive work have steel shanks all the way through the handles so that you can tap on them if necessary. *To remove a rusted screw,* tap the end of a steel-shank screwdriver while holding it at an angle, in order to clean out the screw slot. After the slot is cleaned, holding the screwdriver vertically and tapping on the handle will seat it in the slot and help to jar rusted threads loose.

Not enough emphasis can be placed on selecting the *correct-sized screwdriver* so that the thickness of the blade fits the screw slot, which keeps the slot from burring and reduces the force required to keep the blade in the slot. A screwdriver which slips is dangerous. Clamp the work in a vise while removing screws; otherwise, the screwdriver

17

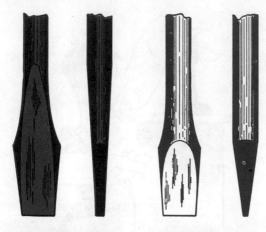

Ground Correctly   *Ground Wrong*

A correctly ground screwdriver blade has its sides parallel. Courtesy Federal-Mogul Service.

most parallel. When dressing the blade, grind it so that the faces taper in very slightly for a short distance back of the tip so that it will stay down in the slot. A blade with too much taper rises out of the slot and may slip off the screw head.

A screwdriver in a leg pocket of your coveralls should be carried *point down*, as bad scratches are possible if it is carried point up. The exposed blade can also mar the finish of a car when you lean over the fender. Sharp-edged tools should be carried in a covered sheath, not in your pocket, as stab wounds may result.

may slip and puncture your palm, which is very painful and makes a wound difficult to treat.

The tip of a *correctly ground screwdriver blade* should have the sides al-

Easy does it! Courtesy General Motors Corporation.

Wrenches

Wrenches are designed to be inserted from the side of a nut (as in the case of an open-end, adjustable, monkey, or pipe wrench), or over the top (socket or box wrench) to hold it firmly for removing or tightening.

If you have to pull hard on a wrench, make sure that it *seats squarely* or it may slip. Pushing on a wrench is dangerous; if the nut breaks loose suddenly you may skin your knuckles. However, if you do have to push on the wrench, use the palm of your hand.

Box wrenches are very popular because of their secure grip. The wrenches are usually made with twelve notches arranged in a circle, and they are, therefore, called twelve-point wrenches. As they cannot spread on a nut, there is little danger of slippage.

Adjustable wrenches are shaped somewhat like open-end wrenches but have one adjustable jaw. The angle of the opening is $22\frac{1}{2}$ degrees. Although adjustable wrenches are especially con-

18

Pushing on a wrench is the wrong approach to this nutty problem. Courtesy General Motors Corporation.

venient at times, they are not intended to take the place of standard open-end, box, or socket wrenches. Their grip is not as secure, and they are more likely to slip. Smaller adjustable wrenches are principally used when loosening an odd-sized nut.

Adjustable wrenches are not intended for hard service; treat them gently. Whenever you do have to exert any real force, there are two important points to remember: (1) Always place

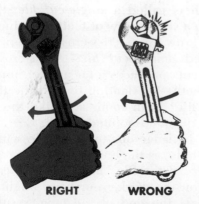

RIGHT   **WRONG**

Always pull so that the strain is against the solid jaw of an adjustable wrench to keep it from slipping. Courtesy General Motors Corporation.

the wrench on the nut so that the pulling force is applied to the strong, stationary side of the handle, as it can withstand the greatest stress. (2) After placing the wrench on the nut, tighten the adjusting knurl so that the jaws fit the nut securely, to prevent slipping.

Hammering on a wrench or extending it with a pipe places an excessive strain on a wrench which it is not designed to take.

Mushroomed chisel—
Flying missile.
Ere you start upon your mission,
Have your tools in good condition.

Chisels

Chisels are used for cutting metal. The one most commonly used is the flat cold chisel to split nuts, cut rivets, cut heads off rusty screws, and remove bushings. The width of the cutting edge denotes its size. The average mechanic's tool kit contains three chisels of $\frac{1}{4}$, $\frac{1}{2}$, and $\frac{3}{4}$ inch sizes.

Always use a chisel that is *big enough for the job*. Use a hammer that is heavy enough. The larger the chisel, the heavier the hammer should be. Ordinarily a chisel should be held in the left hand with the thumb and first finger about an inch from the upper end. Hold the chisel with a steady but rather relaxed grip. If you should miss the chisel and strike your hand, this tends to lessen the effect of the blow. The best practice, of course, is not to miss the chisel! *Keep your gaze on the cutting edge.* Strike one or two light blows to test your swing, and increase the force of the blows as you become more sure.

When chipping, always wear goggles to protect your eyes. If others are working close by, make sure they are protected from flying chips by a screen, or else chip in a direction which is clear of workers. Remember—the time to take precautions is before you start a job, not after someone is injured.

Clamp small pieces of work rigidly in a vise. Chip toward the solid or stationary jaw of the vise and away from yourself.

Each time you sharpen a chisel, inspect the other end to see if it has become upset or mushroomed, as a result of hammering. It is dangerous to use a chisel or punch which has been upset, because fragments may fly off and cause injury. Grind off the extra metal so that the end of the chisel is slightly tapered and comparatively flat across the top.

BEFORE AND AFTER DRESSING

Mushroomed heads should be ground off chisels whenever they are sharpened. Courtesy General Motors Corporation.

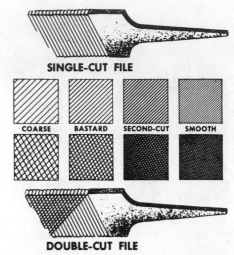

SINGLE-CUT FILE

COARSE   BASTARD   SECOND-CUT   SMOOTH

DOUBLE-CUT FILE

Types of single- and double-cut files. Courtesy General Motors Corporation.

Files

A mechanic's tool kit cannot be considered complete without several files. The portion of the file on which the teeth are cut is called the *face*, and the tapered end which fits into the handle is called the *tang*. The *teeth*, which do the cutting, are set at an angle across the face.

A file with a single row of parallel teeth is called a *single-cut file;* those with a second row of teeth crossing the first row in a criss-cross pattern are called *double-cut files.* Criss-crossing the cuts produces a far greater number of teeth—all slanting toward the tip of the file. Each tooth acts like the end of a diamond-pointed chisel.

It is dangerous to use a file without a handle, as the end of the tang is quite sharp. If the file "hangs up" by catching on the work, your hand might jam against the end of the tang, resulting in a very painful puncture wound. *To put a handle on a file,* select one with

He got the point—do you? Always use a handle on a file. Courtesy General Motors Corporation.

the proper-sized hole for the tang, slip it on, and then tap it on the bench to seat it.

Be sure that the work to be filed *is held securely* because loose work permits the file to chatter, which quickly dulls the teeth. *Exert just enough pressure* to keep the file cutting. Insufficient pressure allows the file to slip over the work which rapidly dulls the teeth.

Prying with a file can ruin your profile. Courtesy General Motors Corporation.

Raise the file slightly on the return stroke in order to clear the work. This does not apply in filing soft metals because drawing the file back over the work aids in cleaning the teeth.

Use a *file brush* frequently to remove the chips from between the teeth. Tapping the end of a file against the vise will dull or even shatter it. Keep your files *hanging in a rack* rather than lying in a drawer with other tools. Files are extremely hard and brittle, and are, therefore, easily damaged by such treatment.

Using a file for *prying* may snap it in two. *Hammering* on a file may cause it to shatter with chips flying off in all directions.

Hacksaws

The two parts of a hacksaw are called the *frame* and *blade*. Practically all hacksaws are made with an adjustable frame designed to take blades which are 8, 10, or 12 inches long. Most frames are made with a *pistol grip.*

When placing a blade in a hacksaw frame, adjust the frame for the length of the blade, allowing sufficient threads to permit the blade to be stretched tightly. Always place the blade on the pins with the teeth pointing toward the *front* of the frame.

To use a hacksaw correctly, the following pointers must be observed: Make steady, slow strokes with even pressure, placing the greatest amount of pressure on the forward stroke and lifting slightly on the return, making each stroke a full one. The saw should be operated at a rate of 40 to 60 strokes per minute. If it is worked too fast, too much heat will be generated which will draw the temper and ruin the blade.

Take it easy—do it right.
You don't have to saw with all your might!
Courtesy General Motors Corporation.

Reduce the number of strokes per minute when cutting harder metal.

Breakage will result if the blade is not tightened properly in the frame. Breakage may also occur if undue strain is placed on the blade by twisting the frame while cutting. It is important that the blade has the correct number of teeth per inch for the metal being cut. Using the wrong blade will shorten its life.

Finer-toothed blades will cut slower but with less risk of tooth breakage. Use blades with 14 teeth per inch for cutting 1 inch or thicker cast iron, machine steel, brass, copper, aluminum, or bronze. Use blades with 18 teeth per inch for cutting from $\frac{1}{4}$ to 1 inch annealed tool steel, high speed steel, rail, or light structural shapes. Use blades with 24 teeth per inch for cutting $\frac{1}{8}$ to $\frac{1}{4}$ inch material. Use blades with 32 teeth per inch for materials thinner than $\frac{1}{8}$ inch.

CHECK YOUR KNOWLEDGE

1. Why is the proper attitude so important in the shop?
2. Why is visiting undesirable during working hours?
3. What danger is there in poking a fellow student for fun?
4. Why is it so important to avoid running in the shop?
5. What is meant by personal caution?
6. What are the seven personal caution practices listed, which can be applied to everyday shop situations?
7. Why is it so important that every injury be reported—no matter how slight?
8. What are two possible results of getting something in your eye?
9. Why should you avoid rubbing your eye if you do get a foreign particle in it?
10. Why is it so important to wash your hands after handling chemicals or before eating?
11. What are some possible results of lifting a heavy object improperly?
12. What is the proper way to stand when lifting a heavy object?
13. How should a long object be carried by one man to protect fellow students?
14. How should stock be arranged to minimize danger of its falling?
15. Why is it so important that guards are in place and working properly before operating power equipment?
16. What procedure should be followed if a guard is missing?
17. Why is it desirable to wear white coveralls?
18. Why should coveralls be changed at least once a week?
19. Why should you remove gloves when working around moving machinery?
20. What three protections are afforded by the use of safety shoes?
21. What are the four most common causes of hand tool accidents?
22. How should tools be stored to minimize hand injuries?
23. How do properly sharpened hand tools minimize cuts and bruises?
24. What is the proper way to grip a hammer handle?

25. How is the hammer head secured to the handle?

26. What protection is needed for a finished steel surface which must be hammered on?

27. What hazard is there in using a steel hammer on hard steel parts?

28. What damage may be caused by using a screwdriver as a pry?

29. What procedure is recommended for removing rusty screws?

30. Why is it so important to select the correct-sized screwdriver for the job?

31. Why should the work be clamped in a vise when removing or replacing screws?

32. How should the screwdriver blade be ground?

33. What precaution is discussed for carrying a screwdriver in your pocket?

34. Why is it dangerous to push on a wrench?

35. What advantage does a box wrench have over an open-end wrench?

36. What is the disadvantage of an adjustable wrench?

37. What two precautions are given for the safe use of adjustable wrenches?

38. Why is it inadvisable to increase the leverage of a wrench?

39. How should a chisel be held?

40. What precaution should be taken against flying chips when using a hammer and chisel?

41. Toward what part of the vise should your blows be directed when using a hammer and chisel?

42. What danger is there in using a chisel with a mushroomed head?

43. What danger is there in using a file without a handle?

44. How much pressure should be kept on the file on the forward stroke? On the return stroke?

45. How should files be stored to minimize dulling the teeth?

46. Why is it dangerous to use a file for prying?

47. How should the chips be removed from the file teeth?

48. How should the hacksaw teeth point when properly installed?

49. What will occur if the hacksaw is worked too fast?

50. What will occur if the blade is not tightened securely in the frame?

Self-Check Tests

TRUE-FALSE

1. A skillful worker is always a safe worker.

2. If you find an article lying on the floor which may be tripped over, the safe procedure is to locate the person who dropped it.

3. Sharp-edged tools should always be stored in a drawer where you cannot accidentally cut yourself.

4. Small injuries need only be tended by stopping the blood flow.

5. One out of every eight disabilities is caused by improper lifting.

6. When lifting a heavy object, use your back muscles by bending over to grasp the object.

7. Gloves are the best protection to prevent cuts when working around machinery.

8. The best place to store hand tools is in a drawer where they can easily be found.

9. A sharp hand tool is much more dangerous than a dull one.

10. Always pull on a wrench when loosening a tight nut.

11. Adjustable wrenches are especially desirable to use because they fit all sizes of nuts and are just as safe as box wrenches.

12. When using an adjustable wrench, place it on the nut so that the pulling force is applied to the stationary jaw.

13. It is important to keep your file clean of chips by tapping it occasionally on the end of the vise.

14. A file is made of good hard steel; therefore it makes an excellent pry.

MULTIPLE CHOICE

1. Small injuries should be: a) ignored; b) washed thoroughly; c) reported immediately.

2. One out of every: a) two; b) four; c) eight; d) sixteen disabilities is caused by improper lifting.

3. When carrying a long object, the front end should be kept: a) low; b) level; c) high.

4. a) $\frac{1}{3}$; b) $\frac{1}{2}$; c) $\frac{2}{3}$ of all shop injuries are caused by misuse of the common hand tool.

AUTO SHOP SAFETY

Falls are the commonest cause of accidents in the shop. Prevent them by keeping your tools off the floor. Be especially careful of creepers which extend partially from under a car. Either lift the creeper off the floor, or push it completely under the car. Stepping unexpectedly on such a "freewheeling" device is an invitation to a hospital.

Spilled oil is slippery. Small oil puddles should be wiped up immediately and large ones covered with an absorbent material.

A *jack handle* is easily tripped over if left in the low position, and it should, therefore, always be raised to its highest point.

Keep your legs under a car when working on a *creeper*. Remember that they may not be visible to the driver of another car. Before getting under a car, make sure that all doors are closed. A very bad head gash is possible if you rise off the creeper and bump your

I BELIEVE I AM IN AN EXCELLENT POSITION TO STATE THAT OIL ON THE FLOOR CREATES A VERY DEFINITE SLIPPING HAZARD!

"Oily" to bed and "oily" to rise . . . didn't make him especially wise! Courtesy National Safety Council.

head on the sharp, bottom edge of an open door.

Make sure that no other student works on an engine while you are working under it, as he may loosen dirt and debris which can fall into your eyes. Before you go under a car, make sure that there are no tools on the fenders or engine. They could be jarred off and fall on you.

Make it a practice to stand to one side of a car in which the engine is being started. Not placing your life in

He's off into the "wild blue yonder"!

someone else's hands is a practical exercise for developing personal caution. Always try to anticipate what could happen, and then take steps to counteract it.

Removing the radiator cap of an engine in which the coolant is boiling is very dangerous, as the excess pressure could blow the cap out of your hands and scald you. In an emergency, the cap may be removed safely by first covering it with rags and turning it to the stop to vent the pressure. After the pressure has been reduced, the cap should be removed while standing at arm's length. Be sure to add water slowly to a hot engine *while it is idling*. Otherwise the cold water, striking the hot cylinder block, may cause such excessive steam pressure and unequal expansion that the block will crack.

Be careful when draining lubricant from an automatic transmission because it may be very hot and can cause severe burns. Touching a hot exhaust manifold can also burn severely.

Compressed air is necessary in the shop, but it must be used with caution and not as a plaything. It can be a dangerous weapon. Air contains many

Look at "Oliver twist" when the drill broke through the thin metal. Hold the drill securely to keep this from happening to you.

small particles of dust and dirt which, when compressed and shot out of a hose nozzle, travel like small bullets. If blown into the eye, they may penetrate the eyeball.

Compressed air is frequently used to blow carbon and dirt particles from engine parts. Use an eye shield to protect you from this flying dust as the particles may not always go in the direction you think they will. Carburetor castings are frequently blown out by compressed air after having been soaked in a chemical cleaning solution. Protect your eyes as there is a strong possibility that some of these passageways reverse direction in the casting. Keep your hands out of this chemical as much as possible since it will degrease your skin and can cause open sores and rashes.

Automotive Electrical Circuits

The purpose of a *fuse* is to protect the electrical equipment should an overload occur in a circuit. Replace any tinfoil-wrapped fuse with a new one

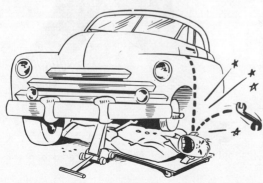

It would have been far better to use an apple to test Newton's theory of gravity.

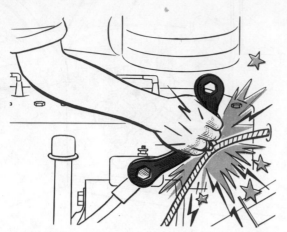

A ring may make contact between the wrench and some metallic object. When it does, it gets "hot" and, brother, will you have trouble on your hands!

Battery

Disconnect the storage battery before starting to work on an engine. This provides assurance against short circuits which might ignite gasoline around the engine. A disconnected battery also prevents accidental cranking of the engine, which could cause injury should your hand get caught in the moving parts.

of the correct size. Wrapping a fuse with tinfoil removes the protection built into the electrical system. A defective, unprotected electrical circuit could short, start a fire, and destroy the car. If a fuse burns out, locate and repair the short circuit before replacing the fuse, otherwise the new fuse will burn out too.

The generator charging circuit is unfused. It is good practice to check this heavy wire from the generator to the regulator, to the ammeter or junction block, and back to the starter solenoid switch for defective insulation. Be sure that the wire is secured by clamps, or wrapped with tape to prevent its moving as vibration could chafe the insulation. If this wire shorts to ground, the car would catch on fire.

Rings must be removed from your fingers before working around electrical wiring as bad burns could result if a ring grounded the circuit.

It's quite revealing what battery acid can do.

When disconnecting a storage battery, remove the ground strap first to prevent accidental shorting should the wrench touch any metallic part of the engine. After disconnecting the ground cable, the hot post cannot be accidentally grounded, as the battery circuit is now incomplete. Of course, the ground cable should be reconnected last when installing a battery.

To test a storage battery, use a hydrometer or meter. Shorting the posts with a pair of pliers causes a spark which could blow up the battery and spray electrolyte in all directions. Battery electrolyte is composed of sulphuric acid and water and is a highly corrosive fluid. Contact with the skin causes acid burns unless quickly washed off with water. Contact with the eyes may cause blindness unless washed out immediately. To wash out the eye, hold your head so that a stream of water from a drinking fountain squirts directly into your eye. Milk is an excellent eye-wash agent for the removal of acids, as it neutralizes them.

Shorting a storage battery with pliers also does a great deal of damage to the battery. The shorted posts melt at the point of contact. The same destructive action is also going on inside of the battery. The heavy current causes internal heating of the plates and cell connectors which, if maintained at all, melts the parts.

Use a battery strap to lift a storage battery, and be sure it is properly applied. The friction catches may slip over the posts, dropping the battery on your foot or smashing its case — spraying acid about. Inspect the grip of the strap clamp on each battery post before plac-

ing a strain on it. Because there is always the possibility of acid leaks, hold a battery away from your body when carrying it.

Be sure to shut off the power switch before disconnecting a storage battery from the charging line; otherwise a spark may occur which could ignite the hydrogen gas generated during the charging process.

Use a brush to remove particles of corrosion from the top of a battery. Brush away from yourself and make sure that no one is in line with the flying particles. Using compressed air to clean a battery is dangerous because it will spray acid and may blow corrosive particles into someone's eyes. *Wash your hands* immediately on completing any battery service and keep them away from your face and eyes while working with acids.

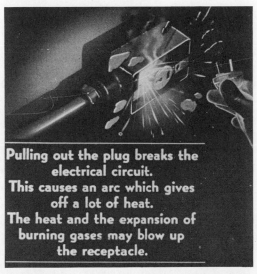

Pulling out the plug breaks the electrical circuit. This causes an arc which gives off a lot of heat. The heat and the expansion of burning gases may blow up the receptacle.

To avoid an arc, be sure that the equipment is not in operation when you pull the plug. Courtesy The Jam Handy Organization.

CAUGHT SHORT

Kill the circuit before it kills you! Courtesy National Safety Council.

Extension Cords

Check your extension cords and portable wiring to make sure that the connections are sound. Take all loops out of extension cords and keep them from crossing aisles. See that all portable tools have a third grounding wire, the purpose of which is to prevent a shock should a defect occur within the tool.

Lifting Devices

Make sure that the car is resting solidly on the jack pad before raising it. Check the support surface just as soon as the wheels clear the floor. Use car stands to support the vehicle when it is raised to the proper height; make sure that the stands are firmly set on the floor. When placing car stands under the front "A" frames, make allowance for their spread as the weight of the car compresses the coil springs.

Make sure that the car is accurately aligned on the lubrication rack and that the attachment pads are properly positioned before raising; otherwise, the car may slip from the rack. Check the pads again for accurate seating just as soon as the rack is raised enough to make contact with the frame. See that there is sufficient clearance all around the car before raising the hoist. After the car is raised, engage the safety pins or legs before working under it. Clear all materials from under the car before lowering it. Stand close to the control valve until the car is safely back on the ground.

When a car is placed on a drive-on type front-end alignment rack, make sure that the ramps are lifted and secured to prevent the car from rolling off. Use two wheel chocks under one rear wheel to keep the car from rolling.

Wire Brush

Use protective goggles or an eyeshield when using the wire brush, as small wire tips always break off when buffing. Stand to one side of the buffer so that small particles will not strike your face. Using a rag to hold the part being buffed is exceedingly dangerous as the rag could catch and be pulled into the revolving brush. You will not be able to let go in time and your hands will be dragged into the brush—the result, a very painful skin abrasion.

Presses

Many automotive parts are secured to shafts with interference fits, which necessitate the use of an arbor or hydraulic press to remove them. Make sure that the part to be removed is securely supported, and that the work lines up with the ram before applying pressure.

When hardened steel parts, such as ball bearings, are to be removed, cover them with a rag to prevent flying particles of steel, as these parts are hard and brittle and fracture easily. The particles are as sharp as glass.

Spray Painting

Breathing paint fumes in the form of spray is exceedingly dangerous. An approved-type respirator should be worn, and all painting done in a booth with an exhaust system, which removes a great deal of the fumes, and the respirator lessens the danger from the remaining fumes.

Spray painting should be done away from any open flame or welding operation. When cleaning a spray booth, use a nonferrous scraper to remove the dried paint—to avoid sparks. Playing with the spray gun by aiming it at anyone is a form of dangerous nonsense which cannot be allowed. Try to keep paint off your skin. The use of paint thinner to remove paint from your hands should be limited because it removes the natural oils and may cause a rash.

Fire Prevention When Working on a Car

The automobile engine operates on gasoline which is a highly flammable substance and, therefore, must be handled with particular care. If spilled, it should be wiped up immediately and the rags placed out of doors to dry. Vaporize the remaining gasoline with compressed air and open the windows to remove the fumes.

Some mechanics use rags instead of brushes for washing parts in solvent. This is bad practice because the disposal of grease-soaked rags always presents a problem in the shop. There is always danger of spontaneous ignition if the rags are laid on top of each other because the chemical action of oxidizing oil generates enough heat to start a fire. If rags are used, they should be placed in covered metal cans or draped over the rim of a metal trash barrel. They must be disposed of every evening—not left in the shop overnight.

An automobile that has a *gasoline leak* in the fuel system is an extremely dangerous fire hazard. The leak must be repaired before the engine is started. The gasoline should be wiped up and the shop vented to remove fumes. Care must be taken to avoid shorts in the electrical system which might cause sparks and ignite the spilled gasoline.

An *improperly tuned engine* is another fire hazard, when it backfires through the carburetor. The presence of spilled gasoline adds to the danger. It is dangerous to run an engine with the carburetor float bowl cover removed because a backfire through the intake manifold may ignite the fuel.

If you discover smoke or fire in a moving vehicle, the cause may be *electrical*. If so, the trouble is probably in the unfused (charging) circuit. To disconnect the battery, remove the cable or cut the main hot wire which connects from the solenoid to the ammeter. Pulling on this wire with your bare hands will cause a very bad burn as it is red hot under the insulation. Use a class "B" type fire extinguisher to put out any flames.

If the fire is caused by burning fuel in the carburetor, it sometimes may be snuffed out by racing the engine, which sucks the flame into the manifold. If this is not successful, shut off the engine and snuff out the flames with a *foam-type* fire extinguisher, blanket, coat, or sand. Water and soda-acid fire extinguishers will spread a gasoline fire because gasoline floats on water. Clean up before attempting to start the engine again.

Automobile parts should be cleaned in solvent rather than gasoline or other flammable fluids. Some mechanics prefer to use gasoline because it is so readily accessible; however, it is quick to ignite from a spark. It is possible to create a spark by striking two metallic objects together. Safer practice is to use solvents which have a high flash point, so do not ignite readily. Most gasolines contain tetraethyl lead, which is poisonous and may cause skin rashes when used for washing parts. Wash your hands thoroughly after using treated gasoline.

Gasoline must be stored in a red safety can with a spring-loaded cover. This is standard procedure so that you will always know that such a can contains gasoline and no other liquid. Keep these cans away from open flames, from the welding stand, and from the hot exhaust pipe of a running engine.

Carbon Monoxide Poisoning

Carbon monoxide (CO), a colorless, odorless gas, is a by-product of all internal combustion engines. When fuel is ignited in a combustion chamber, it is deficient in oxygen, resulting in the formation of carbon monoxide gas.

Carbon monoxide is a deadly poisonous gas because it robs the blood stream of the oxygen needed to support life. The red blood cells carry oxygen to all parts of the body. Carbon monoxide combines with these red blood cells more than 250 times more rapidly then oxygen. The more carbon monoxide in the blood, the less oxygen it can carry. There may be only a small amount of the deadly gas present in the air you breathe, but this gradually accumulates and displaces oxygen in the blood stream, causing the body to suffer from oxygen starvation, as though you were being choked to death. The first symptoms make their appearance when the blood is saturated to about 30 percent. Death occurs when the saturation reaches about 80 percent. The brain is the part of the body most seriously affected; unconsciousness, breath stoppage, and, eventually, death results.

Symptoms vary considerably with the concentration of gas. In mild cases, the symptoms are usually yawning, headache, dizziness, nausea, weariness, ringing in the ears, and later a fluttering or throbbing of the heart. The symptoms may come on so suddenly—or so gradually—that the person may be unaware of trouble until his knees give way. Even though still conscious, he finds out that he cannot walk, crawl, or speak. Unconsciousness and death usually follow.

The best way to treat a carbon monoxide patient is to get him into fresh air quickly—not necessarily the outdoors, especially in cold weather. Take a patient to a room free from gas and comfortably warm. Be quick but not rough.

If breathing has stopped, or is present only in occasional gasps, start rescue breathing at once and continue until natural breathing starts again, or until a physician suggests that you stop. If the patient is moved to fresh air, the carbon monoxide gradually leaves the blood. Some patients cannot eliminate the gas from their system fast enough to avoid being sick. Oxygen helps to drive the carbon monoxide from the blood more quickly.

Pure oxygen does not stimulate breathing. For this reason a mixture of about 7 percent carbon dioxide (CO_2) is administered in cases where natural breathing has stopped. The carbon-dioxide mixture stimulates the breathing center in the brain and causes the patient to breathe more deeply thus driving the carbon monoxide from the blood more rapidly.

Always ask your instructor for permission before starting an engine in the shop. This is necessary for two reasons: He will know if the engine is safe to start because there may be times when pupils of other classes may be working on the same engine, and the instructor will also want to be sure of adequate ventilation to remove exhaust gases. This can be accomplished by piping the fumes to the outside of the building by means of an exhaust manifold connected to the tailpipe of the engine or by opening windows.

CHECK YOUR KNOWLEDGE

1. What is the commonest cause of accidents in the auto shop?
2. What precautions should be observed with regard to creepers?
3. What should be done to puddles of spilled oil?
4. What should be done to jack handles to minimize the danger of tripping over them?
5. What danger is there in working under a car with the door open?
6. What precaution should be taken to protect your eyes when working under a car?
7. Why is it bad practice to stand in front of a car in which the engine is being started?
8. How should a radiator cap be removed if the coolant is boiling?
9. What makes the air hose a dangerous plaything?
10. What precaution is discussed when using an air hose to blow out carburetor passageways?
11. What danger is there in using a tinfoil-wrapped fuse?
12. Why is it so important to inspect periodically the insulation of the generator charging circuit?
13. How can a ring on your finger contribute to a burn?
14. What two assurances are provided by disconnecting the storage battery before starting to work on the engine?
15. Why should the ground cable be disconnected first?
16. What two dangers exist in shorting a battery with a pair of pliers?
17. What should be done if sulphuric acid is splashed in your eye?
18. What precaution must be followed when carrying a battery with a strap?
19. Why must the battery be held away from your body when being carried?
20. Why must the power switch be shut off first before disconnecting a battery from the charging line?
21. How can corrosion be removed safely from the top of a storage battery?
22. How does the third wire (ground) protect you from shock in the event of a defect in a portable power tool?
23. How should extension cords be arranged to minimize the danger of tripping over them?
24. Why is it necessary to support the car with stands before getting under it to work?

25. What precaution is necessary in placing car stands under the front "A" frames?

26. When should the supporting pads of the lubrication rack be checked for alignment with the car?

27. What should be done to the rack in the interest of safety before starting to work under an upraised car?

28. What two safety measures should be observed to secure a car on a wheel alignment rack?

29. Why is a wire brush dangerous?

30. What three safety precautions are given for the use of the wire brush?

31. What danger is there in using a press when working on a hard piece of steel?

32. How can you protect yourself from flying particles of hard steel when pressing off a ball bearing?

33. Why must a respirator be used when spray painting?

34. What precautions against fire should be taken when using a spray gun?

35. Why is it undesirable to use paint thinner for washing your hands?

36. How should spilled gasoline be cleaned up?

37. Why does the disposal of grease- and oil-soaked rags present a problem in the auto shop?

38. What is spontaneous ignition?

39. What two methods are suggested for the disposal of oil-soaked rags?

40. What procedure should be followed when working on an engine with a leak in the fuel line?

41. What makes an improperly tuned engine a fire hazard?

42. How should a fire be handled which is caused by a short in the charging circuit?

43. How should a fire in the carburetor throat be fought?

44. Why is it safer to use cleaning solvent rather than gasoline for the cleaning of parts?

45. How should gasoline be stored for safety?

46. Why does carbon monoxide form in an internal combustion engine?

47. What makes carbon monoxide so dangerous in the blood stream?

48. What organ is most seriously affected by carbon monoxide?

49. What are the symptoms of carbon monoxide poisoning?

50. What is the best way to treat a carbon monoxide poisoned patient?

51. Why is carbon dioxide used in the treatment of carbon monoxide poisoning?

52. What two reasons are given for asking your instructor's permission to start an engine?

Chapter 1

Fundamentals of the Gasoline Engine

The engine of the automobile, power mower, or small boat is of the internal-combustion type. This means that fuel is burned within it. Gasoline vapor is mixed with air and burned to produce pressure which powers the engine. The fuel-and-air mixture is "trapped" inside an airtight cylindrical chamber, which is fitted with a piston that prevents escape of the gas. The compressed mixture is ignited by an electric spark. The resulting burning causes tremendous heat and expansion of the trapped gases. The pressure of the expanding gases pushes the piston down. Movement of the piston powers the vehicle.

This V-8 engine of internal combustion design converts the heat of burning fuel into mechanical energy. Courtesy Buick Motor Division, General Motors Corporation.

This in-line engine of modern design features an overhead camshaft. It is used to power the Pontiac Tempest. Courtesy Pontiac Motor Division, General Motors Corporation.

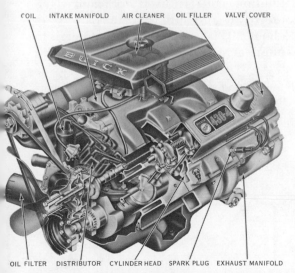

COIL   INTAKE MANIFOLD   AIR CLEANER   OIL FILLER   VALVE COVER

OIL FILTER   DISTRIBUTOR   CYLINDER HEAD   SPARK PLUG   EXHAUST MANIFOLD

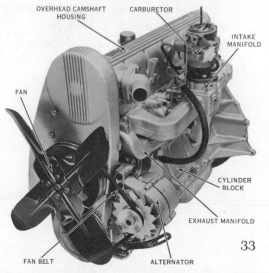

OVERHEAD CAMSHAFT HOUSING   CARBURETOR

INTAKE MANIFOLD

FAN

CYLINDER BLOCK

EXHAUST MANIFOLD

FAN BELT   ALTERNATOR

33

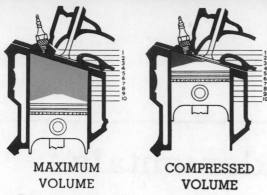

MAXIMUM VOLUME **COMPRESSED VOLUME**

The compression ratio is the difference between the space in the combustion chamber when the piston is at the top and bottom of its stroke. Courtesy The Black & Decker Mfg. Co.

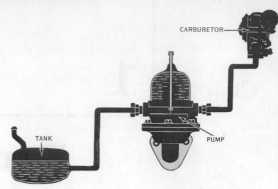

The fuel system consists of a tank, fuel line, pump, and carburetor. Courtesy AC Spark Plug Division, General Motors Corporation

The Combustion Chamber

The combustion chamber is a cylinder, in which a tightly fitted piston slides up and down a distance of approximately three inches. The top of the cylinder is fitted with two valves, or "doors," to let in the fresh fuel-air mixture and to let out the burned gases. A spark plug at the top of the combustion chamber ignites the fuel-air mixture with an electric spark that passes between its electrodes.

Compression Ratio

The smaller the space in which the fuel-air mixture is compressed before firing, the greater the power of the engine. An engine that compresses its fuel-air mixture to one tenth its original volume before firing, is said to have a 10 to 1 compression ratio. Early automotive engines had a compression ratio of 4 to 1.

The Fuel System

Gasoline is brought to the carburetor from the gas tank by means of a fuel pump. Filtered air is drawn through the carburetor by the "sucking" action of the pistons as they move downward in their cylinders.

Liquid gasoline cannot burn; therefore a carburetor is needed to change it into a fine mist and mix it with air into an exactly metered explosive mixture. By the time the mist reaches the cylinder in which it is to be burned, it is turned into a dry gas.

The Ignition System

The ignition system furnishes the electrical spark that starts the fuel-air mixture burning. The principal parts of the ignition system are: storage battery, ignition coil, distributor, and spark plugs.

Because the voltage of the car battery is not enough to jump the gap of a spark plug, a transformer, called an ignition coil, is used to change the electrical pressure of the battery to about 20,000 volts, which is enough to jump across the spark plug gap with

The ignition system furnishes a spark to ignite the fuel-air mixture. Courtesy Delco-Remy Division, General Motors Corporation.

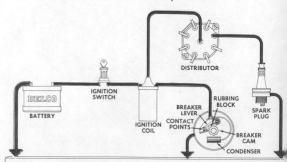

ease. The distributor "times" the spark and sends it to the correct cylinder at the precise instant that the cylinder is ready for combustion.

The Lubricating System

The lubricating system provides a constant flow of filtered oil to all moving parts of the engine. The system consists of an *oil pan* to store the oil, an *oil pump* to circulate it under pressure, a *filter* to remove abrasive particles, and an *oil gauge* to register the pressure under which the system is operating. Many cars use a *signal light* instead of the oil gauge.

The lubricating system contains an oil pan for the storage of the lubricant from where it is pumped to all parts of the engine. Courtesy Chevrolet Division, General Motors Corporation.

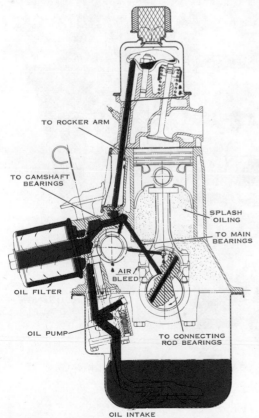

TO ROCKER ARM

TO CAMSHAFT BEARINGS

SPLASH OILING

TO MAIN BEARINGS

AIR BLEED

OIL FILTER

OIL PUMP

TO CONNECTING ROD BEARINGS

OIL INTAKE

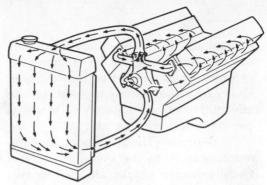

The cooling system carries excess heat from around the combustion area to the radiator, where the air cools it. For details, see Chapter 2. Courtesy Mercury Division, Ford Motor Company.

The Cooling System

An internal combustion engine is essentially a heat engine. That is, it derives its power from burning fuel. Unfortunately, not all of this heat is usable. The temperature of the burning fuel is about 4,500° F., and the melting point of iron is about 2,500° F. You can readily see that the excess heat must be removed to prevent the engine parts from melting.

The cooling system contains liquid which is pumped around hollow jackets surrounding the combustion chambers. Some of the excess heat of combustion is collected by the coolant and carried to the radiator where the air stream removes it to the atmosphere.

Cylinder Block

The cylinder block forms the main structure of the engine. All other parts are fastened to it. Usually made of gray cast iron, it is strongly braced to withstand pressures and vibration. It contains passageways for coolant, cylinder bores for the pistons to slide in, and recesses to hold the camshaft,

35

crankshaft, and valve-operating mechanisms. Some engines have aluminum cylinder blocks with cast iron cylinder sleeves for the pistons to slide in. The advantage of an aluminum block is the great saving in weight.

Four- or six-cylinder blocks are commonly cast with the cylinders in-line. Eight-cylinder blocks are cast in two banks of four cylinders, set 90° to each other, making the engine very compact. The oil pan, at the bottom of the block, holds the lubricating oil. The cylinder heads fasten to the top of the block. They contain the valves and their operating mechanisms and form the cover for the combustion chamber in which the burning fuel is compressed. The *intake* and *exhaust manifolds* attach to the sides of the head. They are pipes which conduct the gases into and out of the engine.

The clutch and transmission are bolted to the back of the block, and these three units together form the power plant.

Bottom view of the block. The main bearings provide a surface in which the crankshaft can turn. This block is especially designed for racing. Note the use of cross bolts to secure each main bearing cap. Courtesy Ford Motor Company.

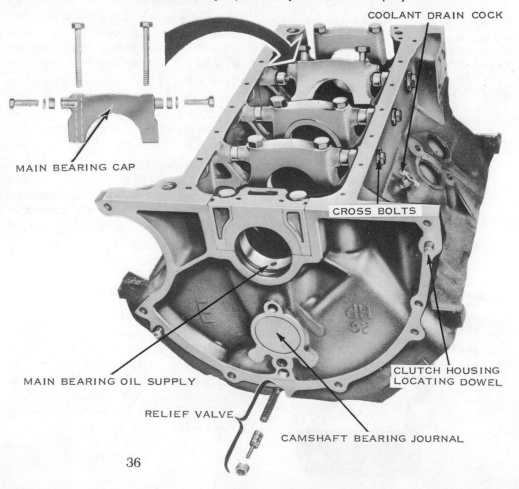

COOLANT DRAIN COCK

MAIN BEARING CAP

CROSS BOLTS

MAIN BEARING OIL SUPPLY

CLUTCH HOUSING LOCATING DOWEL

RELIEF VALVE

CAMSHAFT BEARING JOURNAL

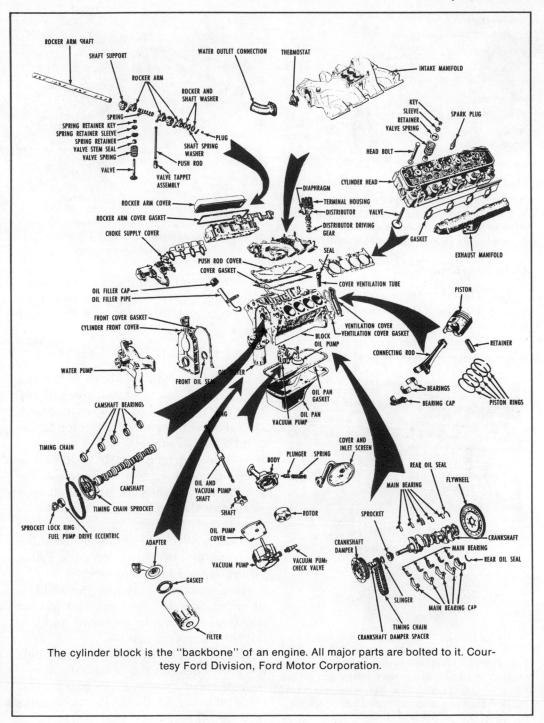

The cylinder block is the "backbone" of an engine. All major parts are bolted to it. Courtesy Ford Division, Ford Motor Corporation.

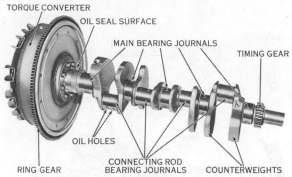

The crankshaft changes the up-and-down motion of the pistons into a rotary one, which operates through the transmission to drive the car. Courtesy Dodge Division, Chrysler Corporation.

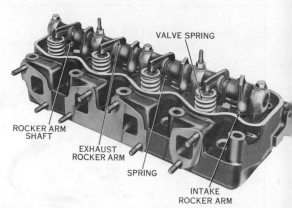

The top of the cylinder head contains the valve operating mechanism. Courtesy Plymouth Division, Chrysler Corporation.

Cylinder Head

The *cylinder head* is bolted to the top of the block. It covers the combustion chamber and holds the valves and their operating mechanisms. Because the cylinder head is closest to the heat of combustion, it contains large coolant chambers to carry excess heat away from the engine. It also contains the spark plugs.

Intake Manifold

The *intake manifold* bolts to the cylinder heads. Made of cast iron, it contains passageways to conduct the fuel-air mixture from the carburetor to the combustion chamber.

The intake manifold is designed to keep the passageways as equal in length as possible. In an unbalanced manifold, the fuel charge is unequally distributed, causing variation in the quantities of fuel fired in each cylinder. Such variations cause uneven firing, vibration, and loss of power.

Heat from the exhaust manifold is directed around the passageways of the intake manifold to warm and dry out the incoming gases.

The intake manifold gasket seals the joint between the manifold and cylinder head to prevent the entrance of air which would throw the carburetor mixture off balance.

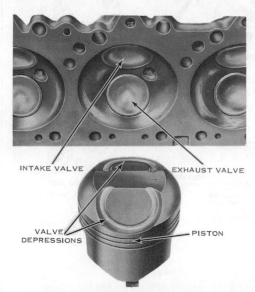

The cylinder head forms the top of the combustion chamber. It contains valves and a hole for the spark plug. This hemispherical combustion chamber is used in some racing engines. Courtesy Dodge Division, Chrysler Corporation.

38

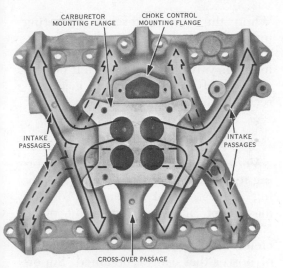

CARBURETOR MOUNTING FLANGE   CHOKE CONTROL MOUNTING FLANGE

INTAKE PASSAGES   INTAKE PASSAGES

CROSS-OVER PASSAGE

The intake manifold conducts the fuel-air mixture from the carburetor to the combustion areas. Courtesy Dodge Division, Chrysler Corporation.

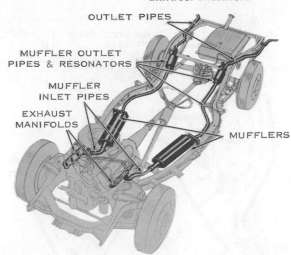

OUTLET PIPES

MUFFLER OUTLET PIPES & RESONATORS

MUFFLER INLET PIPES

EXHAUST MANIFOLDS

MUFFLERS

The burned gases are passed through a muffler and resonator before being discharged into the atmosphere. Courtesy Ford Division, Ford Motor Company.

Exhaust Manifold

The *exhaust manifold* is essentially a tube for carrying the burned gas from the engine to the muffler, where it is discharged into the air. It is made of cast iron and is generally installed with a special asbestos gasket to seal the joint between it and the cylinder head. Some late-model V-8 engines do not use an exhaust manifold gasket and some have a thin, shim-type gasket in place of the usual asbestos gasket.

Manifold Heat Control

On "V"-type engine blocks, one exhaust manifold is blocked by a thermostatically controlled valve. The valve prevents the exhaust gases from freely entering the muffler when the engine is cold. The blocked gases are diverted through a passageway to a chamber cast around the intake manifold. The hot exhaust gases heat the intake manifold, vaporize the gas, and thereby assist in warming the engine rapidly.

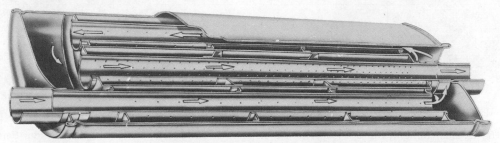

The muffler is a straight-through device which contains gradually expanding chambers that decrease the pressure—and thereby the sound. Courtesy Lincoln Division, Ford Motor Company.

39

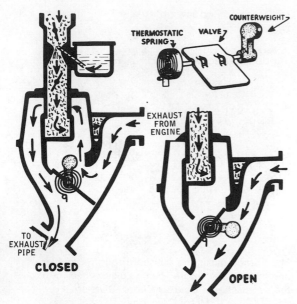

The manifold heat control valve forces the hot exhaust gases to pass around the intake manifold in order to heat and dry out the fuel-air mixture. Courtesy Pontiac Motor Division, General Motors Corporation.

When the engine reaches operating temperature, the manifold heat control thermostat spring relaxes and allows the valve to open to permit normal passage of the hot exhaust gases directly to the muffler.

Tuned Manifolds

Volumetric efficiency is an engineering term used to described the "breathing" efficiency of an engine, or the movement of air into and out of it. Naturally, raising the volumetric efficiency of an engine increases the amount of power that can be obtained. Supercharging is one well-known method of increasing the amount of air that enters an engine, but a supercharger can cause problems regarding space and service. Tuning the intake and exhaust manifolds is a simpler method, based on principles from the science of physics.

Tuned manifolds use the principles of *inertia* and *resonance* to obtain supercharging effects. They work by recovering some of the pumping energy that every engine expends in drawing in

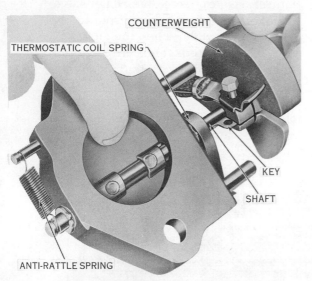

The exhaust butterfly valve, located in the exhaust pipe, is controlled by a thermostatic coil spring. Courtesy Dodge Division, Chrysler Corporation.

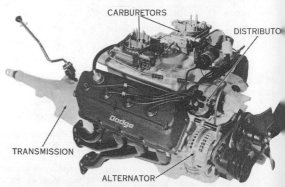

This Dodge Hemi-engine has two four-barrel carburetors mounted on a tuned intake manifold for added torque at high engine speeds. Courtesy Dodge Division, Chrysler Corporation.

These six illustrations show the sequential steps in which the exhaust pipe configurations were laid out for dynamometer testing in order to develop maximum torque for the Ford racing engine used at the Indianapolis Speedway and elsewhere. Courtesy Ford Motor Company.

These tuned intake stacks supply air to the induction system of the Chrysler fuel-injected Hemi-engine. Courtesy Chrysler Corporation.

This is the final version of the Ford racing engine, with the exhaust pipes tuned to a half wave length. Courtesy Ford Motor Company.

41

the fresh air-fuel mixture and in expelling the exhaust gases. Once a column of air is started in motion in a long tube, inertia keeps it moving. This force is used to drive additional quantities of the air-fuel mixture into the cylinder, past the partially closed intake valve.

In addition, if the length of the tubing is calculated with care, each long branch acts like an organ pipe in which a compression wave travels back and forth at the speed of sound. The compression wave is caused by the closing of the intake valve. Racing engines are designed so that the compression wave arrives at the partially closed intake valve just in time to pack more of the air-fuel mixture into the combustion chamber. An increase in volumetric efficiency also increases engine torque at a certain speed.

In a similar manner, the length of the exhaust manifold and related tubing can be calculated so that part of the wave (called the *rarification* part) reaches the partially closed exhaust valve in time to help draw out burned gases. This leaves additional space for the fresh incoming gases, also raising volumetric efficiency.

Service Procedures

Due to the heat of combustion, cylinder head and exhaust manifold castings sometimes warp. Such a condition frequently results in a leak. To true up warped castings, and to replace gaskets, it is necessary to remove the manifolds and/or cylinder heads.

Troubleshooting

Exhaust gasket leaks can be felt by placing your hand close to the suspected area. Rapid acceleration of the

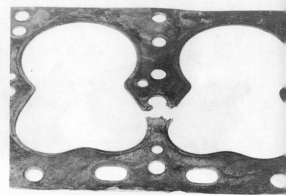

A blown cylinder head gasket allows the compression to leak between two cylinders. Courtesy Federal-Mogul Service.

engine will send a blast of hot exhaust gases where a gasket is defective. A *leaky intake gasket* can be tested by squirting kerosene around the suspected area. If the gasket is defective, the engine will suck the fluid into the manifold, and the engine speed will change.

A cylinder head gasket, blown out between two cylinders, can be checked with a compression gauge. Such a defective condition is evidenced by a lack of compression between two adjacent cylinders.

Replacing a Cylinder Head and/or Manifold Gaskets on a Dodge Slant-Six Engine

A *manifold* conducts the air-fuel mixture from the carburetor to the combustion chambers in the engine through the intake manifold, and it directs the burned gases to the muffler through the exhaust manifold. These two are joined together so that the heat from the exhaust gases warms and dries out the incoming gases. This junction is called the *manifold heat control*. If the gasket at this joint blows out, exhaust

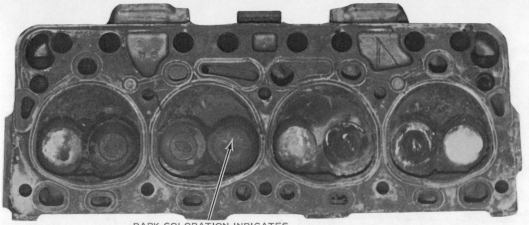

DARK COLORATION INDICATES
DEFECTIVE EXHAUST VALVE

After removing the cylinder head, note the coloration of each exhaust valve. Those cylinders in which the exhaust valve coloring is light have been operating at normal temperatures; the heat of combustion has burned off the carbon. In the second cylinder, note that the exhaust valve is dark, meaning that combustion was relatively cool because of compression lost through the burned valve.

fumes will reach the passenger compartment. This can also happen if the gasket between the block and exhaust manifold blows out. If the intake manifold gasket leaks, the engine will suck in air, and the air-fuel mixture will be out of balance. In either case, it is necessary to install new gaskets.

Tools and Equipment

Dodge (or Chrysler) Slant-Six engine; $\frac{1}{2}''$, $\frac{9}{16}''$, and $\frac{5}{8}''$ combination end wrenches; $\frac{7}{16}''$, $\frac{1}{2}''$, $\frac{9}{16}''$, $\frac{5}{8}''$, $\frac{11}{16}''$, and $\frac{13}{16}''$ sockets; 6″ extension, speed handle, flex handle, and ratchet; pliers; screwdriver; feeler gauges.

PROCEDURE

DISASSEMBLING

Note: *Replacing the cylinder head gasket and replacing the manifold gaskets are two related jobs that are detailed in this sequence. Follow all of the sequential steps to complete both jobs, or cover illustrated steps ① to ⑧ and ㉒ to ㉛ for replacing the manifold gaskets. To replace the cylinder head gasket, it is not necessary to take off*

the manifolds; therefore follow illustrated steps ① to ③ and ⑨ to ㉛ to complete this job.

AIR CLEANER

OIL FILLER CAP

①

① Remove the air cleaner and the oil filler cap, along with the closed crankcase vent line. This line allows filtered air to enter the crankcase to replace the fumes drawn out by the closed ventilator system. If the cylinder head is to be removed, drain the cooling system and remove the coolant inlet and outlet hoses.

43

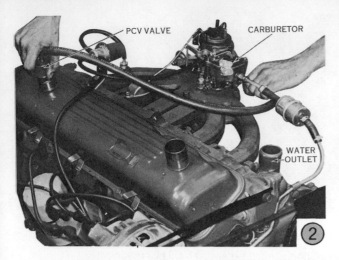

PCV VALVE   CARBURETOR

WATER OUTLET

(2)

② Remove the PCV (Positive Crankcase Ventilator) valve and the line which connects to the fitting on the carburetor base. The vacuum of the intake manifold is used to draw some of the corrosive fumes from the crankcase into the intake manifold, to be burned in the combustion chambers.

③ Disconnect the fuel line at the carburetor. **Caution:** *Use two wrenches to keep from twisting the pipe and breaking out the rear of the carburetor.* Disconnect the distributor vacuum sensing unit from the carburetor and intake manifold. This unit senses the varying loads on the engine resulting from acceleration and deceleration, and causes the distributor to advance or retard the ignition timing. This, in turn, controls exhaust emissions.

④ Disconnect the throttle and choke control rods at the carburetor.

⑤ Remove the carburetor retaining nuts, then take off the carburetor.

⑥ Remove the choke housing retaining bolts and take off the thermostatic coil and housing assembly.

⑦ Remove the nuts, washers, and bridges that hold the manifolds to the cylinder head, then take off the manifold assembly. Scrape off all gasket material. Separate the two manifolds if it is necessary to service the exhaust manifold heat control valve.

⑧ To disassemble the heat control valve, remove the nut and bolt, slide out the lock, and pry off the counterweight. Slip off the thermostatic spring and the retainer. Apply penetrant to the heat control valve. **Caution:** *Lubricating oil must never be used on this valve or it will carbonize and cause the valve shaft to seize.* The purpose of this valve is to direct exhaust heat up

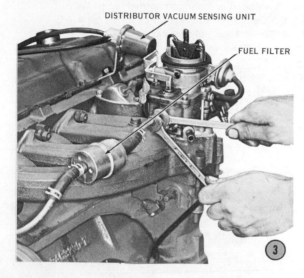

DISTRIBUTOR VACUUM SENSING UNIT

FUEL FILTER

(3)

AUTOMATIC CHOKE CONTROL

(4)

44

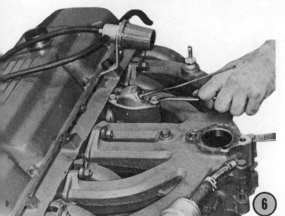

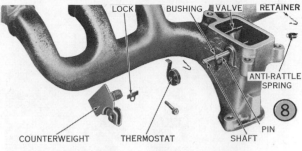

LOCK   BUSHING VALVE   RETAINER

COUNTERWEIGHT   THERMOSTAT   SHAFT

ANTI-RATTLE SPRING

PIN

against the intake manifold; thus the incoming air-fuel mixture will be vaporized by the exhaust heat during the warm-up period. A thermostat is required to allow the valve to open when the engine warms up so that the intake manifold does not become excessively hot, which would reduce volumetric efficiency.

Cylinder Head Removal

Note: *If only the manifolds are to be removed, skip to illustrated Step ㉒ for the assembly. Steps ⑨ through ㉑ are for removing the cylinder head on the Dodge Slant-Six engine.*

⑨ Remove the distributor vacuum sensing control valve.

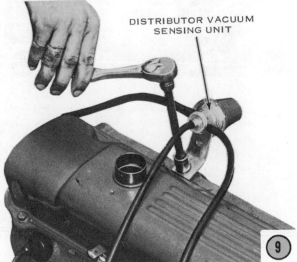

DISTRIBUTOR VACUUM SENSING UNIT

ROCKER ARM COVER
ALTERNATOR   DRIVE BELT   SUPPORT BRACKET

10

ROCKER ARM SHAFT
PUSH RODS

1

11

1

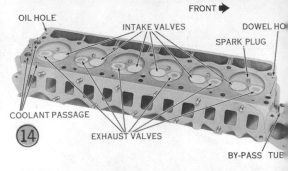

FRONT ➡

OIL HOLE
INTAKE VALVES   DOWEL HO
SPARK PLUG

COOLANT PASSAGE
EXHAUST VALVES
14
BY-PASS TUBE

⑩ Take off the alternator, support bracket, and drive belt. Remove the rocker arm cover.

⑪ Disconnect the spark plug wires, then take out the spark plugs, using a $^{13}/_{16}''$ deep spark plug socket. **Caution:** *Support the end of the wrench; otherwise, it will tilt and crack the porcelain.* Remove the aluminum spark plug tubes.

⑫ Loosen the rocker arm shaft support retaining bolts, then lift off the shaft and rocker arm assembly. Lift out the push rods.

⑬ Take out the cylinder head bolts and lift off the cylinder head. Discard the gasket and scrape the carbon from the head and block.

⑭ Use a piece of baling wire to trace the coolant passageways (ports) through the head and block. Trace them from the manifold side of the head to the underside of the valve heads. Look at the manifold assembly to see which are intake passageways and which are exhaust. *Why are the intake valves larger than the exhaust valves, even though both pass the same volume of gases?* Trace the oil passageway from the underside of the rear of the cylinder head to the rear rocker arm support. Note that this one pedestal does not have threads to the top as do the other pedestals. This is to allow space for the oil to flow into the rocker arm shaft.

⑮ Clean all the gasket surfaces of the cylinder block and head. Coat a new gasket with sealer and position the gasket over the dowels on the block. Install the cylinder head. Tighten the cylinder head bolts to 65 ft-lbs. (foot-pounds) torque in the sequence shown. Repeat the tightening procedure with the torque wrench set to the same figure.

⑯ Install the push rods with the ball ends down. The cupped ends must face up.

⑰ If the rocker arm assembly was taken apart for cleaning or replacing worn parts, assemble it as shown. Note the flat section on the front end of the shaft which must face up for proper rocker arm lubrication.

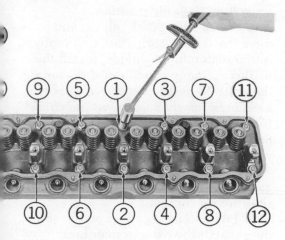

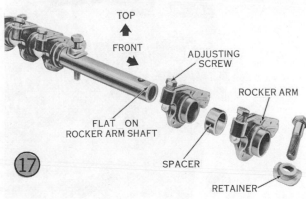

47

⑱ Install the rocker arm assembly with the flat section facing up and toward the front of the engine. Install the rocker shaft retainers between the

rocker arms so that they seat on the rocker arm shaft and not on the extended part of the bushings. Be sure to install the long retainer in the center position only. Install the rocker arm shaft bolts, with the one long bolt at the end, and then tighten the bolts to 25 ft-lbs. torque.

⑲ Make a preliminary valve adjustment by turning the crankshaft until No. 1 piston is at top dead center (TDC), firing position. Both valves of No. 1 cylinder will be closed, and the index mark on the front pulley will be aligned with the "O" mark on the timing tab. Adjust the clearance of these two rocker arms to 0.010″ for the intake valve and 0.020″ for the exhaust valve. **Note:** *This is only a preliminary adjustment; a final adjustment must be made after the engine is normalized (warmed to operating temperature).* Turn the crankshaft until the next piston is at TDC, then adjust the two valves of this cylinder. Continue bringing each piston to TDC, using the firing order of the engine as a guide, and adjusting its valves. **Note:** *The position of the distributor rotor can be used as a guide to determine which cylinder is approaching its firing position.*

⑳ Clean the spark plugs and gap them to 0.035″. Slip the spark plugs into the aluminum shields, install them in the cylinder head, and then torque them to 30 ft-lbs. **Note:** *No gasket is used between the spark plug and shield.* Connect the spark plug wires. Use the firing order of the engine as a guide, which is 1−5−3−6−2−4.

㉑ Position a new rocker arm cover gasket on the cylinder head, then install the rocker arm cover.

㉒ Position new gaskets on the studs, then install the exhaust manifold.

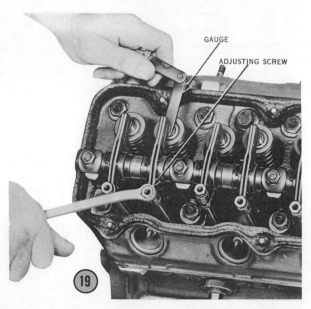

GAUGE

ADJUSTING SCREW

SPARK PLUG   SHIELD

(23) Install the intake manifold.

(24) Install and tighten all bolts and nuts snugly.

(25) This shows how the conical washers are installed as exhaust manifold retainers.

49

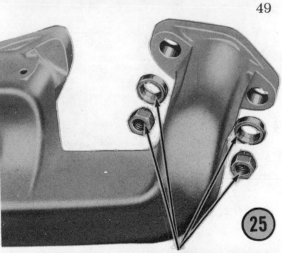

CONICAL NUTS AND WASHERS

(26)

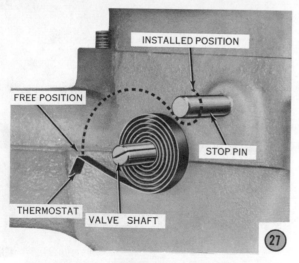

INSTALLED POSITION

FREE POSITION

STOP PIN

THERMOSTAT   VALVE SHAFT

(27)

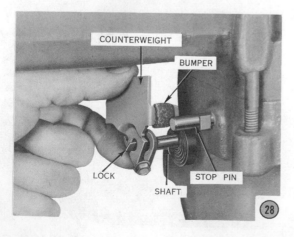

COUNTERWEIGHT

BUMPER

LOCK

STOP PIN

SHAFT

(28)

㉖ After both manifolds are aligned with the cylinder head, tighten the three bolts holding the intake manifold to the exhaust manifold, then torque the nuts holding the manifolds to the cylinder head to 10 ft-lbs. Connect the muffler inlet pipe to the exhaust manifold.

㉗ Turn the valve shaft to its extreme clockwise position, then slip a new thermostat into the shaft slot, with the outer end in the lower left-hand position as shown. Wrap the outer end of the thermostatic spring clockwise and engage it under the stop pin.

㉘ Place the counterweight on the shaft, with the shield in the upward position, then slip the lock into the shaft slot. Center the counterweight on the shaft, and turn the assembly counterclockwise until the bumper passes the stop pin. Press the counterweight onto the shaft until it is seated, then tighten the clamp bolt. Make sure that the anti-rattle spring is in place on the opposite end of the shaft. Test the valve for proper operation.

㉙ Install the alternator and drive belt. Adjust the belt deflection to $\frac{1}{4}''$ for a used belt (or $\frac{1}{8}''$ for a new belt) with a load of 5 lbs. The deflection must be measured at the midpoint of the largest span. Attach the fuel line, carburetor, and distributor vacuum sensing valve. **Caution:** *Use two wrenches on all fittings to keep from twisting the fuel line.* Install and connect the automatic choke.

㉚ Install the PCV valve and hose to the carburetor. Replace the air cleaner, oil filler cap, and hose. Connect the coolant hoses and fill the radiator. Check the oil dipstick and add oil as necessary to bring the level to the "full" mark.

㉛ Start the engine and adjust the idle speed to 550 revolutions per minute (rpm) with the headlights turned on. **Note:** *Use of headlights is necessary to cause the alternator to charge, which places an additional load on the engine.* After normalizing, idle the engine and adjust the rocker arm clearance to 0.010″ for the intake and 0.020″ for the exhaust valves. Connect the timing light to No. 1 cylinder spark plug high-tension wire. Connect the low-tension wires to the battery terminals. Direct the neon light toward the timing tab, then turn the distributor housing until the index mark aligns with the specified degree mark as follows: Set the ignition timing to 5° BTDC (before top dead center) for the 170 cu. in. engine, 2½° BTDC for the 225 cu. in. engine, or 5° ATDC (after top dead center) for the CAS engine (with Cleaner Air System). Adjust the idle mixture and the idle speed to 550 rpm with the transmission in neutral on an engine without CAS or 650 rpm in neutral with CAS.

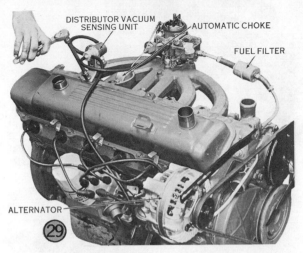

Replacing a Cylinder Head Gasket on a Chevrolet V-8 Engine

A V-8 engine consists of two banks of four cylinders each and two cylinder heads. The intake manifold is located between the cylinder banks and is secured to each cylinder head. Its position between the heads makes it a convenient cover for the valve actuating mechanism. The exhaust manifolds are attached to the cylinder heads on the opposite side of the intake manifold. To remove a cylinder head from a V-8 engine, it is necessary to take off the intake and exhaust manifolds first.

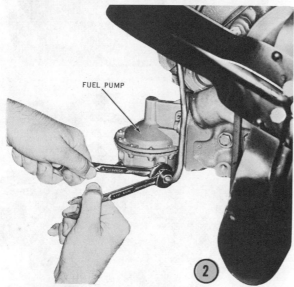

AIR CLEANER

1

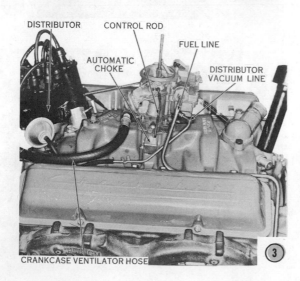

FUEL PUMP

2

DISTRIBUTOR   CONTROL ROD

AUTOMATIC
CHOKE

FUEL LINE

DISTRIBUTOR
VACUUM LINE

CRANKCASE VENTILATOR HOSE

3

Tools and Equipment

Chevrolet 283 or 327 cu. in. engine; $3/8''$, $7/16''$, $1/2''$, $9/16''$, $5/8''$, and $1''$ combination end wrenches; torque wrench, ratchet, speed handle, flex handle, and $3''$ and $6''$ extensions; $7/16''$, $1/2''$, $9/16''$, $5/8''$, $11/16''$, and $13/16''$ (deep) sockets; screwdriver; feeler gauges; pliers.

PROCEDURE

DISASSEMBLING

① Drain the cooling system and remove the inlet and outlet hoses. Remove the wing nut holding the air cleaner to the carburetor, then lift off the air cleaner.

② Disconnect the fuel line at the fuel pump. **Caution:** *Use two wrenches on fuel line fittings to keep from twisting off the line.*

③ Disconnect the fuel line at the carburetor. Use two wrenches to keep from damaging the line and the carburetor fitting. Disconnect the choke rod at the choke lever by prying off the clip. Pry off the thermostat cover, then remove the choke control rod by sliding it out of the thermostatic coil. Slide off the crankcase ventilator hose. Remove the vacuum line and rubber tube to the distributor. Use two wrenches on the fitting at the carburetor.

④ Remove the carburetor flange nuts and lift off the carburetor.

⑤ Disconnect the spark plug wires. Use a screwdriver to unlatch the distributor cap by pressing down on the retaining screws and turning them a quarter turn. Turn the crankshaft until the rotor is pointing to the front of the engine. Remove the distributor retaining bolt, then lift out the distributor. Note that the rotor turns counterclock-

INTAKE MANIFOLD

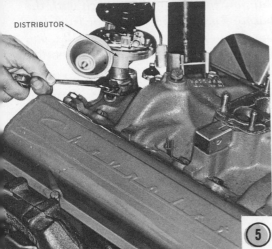

DISTRIBUTOR

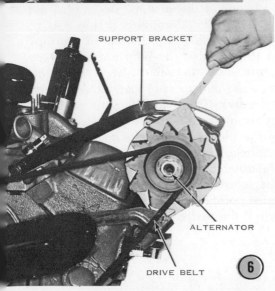

SUPPORT BRACKET

ALTERNATOR

DRIVE BELT

wise as you lift it out because of the spiral drive gear at the bottom of the shaft. It is important, therefore, when installing the distributor to position it so that the rotor is slightly past the straight-ahead position.

⑥ Disconnect the main and field wires at the alternator. **Caution:** *Because the main lead to the alternator is live, it is extremely important to disconnect the ground cable at the battery to avoid damaging the unit.* Disconnect the alternator support bolt, push the alternator toward the engine, and remove the drive belt. Take off the alternator and its support bracket.

⑦ Take off the intake manifold retaining bolts, then lift off the intake manifold. Remove all old gasket material and seals.

⑧ Take out the rocker arm cover retaining bolts and lift off the cover. Remove the gasket.

53

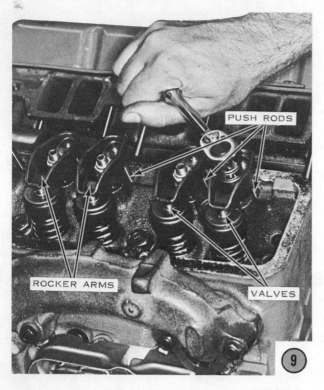

PUSH RODS

ROCKER ARMS

VALVES

9

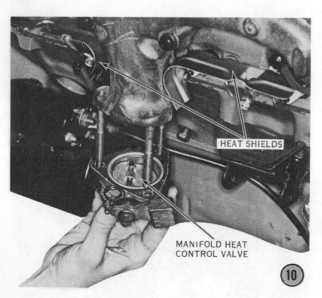

HEAT SHIELDS

MANIFOLD HEAT
CONTROL VALVE

10

9 Take off the rocker arm pivot nuts, lift off the rocker arms, and take out the push rods.

10 Remove the muffler inlet pipe and the exhaust manifold heat control valve. Check the valve to be sure that it is free; if it is not, apply penetrant. **Caution:** *Don't use oil on the shaft of this valve as it will carbonize from the exhaust heat and the valve will stick.* Take off the heat shields above the spark plugs.

11 Take out the spark plugs. **Caution:** *Support the end of the wrench with the palm of your hand to keep it from tilting. If the end of the wrench tilts, you will crack the spark plug insulator.*

12 Using a screwdriver, bend back the tabs on the French locks. Remove the exhaust manifold. Note that there are no gaskets between the manifold and cylinder head.

13 Take out the cylinder head bolts, then lift off the head. Remove the gasket.

14 After removing the cylinder head, scrape the carbon from the head, block, and tops of the pistons. Be careful not to score the aluminum piston heads. Note the valve depressions in the tops of the pistons. *(A) Why are there four depressions in each piston head although there are only two valves in each cylinder?* Trace the coolant passages by probing through the holes in the top of the block. *(B) Is there a coolant passageway between the cylinders?* Note the notch in each piston head to indicate the correct installation. The notches must point toward the front of the engine when the pistons are installed.

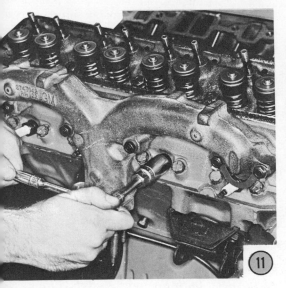

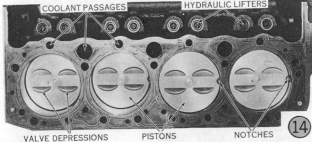

FRENCH LOCKS

COOLANT PASSAGES   HYDRAULIC LIFTERS

VALVE DEPRESSIONS   PISTONS   NOTCHES

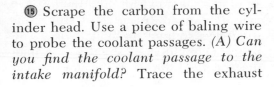

⑮ Scrape the carbon from the cylinder head. Use a piece of baling wire to probe the coolant passages. *(A) Can you find the coolant passage to the intake manifold?* Trace the exhaust passageways (ports) from the outside of the cylinder head to the exhaust valve heads. Trace the intake passageways to the intake valve heads. *(B) Which are the larger valves—intake or exhaust? (C) Why is one valve in a cylinder smaller than the other, even though both pass the same volume of gas into and out of the cylinder?*

GASKET

DOWEL PIN

⑯ Remove the thermostat housing and the thermostat from the intake manifold. Test the thermostat by suspending it in a container of water that can be heated. Use a thermometer to see if the thermostat opens at the specified temperature of 177°-183° F. **Caution:** *Do not allow the thermometer to touch the container.* (A) Why? Some cars with heaters may have thermostats that open at 190° F. *(B) What advantage would a high-temperature rated thermostat have in such a vehicle?*

Assembling

⑰ Position a new cylinder head gasket on the block. **Caution:** *The gasket surfaces on both the head and the block must be clean and free of nicks or heavy scratches.* The threads of the cylinder head retaining bolts and the threads in the block must be cleaned. Dirt will affect the torque. Do not use any gasket sealer on composition steel-asbestos gaskets. Coat both sides of all-steel gaskets with sealer. **Caution:** *Too much sealer may hold the beads of the gasket away from the head or block.* Guide the cylinder head into place over the dowel pins and gasket. Coat the threads of the cylinder head bolts with sealing compound and tighten with your fingers.

⑱ Tighten the cylinder head bolts to 60-70 ft-lbs. torque, in the order shown in the next diagram.

⑲ This diagram shows the proper sequence for tightening the cylinder head bolts for the Chevrolet small block engines. All car manufacturers provide similar diagrams for tightening the cylinder head evenly. Using this sequence, tighten the bolts twice. The first time tighten to slightly less than the specified torque rating; the second

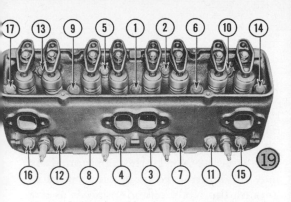

time tighten fully as specified. **Caution:** *Uneven tightening of the cylinder head bolts will cause distortion of the block which will result in uneven wear, oil pumping, and power loss through escaping gas, often called "blow-by."*

⑳ Replace the exhaust manifold. French tab locks are used on the end bolts. **Caution:** *If the tabs are broken, replace the locks.* Be sure that the surfaces are clean, as no gasket is used between the head and exhaust manifold. Tighten the manifold retaining bolts evenly, then fasten the French locks by bending a tab up against the flat side of each retaining bolt.

㉑ Install the heat shields and the spark plugs which have been cleaned and gapped to 0.035″. **Caution:** *Don't tilt the spark plug socket, or you will crack the insulator.* Tighten the spark plugs to 20-25 ft-lbs. torque. **Caution:** *Over-tightening will cause the gaps to close up, which will result in uneven idling.*

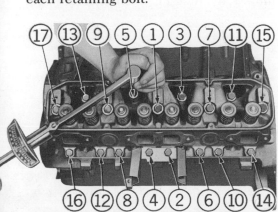

This is the sequence for tightening cylinder head bolts on all of the larger Chrysler engines. Note that the bolts are tightened in a regular pattern, starting from the center and working evenly and alternately out to the ends. This tightening pattern can be used successfully on any comparable engine.

PUSH RODS

(24) Adjust the valve lash. When the lifter is on the base circle of the camshaft lobe, adjust as follows: Turn the crankshaft until the mark on the torsional damper lines up with the center of the "0" mark on the timing tab and the engine is at the No. 1 firing position. This may be determined by placing your fingers on the No. 1 cylinder valves as the mark on the damper approaches the "0" mark on the front cover. If the valves are not moving, the engine is at the No. 1 firing position. If the valves move as the mark approaches the timing tab, the engine is at No. 6 firing position, and the crankshaft should be rotated one more revolution in order to reach the No. 1 position.

The *hydraulic lifter lash adjustment* is made by backing off the rocker arm stud nut until there is play in the push rod, then tightening the nut to remove all clearance between push rod and rocker arm. This position can be determined by rotating the push rod with

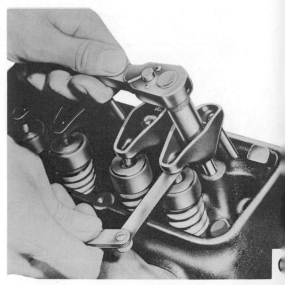

(22) Replace the cleaned manifold heat control valve and the muffler inlet pipe. Install the push rods. Either end can go up in this engine since the oil passage openings are identical at both ends.

(23) Replace the rocker arms and secure them in position with special conical adjusting nuts.

your fingers as the nut is tightened. When the push rod does not turn, all play is removed, and this is known as the *zero-lash position*. Now, turn the adjusting nut an additional turn to position the hydraulic lifter plunger in the center of its travel.

With the engine at the No. 1 firing position, the following valves may be adjusted:

Exhaust—1, 3, 4, & 8
Intake—1, 2, 5, & 7

Turn the crankshaft one revolution until the "0" mark and the damper mark are again in alignment. This is No. 6 cylinder firing position, and the following valves should be adjusted:

Exhaust—2, 5, 6, & 7
Intake—3, 4, 6, & 8

The *mechanical lifter lash adjustment* is made by inserting a feeler gauge of the specified thickness between the end of the valve stem and the rocker arm face, as shown. After positioning No. 1 piston at the firing position, adjust the following valves:

Exhaust—4 & 8
Intake—2 & 7

Turn the crankshaft ½ revolution (180°) clockwise and adjust the following valves:

Exhaust—3 & 6
Intake—1 & 8

Turn the crankshaft another ½ revolution until the "0" mark and the torsional damper marks are again in alignment. This is No. 6 firing position. Adjust the following valves:

Exhaust—5 & 7
Intake—3 & 4

Turn the crankshaft another ½ turn and adjust the following valves:

Exhaust—1 & 2
Intake—5 & 6

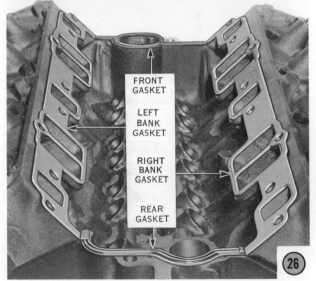

FRONT GASKET

LEFT BANK GASKET

RIGHT BANK GASKET

REAR GASKET

㉕ Position a new gasket on top of the cylinder head, then replace the rocker arm cover. Install and tighten the cover bolts.

㉖ Be sure that all gasket material has been removed from the intake manifold mating surfaces, then install new gaskets and seals as shown. Be sure that the ends of the seals are positioned properly, or an oil leak will result.

27

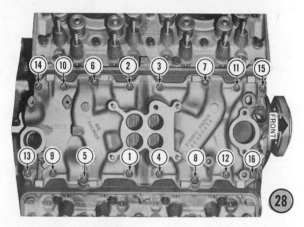

28

29

27 Install the thermostat and its housing on the intake manifold. Replace the intake manifold. Tighten the bolts evenly, but not too tightly. They will be torqued properly in the next step.

28 Torque the intake manifold retaining bolts to 25-35 ft-lbs. in the sequence shown. The proper torque and sequence for tightening these bolts is extremely important to prevent distortion which will result in oil and air leaks.

29 If the crankshaft has not been turned, install the distributor. Remember that the spiral drive gear will cause the rotor to turn clockwise as you insert the unit. Make allowance for this by inserting the distributor with the rotor pointing about $\frac{1}{8}$ turn counterclockwise from the straight-ahead position. The tongue at the bottom end of the distributor shaft must mesh with the slot in the oil pump driveshaft. You may have to turn the crankshaft slightly until it meshes properly. When the two parts are in alignment, the distributor will drop into place so that the shoulder on the shaft is even with the machined boss on the intake manifold. When properly positioned, secure the distributor with the hold-down clamp and bolt. If the crankshaft has been turned with the distributor removed to adjust the valves, it will be necessary to retime the distributor to the engine as follows: Locate No. 1 piston at the firing position by removing the spark plug from No. 1 cylinder and cranking the engine until compression is felt as the piston rises. Continue cranking until the timing mark on the crankshaft pulley lines up with the timing tab attached to the engine front cover. Position the distributor in the intake manifold so that the rotor points toward No. 1 spark plug terminal in the

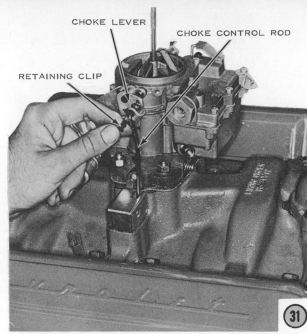

CHOKE LEVER

CHOKE CONTROL ROD

RETAINING CLIP

③⓪

③①

distributor cap. Press the distributor down firmly and engage the cranking motor a few times until the distributor drops into place properly. Install the hold-down clamp and bolt, tightening the bolt snugly. Turn the distributor body slightly counterclockwise until the ignition contact points just open, then lock it in this position.

③⓪ Install the distributor cap, making sure that the rotor is pointing toward No. 1 spark plug wire terminal. Lock the distributor cap by depressing the latches and turning them a quarter turn until the ends lock under the distributor body. Install the spark plug wires. **Caution:** *The wires must be inserted in the support brackets as numbered in order to prevent cross-firing.*

③① Position a new gasket on the carburetor flange, then install the carburetor. Tighten the four retaining nuts evenly. **Caution:** *Uneven tightening will crack the flange.* Install the choke control rod and secure it to the choke lever by means of the retaining clip as shown.

③② Install the crankcase ventilator hose, distributor vacuum line, and the fuel line. **Caution:** *Be sure to use two wrenches on all fittings to keep from twisting the lines.* Connect the throttle control rod.

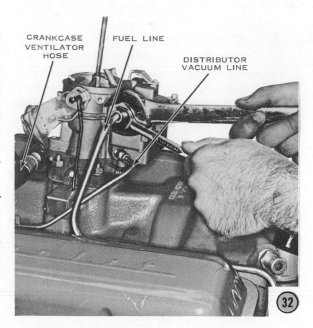

CRANKCASE VENTILATOR HOSE

FUEL LINE

DISTRIBUTOR VACUUM LINE

③②

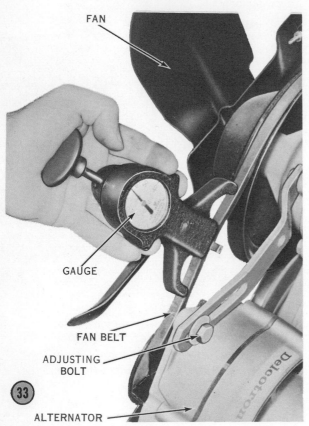

FAN

GAUGE

FAN BELT

ADJUSTING BOLT

33

ALTERNATOR

33 Install the alternator and its support brackets. Install the drive belt and use a tension gauge to adjust the belt tension to 70 lbs. ±5 lbs. with a used belt or to 90 lbs. ±5 lbs. with a new belt. Connect the main and field leads to the alternator, then reconnect the battery ground terminal.

34 Clean the air cleaner element by blowing compressed air through it in a reverse direction. **Caution:** *Don't hold the air nozzle too close to the element, or you will damage it.* The element should be replaced each 12,000 miles of service. Install the air cleaner on the carburetor with the word "front" facing the front of the engine. Tighten the wing nut.

35 Connect all coolant hoses and fill the cooling system. Check the dip stick to be sure that the oil level is up to the *full* mark. Add oil as required. Start the engine and adjust the idle speed to 600 rpm. Before adjusting the valve-stem-to-rocker-arm clearance, it is extremely important that the engine be thoroughly normalized (warmed to operating tem-

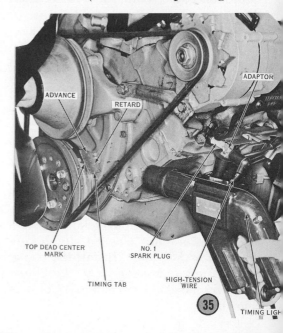

ADVANCE

RETARD

ADAPTOR

TOP DEAD CENTER MARK

NO. 1 SPARK PLUG

TIMING TAB

HIGH-TENSION WIRE

35

TIMING LIGH

perature). Valve clearances will change considerably—as much as 0.005"—during this warm-up period. Engines should be run 15-20 minutes in order to normalize all parts. Covering the radiator will not hasten this process as the expansion of the valves, push rods, cylinder head, and block is relative to the oil temperature. Therefore, only after the oil temperature is stabilized do these parts stop expanding, and valve clearance changes cease to occur. To adjust hydraulic lifters, back off the valve rocker arm nut with the engine idling, until the rocker arm starts to clatter, then turn the nut down slowly until the noise just stops. This is the *zero-lash position*. Now, turn the nut down an additional ¼ turn, pause 10 seconds until the engine runs smoothly, and repeat the ¼ turns until the nut is down one full turn from the zero-lash position.

Caution: *This one-turn preload adjustment must be done slowly to allow the lifter time to adjust, so there will be no interference between the inlet valve head and the top of the piston.* If the valve head does strike the piston, a bent valve or push rod will result. With mechanical lifters, turn the rocker arm stud nut as needed to obtain the specified valve lash as measured between the rocker arm and the valve stem. Stop the engine to connect a timing light. Install an adaptor between No. 1 spark plug and the high-tension wire so that you can connect the timing light high-tension wire to it. Connect the two primary wires to the terminals of the battery. Start the engine and direct the neon light at the timing tab. Adjust the position of the distributor until the index on the impulse neutralizer is aligned with the correct timing mark for the engine.

CHECK YOUR KNOWLEDGE

1. What is the basic difference between an internal and external combustion engine?
2. Explain the purpose of each of the following parts of the fuel system: gas tank, fuel pump, carburetor, and intake manifold.
3. What is the advantage of a high compression ratio?
4. What is the function of the ignition system?
5. Why is an electrical discharge of 20,000 volts required to fire the fuel-air mixture?
6. What is the temperature of the burning fuel?
7. What is the purpose of the lubricating system?
8. Describe a cylinder head.
9. What four parts does the cylinder head contain?
10. Why is it so important for the intake manifold to provide equi-distant passageways to the combustion chambers?
11. Why must the exhaust manifold gaskets be made of special heat resisting material?
12. What is the purpose of the exhaust manifold heat control?
13. What is the test for a leaky exhaust manifold gasket? Intake manifold gasket? Cylinder head gasket?

Self-Check Tests
TRUE-FALSE

1. Liquid gasoline cannot burn.
2. The compression ratio of today's engines often reaches 20 to 1.
3. Newer cars are equipped with 12 volt storage batteries to provide a larger spark across the spark plug electrodes.
4. Most automotive engines are liquid cooled.
5. The power plant consists of the engine, clutch, and transmission.

6. The intake manifold conducts the burned gases from the combustion chamber to the muffler.
7. The manifold heat control dries out the incoming gases.
8. A defective exhaust manifold gasket will cause the engine to miss on two adjacent cylinders.

MULTIPLE CHOICE

1. The engine which powers our modern automobile is of the: a) external; b) internal; c) pulse-jet combustion type.
2. The fuel-air mixture is drawn through the carburetor by the sucking action of the: a) piston; b) valves; c) intake manifold; d) fuel pump.
3. The combustion chamber is: a) square; b) rectangular; c) cylindrical.
4. The compression ratio of today's engines often reaches: a) 4−1; b) 6−1; c) 10−1.
5. Which of the following parts does *not* belong to the ignition system: a) spark plug; b) fuel pump; c) distributor; d) battery?
6. The temperature of the burning fuel often reaches: a) 2,500°; b) 3,500°; c) 4,500° F.
7. Which of the following is *not* a part of the lubrication system: a) carburetor; b) oil pump; c) filter; d) gauge?
8. The V-type engine has almost superseded the in-line engine because it is: a) more economical; b) more powerful; c) shorter in length.
9. The cylinder head contains the: a) oil pump; b) valves; c) heat control.
10. The intake manifold conducts the: a) fuel-air mixture to the carburetor; b) burned gases to the muffler; c) the fuel-air mixture to the combustion area.
11. The exhaust gases contain: a) carbon monoxide; b) carbon dioxide; c) fuel-air mixture.
12. The manifold heat control valve is located in the: a) exhaust; b) intake; c) cooling manifold.
13. A defective intake manifold gasket can be detected: a) with a compression gauge; b) with a gasoline squirt can; c) by hand.

COMPLETION

1. Gasoline is brought to the carburetor from the gas tank by a _____.
2. A _____ _____ ignites the fuel-air mixture by passing a spark between its electrodes.
3. The ignition _____ supplies the high voltage required to jump across the spark plug gap.
4. The oil _____ removes harmful abrasive particles before they can be circulated with the lubricating oil.
5. The _____ and _____, together with the completely assembled engine block, form the power plant.
6. The _____ _____ conducts the fuel-air mixture from the carburetor to the combustion chamber.
7. Heat from the exhaust manifold _____ _____ is used to dry out the incoming gases.

MATCHING

1. Carburetor
2. Spark plug
3. Cylinder
4. Filter
5. Radiator
6. Valves
7. Manifold heat control

a. Cooling system
b. Ignition system
c. Combustion chamber
d. Fuel system
e. Lubrication system
f. Exhaust system
g. Cylinder head

Chapter 2

The Cooling System

The internal combustion engine is essentially a heat engine. That is, it develops its power through the burning of fuel which creates the expansive force needed to drive the piston down the cylinder. The temperature of the burning fuel often reaches 4,500° F. If this were not reduced, engine parts would melt.

It is the duty of the cooling system to carry off this excess heat before the engine is damaged. However, the cooling system has another duty — it must maintain enough heat in the engine for it to operate at maximum efficiency.

Transfer of Heat

Heat can be transferred from one medium to another in three ways: *conduction, convection* and *radiation*. The automobile engine utilizes all three of these methods. After combustion, the unwanted heat passes through the cylinder head metal by *conduction* and into the coolant fluid which surrounds it. The coolant acts as a transfer agent, carrying the heat to the radiator for dissipation to the atmosphere. The coolant is circulated within the system by a centrifugal pump and by *convection* currents. As the heated coolant expands, it becomes lighter than the surrounding liquid. The positions of the hoses, radiator outlet, and inlet are so designed as to take advantage of these *convection* currents. The heated coolant transfers its energy through the metal walls of the radiator *(conduction),* which *radiates* the heat to the surrounding air.

Types of Cooling Systems

In general, engines are either air or liquid cooled. Air-cooled engines have separate cast cylinders so air can be circulated around them to remove the heat. The tops of such cylinders are finned to increase the heat dissipating area.

Liquid-cooled engines circulate a liquid around the hottest parts to remove excess heat. The heated liquid is carried to the radiator where the air cools it. Basically, a liquid-cooled engine is air cooled because, in the final analysis, the coolant is only an agent for transferring the heat to the radiator where air cools it.

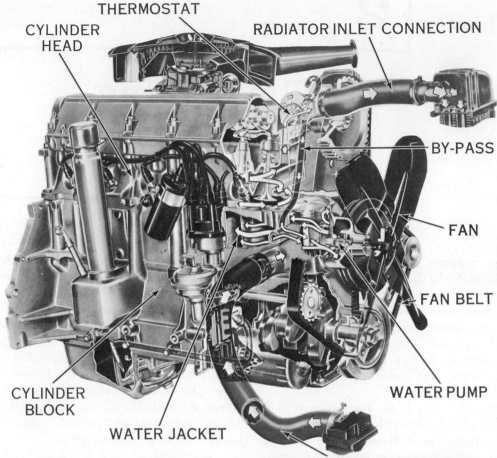

THERMOSTAT

CYLINDER HEAD

RADIATOR INLET CONNECTION

BY-PASS

FAN

FAN BELT

WATER PUMP

CYLINDER BLOCK

WATER JACKET

RADIATOR OUTLET CONNECTION

The engine contains a hollow chamber around the combustion area of the head and around the cylinder area of the block. While passing through this chamber, the coolant collects the excess heat of combustion. The heated coolant is then circulated to the radiator, where the passing air removes the heat. Courtesy Pontiac Motor Division, General Motors Corporation.

Parts of the Cooling System

The *coolant* is circulated by a centrifugal pump which is driven by a fan belt from the crankshaft pulley, and is sealed against leakage by a spring-type washer.

The *fan* blades are unequally spaced to minimize vibration. On some engines, a detachable clutch allows the fan to idle when the engine is cool

enough. This saves about 10% of the engine horsepower.

A *thermostat* restricts the flow of coolant to the radiator until the right temperature is reached. This minimizes the length of time required for warm-up. The thermostat contains a bellows which expands when heated to open a valve and permit normal circulation of the coolant.

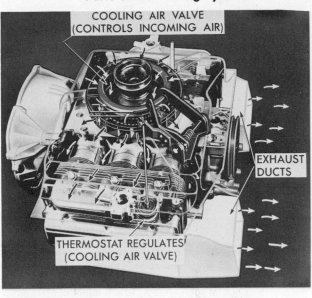

A cellular radiator core. The black arrow shows the path the coolant follows. The folded fins increase the heat radiating area. Courtesy Harrison Radiator Division, General Motors Corporation.

The Corvair engine is air-cooled. Note that the fins are larger around the combustion chamber than around the lower part of the cylinders. Larger fins increase heat radiating area. Courtesy Chevrolet Motor Division, General Motors Corporation.

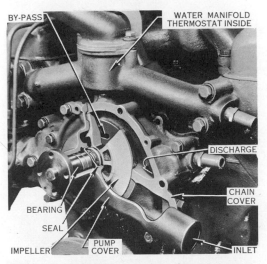

A cutaway section of a fin-and-tube radiator core. The black arrow shows the path the coolant follows. The fins increase the heat radiating area. Courtesy Harrison Radiator Division, General Motors Corporation.

This cutaway section shows how the water pump operates. The vanes of the impeller whirl the water around, centrifugal force throwing it outward to the discharge port. The inlet feeds to the center of the impeller. Courtesy Buick Motor Division, General Motors Corporation.

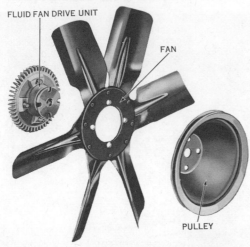

FLUID FAN DRIVE UNIT

FAN

PULLEY

Note how the fan blades are unequally spaced to minimize vibration. The fluid fan drive unit contains silicone fluid, which allows some slippage at high speeds, where minimum fan effect is desired. Courtesy Chrysler Division, Chrysler Corporation.

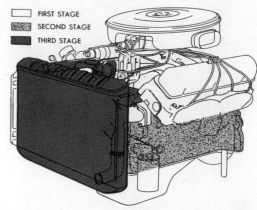

☐ FIRST STAGE

▨ SECOND STAGE

■ THIRD STAGE

The Mercury engine cooling system operates in three stages. When the engine is started, circulation occurs only around the cylinder heads. When the coolant warms, a thermostat opens allowing circulation through the block. And when the engine reaches operating temperature, the coolant is circulated through the radiator as well. Courtesy Lincoln-Mercury Division, Ford Motor Company.

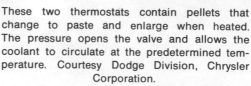

VALVE

POWER UNIT

A *by-pass* allows limited circulation past the closed thermostat until the correct operating temperature is reached. The coolant is directed around the block, instead of to the radiator, whenever the thermostat is closed. This provides a uniform temperature throughout the engine, eliminating hot spots and uneven expansion, and improving exhaust valve life.

The boiling point of water, 212° F at sea level, drops rapidly with altitude because the air pressure decreases. The normal operating temperature of an internal combustion engine is about 180° F and increases rapidly when the engine is pulling up a long steep grade

These two thermostats contain pellets that change to paste and enlarge when heated. The pressure opens the valve and allows the coolant to circulate at the predetermined temperature. Courtesy Dodge Division, Chrysler Corporation.

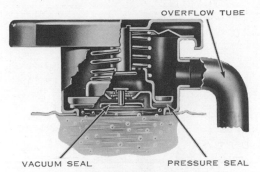

OVERFLOW TUBE

VACUUM SEAL   PRESSURE SEAL

A pressurized cooling system cap contains a pressure seal which opens at 14 psi, and a vacuum seal which opens when the pressure goes below atmospheric as the liquid cools and contracts.

because of the additional fuel supplied by the opened throttle. When the increased engine temperature meets the lowered boiling point of the coolant, it begins to boil.

To combat this unpleasant situation, engineers have pressurized the cooling systems of modern automobiles. By raising the pressure on the coolant to 14 pounds to the square inch (psi), the liquid does not boil until a temperature as high as 232° F is reached. This increases the margin of safety between the boiling and operating temperatures under heavy-load operating conditions.

The filler cap contains a pressure-relief valve which opens at 14 psi to prevent dangerous build-up of pressure which could split the radiator. A "reverse" valve in the cap allows air to enter the system when the engine cools, preventing the formation of a vacuum which could collapse the hoses.

Antifreeze

Water freezes at 32° F at sea level and expands when it does. If allowed to do so in the confined space of the coolant

chambers, the block would crack. To minimize this danger when outside temperature drops below freezing, a chemical is added to the coolant to lower its freezing point.

Either of two antifreeze agents is commonly used: alcohol or Ethylene Glycol. Alcohol makes only a temporary solution, since engine operating temperatures are often close to the boiling point of the alcohol, which hastens loss by evaporation.

The Ethylene Glycol solutions are often termed "permanent" types, since their boiling point is much higher than the operating range of the engine temperature; therefore they resist evaporation.

Antifreeze solutions are mixed with the coolant in varying proportions according to the temperature expected. The lower the temperature, the more antifreeze must be added. The strength of the solution can be tested with a hydrometer similar to the type used for testing the solutions of batteries, but equipped with a scale adapted to the density of antifreeze solutions.

Service Procedures

Unless water in the cooling system is treated with a corrosion preventive, rust and scale may eventually clog water

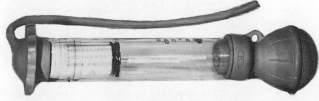

A hydrometer is used to measure the specific gravity of the coolant to determine the antifreeze content. Courtesy E. I. du Pont de Nemours & Company.

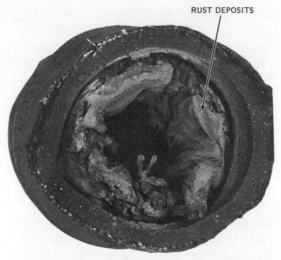

RUST DEPOSITS

Rust deposits build up in an unprotected cooling system. Note how little passageway is left for the coolant.

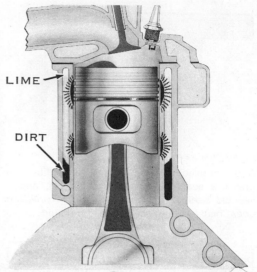

LIME

DIRT

One of the dangers of rust and lime formations is hot spots caused by the insulating quality of the deposits. These soon result in local overheating, burning off the lubricant, and eventually scuffing. Courtesy Perfect Circle Corporation.

passages in the radiator and water jackets. This raises engine operating temperatures, affecting engine performance and economy of operation.

Two common causes of corrosion are: (1) air drawn into the system from a low liquid level in the radiator, a leaky water pump, or a loose hose connection;

This block was broken away to show the rust and corrosion deposits which form and block passageways. These deposits can be minimized by using a rust inhibitor. Courtesy E. I. du Pont de Nemours & Company.

(2) exhaust gas which may be blown into the cooling system past a leaking cylinder head gasket or through a crack.

Service procedures consist of replacing a worn fan belt, testing and replacing a defective thermostat, repairing a defective or leaky water pump, and cleaning the cooling system.

Troubleshooting

Test for a clogged radiator by warming the engine to operating temperature and then turning it off. Feel the radiator. It should be rather hot at the top and warm at the bottom, with a gradual temperature change between. Cold sections indicate *clogged areas.*

A *defective head gasket* may allow exhaust gases to leak into the cooling system. These gases combine with the water to form acids which hasten corro-

BEFORE INSTALLING WATER PUMP...

1 DISCONNECT BATTERY

2 DRAIN COOLANT
Thoroughly flush and drain the cooling system.

3 CHECK HOSES, CLAMPS, RADIATOR
Examine the hoses, clamps, and the radiator and cap. Repair or replace if necessary.

4 GAIN WORKING ROOM
If necessary for working room, remove the radiator, fan shroud and other components. A few minutes spent analyzing adjacent components and removing those in the way may save you hours of lost labor.

5 REMOVE BELTS
Remove all belts that ride on the fan pulley. On some late models, such as front wheel drive Escort/Lynx and Mazda 626, the water pump is powered by the camshaft drive (timing) belt. In these cases refer to manufacturer's recommendations concerning camshaft drive belt installation and tension adjustment.

6 REMOVE THE FAN
Remove the fan and inspect it carefully. IMPORTANT: A flying fan blade can be deadly! If you detect any evidence of cracks or bends in a fan, replace it. Never try to straighten or repair a fan.

7 INSPECT FAN CLUTCH
If a fan clutch is present, check it for evidence of fluid leakage. If the fan spins more than five revolutions when turned by hand, the fan clutch mechanism should be replaced. FAULTY FAN CLUTCHES ARE A MAJOR CAUSE OF OVERHEATING.

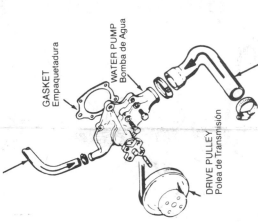

HOSE (FROM HEATER)
Manguera (del Calentador)

GASKET
Empaquetadura

WATER PUMP
Bomba de Agua

DRIVE PULLEY
Polea de Transmisión

LOWER RADIATOR HOSE
Manguera Inferior del Radiador

ANTES DE INSTALARLO LA BOMBA DE AGUA ...

1 DESCONECTE LA BATERIA

2 VACIE EL LIQUIDO REFRIGERANTE
Vacíe completamente el sistema refrigerante.

3 COMPRUEBE LAS MANGUERAS, ABRAZADERAS Y RADIADOR
Examine las mangueras, abrazaderas, y el radiador y su tapa. Repare o reemplace si es necesario.

4 GANE ESPACIO PARA TRABAJAR
Si es necesario ganar más espacio para trabajar, retire el radiador, anillo de refuerzo del ventilador y otras piezas. Gastando unos pocos minutos analizando las piezas cercanas y retirando las que están en su campino, le puede ahorrar horas de trabaho perdido.

5 RETIRE LAS CORREAS
Retire todas las correas que van en la polea del ventilador. En algunos vehiculos de modelo último, como Escort/Lynx y Mazda 626 de tracción delantera, la bomba de agua es accionada por la correa del mecanismo del eje de levas (regulador de encendido). En estos casos, consulte las recomendaciones del fabricante del vehiculo para instalar y ajustar apropiadamente esta correa.

6 RETIRE EL VENTILADOR
Retire el ventilador e inspecciónelo con cuidado. IMPORTANTE: Una hoja o paleta del ventilador que se desprenda puede ser fatal. Si detecta cualquier evidencia de rajadura o doblez en el ventilador, reemplácelo. Nunca trate de enderezar o reparar un ventilador.

7 COMPRUEBE EL EMBREAGUE DEL VENTILADOR
Si hay un embreague del ventilador, examínelo para evidencia de líquido perdiendo. Si al hacer girar el ventilador con la mano dá más de 5 vueltas, el mecanismo del embreague del ventilador debe ser reemplazado. EMBREAGUES DE VENTILADOR DEFECTUOSOS SON UNA CAUSA MAYOR DE RECALENTAMIENTO.

WATER PUMP TROUBLESHOOTING
FALLAS MECANICAS EN LA BOMBA DE AGUA

SYMPTOMS — FALLAS

PROBABLE CAUSES
CAUSAS PROBABLES

PROBABLE CAUSES / CAUSAS PROBABLES	Overheating / Recalentamiento	Leaks at water pump bolts / Pérdidas de líquido por los pernos de la bomba de agua	Leaks at gasket / Pérdidas de líquido por la empaquetadura	Scraping noise when pump shaft is turned / Ruido de "raspado" cuando el eje de la bomba es girado
Low coolant level / Poco líquido refrigerante	●			
Air pocket in coolant system / Aire en el sistema refrigerante [1]	●			
Faulty fan clutch / Embreague defectuoso del ventilador	●			
Inoperative electric coolant fan / Ventilador eléctrico no funciona	●			
Restricted exhaust system / Sistema de tubo de escape obturado	●			
Retarded spark timing / Regulador de encendido de bujías retardado	●			
Bolts go through cooling system / Los pernos atraviezan el sistema refrigerante [2]		●		
Mounting surface unclean / Superficies de montaje sucias			●	
Gasket misaligned / Empaquetadura malposicionada			●	
Pump bolts not properly tightened / Pernos de la bomba malajustados			●	
Rust deposits from mounting surface entering pump / Depósitos de óxido en las superficies de montaje de entrada de la bomba				●
Pump installed without gasket / Bomba instalada sin empaquetadura				●
Excessive side play in pump / Demasiado vibración lateral en la bomba [3]				●

[1] Allow engine to cool; restart and run with radiator cap removed and fill as necessary.
Deje enfriar el motor del vehículo; luego vuelva a hacerlo funcionar teniendo la tapa del radiador retirada y heche más líquido si es necesario.

[2] Apply sealant to threads.
Aplique líquido sellador a las roscas de los pernos.

[3] Bearings damaged from overtight belt.
Cojinetes dañados por una correa demasiado ajustada.

NOTE: A common cause of overheating in cars equipped with electrically operated radiator fans is a malfunction in fan control circuits. This may be a blown fuse, a faulty thermoswitch, etc. After the remanufactured pump is installed and the cooling system refilled, run the engine until the coolant reaches the temperature at which the fan should switch on. If it does not do so, refer to the manufacturer's recommendations for troubleshooting the fan circuit.

NOTA: Una causa muy común de recalentamiento en vehículos equipados con ventiladores de control eléctrico es malfuncionamiento en los circuitos de control del ventilador. Esto puede ser un fusible quemado o un interruptor de temperatura quebrado, etc. Una vez que la bomba de repuesto ha sido instalada y se ha vuelto a llenar el sistema refrigerante, haga funcionar el motor del vehículo hasta que el líquido refrigerante alcance una temperatura a la cual el ventilador empieza a funcionar. Si ésto no ocurre, consulte las recomendaciones del fabricante del vehículo por probables fallas en el circuito del ventilador.

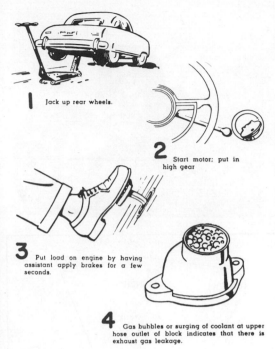

1 Jack up rear wheels.

2 Start motor; put in high gear

3 Put load on engine by having assistant apply brakes for a few seconds.

4 Gas bubbles or surging of coolant at upper hose outlet of block indicates that there is exhaust gas leakage.

To test for a cracked block, place a load on the engine, with the top water hose removed so that you can see the bubbles formed by the exhaust gases passing through the coolant. Courtesy E. I. du Pont de Nemours & Company.

cars with a 14 psi cap.) If the pressure drops, check all points for an exterior leak.

If you cannot locate an exterior leak, after the gauge shows a drop in pressure, detach the tester and run the engine until it reaches operating temperature. Reattach the tester and pump it to 7 psi pressure while the engine is running. Race the engine and, if the dial fluctuates, it indicates a combustion leak. **Caution:** *Pressure builds up fast! Never let the pressure exceed 15 psi. Release excess pressure immediately.*

To trace a combustion area leak further in a V-8 engine, detach the wires from one bank of spark plugs. Run the engine on the connected bank. If the needle continues to fluctuate, the leak is in the operating bank; otherwise, the leak is in the other bank.

Check the oil dip stick; if water globules appear mixed with the oil, a serious *internal leak* is in the block.

sion. To check for such exhaust leaks, drain the coolant until the level is just above the top of the cylinder head. Disconnect the upper radiator hose and remove the thermostat and fan belt. Start the engine and accelerate it quickly several times. At the same time, note any appreciable water rise or the appearance of bubbles, indicating exhaust gases passing into the system.

To test a pressure cooling system for *leaks*, wipe the radiator filler cap seat clean. Drain some water until the level is ½ inch below the neck of the radiator. Attach the tester and apply 15 psi pressure. (Use 15 psi pressure only on

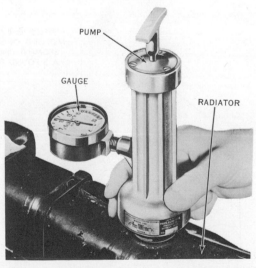

PUMP

GAUGE

RADIATOR

A gauge can be used to find a leak in a pressurized cooling system by building up pressure with the attached pump. Courtesy Dodge Division, Chrysler Corporation.

Drive belts must be tensioned properly so that they do not slip, if too loose, or damage the bearings, if too tight. The adjustment can be made according to the procedure on page 73 (and shown below), known as the belt-deflection method. The Borough's strain gauge is a precision tool for determining the applied pressure. Courtesy Chevrolet Motor Division, General Motors Corporation.

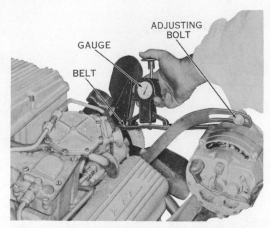

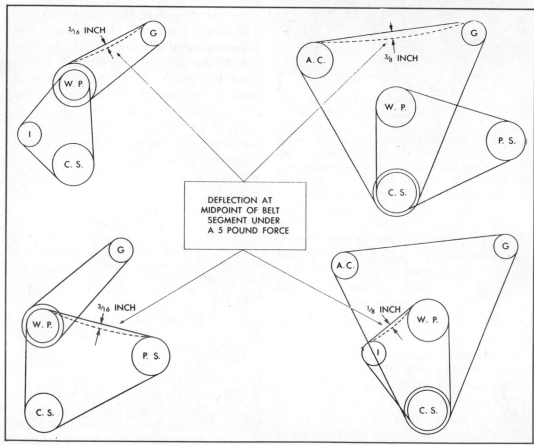

This diagram shows the various belt arrangements possible on a Dodge engine, C.S., crankshaft; W.P., water pump; G., generator; A.C., air conditioning; P.S., power steering; I., idler. Courtesy Chrysler Corporation.

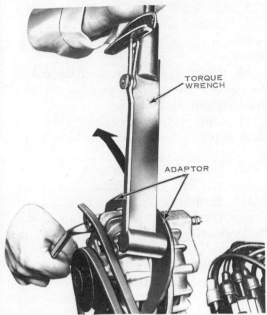

TORQUE
WRENCH

ADAPTOR

Some manufacturers design the bracket with a square hole for the insertion of a torque wrench so that a specified tension can be placed on the belt. Notice the *wheel and axle* arrangement that drives the generator. *What class lever* is the torque wrench? Courtesy Chrysler Corporation.

Replacing a Fan Belt

The V-type fan belt is used on all modern engines to drive the water pump, fan, alternator, and compressors. It does not slip when properly adjusted, because of its wedge-shaped bearing surface. If the belt is too tight, there will be excessive friction and considerable wear on the bearings. If the belt is too loose, it will vibrate and howl as it slips and chatters over the pulleys; the alternator output and water circulation will be affected.

The proper belt adjustment varies with the different manufacturers and will have to be looked up for each model car.

Tools and Equipment

$\frac{1}{2}$ and $\frac{9}{16}$ inch combination-end wrenches; pry bar; torque wrench; $\frac{3}{4}$ and $\frac{11}{16}$ inch sockets; Borough's strain gauge.

PROCEDURE

1. Loosen the bolts holding the slotted brace to the alternator and to the engine.

2. To replace the drive belt, move the alternator toward the block as far as it will go to provide maximum clearance.

3. Adjust the new belt so that it deflects the specified distance when normal thumb pressure is applied midway between the alternator and fan pulleys.

4. If the power steering pump belt must be replaced, the pump bracket bolts are loosened and the pump moved in toward the engine to provide clearance.

5. Test the pump drive belt tension for slippage by using a torque wrench applied to the drive pulley retaining nut. A *new* belt is correctly adjusted when it will slip in the pulley when 40-45 foot-pounds torque is applied. With a *used* belt, the torque should be 30-35 foot-pounds.

6. Tighten the retaining bolts securely.

Reverse Flushing

Use a good cleaning solution to loosen the rust and scale before flushing. The manufacturer's instructions should be followed exactly. After chemical cleaning, the system is flushed with water and air under pressure in a direction opposite to the normal flow. This reverse action loosens the corrosion deposits and forces them out.

73

FLUSHING GUN

To reverse-flush the block, first remove the thermostat; otherwise, the cold water will close it and prevent circulation. Courtesy Plymouth Division, Chrysler Corporation.

Tools and Materials

Chemical cleaner, reverse flushing equipment, screwdriver, $\frac{1}{4}$, $\frac{3}{8}$, $\frac{7}{16}$, $\frac{1}{2}$ and $\frac{9}{16}$-inch wrenches.

PROCEDURE

To Clean the System

1. Drain the cooling system completely.

2. Remove the thermostat housing, and then the thermostat.

3. Refill the cooling system to about 3 inches from the top.

4. Add the chemical cleaning solution.

5. Cover the radiator and run the engine until the temperature reaches 180° F.

6. Remove the radiator cover and continue to run the engine for another 20 minutes, but do not allow it to boil.

7. Stop the engine and drain the solution. **Caution:** *Be careful not to scald yourself.*

To Reverse Flush the Radiator

8. Remove the upper and lower radiator hoses, and replace the radiator cap.

9. Attach a long piece of hose to the top radiator connection to carry the water away from the engine compartment.

10. Attach a piece of hose to the radiator outlet connection and insert the flushing gun in this hose.

11. Connect the water hose of the gun to a water outlet and the air hose to an air line.

12. Turn on the water and, when the radiator is full, turn on the air in short blasts, letting the radiator fill between blasts. **Caution:** *Be careful to apply the air gradually, as a clogged radiator can stand only a limited pressure before it comes apart at the seams.*

13. Continue flushing and blowing air through the radiator until the water is clear.

The pressure flushing gun has fittings to allow fluid and compressed air to pass into the radiator. When the radiator is full, the operator can turn on the valve to allow air pressure to blast the rust from the system. Courtesy Plymouth Division, Chrysler Corporation.

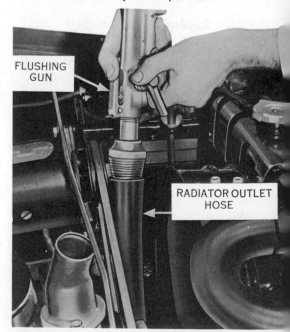

FLUSHING GUN

RADIATOR OUTLET HOSE

To Reverse Flush Block and Head

14. With the thermostat removed, attach a long hose to the water pump inlet and a short hose to the water outlet connection at the top of the engine.

15. Insert the flushing gun into the short hose.

16. Turn on the water and, when the engine water jacket is full, turn on the air in short blasts.

17. Continue flushing and blowing air through the block and head until the water is clear.

18. Direct compressed air behind the radiator core to blow out dirt and bugs from the air passages.

To Clean the Heater Core

19. Disconnect both hoses from the heater.

20. In a similar manner, use the air and water valves to blow out the rust and corrosion. Be careful not to use too much pressure, which will damage the core.

Testing Thermostats

Thermostats contain metals that expand and contract with temperature changes. They are used for automatic temperature control. All modern cars have thermostatically controlled cooling systems to block circulation while the engine is cold. The heat from the burning fuel warms the coolant quickly. As soon as it reaches the temperature at which the thermostat is set, the valve opens and permits normal circulation. In extremely cold weather, the thermostat valve may remain partially closed.

Tools and Equipment

$\frac{1}{2}$ and $\frac{9}{16}$-inch end wrenches; screwdriver; pot of water; thermometer; gas stove; thermostat unit.

PROCEDURE

1. Drain the water from the radiator.

2. Remove the top water hose and outlet pipe.

3. Remove the thermostat valve and inspect for temperature rating.

4. Heat a pot of water containing the thermostat and thermometer. For equalized temperatures, see that neither the thermostat nor the thermometer touches the bottom of the pot. They may be suspended by a string from a stick laid across the top.

5. The thermostat should open when the water reaches the temperature stamped on the side of the valve.

6. Replace the thermostat valve in the top of the cylinder head.

7. Install the top casting and water hose, using a new gasket.

8. Fill the radiator with water and inspect for leaks. Recheck the coolant level after the engine is warm.

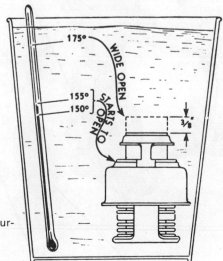

Testing a thermostat-opening temperature. Courtesy American Motors Corporation.

Repairing a Water Pump

The water pump has an impeller driven by a shaft which extends out through the front of the pump housing. In order to keep the coolant inside the housing, a packing gland is used around the shaft. After long wear, a leak may develop at this point.

Modern water pumps cannot be re-packed because they are built with self-sealing devices. A spring presses against a packing washer which seals the joint between the shaft and housing. When this type of pump leaks, the ball bearings rust, and the entire pump must be rebuilt or exchanged.

Tools and Equipment

Water pump; screwdriver; ½ and ⁹⁄₁₆-inch combination end wrenches; repair kit.

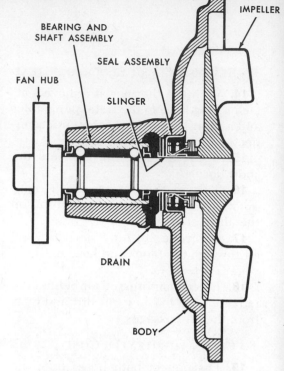

The modern water pump seal rotates with the impeller shaft and is compressed against the pump housing by a spring. A graphite washer reduces friction and provides lubrication.

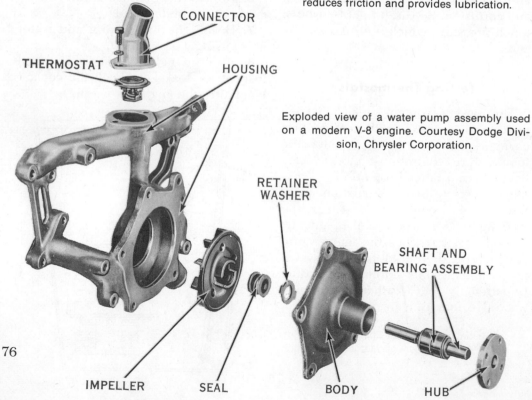

Exploded view of a water pump assembly used on a modern V-8 engine. Courtesy Dodge Division, Chrysler Corporation.

76

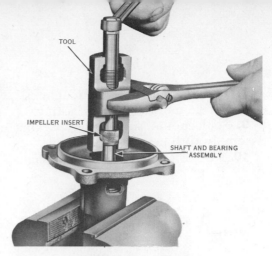

After the plastic impeller is split, the insert must be removed by a special tool. *What three simple machines* can you find in this picture? Courtesy Dodge Division, Chrysler Corporation.

1. Drain the water.

2. Loosen the alternator. Remove the fan belt and water pump.

3. Remove the fan blades, if necessary, to take off the pump.

4. Press off the pulley and hub. On late-model Chrysler product engines, the plastic impeller must be split with a chisel to remove it.

5. Remove the shaft and impeller. Trace the path of the fluid as it enters from the center of the pump housing and is thrown off to one side by centrifugal force.

6. Remove the packing and spring assembly. Note how the spring presses the packing against the face of the pump housing, sealing it against water leaks.

On Chrysler products using plastic impellers, the plastic must be split with a chisel. Courtesy Dodge Division, Chrysler Corporation.

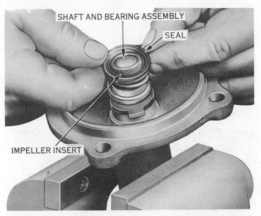

Assembling the new seal. Courtesy Dodge Division, Chrysler Corporation.

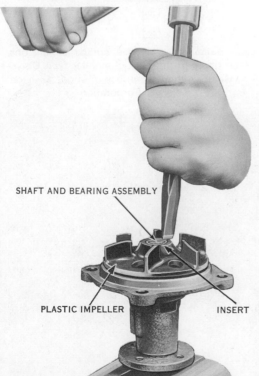

The seat must be resurfaced so that the new seal will not leak. Courtesy Miller Mfg. Co.

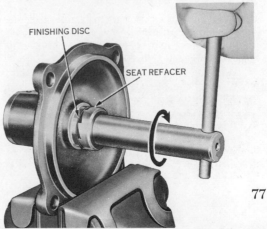

7. Test the bearings for roughness.

8. Reface the water pump casting.

9. Replace the spring and packing assembly with new parts.

10. Install a new impeller and shaft.

11. Install the hub assembly.

12. Install the fan blades.

13. Install the pump on the engine, using a new gasket. **Caution:** *Be sure that the old gasket has been completely removed; otherwise, it will leak.*

14. Fill the radiator with coolant and check for leaks.

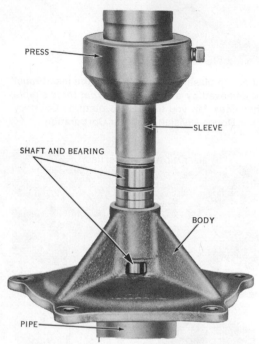

Pressing a new shaft and bearing assembly into the pump housing. Courtesy Chrysler Corporation.

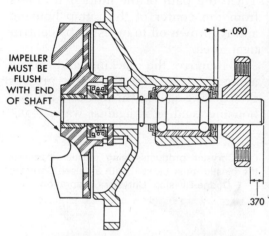

Each pump assembly has critical dimensions. These apply to the plastic-impeller type Chrysler water pump. Courtesy Dodge Division, Chrysler Corporation.

CHECK YOUR KNOWLEDGE

1. Why is it so important to remove excess heat from the engine?

2. What are the two purposes of the cooling system?

3. What is the purpose of the thermostat?

4. What is the purpose of the by-pass?

5. What is the advantage of a pressurized cooling system?

6. Why is it so important to protect the engine against freezing?

7. What are the two commonly used types of antifreeze?

Self-Check Tests

TRUE-FALSE

1. The cooling system has but one purpose: to remove from the engine all the heat possible.

2. Basically, a liquid cooled engine is air cooled.

3. A "V"-type belt is used because its shape increases the contact area and reduces slippage.

4. The thermostat opens when the engine cools and closes when it reaches operating temperature.
5. Engine operating temperatures are often close to the boiling point of alcohol, which hastens evaporation.

MULTIPLE CHOICE

1. Which one of the following is *not* a part of the cooling system: a) pump; b) thermostat; c) belt; d) filter?
2. Partial block circulation, when the engine is cold, is provided by the: a) fan; b) by-pass; c) thermostat; d) manifold heat control valve.
3. The strength of the antifreeze solution can be tested with a: a) thermometer; b) thermostat; c) voltmeter; d) hydrometer.

COMPLETION

1. Engines are either _____ or _____ cooled.
2. The coolant is circulated by a _____ vane-type pump.

3. The fan blades are unevenly spaced to minimize _____.
4. The _____ restricts the flow of coolant until a predetermined temperature is reached.
5. Most cooling systems are pressurized to about _____ psi.
6. A permanent type of antifreeze is _____.
7. Two common causes of corrosion are _____ and _____ _____.

MATCHING

1. Heat transfer device	a. Antifreeze
2. Thermostat	b. Partial circulation with cold engine
3. Ethylene Glycol	c. Radiator
4. By-pass	d. Restricts circulation when engine is cold
5. Pressure-type radiator cap	e. Increased boiling point

For an engine to run efficiently, it must be tuned properly. This night-school instructor is demonstrating the use of precision equipment in tuning this engine.

Chapter 3

The Lubricating System

Without proper lubrication, an engine would soon wear out; in fact, it would not even operate. Lubricants provide a liquid film on which the metallic parts ride so that sliding friction is replaced by fluid friction. Metal never touches metal when proper lubrication is supplied.

Lubricants also seal the gap between parts. If it were not for this sealing property, the gases could not be trapped and squeezed between the piston and cylinder head, and the engine would not run.

Another duty of the lubricant is to carry friction and combustion heat to the crankcase, where it is conducted through the oil pan metal and carried away by the passing air.

Fluid and Sliding Friction

Friction is the resistance offered to the movement of one body over another and is caused by the unevenness of the surfaces. No metallic surface is perfectly smooth. If examined under a powerful microscope, the finest honed

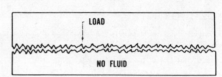

Sliding friction results when the peaks of one surface drop into the valleys of the other. Courtesy Clevite Service Corporation.

area will show "mountains" and "valleys." When such surfaces move over each other, friction results.

Friction is both troublesome and helpful to the engineer. Without friction, the tires would not be able to push against the road and the car would not move; the brakes would not be able to stop the car from rolling, once it started. Yet friction always results in heat, which is a form of wasted energy when we must get rid of it.

Another friction problem involves any shaft that has to revolve in a support; we call such supports *bearings*. Unless friction is minimized, the heat soon melts the parts and seizure occurs. Engineers use several devices to overcome bearing friction. For example, knowing that rolling friction is much

80

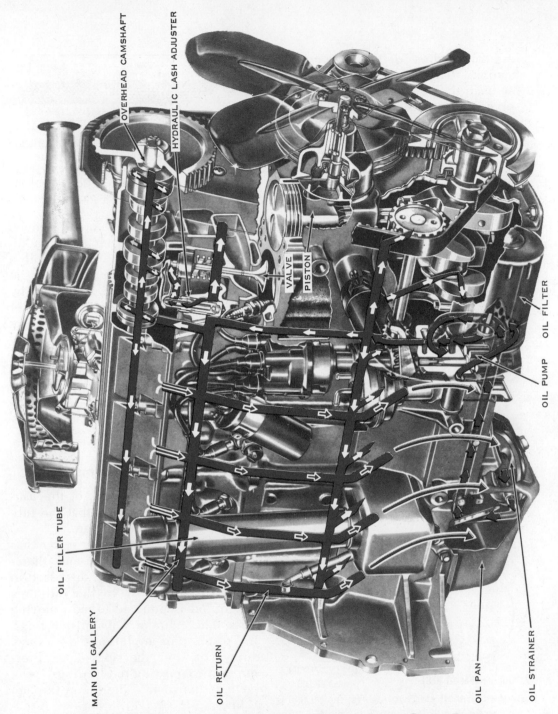

OVERHEAD CAMSHAFT

HYDRAULIC LASH ADJUSTER

VALVE

PISTON

OIL FILTER

OIL PUMP

OIL FILLER TUBE

MAIN OIL GALLERY

OIL RETURN

OIL PAN

OIL STRAINER

Diagram of the oil path in the full-force lubricating system used on the Pontiac Tempest 6-cylinder, overhead camshaft engine. Courtesy Pontiac Division, General Motors Corporation.

less than sliding friction, they use ball bearings. They use *dissimilar* metals for bearing surfaces, because they observed that friction varies with the nature of the surfaces in contact; surface irregularities of dissimilar metals

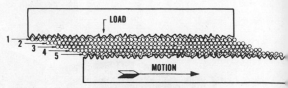

do not line up with each other as much as do those of similar metals. In addition, moving parts are supplied with a film of *lubricant* to separate them so that sliding friction is replaced by fluid friction.

Lubricants reduce friction because of their low *cohesion* (the force keeping the molecules together) which allows the molecules to move over each other with relatively low resistance. Lubricants have high *adhesion* qualities (the ability to stick to other materials), and so stay in place.

Types of Systems

Automobile engines are of the *wet-sump* type, which means that the lubricant is stored in the oil pan.

The *full-force lubricating system* has superseded all other types and, therefore, will be the only one discussed in detail in this book. In the full-force system, oil is pumped to most moving parts. The cylinder walls, piston rings, and piston pins are lubricated by spray thrown off from the sides of the pressure-fed connecting rod bearings.

Oil is drawn into the pump through a fine-mesh strainer, where it is delivered under pressure to an oil gallery or "header" line drilled lengthwise in the block. Feeder tubes extend from

Friction always results in heat, as shown by this dramatic picture of a brake being applied until it smokes. Courtesy Ford Division, Ford Motor Company.

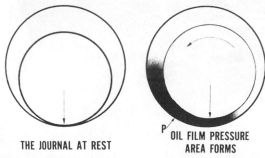

THE JOURNAL AT REST | OIL FILM PRESSURE AREA FORMS

Before the shaft starts to revolve, the oil film is squeezed out and boundary lubrication is present. After the oil film wedge forms, pressure holds the shaft from making metal-to-metal contact. Courtesy Clevite Service Corporation.

82

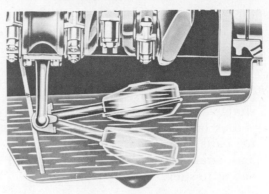

The floating-type oil strainer picks up the oil from the top, where it is cleanest.

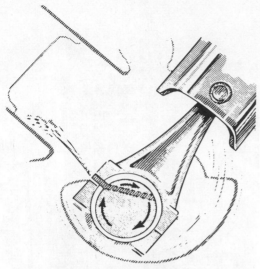

The oil spurt hole in the rod bearing lubricates the cylinder walls. Courtesy Ford Division, Ford Motor Company.

this main line to main and camshaft bearings. The main bearings are grooved so that oil can be forced into the drilled crankshaft, where it is directed under pressure to the connecting rod bearings. An oil "spit" hole, on the top thrust side of each connect-

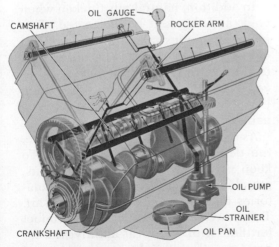

Diagram showing the path of the oil in a V-8 engine.

ing rod, sprays oil onto the cylinder walls for lubricating the pistons and rings.

The valve mechanism requires special lubrication. Oil leakage from the sides of the rod bearings sprays a fine mist around the valve operating mechanism. Hydraulically operated tappets require their own pressurized supply. Rocker arms are provided with a pressurized line from the main oil gallery.

The full-pressure system affords positive lubrication at all times. This advantage is lost by engines having excessively worn bearings. Excessive quantities of oil are thrown off the sides of such a bearing, onto the cylinder wall—too much for even the best set of rings to control—and oil burning usually results.

Development of Engine Lubricants

A "straight-run" product, a low-grade refinement of petroleum crude, was adequate for lubricating the early automobile engine. However, the modern internal combustion gasoline engine is very demanding of lubricating

83

oil. The constant churning and spraying mixes the oil with air, which increases oxidation and foaming. The products of combustion are water and acid. The mixing of these undesirable products with dust and dirt forms a sludge-and-resin type varnish which settles out and deposits over all internal parts. This "goo" plugs small holes and strainers, and causes rings and valves to stick.

A thermofor catalytic cracking unit. (TCC). The gasoline vapors are "cracked" and turned into blending stocks of high quality. Courtesy Mobil Oil Company.

The bubble tower (crude unit still)—where the heated oil rises in vapor form through bubble trays, coming out of the tower at various levels in "fractions" ranging from light gases at the top, through gasoline distillates and fuel oils to residuals at the bottom. Courtesy Mobil Oil Company.

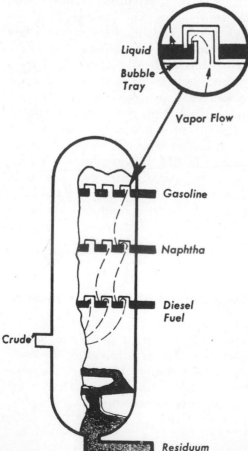

Liquid

Bubble Tray

Vapor Flow

Gasoline

Naphtha

Diesel Fuel

Crude

Residuum

In addition, natural oils thicken when cold, and thin out when heated. This is highly undesirable in our modern, closely fitted engines because such oils do not provide a free-moving lubricant when the engine is cold and, when it is hot, provide too thin a film between parts.

As engine speeds and power increase, the demands on oil also increase. To keep pace with engine developments, petroleum engineers set up laboratories to test and improve nature's art. Today, we have a highly refined product fortified with chemical additives, a far cry from the straight-run products of 40 years ago.

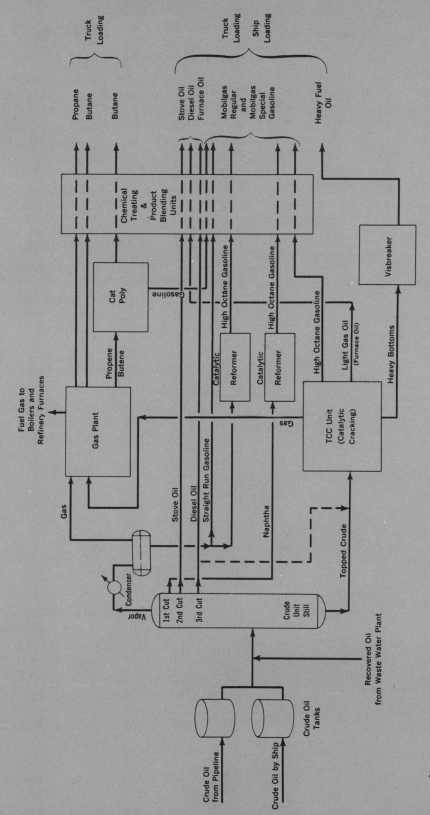

Diagram showing the processing of crude oil. Courtesy Mobil Oil Company.

85

Types of Oil

The control of sludge, varnish, moisture, and corrosive acids depends on (1) the quality of oil and additives, (2) engine operating temperature, and (3) the type of driving. The deposits form under both low- and high-speed driving conditions, but generally form more rapidly in cold weather during city driving. Thus, considerable periods of stop-and-go driving constitute *severe* conditions insofar as oil is concerned.

Sludge is reduced by an additive having detergent (cleansing) characteristics, varnish deposits by oxidation inhibitors, and bearing corrosion by corrosion-preventive additives. To differentiate in additive content, the Society of Automotive Engineers (S.A.E.) designates oil as follows:

ML (motor car, light service): For engines not critically affected by sludge and varnish deposits.

MM (motor car, medium service): Has additives to reduce sludge, varnish, and acid formations.

MS (motor car, severe service): Has enough additives to minimize the formation of sludge, varnish, and acids under normal driving conditions.

The control laboratory where samples of the various products are continuously tested for purity and content. Courtesy Mobil Oil Company.

Additives

Detergents

Under the high temperature of engine operation, some oil is burned. Carbon and oxidized products, mixed with dust, form abrasives which increase wear on the moving parts of the closely fitted engine. Additives of the detergent-dispersive type suspend the contaminants in exceedingly fine particles which do not form into harmful deposits.

Pour-point Depressants

Oil thickens as the temperature drops. This means that, in cold weather, poor lubrication results until the oil warms. A chemical is added to make the oil flow freer at low temperatures.

Anti-foam Agents

All oils foam to some extent from the vigorous agitation and aeration (air-mixing) in an automobile engine. Excessive foaming causes loss of oil from breather outlets and introduces air bubbles in the oil film, lowering its pressure resistance. To minimize foaming, a chemical is added to the oil to weaken the bubble structure and release the air.

Rust Protection

Low operating temperatures, the result of short trips and delayed warm-ups because of defective thermostats in the cooling system and exhaust manifold, cause water to form in the crankcase and mix with the lubricating oil. The water, resulting from the products of combustion, condenses on the cold metallic parts of the engine. In the

86

liquid solution are small amounts of acids, which result from the combustion of petroleum fuels. These acids accumulate in strength and cause corrosion.

Acid counteragents are placed in the oil to form a coating which prevents acid action with the metal. Frequent oil changes are necessary to remove the acid formation *if the average trip length is short.*

Viscosity

S.A.E. numbers refer to the flow characteristics of an oil. The lower viscosity oils, or "thinner" oils, such as S.A.E. 10 or S.A.E. 10W, are designed for cold weather to provide fast starting and instant lubrication. The higher viscosity oils, or "thicker" oils, such as S.A.E. 20 or S.A.E. 30, are designed for warm weather to provide good lubrication and low oil consumption under high operating temperatures.

Multiple viscosity oils, such as S.A.E. 10-30, are designed to combine fast starting and instant lubrication, characteristics of the thinner oils, with the warm-weather operating characteristics of the thicker oils.

Oil Changes

Motor oil does not wear out, but it becomes contaminated by dust, carbon, water, gasoline, and acids from the process of combustion. Changing it at regular intervals is the only way to remove these impurities, even though a filter is used. To be safe, the filter element should be changed each time the oil is changed.

The life span of engine oil depends on operating conditions. When the car

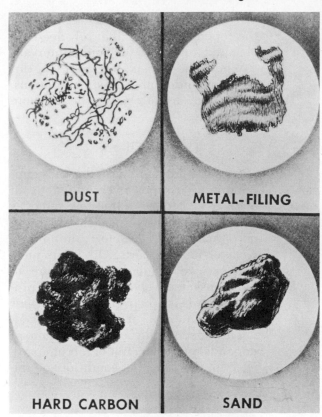

DUST

METAL-FILING

HARD CARBON

SAND

Abrasive particles found in the oil of any automobile engine. Courtesy Purolator Products, Inc.

is driven in cold weather in the city for house-to-house calls, as by doctors and salesmen, the oil should be changed every 500 miles. Under average winter driving conditions, when most of the driving is in the city with only occasional highway driving, the oil should be changed every 1,000 miles. Under average summer driving conditions, with the car operating under mixed city and highway driving, such as town driving during the week with a highway trip on week-ends, the oil should be changed every 4,000 miles.

When the car is driven exclusively on the open highway, the oil need be changed only at 5,000 mile intervals.

When the car is operated on dirt roads or under other dusty conditions, it is necessary to change the oil more frequently.

Oil Filters

An oil filter is one of the most important accessories ever added to an engine. Effective filtration removes most of the abrasive particles from the oil stream and, therefore, minimizes wear of moving parts. Oil filters must be serviced regularly if they are to function effectively. The service procedure consists of replacing the filter element whenever it becomes clogged.

The effective life of a filter element depends on the amount of foreign particles in the oil, the condition of the

This is a picture of a clogged oil filter. Evidently it cannot do the oil any good in this condition. Courtesy Purolator Products, Inc.

engine, and the amount and kind of dust in the area where the car is driven. Because it is difficult to see the extent of contamination in some filters, it is best, as stated earlier, to replace the element each time the oil is changed. This will assure a filtered supply of oil for longer engine life.

An engine with poor rings has more "blow-by" and carbon in the oil stream than does a new engine. Obviously, a worn engine needs more frequent element changes than a new one, but the safest way is to change the oil and filter element at the same time.

Oil filter systems are of two types: full-flow and by-pass. In the full-flow system, all of the oil is made to pass through the filter before it is sent to the moving parts of the engine. A valve, incorporated in the filter, opens when the element becomes clogged; therefore a constant stream of lubricating oil (though unfiltered) is always assured.

In the by-pass system, a secondary stream of oil is forced through the filter. The filter is installed in the by-pass valve line and, when the pressure exceeds the working pressure of the engine, the by-pass valve opens, allowing the extra oil to return to the crankcase through the filter.

Crankcase Ventilation

Gasoline, water, carbon, and dirt normally find their way into the crankcase of a gasoline engine. These substances unite chemically to form sludge, a gummy, tarry substance which sticks to valve stems and piston rings causing them to operate ineffectively, resulting in a steady loss of power.

This is the way the oil strainer plugs up with sludge. Courtesy Magnus Chemical Company.

Much engineering research is going on to minimize these deposits as much as possible. The most effective way to do this, researchers say, is to remove as many of the foreign agents as possible before they have a chance to unite chemically. To do this, oil filters are used to remove the insoluble particles, dirt and carbon, while crankcase ventilators remove the soluble agents, water and gasoline.

One gallon of water is formed by the combustion of each gallon of gasoline. Blow-by carries some of this vapor past the piston rings into the crankcase. Raw gasoline, especially from overchoking when the engine is cold, runs past the piston rings and thins out the oil. Inasmuch as the lubricating oil is heated well above the boiling point of water and gasoline on long runs, these liquids turn to vapor and can be drawn from the crankcase by passing air through it. On short runs where the engine oil seldom reaches a high temperature, more of the harmful liquids remain in solution to contaminate the oil.

Crankcase ventilators are provided on all engines to remove these vapors. In general, older engines depended on a vacuum, built up behind an outlet pipe, to suck the vapors from the crankcase. These pipes were always located so as to remove the vapors from the rear of the valve chamber. The angle of the bottom of the pipe was such that air passing by created a vacuum. This was known as the road-draft system of crankcase ventilation. It had one basic weakness in that it operated efficiently only at high road speeds. At low road speeds, an air draft is almost nonexistent and so the system was very ineffective.

Modern design requires a positive type ventilator in which the vapors are sucked into the intake manifold through a vacuum-actuated valve or carried into the induction system by the air passing through the carburetor.

The valve opens during periods of acceleration as the vacuum drops. Should the valve clog with carbon, pressure built up in the crankcase will force oil from the main bearings. Should the valve fail to seat, it will be impossible to make the engine idle properly. This system has been required by law since 1968 in order to minimize air pollutants and so lessen smog.

It is important in servicing these installations for the oil filler tube cap and vacuum valve to be cleaned frequently. The caps are made with a gauze filtering element to keep the dirt out of the incoming air. In service, they become clogged, which nullifies the benefits of the entire ventilation system. When the caps are very badly clogged, it is better to replace them as the cost is nominal. The valves clog and must be cleaned. When replacing such a valve, make sure that it is the correct one for that engine, as the air vent and spring vary with each model.

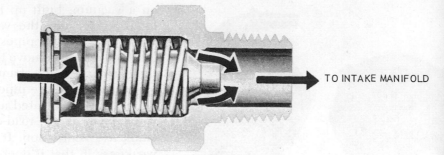

FROM CRANKCASE
AND/OR ROCKER
ARM COVER

TO INTAKE MANIFOLD

LOW SPEED OPERATION—HIGH MANIFOLD VACUUM

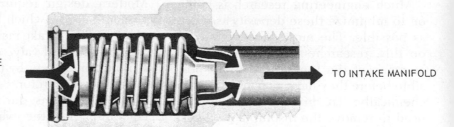

FROM CRANKCASE
AND/OR ROCKER
ARM COVER

TO INTAKE MANIFOLD

HIGH SPEED OPERATION—LOW MANIFOLD VACUUM

Diagram showing the operation of the PCV valve
during periods of high speed operation (bottom
view) and when idling. Note that the spring forces
the valve off its seat during low-vacuum operating
conditions, when it is most effective in drawing
the vapors from the crankcase.

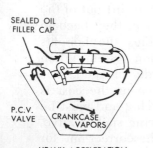

SEALED OIL
FILLER CAP

P.C.V.
VALVE

CRANKCASE
VAPORS

**HEAVY ACCELERATION
OR
HIGH ROAD SPEED**

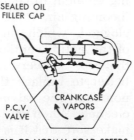

SEALED OIL
FILLER CAP

P.C.V.
VALVE

CRANKCASE
VAPORS

IDLE OR NORMAL ROAD SPEEDS

Since 1964, many manufacturers have
used the "closed" ventilation system in
which fresh air is obtained from the air
cleaner. In these systems, the filtering
element is in the air cleaner rather than
in the oil filler cap.

Operating conditions of crankcase ventilating
system, using a PCV valve. The illustrations show
the flow of vapors in the closed-type of system
formerly known as the California type, now used
on most cars manufactured since 1958.

Service Procedures

Lubrication, changing engine oil, cleaning the crankcase ventilator filters, and the PCV valve, and replacing the oil filter cartridge are the services most commonly performed. Infrequently, oil pumps wear, by-pass valves stick, and oil lines become plugged.

Troubleshooting

The color of the oil on the dip stick is not a fair indicator of the amount of dirt in the oil because acids and other chemical contaminants are not visible, and detergent oils discolor quickly anyway.

Low oil pump pressure is frequently due to worn connecting rod bearings and mains. This can be detected when the engine is disassembled by using a bearing oil leak detector. When performing an engine overhaul, it is good practice to disassemble the engine oil pump and inspect it for worn parts.

With the positive crankcase ventilation (PCV) system operating normally, about $1/4$ of the air used in the idle mixture is supplied through the ventilator valve. Therefore, if the ventilator system air supply is shut off, the idle speed will be noticeably reduced. To check this out, connect a tachometer, start the engine, and then squeeze the crankcase ventilator hose tightly. The idle speed should drop 60 rpm or more if the system is functioning properly.

To check out the system in detail, locate and disconnect the PCV valve, leaving the hose attached. Start the engine and hold your finger over the end. If the valve is working properly, a strong vacuum should be felt. Remove the valve and shake it. A clicking noise indicates that the valve is free; otherwise, it must be replaced. After servicing the valve, remove the oil filler cap and hold a piece of cardboard over the filler pipe opening. After the engine has idled about a minute, enough vacuum should be built up to hold the cardboard against the opening if the system is operating efficiently. On older engines with excessive blow-by, the vacuum may be overcome by the gases by-passing the piston rings.

Changing Engine Oil

Oil in the crankcase must be changed at regular intervals because it becomes contaminated. If the engine has been run a long time with dirty oil, it is good practice to flush the crankcase with two or three quarts of the same oil that is to be used in the engine. This will remove most of the dirty oil remaining in the passageways and bearings. Flushing oils and solvents should not be used, as some of these poorly refined liquids will remain to contaminate the new oil. **Caution:** *Do not mix oil brands, because the chemical additives may not be compatible.*

Tools and Equipment

Engine; drain pan; crescent wrench; 5 qts. of engine oil; 5 qt. oil measure.

PROCEDURE

1. To be sure the oil is thin enough to flow properly, warm the engine to operating temperature.
2. Place the drain can under the plug of the oil pan to catch the oil.
3. Remove the plug and allow the oil to drain completely.

The plug to be removed when draining oil from the engine.

4. Replace the drain plug. **Caution:** *Make sure it is tight.*

5. Consult the specification chart for the number of quarts and the S.A.E. number of the oil for this engine according to the climate and season.

6. Fill with the required number of quarts through the crankcase filler tube.

7. Start the engine and allow it to idle a few moments so that the oil circulates through the passageways, and then shut it off.

8. Measure the oil level by wiping off the dip stick and pushing it down as far as it will go. Pull out the stick and check the level of the oil against the marking. Add oil, as required, to bring the level to the dip stick "Full" mark.

Replacing Oil Pan Gaskets

The oil pan is bolted to the block by many bolts. A cork gasket keeps the oil from leaking; however, lots of oil is lost by oil pan leaks when the gasket loosens. Notice the oil drippings on the road, especially following a

rough spot. Look under your car and note whether the pan is oily. Let the engine run over some clean newspapers and note the oil drippings. The remedy is to replace the oil pan gasket.

Oil breathers and intake screens should be cleaned at the same time because dirty breathers hold the blow-by pressure inside the crankcase, forcing oil out of the main bearings.

Tools and Equipment

Engine; $\frac{1}{2}$ inch cub socket and speed handle; drain pan; crescent wrench; engine oil; 5 qt. oil measure.

PROCEDURE

1. Drain the engine oil into a clean bucket.

2. Remove the oil pan bolts, and then the oil pan. On many cars it is necessary to remove the tie-rod first. On all V-8's the exhaust crossover pipe must be removed. Many engines require that the engine be lifted two or three inches to clear the crossmember.

3. Replace and tighten the drain plug.

4. Scrape the old gasket off the block and pan.

5. Clean the pan in solvent.

6. Clean the oil pump intake screen.

7. Clean the oil pan breather screen.

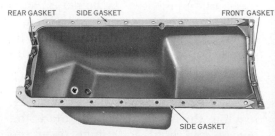

REAR GASKET   SIDE GASKET   FRONT GASKET

SIDE GASKET

The oil pan gaskets in place on the Slant-6 Dodge and Plymouth engines. Courtesy Plymouth Division, Chrysler Corporation.

LUBRICATION AND MAINTENANCE CHART

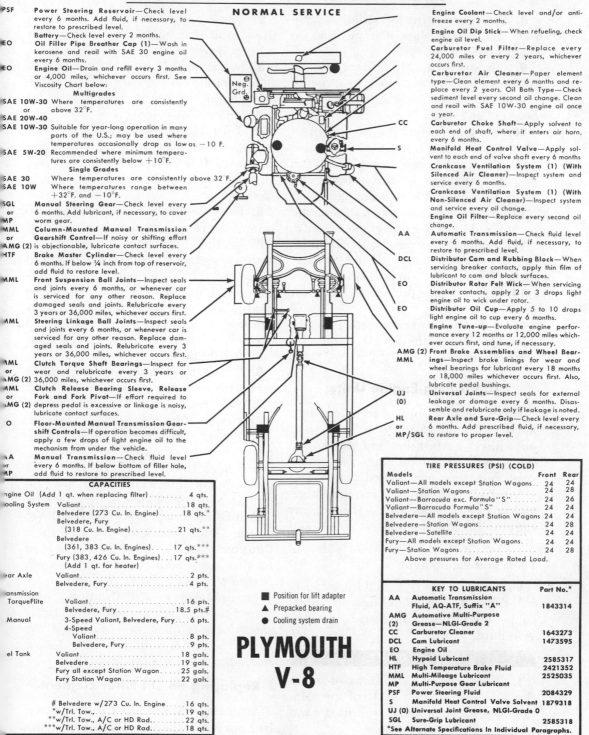

PSF   **Power Steering Reservoir**—Check level every 6 months. Add fluid, if necessary, to restore to prescribed level.

Battery—Check level every 2 months.

EO   **Oil Filler Pipe Breather Cap (1)**—Wash in kerosene and reoil with SAE 30 engine oil every 6 months.

EO   **Engine Oil**—Drain and refill every 3 months or 4,000 miles, whichever occurs first. See Viscosity Chart below:

Multigrades

SAE 10W-30 Where temperatures are consistently
or above 32°F.
SAE 20W-40

SAE 10W-30 Suitable for year-long operation in many parts of the U.S.; may be used where temperatures occasionally drop as low as −10 F.

SAE 5W-20 Recommended where minimum temperatures are consistently below +10°F.

Single Grades

SAE 30 Where temperatures are consistently above 32 F.

SAE 10W Where temperatures range between +32°F. and −10°F.

SGL **Manual Steering Gear**—Check level every
or 6 months. Add lubricant, if necessary, to cover
MP worm gear.

MML **Column-Mounted Manual Transmission**
or **Gearshift Control**—If noisy or shifting effort
AMG (2) is objectionable, lubricate contact surfaces.

HTF **Brake Master Cylinder**—Check level every 6 months. If below ¼ inch from top of reservoir, add fluid to restore level.

MML **Front Suspension Ball Joints**—Inspect seals and joints every 6 months, or whenever car is serviced for any other reason. Replace damaged seals and joints. Relubricate every 3 years or 36,000 miles, whichever occurs first.

AML **Steering Linkage Ball Joints**—Inspect seals and joints every 6 months, or whenever car is serviced for any other reason. Replace damaged seals and joints. Relubricate every 3 years or 36,000 miles, whichever occurs first.

MML **Clutch Torque Shaft Bearings**—Inspect for
or wear and relubricate every 3 years or
AMG (2) 36,000 miles, whichever occurs first.

MML **Clutch Release Bearing Sleeve, Release**
or **Fork and Fork Pivot**—If effort required to
AMG (2) depress pedal is excessive or linkage is noisy, lubricate contact surfaces.

O   **Floor-Mounted Manual Transmission Gearshift Controls**—If operation becomes difficult, apply a few drops of light engine oil to the mechanism from under the vehicle.

A   **Manual Transmission**—Check fluid level
or every 6 months. If below bottom of filler hole,
MP add fluid to restore to prescribed level.

Engine Coolant—Check level and/or antifreeze every 2 months.

Engine Oil Dip Stick—When refueling, check engine oil level.

Carburetor Fuel Filter—Replace every 24,000 miles or every 2 years, whichever occurs first.

Carburetor Air Cleaner—Paper element type—Clean element every 6 months and replace every 2 years. Oil Bath Type—Check sediment level every second oil change. Clean and reoil with SAE 10W-30 engine oil once a year.

CC   **Carburetor Choke Shaft**—Apply solvent to each end of shaft, where it enters air horn, every 6 months.

S   **Manifold Heat Control Valve**—Apply solvent to each end of valve shaft every 6 months

Crankcase Ventilation System (1) (With Silenced Air Cleaner)—Inspect system and service every 6 months.

Crankcase Ventilation System (1) (With Non-Silenced Air Cleaner)—Inspect system and service every oil change.

Engine Oil Filter—Replace every second oil change.

AA   **Automatic Transmission**—Check fluid level every 6 months. Add fluid, if necessary, to restore to prescribed level.

DCL   **Distributor Cam and Rubbing Block**—When servicing breaker contacts, apply thin film of lubricant to cam and block surfaces.

EO   **Distributor Rotor Felt Wick**—When servicing breaker contacts, apply 2 or 3 drops light engine oil to wick under rotor.

EO   **Distributor Oil Cup**—Apply 5 to 10 drops light engine oil to cup every 6 months.

Engine Tune-up—Evaluate engine performance every 12 months or 12,000 miles whichever occurs first, and tune, if necessary.

AMG (2) **Front Brake Assemblies and Wheel Bear-**
MML **ings**—Inspect brake linings for wear and wheel bearings for lubricant every 18 months or 18,000 miles whichever occurs first. Also, lubricate pedal bushings.

UJ **Universal Joints**—Inspect seals for external
(0) leakage or damage every 6 months. Disassemble and relubricate only if leakage is noted.

HL **Rear Axle and Sure-Grip**—Check level every
or 6 months. Add prescribed fluid, if necessary,
MP/SGL to restore to proper level.

CAPACITIES

Engine Oil (Add 1 qt. when replacing filter)		4 qts.
Cooling System	Valiant	18 qts.
	Belvedere (273 Cu. In. Engine)	18 qts.*
	Belvedere, Fury (318 Cu. In. Engine)	21 qts.**
	Belvedere (361, 383 Cu. In. Engines)	17 qts.***
	Fury (383, 426 Cu. In. Engines)	17 qts.***
	(Add 1 qt. for heater)	
Rear Axle	Valiant	2 pts.
	Belvedere, Fury	4 pts.
Transmission		
TorqueFlite	Valiant	16 pts.
	Belvedere, Fury	18.5 pts.#
Manual	3-Speed Valiant, Belvedere, Fury	6 pts.
	4-Speed	
	Valiant	8 pts.
	Belvedere, Fury	9 pts.
Fuel Tank	Valiant	18 gals.
	Belvedere	19 gals.
	Fury all except Station Wagon	25 gals.
	Fury Station Wagon	22 gals.

Belvedere w/273 Cu. In. Engine......16 qts.
*w/Trl. Tow.......................19 qts.
**w/Trl. Tow., A/C or HD Rad......22 qts.
***w/Trl. Tow., A/C or HD Rad......18 qts.

■ Position for lift adapter
▲ Prepacked bearing
● Cooling system drain

PLYMOUTH V-8

TIRE PRESSURES (PSI) (COLD)

Models	Front	Rear
Valiant—All models except Station Wagons	24	24
Valiant—Station Wagons	24	28
Valiant—Barracuda exc. Formula "S"	24	26
Valiant—Barracuda Formula "S"	24	24
Belvedere—All models except Station Wagons	24	24
Belvedere—Station Wagons	24	28
Belvedere—Satellite	24	24
Fury—All models except Station Wagons	24	24
Fury—Station Wagons	24	28

Above pressures for Average Rated Load.

KEY TO LUBRICANTS

		Part No.*
AA	Automatic Transmission Fluid, AQ-ATF, Suffix "A"	1843314
AMG (2)	Automotive Multi-Purpose Grease—NLGI-Grade 2	
CC	Carburetor Cleaner	1643273
DCL	Cam Lubricant	1473595
EO	Engine Oil	
HL	Hypoid Lubricant	2585317
HTF	High Temperature Brake Fluid	2421352
MML	Multi-Mileage Lubricant	2525035
MP	Multi-Purpose Gear Lubricant	
PSF	Power Steering Fluid	2084329
S	Manifold Heat Control Valve Solvent	1879318
UJ (0)	Universal Joint Grease, NLGI-Grade 0	
SGL	Sure-Grip Lubricant	2585318

*See Alternate Specifications In Individual Paragraphs.

Points of lubrication. Courtesy Plymouth Division, Chrysler Corporation.

8. Place a coating of sealer on the new gasket and place it in position on the oil pan.

9. On some cars, it is necessary to tie the gasket to the block in order to insert the gasket ends under the main bearing cork seals.

10. Tie the gasket to the oil pan. Start in the corner and tie every third hole. Keep the knot away from the gasket. The string remains and does no harm, providing it is thin enough.

11. Place the pan in position. Be careful not to jar the gasket out of place.

12. Replace the pan bolts. **Caution:** *Do not tighten until all are started.*

13. Tighten the pan bolts evenly.

14. Replace the tie-rod and exhaust pipe.

15. Fill the crankcase with new engine oil. Check the level on the dip stick.

Lubricating Engine Units

Every bearing point of an automobile must have lubrication or it will wear out quickly. Most bearing points are lubricated by the oil from the crankcase, but there are several places outside of the engine that require lubrication every 1,000 miles. Other parts require lubrication only at 5,000 and 10,000 mile periods.

Tools and Equipment

Oil can; clean rag; multi-purpose, ball-bearing, and wheel-bearing lubricants; engine oil; automatic transmission fluid.

PROCEDURE

1. Place *one* or *two* drops of oil in the oil cups at both ends of the generator. Alternators are prelubricated and need no further attention.

2. Place *one* or *two* drops of oil in the cup at rear of starting motor, if an oil cup is provided.

3. Saturate the felt washers between the top of the battery case and the cable connections (if used) with engine oil to minimize corrosion.

4. Turn the oil cup at the base of the distributor one full turn. Some distributors are lubricated with an oil can, and some are prelubricated when manufactured.

5. Remove the distributor cap and rotor. Apply a *very small amount* of ball bearing lubricant to the distributor cam surface. Apply a few drops of oil to the felt in the center of the distributor shaft and *one* or *two* drops to the breaker lever pivot. **Caution:** *Excess lubrication will get on the points and cause hard starting.* Replace the rotor and distributor cap.

6. Use a few drops of light engine oil on the gearshift idler lever bushing.

7. Fill the steering gear housing with chassis lubricant.

8. Place a few drops of oil on all control rods.

9. Check the level of the automatic transmission lubricant. Add the required number of quarts of automatic transmission fluid to bring the level to the "Full" mark on the dip stick. **Caution:** *Use the fluid type specified by the manufacturer, as some are not compatible with fluids that may have been used previously.* **Caution:** *Some manufacturers specify that the engine should be idling when checking the fluid level. It is always best to follow the manufacturer's specifications.*

Replacing an Oil Filter Element

After about 5,000 miles, or less under bad operating conditions, the filter ele-

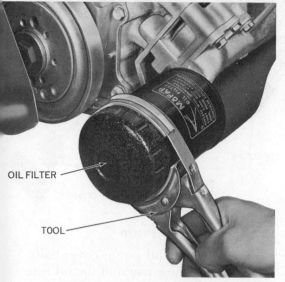

OIL FILTER

TOOL

Removing an oil filter element. Note the use of the tool which is a second class lever. Courtesy Chrysler Division, Chrysler Corporation.

ment becomes fouled with sludge and cannot filter the oil efficiently. Such a filter element must be replaced.

Tools and Equipment

$9/16$ and $5/8$ inch sockets; 5 inch extension; ratchet; drain bucket; lift.

PROCEDURE

1. Locate the filter. If it is not accessible from the top, place the car on a lift or over a pit to get to the filter.

2. Place the drain bucket under the filter to catch the leaking oil.

3. Loosen the center bolt, if so equipped, and then drain the filter.

4. Turn the open end of the filter up and remove it from the engine compartment.

5. Remove the old gasket from the filter base, and clean the base thoroughly.

6. Install a new base gasket. Be sure that it is completely seated in the recess.

7. Re-install the assembled filter on the base.

8. Tighten the center bolt, if so

equipped, while rotating the shell in both directions to insure even seating. **Caution:** *Do not overtighten or you may distort the shell.*

Repairing an Oil Pump

Under a pressure as high as 40 pounds to the square inch, the oil pump supplies oil to moving engine parts. The oil is drawn into the pump from the pan through a screen and forced through tubing to each bearing and bushing. If the screen clogs or the pump fails, the engine will be ruined.

Tools and Equipment

Gear-type oil pump; rotor-type oil pump; by-pass valve; $7/16$ and $1/2$ inch combination end wrenches; screwdriver; two qts. of oil for testing.

PROCEDURE

GEAR-TYPE OIL PUMP

1. Remove the screen from the pump.

2. Take out the bolts holding the cover in place.

3. Remove the cover.

4. Slip the *driven* gear out by turning the pump upside down.

5. Remove the *driving* gear by forcing the shaft through the housing.

6. Inspect the gears, shaft, and cover for wear.

7. Reassemble the gears and turn the shaft to see the principle of operation. Note how each gear tooth carries oil around each side of the pump housing. The oil cannot return because of the meshed teeth. Illustration, page 96.

8. Replace the cover, using a new gasket.

9. Test the pump for proper operation by inserting it in a pan of oil. Use an electric drill to drive the shaft.

95

Exploded view of a gear-type oil pump. This unit is used on the Pontiac Tempest overhead camshaft engine and contains a place for the oil filter, pressure regulating and by-pass valves, and provision for driving the distributor.

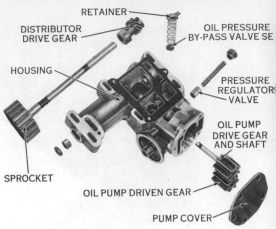

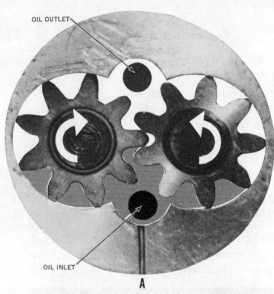

A

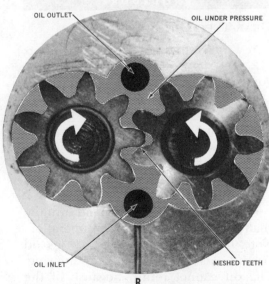

B

Diagram showing the operation of a gear-type oil pump. Each gear tooth picks up a pocket of oil, which it transports around the outside of the case. The oil is prevented from returning by the meshed teeth.

ROTOR-TYPE OIL PUMP

1. Remove the oil pump cover bolts.

2. Remove the cover and the oil ring seal.

3. Remove the pump rotor and shaft.

4. Remove the outer rotor body.

5. Clean the parts with solvent.

6. To understand its action, assemble the outer and inner rotors, see page 97.

• Turn the shaft. Note that chamber #4, view A, increases in size in views B and C. This creates a vacuum which sucks oil into the pump.

• As the parts of the pump revolve, chamber #4 expands until the inlet port is no longer uncovered.

• On the pressure side, follow chamber #1, starting at view A. Note that the "filled" chamber has just uncovered the outlet port.

• As chamber #1 continues to contract in views B and C, it grows smaller, putting pressure on the trapped oil until it is fully discharged.

• In view C, the emptied chamber #5 is ready to start the inlet cycle again.

7. Install a new oil seal.

8. Replace the cover.

9. Tighten the cover screws securely.

10. Dip the pump into a pan of clean oil and test its operation by driving it with an electric drill.

96

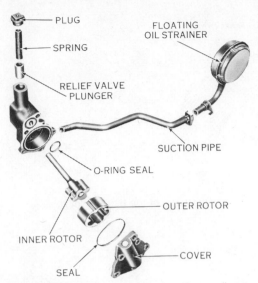

PLUG

SPRING

RELIEF VALVE
PLUNGER

FLOATING
OIL STRAINER

SUCTION PIPE

O-RING SEAL

OUTER ROTOR

INNER ROTOR

SEAL

COVER

An exploded view of a rotor-type oil pump. Courtesy Plymouth Division, Chrysler Corporation.

By-Pass Valve

1. Remove the cover bolt.

2. Remove the spring and the plunger.

3. To understand its operation:

• Probe to the right of the plunger seat with a fine wire in order to find the crankcase oil pressure hole.

• Insert the plunger and spring. Note that the hole to the left of the plunger is open to the oil pan drain.

• Oil under pressure is always at the right side of the plunger, and the spring on the left side of it balances this pressure. As long as the oil pressure is less than the spring pressure, the plunger remains on its seat.

• At high speeds, or when the oil is cold and thick, the pressure increases and forces the plunger off its seat.

• Excess oil is returned to the oil pan, thus keeping the pressure constant. This same mechanism is used on all pressure safety valves.

4. Re-assemble the cover.

Operation of the rotor-type oil pump.

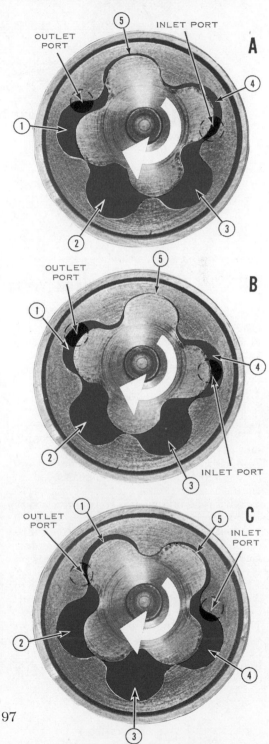

OUTLET PORT — INLET PORT — A

OUTLET PORT — B — INLET PORT

OUTLET PORT — C — INLET PORT

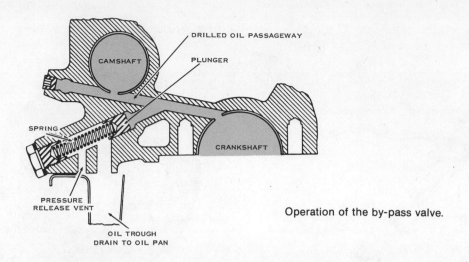

Operation of the by-pass valve.

CHECK YOUR KNOWLEDGE

1. What are the three purposes of lubrication?
2. What is a wet-sump type of lubricating system?
3. What is meant by a full-force lubricating system?
4. How are the piston rings lubricated?
5. What is the purpose of the oil "spit" hole in the connecting rod?
6. Why is the internal combustion engine said to be hard on lubricating oils?
7. What are the four forms of harmful deposits which form in the crankcase of an engine?
8. What type of driving is considered severe on engine lubricants?
9. What are the three types of engine lubricants classified by the Society of Automotive Engineers (S.A.E.) and the types of engine service conditions they are meant to cover?
10. What does a detergent additive do to the lubricant? Pour-point depressant? Anti-foam agent? Rust preventive?
11. What are the two types of oil filter systems?
12. How is it possible to remove harmful liquids from the lubricating oil through a crankcase ventilator?

Self-Check Tests

TRUE-FALSE

1. The lubrication system cools by carrying frictional heat to the radiator, where the air removes it.
2. In the full-force system of lubrication, some of the oil is sprayed onto moving parts.
3. The only disadvantage of the full-pressure lubricating system is that it forces excessive quantities of oil from the sides of worn bearings.
4. The products of combustion are water and acid.
5. Crude oil requires very little chemical changing to make it a perfect lubricant for the internal combustion engine.
6. The severest condition imposed on engine lubricants is continued high-speed driving.
7. The higher the viscosity number of an oil, the thicker it is.
8. In the full-flow filtering system, a clean supply of oil is always assured because the entire oil supply has to pass through the filter element constantly.
9. Most harmful products of combustion are in vapor form in the crankcase and are

automatically removed if the engine is operated at a constant high speed.

MULTIPLE CHOICE

1. Automobile lubricating systems are of the: a) dry sump; b) wet sump; c) short sump type.
2. The cylinder walls are lubricated by oil from the: a) gallery; b) oil pump; c) spit hole.
3. Which of the following terms does *not* apply to engine oils: a) detergent; b) depressant; c) anti-knock; d) anti-foam?
4. High viscosity oils flow: a) freely; b) sluggishly; c) the same as compared with the flowing action of low viscosity oils.
5. Under continued high-speed driving, engine oil should be changed every: a) 500; b) 1,000; c) 2,000; d) 5,000 miles.
6. Oil filter elements should be changed at: a) 8,000 miles; b) 16,000 miles; c) each time the oil is changed.
7. Crankcase ventilation does *not* remove one of the following from the engine oil: a) water; b) gasoline; c) acid; d) blow-by vapors.

COMPLETION

1. _____ seal the gap between moving parts of the engine.
2. Sludge is reduced by using a compounded engine oil having _____ _____ characteristics.
3. _____ is a term applied to the free-flowing characteristics of a lubricating oil.
4. Under average summer driving conditions, engine oil should be changed every _____ miles.

MATCHING

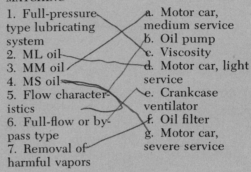

1. Full-pressure type lubricating system
2. ML oil
3. MM oil
4. MS oil
5. Flow characteristics
6. Full-flow or by-pass type
7. Removal of harmful vapors

a. Motor car, medium service
b. Oil pump
c. Viscosity
d. Motor car, light service
e. Crankcase ventilator
f. Oil filter
g. Motor car, severe service

Chapter 4

Valve Mechanisms

While there are several possible valve arrangements, only one is in common use today—the "I"-head. This engine has its valves in the cylinder head. It is often called an overhead valve engine because the combustion chamber is directly over the cylinder bore.

Valves let the fuel-air mixture into the cylinder and let the burned gases out. They are the "doors" of the combustion chamber. The valves are opened by cams on the camshaft and are closed by springs. In an "I"-head engine (with the valves in the cylinder head), the valves are opened by rocker arms which are operated by tappets and push rods.

The intake valve opens when the piston is moving down the cylinder to draw in the fuel-air mixture. The exhaust valve opens when the piston is moving up to force the burned gases from the combustion chamber.

The valve operating mechanism of an "I"-head engine. Note the first class lever used as a rocker arm and the camshaft (inclined plane) which opens the valve.

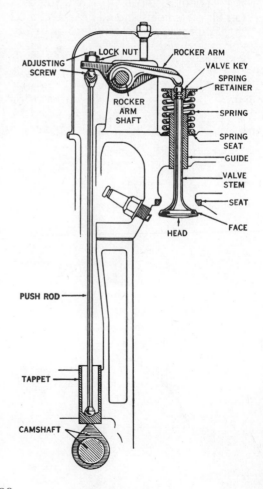

100

The valve head is machined with a face angled either 30° or 45° to the valve stem. The valve seat is ground to the same angle so that, when the two parts are held together by spring pressure, they seal airtight.

The operating conditions of the two valves are entirely different. The *intake valve* is "bathed" in a cool, clean fuel-air mixture each time it opens, while the *exhaust valve* is bathed in flaming hot exhaust gases. The exhaust valve is usually made of special heat resisting steel and its seat in the block is also made of special steel to resist burning. It is machined in the form of a ring and pressed into a recess cut around the valve port. The hardened valve seat is able to withstand the abusive operating conditions better.

One of the main jobs of the cooling system is to prevent the exhaust valves from burning. Distribution tubes are used to direct streams of coolant around the valve seats and guides. The valves are cooled by a transference of their heat, through the valve seat and guide, to the coolant chambers, from where it is carried away.

Rotating exhaust valves are used in some engines to minimize distortion and blow-by. By rotating the valve, a new surface is presented to the burning gas each time combustion occurs and the valve face is kept at a more uniform temperature.

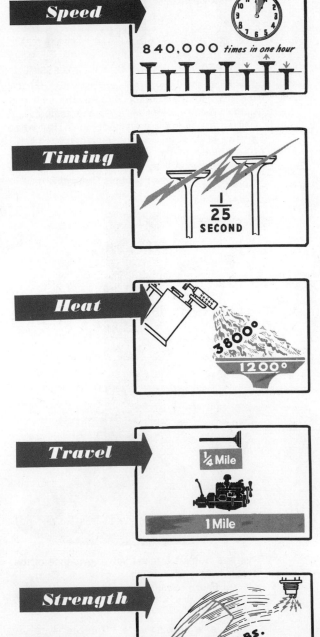

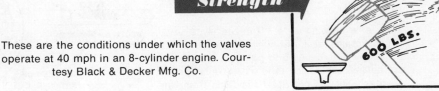

These are the conditions under which the valves operate at 40 mph in an 8-cylinder engine. Courtesy Black & Decker Mfg. Co.

101

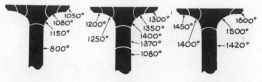

DESIRED   NORMAL   EXCESSIVE

The stem and face of an exhaust valve transfer the heat to the coolant through the seat and guide. With a normal valve, the temperature pattern at the left is usually obtained. But when a valve seats poorly in one section, the temperature pattern at the right is generally obtained. Such a valve will soon burn up. Courtesy The Toledo Steel Products Company.

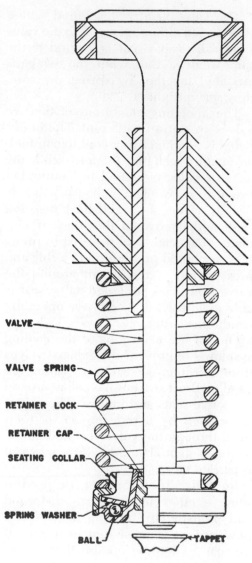

VALVE

VALVE SPRING

RETAINER LOCK

RETAINER CAP

SEATING COLLAR

SPRING WASHER

BALL   TAPPET

This is a burned exhaust valve, evidence of the terrific heat under which it operates. Courtesy Eaton Manufacturing Company.

This is a drawing of a "Rotocap"-type valve, which rotates at a definite rate because it is driven by the springs and balls which move up an *inclined* ramp each time the valve is opened. Courtesy The Toledo Steel Products Company.

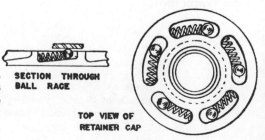

SECTION THROUGH
BALL RACE

TOP VIEW OF
RETAINER CAP

102

Camshaft

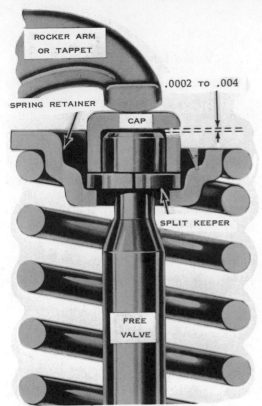

ROCKER ARM OR TAPPET

SPRING RETAINER

.0002 TO .004

CAP

SPLIT KEEPER

FREE VALVE

The camshaft contains lobes which lift the tappet at precisely the right moment of engine operation. Two cams are needed for each cylinder, one for opening the exhaust and one for the intake valve. The camshaft is driven at half-engine speed by means of a timing chain or gear. For each two revolutions of the crankshaft, or four strokes of the piston, the camshaft turns once.

Camshaft gears, which are used on some engines, are made of pressed fiber to minimize noise. Chains are used on most engines because the greater number of engaged teeth lessens the amount of noise.

This is a "free"-type valve-rotating mechanism. When the valve is open, it is free to rotate but the rate is uncertain. Courtesy McQuay-Norris Manufacturing Co.

The camshaft rotates in bearings. It has cams (inclined planes) which push up the tappets that open the valves. The camshaft sprocket is driven by the crankshaft sprocket through the timing chain. The camshaft sprocket must always have twice the number of teeth as the crankshaft sprocket. Can you see why? The small gear on the left end of the camshaft drives the distributor and usually the oil pump.

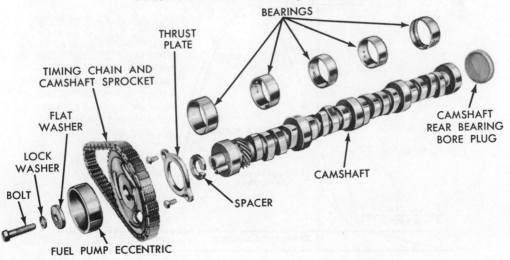

BEARINGS

THRUST PLATE

TIMING CHAIN AND CAMSHAFT SPROCKET

FLAT WASHER

LOCK WASHER

BOLT

FUEL PUMP ECCENTRIC

SPACER

CAMSHAFT

CAMSHAFT REAR BEARING BORE PLUG

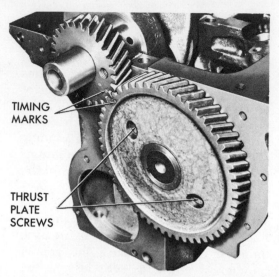

TIMING MARKS

THRUST PLATE SCREWS

Note that there are twice the number of teeth on the camshaft gear (bottom) as on the crankshaft gear. Courtesy Chevrolet Motor Division, General Motors Corporation.

It is very important that the specified valve lash be maintained; otherwise, damage can result, as shown in this diagram of valve operation. Courtesy The Toledo Steel Products Company.

Valve Lash or Clearance

Clearance must be maintained in the valve mechanism to keep the valves from remaining open during operation; however, if too much clearance exists, the valve mechanism will be noisy. Insufficient clearance holds the valves off their seats, resulting in burning and quick destruction.

The clearance is adjustable in "I"-head engines by turning a screw at the rear of the rocker arm. In some engines, the valve lash is adjusted by turning the rocker arm anchor screw. In hydraulically operated lifters, the mechanism is usually self-adjusting.

Hydraulic Valve Lifters

Hydraulic valve lifters automatically adjust the clearance between operating parts to eliminate valve noise. The lifter consists of a body, plunger, spring, check valve, check valve retainer, push rod seat, and seat retainer.

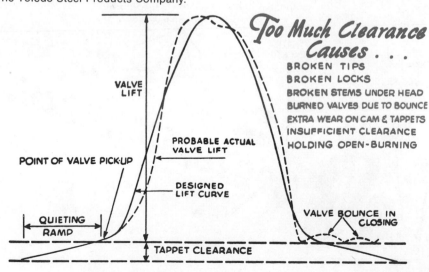

VALVE LIFT

PROBABLE ACTUAL VALVE LIFT

POINT OF VALVE PICK-UP

DESIGNED LIFT CURVE

QUIETING RAMP

TAPPET CLEARANCE

VALVE BOUNCE IN CLOSING

Too Much Clearance Causes . . .

BROKEN TIPS
BROKEN LOCKS
BROKEN STEMS UNDER HEAD
BURNED VALVES DUE TO BOUNCE
EXTRA WEAR ON CAM & TAPPETS
INSUFFICIENT CLEARANCE
HOLDING OPEN-BURNING

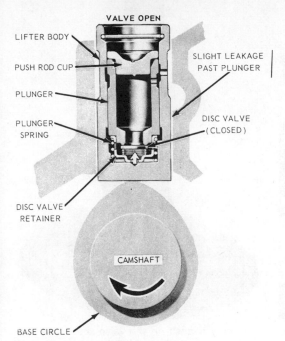

VALVE OPEN

LIFTER BODY

PUSH ROD CUP

PLUNGER

PLUNGER SPRING

DISC VALVE RETAINER

SLIGHT LEAKAGE PAST PLUNGER

DISC VALVE (CLOSED)

CAMSHAFT

BASE CIRCLE

Parts of the hydraulic valve lifter. Courtesy Ford Motor Company.

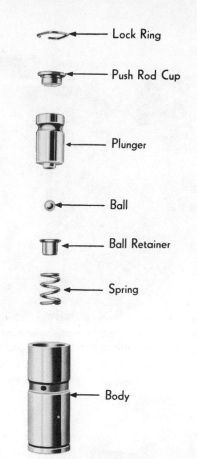

Lock Ring

Push Rod Cup

Plunger

Ball

Ball Retainer

Spring

Body

An exploded view of a hydraulic valve lifter.

When clearance exists between the operating parts, the plunger is expanded by oil pressure until contact is made with the push rod. The oil then becomes a solid connecting unit. When the tappet is lifted, a calculated amount of oil leaks from between the plunger and lifter body. In operation, the lifter expands and contracts continually.

After the engine has been standing for several hours, the valves are held open due to the position of the camshaft. They leak and are noisy when the engine is first started, but they quickly fill with oil when pressure builds up.

Valve Guide Oil Seals

The high vacuum under the head of the intake valve has always created the problem of drawing oil through the valve guide, which is intensified when the guide is worn. Today's engines, with the intake guide in the cylinder head, allow gravity to aid the oil flow.

Testing the hydraulic valve lifter. Reject any lifter that has no resistance.

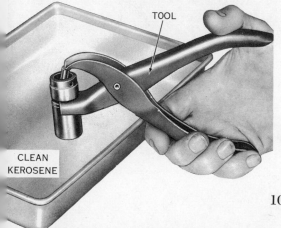

TOOL

CLEAN KEROSENE

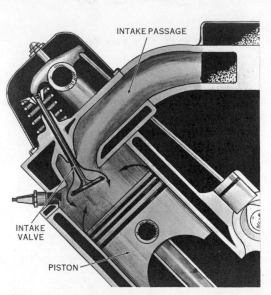

INTAKE PASSAGE

INTAKE VALVE

PISTON

Oil leaks into the combustion chamber past the intake valve guides and piston rings.

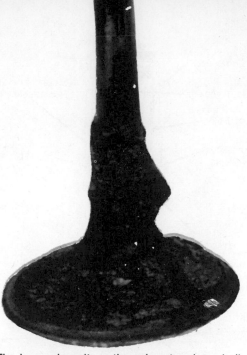

The heavy deposit on the valve stem is an indication of worn valve guides.

Valve seal used on some OHV engines. Courtesy Perfect Circle Corp.

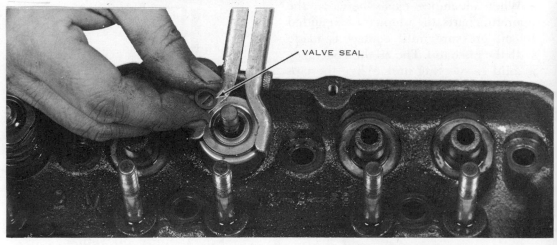

VALVE SEAL

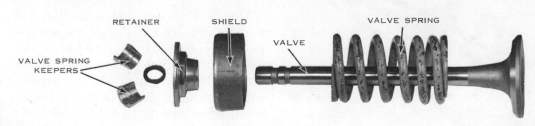

RETAINER

SHIELD

VALVE

VALVE SPRING

VALVE
SPRING
KEEPERS

106

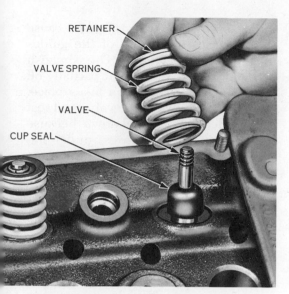

RETAINER

VALVE SPRING

VALVE

CUP SEAL

The valve seal keeps oil from passing by the valve guide. Plymouth Division, Chrysler Corporation.

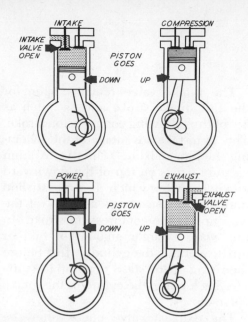

The four strokes of the four-stroke-cycle gas engine (Otto cycle): Intake, compression, power, and exhaust.

To minimize loss, engineers have installed various kinds of seals around the valve stem.

Care must be taken during assembly to install the new seals properly. To test a seal, pour gasoline into the valve spring retainer. If the seal is effective, the gasoline will not leak. Incorrectly installed seals can cause an engine to use as much as five times more oil than normal.

Valve Timing

Intake and exhaust valves do not open and close at the end of the strokes. Engineers have found that they can increase the breathing efficiency of the engine by using the power developed by the rapidly moving gases (inertia). For example, as the exhaust gases leave the combustion chamber at high velocity (expelled by the piston), the intake valve is opened just before the piston reaches TDC of the exhaust stroke. The speed of the rapidly moving exhaust gases causes a slight vacuum in the combustion chamber which starts the intake gases moving. Both inlet and exhaust valves are open at the same time, between 10° and 50°. During this time there is very little piston movement because of the angular position of the crankpin.

A typical valve operating diagram.

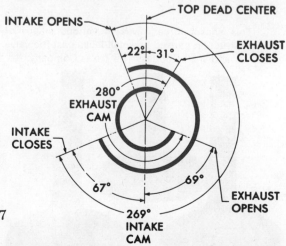

107

The intake valve remains open for the full intake stroke and as much as 65° of the following compression stroke. This is to take advantage of the incoming fuel-air mixture's inertia. A high vacuum exists on top of the downward moving piston which is not satisfied until the piston moves about ⅓ of the way up on the compression stroke. In this way, a larger amount of fuel-air mixture enters the cylinder. Just before the rising piston starts to pump the mixture back out of the cylinder, the intake valve closes.

The exhaust valve opens after the piston has traveled slightly over ⅔ of the way down on the power stroke. At this point, combustion chamber pressure has decreased until it has very little effect on engine power, but it has enough pressure left to start expelling the burning gases. This increases the amount of exhaust gases removed from the combustion area and assists in engine cooling.

Service Procedures

The high temperatures under which exhaust valves work cause operating difficulties which eventually result in the valve face burning and not seating

airtight. The hot exhaust gases cause the lubricant in the top of the guides to burn, forming gum. The sluggish action of the valve holds it partially off its seat while combustion takes place. A small leak between the valve and seat quickly leads to a breakdown because the fiercely burning gases, under tremendous pressure, force their way from the combustion chamber through this small leak. The engine loses power and the valve face receives a tremendous amount of heat in a small area, causing it to burn.

Troubleshooting the Valve Mechanism

Most valve troubles are due to burned valve faces and seats which lower compression and reduce power. Valve stems sometimes gum up and cause sticky valves.

The standard test to determine the efficiency of the valve mechanism is to use a compression tester. The tester is inserted in a spark plug hole, after all the plugs have been removed, and the engine cranked with the starter for

A compression reading can determine with accuracy variations in valve seating ability. Courtesy Ford Division, Ford Motor Company.

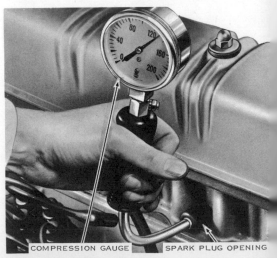

This shows three valves in various stages of destruction caused by small leaks past the valve and seat. Courtesy The Texas Company.

108

COMPRESSION GAUGE   SPARK PLUG OPENING

about four compression strokes. By comparing the cylinder pressures, a weak cylinder is identified. Naturally, the same number of compression impulses must be measured in each cylinder. Any variation over 20 lbs. indicates trouble.

To isolate the faulty condition further, insert a tablespoon of heavy oil on top of each piston and crank the engine several times to distribute the oil around the piston and rings. Retest the compression and, if it raises 20 lbs. or more, the rings are leaking. If the pressure remains the same, the valves are leaking.

Removing and Replacing Valves

Valves let the fuel-air mixture into the combustion chamber, and the burnt gases out. When the valves are closed, they must seat airtight so that compression builds up to the highest point possible. Sometimes the valves burn and do not seat perfectly. In such cases, remove them for reconditioning.

This sectioned view through the Pontiac Tempest overhead camshaft engine shows the relationship between parts. Note that the engine is of "I"-head design. Courtesy Pontiac Motor Division, General Motors Corporation.

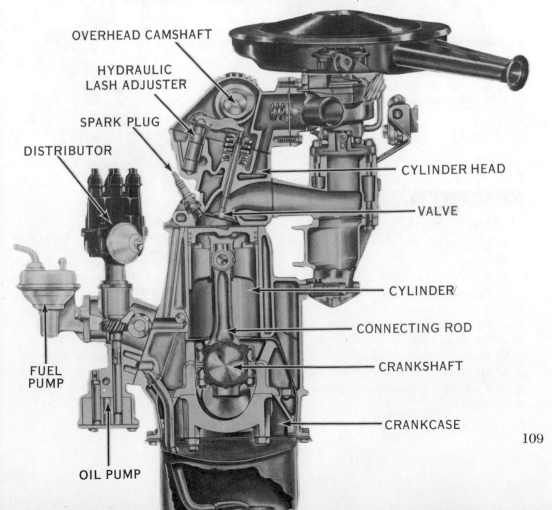

OVERHEAD CAMSHAFT

HYDRAULIC
LASH ADJUSTER

SPARK PLUG

DISTRIBUTOR

CYLINDER HEAD

VALVE

CYLINDER

CONNECTING ROD

CRANKSHAFT

FUEL
PUMP

CRANKCASE

OIL PUMP

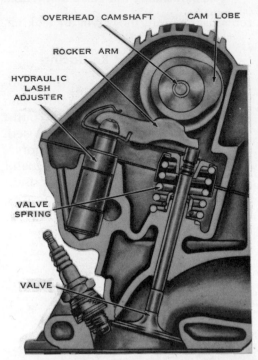

This close-up view shows the valve-operating mechanism used on the Pontiac Tempest overhead camshaft engine. Courtesy Pontiac Motor Division, General Motors Corporation.

Keep all valve parts in holders so that they can be replaced in their original ports. Courtesy Ford Division, Ford Motor Company.

Tools and Equipment

Valve spring compressor; "I"-head engine.

PROCEDURE

"I"-HEAD ENGINE

1. Drain the coolant and remove the manifolds.

2. Remove the spark plugs.

3. Remove the push rod chamber cover.

4. Remove the rocker arm assembly and the push rods.

5. Remove the cylinder head.

6. Remove the valve spring keepers, using an overhead valve spring compressor.

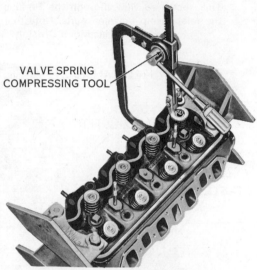

Compress the spring in order to remove the valve keepers. Note the use of holders to keep the cylinder head from contacting the bench. This protects the gasket surface. Courtesy Chrysler Corporation.

7. Remove the valve, spring, and retainer. Repeat for the other valves.

8. Scrape the carbon from the combustion chambers.

9. Clean the valve guides of gum.

10. Recondition the valves and seats.

11. Replace the valves, springs, seals, retainers, and keepers. Be sure that the tapered keepers are properly seated, or they may drop out when the engine starts.

12. Replace the cylinder head using a new gasket.

13. Replace the push rods and rocker arm assembly.

14. Replace the push rod chamber cover. Use new gaskets to avoid leaks.

15. Replace the manifolds using a new gasket set.

16. Replace the coolant.

17. Run the engine for 15 minutes to normalize it before adjusting the valves.

Refacing Valves

The face of the valve becomes pitted and burned through long use until the valve doesn't seat airtight any more. Eventually, the leaking gases tend to warp the valve head. When the valve

Each rocker arm assembly is marked so that it can be replaced correctly. Note the locating arrows used in this Chrysler engine. Ask your instructor, if you are not sure. Courtesy Plymouth Division, Chrysler Corporation.

face is not too badly pitted, a hand-lapping operation will seat the valve airtight again. However, when there are deep pits or grooves, or the head is warped, the valve must be refaced to true it before lapping.

This is the result of careless installation of the valve keepers.

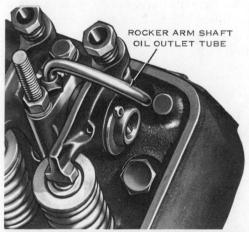

It is generally necessary to position an oil outlet or inlet tube correctly whenever replacing a rocker arm shaft. Ask your instructor, if you are not sure. Courtesy Ford Motor Company.

111

Tools and Equipment

Valve refacing machine; valves to be refaced.

PROCEDURE

1. Check the scale angle to make sure the chuck is set to the correct angle, 45° for a 45° valve and 30° for a 30° valve.

2. Insert the valve stem in the chuck and tighten firmly. The head should extend 1 inch.

3. Locate the *cross* and *in-out* feed handles.

4. Using the two feed handles, locate the valve face directly in front of, and about $1/16$ inch away from the stone.

5. Start the electric motors.

6. Adjust the *in-out* feed handle until the stone lightly contacts the valve face.

7. Turn the *cross* feed handle so that the valve face moves completely across the face of the stone.

8. Adjust the *in-out* feed handle to a slightly deeper cut.

9. Turn the *cross* feed handle again as in step 7, and continue steps 7 and 8 until the valve face is true and without pits.

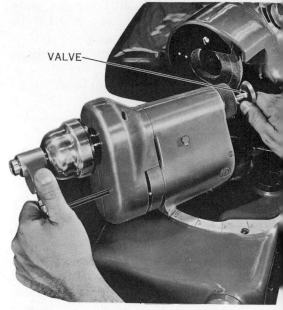

VALVE

Installing the valve into the valve chuck. The head should extend out about 1 inch. Courtesy The Black & Decker Mfg. Co.

CROSS-FEED HANDLE

IN-OUT HANDLE

Grinding the valve face. The handle on the right is the in-out handle and the one on the left is the cross-feed handle. Courtesy The Black & Decker Mfg. Co.

Aligning the valve chuck to the angle of the valve face. Courtesy The Black & Decker Mfg. Co.

VALVE CHUCK

SCALE

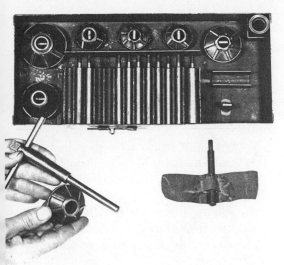

The reamer set for cutting the valve seat. The reamers come in an assortment of sizes and angles to fit each job. They must not be used on hardened valve seat inserts.

2. Clean the guide and valve seat. A dirty guide will cause misalignment of the pilot and cutters.

3. Select a pilot to fit the guide and assemble the correct reamer.

4. A piece of emery cloth, with a hole for the pilot, placed over the reamer cutting face, assists in cutting the first glaze off the seat.

The pilot has a slow taper on top and an adjustable taper on bottom, both of which must be accurately seated. Be sure to follow the instructions carefully. Courtesy The Black & Decker Mfg. Co.

Refacing Valve Seats

In many cases of valve reconditioning, it becomes necessary to retrue the valve seat either because the seat is too wide or is worn unevenly. Reamers of the proper angle can be used on cast-iron valve seats, but hardened exhaust valve inserts require special grinding equipment.

Tools and Equipment

Valve seat reamer set; piece of emery cloth; wooden mallet; valve seat grinding equipment.

PROCEDURE

REAMER

1. Remove the valve and determine the angle of the seat. Many engines use 45° exhaust valve seats and some use 30° seats for intake valves.

113

5. With even pressure, take a light cut to true the seat. **Caution:** *Never turn the reamer backwards.*

6. If the seat is over ⅛ inch wide, it must be narrowed by using the 60° and 15° reamers.

7. Cut carefully until the seat is 1/16 inch wide.

8. A final light cut with the 45° finish reamer will bring the seat width to the required 3/32 inch.

9. To change reamers, tap the end of the pilot with a wooden mallet. **Caution:** *Never use a steel hammer or the end of the pilot will swell and not enter the guide.*

STONE

1. Insert the pilot in the cleaned guide.

2. Raise the pilot ½ inch to lift the top taper out of contact with the guide.

3. Turn the pilot handle to the right to tighten the bottom taper.

4. Release the bottom taper by turning the pilot handle a half turn to the left.

5. Press the pilot down to seat the top taper.

6. Retighten the handle a half turn to the right to seat both tapers.

7. Select the proper stone; 45° or 30° depending on the angle of the seat; white stone for hardened inserts, black stone for softer cast-iron seats.

8. Assemble the stone to the stone holder.

9. True the stone with the diamond dresser. **Caution:** *Keep a firm downward pressure on the driver to avoid stone bounce.*

10. Clean the pilot and lubricate it with *one* drop of oil.

11. Assemble the stone and holder on the pilot.

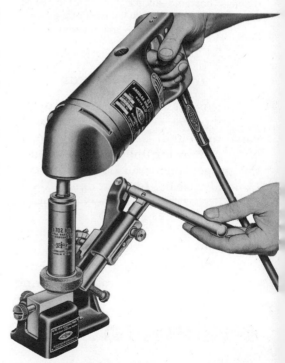

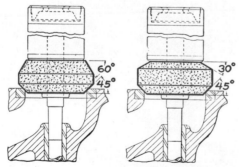

The stones come in various angles. The 30° stone is used to narrow a 45° seat and the 60° stone can be used to remove stock from the inside of the valve port, moving the seat outward. Courtesy Albertson & Company, Sioux Tools.

Truing up the stone. Make sure that the cutter is adjusted to a 45° angle when dressing a 45° stone and keep pressure on the driver to keep the stone from bouncing. Courtesy Sioux Tools, Inc.

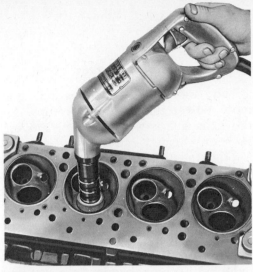

Dressing a valve seat. Lift the driver slightly so that the stone bounces, in order to clear it of grinding debris. Courtesy Plymouth Division, Chrysler Corporation.

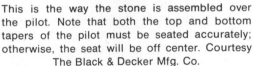

This is the way the stone is assembled over the pilot. Note that both the top and bottom tapers of the pilot must be seated accurately; otherwise, the seat will be off center. Courtesy The Black & Decker Mfg. Co.

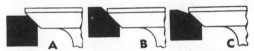

A correctly ground seat should be located in the center of the valve face, as at "A." If the seat gets too wide, as at "B," narrow it with a 30° stone, removing stock at the top until it seats, as at "C." Courtesy The Black & Decker Mfg. Co.

12. Support the driver slightly to allow the stone to bounce so it can clean itself.

13. Start the drive motor and lightly grind the seat. **Caution:** *Do not grind too long or you will widen the seat excessively.*

14. Lift the stone and holder to inspect the seat.

15. Continue grinding until the entire seat is free of pits and burnt sections and is ³⁄₃₂ inch wide.

16. If the seat is too wide or uneven, use a 20° roughing stone to narrow it.

17. If the face of the valve is ground to as fine a finish as the seat, it may be assembled after oiling. Lapping compound should not be used, as it will roughen the fine surface produced by the stone.

A dial indicator can be used to measure the out-of-roundness of the valve seat. Do not pass any seat over 0.002 inch out of round. Courtesy Ford Division, Ford Motor Company.

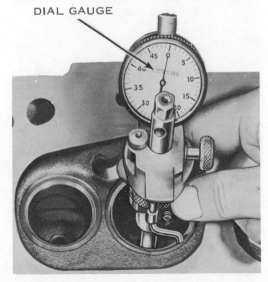

DIAL GAUGE

115

Lapping Valves

The higher the compression, the more power the engine develops. As the exhaust gases pass by the valves, they are heated red hot and beaten forcibly against their seats hundreds of times per minute. Often a small grain of white hot carbon is caught between the valve and seat where it burns a pit into both parts. These burnt spots become larger and larger, as grains of burning carbon now have a place to lodge, until the valve does not seal the combustion chamber anymore. In this case, the valve needs lapping in order to seat it airtight again.

Tools and Equipment

Suction cup and handle; valve lapping compound; rag; valves; engine block; lacquer thinner; guide cleaner.

PROCEDURE

1. Clean the valve and stem of carbon by scraping and buffing.

Clean the valve face and stem of carbon and gum by buffing. Use a face shield to avoid flying particles. Make sure that all gum is completely removed—not burnished on the stem. Courtesy The Black & Decker Mfg. Co.

WIRE BRUSH

Clean the combustion chamber, using a wire brush to break out small carbon particles that stick firmly. Courtesy The Black & Decker Mfg. Co.

2. Clean the block, port, and guide by scraping and brushing. Be especially careful to clean the guide of all gum. Use a guide buffer and lacquer thinner to dissolve the gum. It is gum in the exhaust valve guides which causes them to stick and burn.

3. Apply enough fine lapping compound to coat the face of the valve. **Caution:** *Do not use too much, or the excess will get into the working parts and damage the engine.*

4. Attach the suction cup to the top of the valve by moistening and pressing.

5. Place the valve and suction cup handle into its proper port. If the valve is held open on an "L"-head engine, turn the crankshaft until the valve seats. Sometimes the tappet adjustment must be lowered.

6. Lap the two surfaces lightly together by rotating the handle between the palms of your hands. Change the position of the handle often and lift slightly. The pressure of lapping forces the compound away from the grinding

116

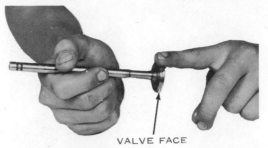

VALVE FACE

Apply valve grinding compound to the face of the valve. Apply only enough to cover the face.

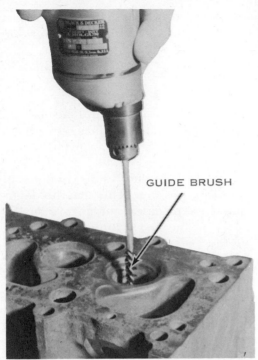

GUIDE BRUSH

Clean the valve guide with this special guide brush. Be careful not to tilt the drill or you will snap the brush. Use some lacquer thinner applied with an oil can to dissolve the gums. Courtesy The Black & Decker Mfg. Co.

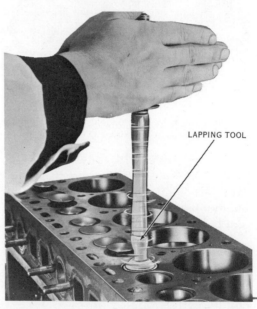

LAPPING TOOL

Lap the valve to its seat by rotating it. This suction cup holder is very handy for this work. Moistening the rubber helps to hold it to the valve head.

surfaces and lifting the valve brings the compound back to the center of the valve face.

7. To inspect, clean the lapped surfaces with a damp rag.

8. Continue lapping until the rings on the valve and seat are even and grey, with all black pits removed.

9. Clean all traces of lapping compound from the seat and valve. **Caution:** *Make sure that you have removed every particle of compound or the engine will be damaged.*

10. Lubricate the valve stem, face, and seat before assembling to keep the parts from rusting.

Adjusting Valves

Valves must close completely to develop power. Therefore a slight clearance must always exist between the valve stem and the tappet to allow for heat expansion. Too much clearance will cause the valve mechanism to be

117

STEP-TYPE FEELER GAUGE

Adjusting the valve clearance in the OHV engine. Courtesy Ford Motor Company.

noisy; too little will cause the valves to remain open slightly and leak compression. Some engines allow for adjustment of valve clearance by means of a bolt in the rocker arm.

Tools and Equipment

Overhead valve adjusting tool; feeler gauge; "I"-head engine; Chevrolet V-8 engine with hydraulic lifters.

PROCEDURE

"I"-HEAD ENGINE

1. It is especially important to normalize an overhead valve engine before adjusting the valves because the clearances change as much as 0.005 inch between a cold and hot engine.

2. Tighten the cylinder head and rocker arms with a torque wrench because the tightness of these bolts also affects the clearance.

3. With the engine running, adjust the screw at the rear of the rocker arm to obtain the specified clearance.

CHEVROLET V-8 ENGINE WITH HYDRAULIC LIFTERS

1. Crank the engine until the mark on the harmonic balancer lines up with the center of the "O" mark on the timing tab.

2. Make sure that No. 1 cylinder is in the firing position. This may be determined by placing your fingers on the valves of the first cylinder as the mark on the balancer comes near the "O" mark on the front end cover. If the valves are *not* moving, the engine is in the No. 1 firing position. If the valves move as the mark comes up to the timing tab, the engine is in No. 6 firing position, and it should be turned one more revolution to reach the No. 1 position.

Some engines require that the entire rocker arm be moved to adjust the tappets. Courtesy Chevrolet Division, General Motors Corporation.

118

3. With the engine in the No. 1 firing position, the following valves should be adjusted: exhaust—1, 3, 4, 8; intake—1, 2, 5, 7.

4. Adjust each valve by backing off the adjusting nut (rocker arm stud nut) until there is play in the valve push rod, and then tighten just enough to remove all the push rod-to-rocker arm clearance. This may be determined by rocking the push rod as the nut is tightened. When the rod does not readily move in relation to the rocker arm, the clearance is eliminated.

5. Now, tighten each adjusting nut an additional ¾ turn to place the hydraulic lifter plunger in the center of its travel.

6. Crank the engine one revolution until the pointer "O" mark and harmonic balancer mark are in alignment. This is No. 6 firing position, and the following valves should be adjusted: exhaust—2, 5, 6, 7; intake—3, 4, 6, 8.

7. Hydraulic tappets can also be adjusted with the engine running by

The timing gear retaining bolts can be reached through the gear on the 6-cylinder Chevrolet engine. Courtesy Chevrolet Motor Division, General Motors Corporation.

loosening the adjustment until the valve clatters, and then tightening the adjustment slowly until all noise just disappears. Now, tighten the adjustment screw one full turn to bring the hydraulic tappet to the center of its operating position. **Caution:** *Valve adjustments, with the engine running, must be made only on a thoroughly warmed engine, and the nut must be turned slowly, allowing time for the lifter plunger to reposition itself; otherwise, damage to the valve and push rod will result because of the very small clearance between the valve head and the piston.*

Replacing a Timing Gear

The valves are opened by means of cams on the camshaft. The time of opening and closing must be exact in relation to piston travel. The camshaft must be driven by some positive means such as gears or a chain. After long use, the chain or the fiber camshaft gear wears enough to become noisy. When replacing this gear, be sure to mesh the teeth properly or the valves will not operate in time.

Tools and Equipment

Chevrolet short block; gear puller; ½ and ⁹⁄₁₆ inch sockets; ½ and ⁹⁄₁₆ inch combination end wrenches; ratchet handle.

PROCEDURE

1. Wipe off both gear edges to locate the register marks.

2. Turn the crankshaft until the old marks mesh.

3. Remove the camshaft gear bolts. Use a gear puller to remove the gear.

4. Install the new gear by lining up

the register marks. Then turn the crankshaft until the gear keyway lines up with the keyway of the camshaft. Push the gear in place.

5. Test the valve operation by turning the crankshaft through the four strokes of the four-cycle engine: intake, compression, power, and exhaust. Check the valve action against piston movement.

6. Test the valve timing in the following manner: Turn the crankshaft until No. 1 piston is at TDC firing position. The two valves of the last cylinder should be in the rocking position. That is, the exhaust valve should be just closing and the intake just opening. A slight movement either way will release one valve and tighten the other. In other words, the rocking position is a point in valve action where both intake and exhaust valves are slightly open at the same time. This is also known as *valve overlap.*

7. Tighten the gear retaining bolts.

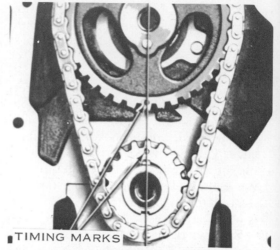

TIMING MARKS

Most engines are designed so that the timing marks align through the shaft centers, as shown in this illustration.

KEYWAY   TIMING MARK

KEYWAY   TIMING MARK   12 PINS BETWEEN MARKS

Buick and some Ford models require a specified number of pins or teeth between the timing marks, as shown in this illustration. Be sure to check the specifications before installing timing gears; and, too, be sure to check the valve timing by means of the "rocking" position, in order to make sure. Courtesy Ford Division, Ford Motor Company.

TIMING MARKS

THRUST PLATE SCREWS

The timing marks must match when the gears are assembled.

Replacing a Timing Chain

Many manufacturers use short chains to drive the camshaft. Chains have many more teeth in mesh than do gears, therefore they run more quietly. Short chains cannot be adjusted; they must be replaced when worn. If the chain is stretched, the valves will open and close later and thus affect engine performance.

Tools and Equipment

Plymouth short block; gear puller; $\frac{1}{2}$ and $\frac{9}{16}$ inch sockets; $\frac{1}{2}$ and $\frac{9}{16}$ inch combination-end wrenches.

PROCEDURE

1. Wipe off both gear edges to locate the register marks.

2. Turn the crankshaft until the marks are in line with a center line drawn through the two shafts.

3. Remove the camshaft gear retaining bolts and gear. Remove the chain.

4. Replace the chain by lining up both gear markings with a straightedge through the shaft centers. **Note:** *Some chains are installed with a specified number of teeth between marks as shown in the accompanying illustration.*

5. Turn the crankshaft until the camshaft gear bolt holes line up with the holes in the camshaft hub. Push the gear into position and tighten the bolts securely.

6. Test the valve operation by going through the four strokes of the four-cycle gasoline engine: intake, compression, power, and exhaust. Check the piston movement against the valve action.

7. Test the valve operation by means of the *rocking* position.

CHECK YOUR KNOWLEDGE

1. What are two purposes of valves?
2. Where are the valves positioned in an "I"-head engine?
3. Why must the exhaust valve be made of a different kind of steel from that of the intake valve?
4. What is the advantage of a rotating valve?
5. Why are two cams per cyclinder needed?
6. What advantage has a chain drive over a gear drive?
7. Why is it necessary to have valve clearance?
8. How much clearance is required in a hydraulically operated valve lifter?
9. What are the five parts of the hydraulic valve lifter?
10. What expands the hydraulic valve lifter?
11. What causes the hydraulic valve lifter to compress?
12. Why has the problem of oil leaking past worn guides been intensified with the universal adoption of the "I"-head engine?
13. What test is suggested for finding leaking valve oil seals?
14. Why is the intake valve of the gasoline engine opened before top dead center of the exhaust stroke?
15. Why is the exhaust valve opened during the power stroke?

Self-Check Tests

TRUE-FALSE

1. Intake valves are subjected to higher temperatures than exhaust valves.
2. The camshaft opens and closes the valves.
3. The camshaft is driven at half engine speed.

4. The valve adjustment is made, in some cases, by moving the entire rocker arm up or down.

5. There is a calculated amount of oil leakage between the plunger and body of a hydraulic valve lifter to cause expansion of the unit which takes up excessive play in the valve mechanism.

6. Oil seals are required to minimize oil leakage around worn intake guides.

MULTIPLE CHOICE

1. The valves are closed by the: a) tappet; b) camshaft; c) valve spring.

2. For each four strokes of the piston, the camshaft turns: a) once; b) twice; c) four times; d) eight times.

3. In hydraulically operated valve lifters, the clearance should be adjusted by: a) turning a screw in the tappet; b) turning the rocker arm; c) turning an anchor screw to move the entire rocker arm up or down; d) no adjustment needed.

4. Which of the following is *not* a part of a hydraulic valve lifter: a) ball check valve; b) plunger; c) pump; d) push rod seat?

5. The exhaust valve opens after the piston has traveled slightly over: a) $\frac{1}{3}$; b) $\frac{2}{3}$; c) $\frac{3}{4}$ of the way down on the power stroke.

COMPLETION

1. At _____ mph, an eight cylinder engine opens and closes its valves at the rate of 840,000 times in one hour.

2. The temperature of the exhaust valve often reaches _____ degrees.

3. Camshaft gears are made of _____ to minimize noise.

4. _____ _____ _____ automatically adjust the clearance between operating parts of the valve mechanism.

5. The intake valve remains open for the full intake stroke and as much as _____ degrees of the following compression stroke.

MATCHING

1. "I"-head
2. Camshaft
3. Hydraulic valve lifter
4. Four-stroke cycle
5. Valve timing

a. Opens valves
b. Self adjusting
c. Cycle of valve operation
d. Overhead valve arrangement
e. Principle of gas engine operation

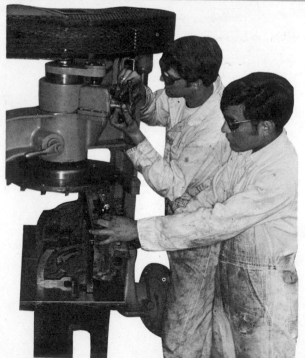

These students in Los Angeles Trade-Technical College are truing a cylinder head on a milling machine.

Chapter 5

Piston, Crankshaft, and Connecting Rod Assembly

Piston

As discussed in previous chapters, the piston slides in the cylinder a distance of about three inches. It receives the pressure of the expanding gas and transmits its power to the crankshaft by means of a connecting rod which is secured to the piston by a piston pin. The crankshaft and connecting rods change the sliding motion to a rotary one.

The piston of a modern engine is made of a very light alloy of aluminum to conserve energy needed to move it as it reverses direction of travel twice for each crankshaft revolution. The piston contains three grooves around its top for the installation of piston rings to seal the space between the piston and cylinder wall.

Pistons are cam ground—that is, they are slightly oval in shape so that they

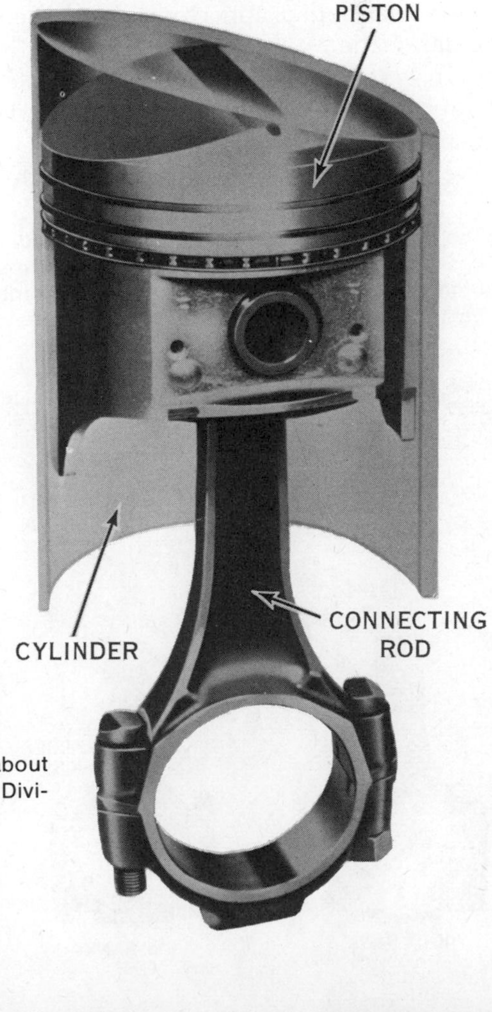

PISTON

CYLINDER

CONNECTING ROD

The piston slides up and down in a cylinder about a distance of 3 inches. Courtesy Chevrolet Division, General Motors Corporation.

123

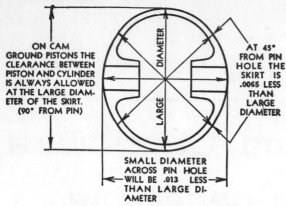

ON CAM GROUND PISTONS THE CLEARANCE BETWEEN PISTON AND CYLINDER IS ALWAYS ALLOWED AT THE LARGE DIAMETER OF THE SKIRT. (90° FROM PIN)

DIAMETER

LARGE

AT 45° FROM PIN HOLE THE SKIRT IS .0065 LESS THAN LARGE DIAMETER

SMALL DIAMETER ACROSS PIN HOLE WILL BE .013 LESS THAN LARGE DIAMETER

Modern pistons are cam-ground so that they fit the cylinder bore very closely across the thrust faces, but have room on the sides for expansion from heat.

fit the cylinder closely across the *thrust faces,* and have clearance across the *piston-pin sides.* As the engine warms up, the piston expands sideways. A fully warmed piston expands to a circular shape.

In certain piston designs, the piston pin is offset as much as $5/64$ inch from the center line to reduce piston slap. As such a piston passes top dead center,

The piston pin is offset so that the skirt loading changes smoothly as the piston moves across both top and bottom dead center. This contributes to quiet operation. Courtesy Pontiac Motor Division, General Motors Corporation.

the piston skirt loading (pressure on the skirt) changes smoothly from one side to the other because the bottom of the piston moves across the bore before the top, which greatly reduces the lateral force.

Piston slap is reduced in other designs by controlling expansion. Some pistons contain metal struts which oppose expansion of the piston when hot. Others contain slots—a horizontal one which interrupts the path of heat to the skirt, and a vertical one which allows the skirt to expand without increasing piston size.

Rings

Usually three cast-iron rings are used to seal the space between the piston and cylinder wall. They hold the compressed gases in the combustion chamber and keep lubricating oil out. They also transfer combustion heat from the pistons to the cylinder walls.

Piston rings have specialized duties. The top ring is a *compression ring;* its main purpose is to seal against combus-

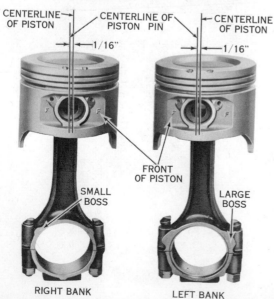

CENTERLINE OF PISTON

CENTERLINE OF PISTON PIN

CENTERLINE OF PISTON

1/16"

1/16"

FRONT OF PISTON

SMALL BOSS

LARGE BOSS

RIGHT BANK

LEFT BANK

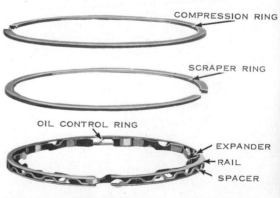

COMPRESSION RING

SCRAPER RING

OIL CONTROL RING

EXPANDER

RAIL

SPACER

The piston rings which encircle the piston keep the compression up and the oil down. Courtesy Buick Motor Division, General Motors Corporation.

124

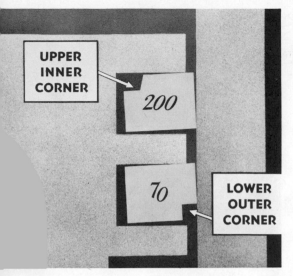

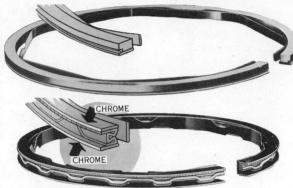

A scraper ring (top) with an expander to provide more unit wall pressure, and a multipiece oil ring (bottom) with chromed edges. Courtesy Hastings Manufacturing Company.

Modern compression rings are grooved so that they twist in operation to present a point contact to the walls and to the piston grooves for more efficient sealing. Courtesy Perfect Circle Corporation.

tion pressures. Being close to the heat of combustion, no spring expander is used behind it. The *scraper ring,* in the second groove of the piston, also holds back compression and usually contains a groove along its bottom edge to scrape lubricant from the cylinder wall on the down stroke. Sometimes a steel segment

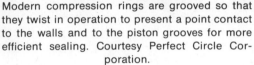

The expander of a multi-piece oil ring is designed to keep the steel rails in firm contact with the sides of the grooves, as well as the edges of the rails in firm contact with the cylinder walls. Courtesy Perfect Circle Corporation.

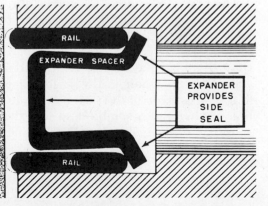

ring is installed under the cast-iron section. The lowest ring is specifically designed to remove excessive quantities of lubricant. However, enough oil must pass to lubricate the upper two rings; otherwise, scuffing occurs. *Oil control rings* have thin side rails to scrape the oil from the walls, and a slotted inner spacer to allow the oil to drain back.

Crankshaft

The crankshaft and rods change the sliding movement of the pistons into a rotary motion. The rear end of the crankshaft delivers the power to the rear drive mechanism.

The power flow of an internal combustion engine is not smooth; it consists of individual power thrusts which weaken rapidly as the pistons move down the cylinders. To keep the crankshaft turning smoothly between power impulses, a flywheel absorbs power from each piston thrust, and transfers the energy to the shaft while the other pistons are coasting.

125

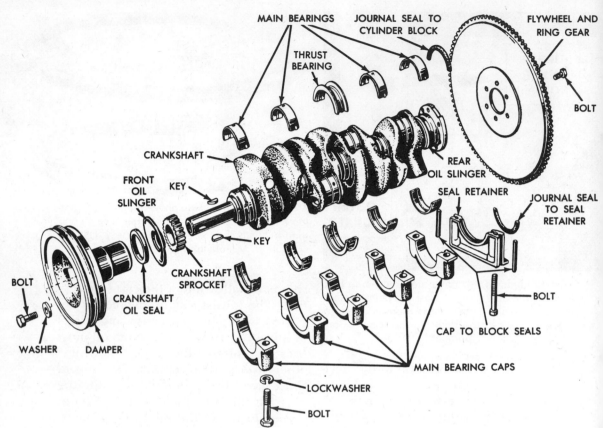

The crankshaft and its associated parts. Courtesy Ford Motor Company.

Besides smoothing out power impulses, the flywheel contains a ring gear which is engaged by the starting motor gear. In addition, the rear face of the flywheel is machined to drive the clutch friction plate.

On a long crankshaft, the alternate firing cylinders tend to "wind up" the shaft, causing torsional strains and vibration. To offset this, a small flywheel or *impulse neutralizer* is installed on the front end of the shaft.

Connecting Rods

The connecting rod has a bushing at one end to hold the piston pin and a bearing on the other to fit around the crankshaft journal. The latter is often called the *big end*. The small end of the connecting rod moves in a line with the piston. The big end moves around in a circle with the crankshaft throw.

The piston-pin end of the rod is lubricated by spray. Most connecting rods have a small hole drilled through the big end. As the crankshaft turns, a jet or spurt of oil is sprayed onto the cylinder wall. This spurt hole is always installed to the thrust side of the piston on an in-line engine and assembled so that the spurt holes face up on a V-8 engine.

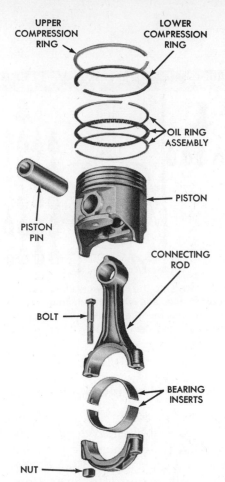

UPPER COMPRESSION RING

LOWER COMPRESSION RING

OIL RING ASSEMBLY

PISTON

PISTON PIN

CONNECTING ROD

BOLT

BEARING INSERTS

NUT

An exploded view of the connecting rod and piston assembly. Courtesy Ford Motor Company.

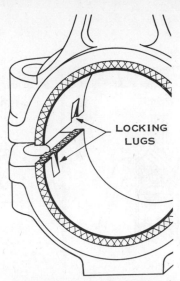

LOCKING LUGS

The locking lugs keep the bearing insert from moving when properly assembled in the rod and cap.

A tri-metal bearing has a knurled surface filled with lead alloy by electroplating. Courtesy Federal-Mogul Service, Inc.

Bearings

Bearings reduce friction, minimizing wear. Each connecting rod has a bearing surface in contact with the crankshaft journal to allow the rotating parts to turn smoothly. The crankshaft rotates in main bearings supported by webbings in the crankcase. Only one main bearing has thrust surfaces to take care of crankshaft end play.

Usually bearings are made of soft metal such as babbitt, which is a composition of antimony, tin, lead, and copper in varying amounts. Copper-lead type bearings resist heavier strains and greater heat. Modern engines use precision-bearing inserts which can be replaced when worn. They have a steel backing to which a very thin layer of bearing metal is applied.

A bearing is fitted with a small amount of clearance between it and the part it serves. This space carries the lubricant on which the bearing rides, preventing metal-to-metal contact.

127

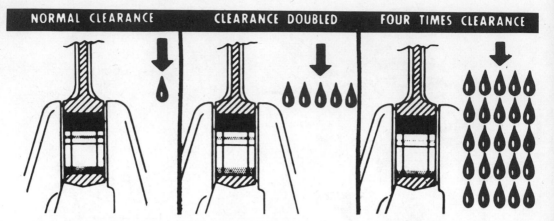

| NORMAL CLEARANCE | CLEARANCE DOUBLED | FOUR TIMES CLEARANCE |

The bearing clearance determines how much oil is thrown onto the cylinder walls. When the clearance is doubled, the oil throw off is multiplied by five, and when the clearance is four times normal, the oil throw off is 25 times that of a normal bearing. Naturally, even the best set of rings cannot control this much oil. Courtesy Hastings Manufacturing Company.

There must be a very small space between the shaft and bearing for oil. It is generally about 0.001″ to 0.002″. Courtesy Clevite Service Corporation.

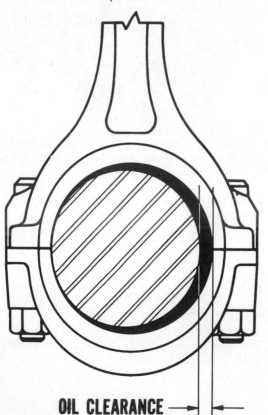

OIL CLEARANCE ←→

Service Procedures

The piston, crankshaft, and connecting rod assembly is serviced as a unit. Generally, piston rings are replaced to correct oil consumption and restore engine efficiency. However, piston rings are seldom, if ever, installed without servicing the other mechanical parts of the engine.

Connecting-rod bearings that have too much clearance, even though not worn enough to be noisy, throw excess quantities of lubricant onto the cylinder walls, which even the best set of piston rings cannot control. Therefore, to assure satisfactory performance, service the bearings at the same time new rings are installed.

When installing rings, pistons must be expanded, new piston pins fitted, connecting rods aligned, bearings replaced, valve mechanism reconditioned, and the engine tuned for best performance. This is called an *engine overhaul.*

128

Troubleshooting

Burning oil is evidenced by blue smoke from the exhaust. This is especially noticeable on acceleration. The oil that by-passes the piston rings enters the combustion chamber and burns. An especially good indication of worn piston rings is the heavily coated, oily combustion chamber. Removing the spark plugs will show if the condition is localized to one or two cylinders or is general throughout the engine.

Engine noises are difficult to locate without considerable experience. The use of a stethoscope is recommended to localize and identify noises.

A stethoscope is handy to locate the source of a noise.

Removing, Cleaning, and Inspecting the Connecting Rod Assembly

To overhaul an engine, it is necessary to remove, clean, and recondition all moving parts. After cleaning, the parts are inspected for defects, measured for wear, and new parts ordered to replace the worn ones.

Tools and Equipment

V-8 engine; $\frac{7}{16}$, $\frac{1}{2}$, $\frac{9}{16}$, $\frac{5}{8}$ and $\frac{3}{4}$ inch box, open-end wrenches; cub socket set; crescent wrench; drain bucket; screwdriver; hammer; jack; ridge removing tool; carbon scraper; ring groove cleaner; inside and outside micrometers; auxiliary starter switch; 0.002, 0.0025, and 0.003 inch feeler gauge stock; spring scale.

PROCEDURE

REMOVAL

1. Remove the oil pan and the cylinder heads. Disconnect the high tension lead wire at the coil. Disconnect the wire at the "S" terminal of the starter solenoid. Connect an auxiliary starter cable to the positive terminal of the battery and the "S" terminal of the solenoid.

2. "Bump" the engine with the auxiliary starter switch until the piston to be removed is at BDC (Bottom Dead Center). Before removing the cylinder ridge, insert a clean cloth into the cylinder bore to prevent steel chips and carbon from falling onto the piston rings. Remove the ridge, being careful not to cut into the ring travel area. Remove the cloth and wipe the bore clean. Do this for each cylinder.

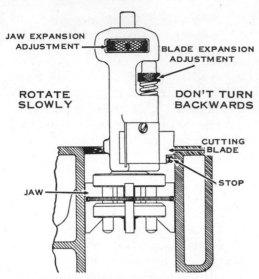

JAW EXPANSION ADJUSTMENT

BLADE EXPANSION ADJUSTMENT

ROTATE SLOWLY

DON'T TURN BACKWARDS

CUTTING BLADE

JAW

STOP

A ridge reamer is used to cut out the ridge.

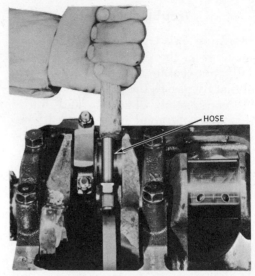

HOSE

A tube placed over the connecting rod bolt keeps the threads from contacting the shaft and damaging it. Courtesy Oldsmobile Division, General Motors Corporation.

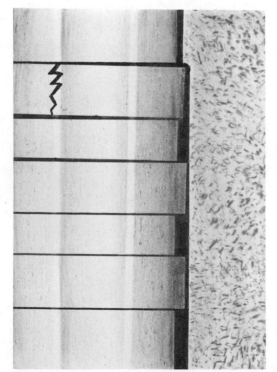

If the ridge is not removed, a new top ring will strike it and break.

3. Using the auxiliary starter switch, rotate the crankshaft to position the respective journals at approximately BDC for removal of each connecting rod and piston assembly.

4. Remove the connecting rod bearing cap and bearing inserts. Using a wooden hammer handle, push the connecting rod and piston assembly out of the cylinder bore. Use care to prevent the connecting rod from striking the cylinder bore or the threads from scratching the crankshaft journal. If the bore is scored or nicked while removing the assembly, it will have to be honed or rebored to repair the damage.

5. Replace the bearing inserts and cap on each connecting rod so that the numbered sides match.

CLEANING AND INSPECTING

1. Clean each machined surface of the cylinder block of old gasket mate-

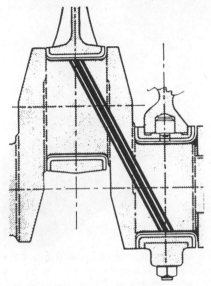

The oil passageways are drilled through the crankshaft from one bearing to another. Now you can see why it is very important to clean the oil holes in the crankshaft thoroughly.

This is a defective bearing with excessive clearance, as evidenced by its dark coloration.

This light gray coloring is an indication that this bearing is operating with the correct clearance.

rial. Clean all parts in solvent and blow dry. Carefully inspect for scored bores, cracks, or water leaks. Minute cracks may be found by coating the suspected areas with a mixture of 75% light engine oil and 25% kerosene. After wiping the area clean, immediately apply a coating of zinc oxide disolved in wood alcohol. If any cracks are present, the white coating will discolor at the defective area.

2. Check each cylinder bore for taper and out-of-round conditions. Measure the diameter of the bore at the top of the piston ring travel, crosswise of the block. Next, take a measurement lengthwise of the block. The difference between the readings is the out-of-round wear. Repeat the measurements at the bottom of the ring travel to check for taper. The difference between the diameters, measured at the top and bottom of the bore, is the taper of the bore.

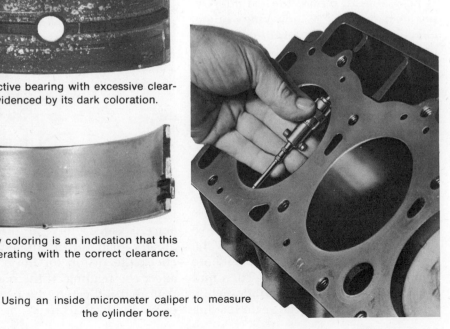

Using an inside micrometer caliper to measure the cylinder bore.

A dial gauge can be used to measure the amount of taper in a cylinder. Courtesy Buick Motor Division, General Motors Corporation.

These students in Los Angeles Trade-Technical College are checking a cylinder with a micrometer to determine the amount of wear.

3. If the cylinder bore wear does not exceed 0.008 inch, new piston rings will give satisfactory service. If the wear is between 0.008 inch and 0.018 inch, it is advisable to rebore the cylinders to the next oversize as new rings cannot effectively control oil burning with this much taper. When the cylinder is worn to this extent, the use of ring sets with severe expanders is not advised because it will result in a noticeable drop in power. Over 0.018 inch taper requires a rebore job because rings cannot operate properly under these conditions.

4. Check the piston fit with a length of ½ inch wide feeler stock. The feeler should extend the entire length of the piston, 90° from the piston pin holes. Hold the piston in the cylinder bore so that the end is about 1½ inch below the top of the block and the piston pin bore is parallel to the crankshaft. Then pull the feeler stock from the cylinder while noting the reading. If the scale reading

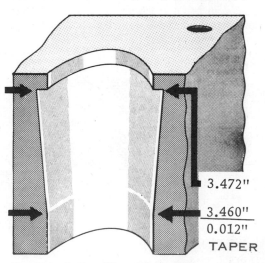

3.472"
3.460"
0.012"
TAPER

The taper is the difference in readings between the top and bottom of a cylinder.

conforms to the limits below, the clearance is satisfactory. If the reading is greater than the maximum pull limit, check the piston for burrs which may affect the reading. If the reading is less than that indicated, the piston must be expanded back to size.

A micrometer should be used to determine actual gauge size as shown. The indicator needle must first be zeroed with the gauge in the bottom of the cylinder bore. Courtesy Buick Motor Division, General Motors Corporation.

A boring bar is used to true up the cylinder walls to the next oversize when the wear is excessive. Courtesy Kwik-Way Division, Cedar Rapids Engineering Company.

This student is learning to measure the cylinder bore and center the boring bar.

Fit New Piston in New Bore		Fit New Piston in Used Bore		Fit Used Piston in Used or New Bore	
Feeler Thickness (Inches)	Pull (lbs.)	Feeler Thickness (Inches)	Pull (lbs.)	Feeler Thickness (Inches)	Pull (lbs.)
.002	5-10	.0025	5-10	.003	5-10

Checking the fit of a piston in a rebored cylinder. Courtesy Ford Motor Company.

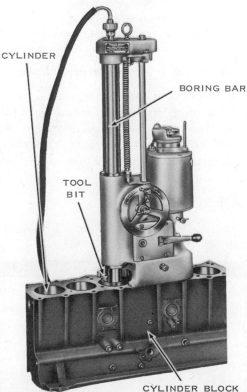

CYLINDER

BORING BAR

TOOL BIT

CYLINDER BLOCK

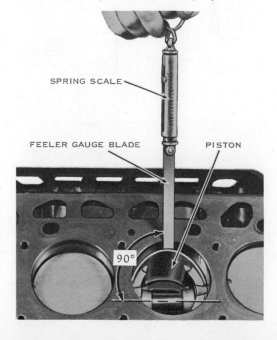

SPRING SCALE

FEELER GAUGE BLADE

PISTON

90°

133

5. Before installing new rings, remove the glaze to assist in seating the rings.

6. If the original pistons are to be used with new rings, they must be thoroughly cleaned in carbon-removing solvent. **Caution:** *Never buff the sides of a piston, as this will round off the ring lands.* Clean the oil holes or slots, being careful not to score or remove metal from the ring grooves, because the new rings must make a seal against these surfaces.

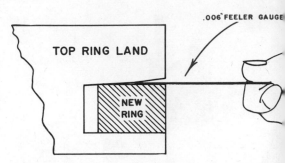

Testing the wear of a top ring groove. A .006" feeler gauge blade must not enter over halfway.

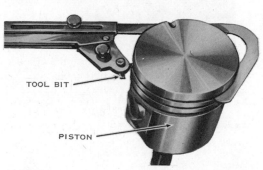

Cleaning the ring grooves of a piston. Courtesy Ford Motor Company.

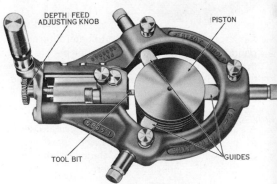

This is the tool used to true up the top ring groove. Courtesy Perfect Circle Corporation.

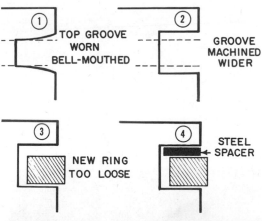

This series of drawings show how a top ring groove is widened and a spacer installed above the ring to take up the extra space.

Reading a Micrometer Caliper

Learn how to read a micrometer to be able to order the proper-sized parts for replacement purposes. The caliper is called a micrometer for short. A micrometer measures to one thousandth of an inch (0.001 inch).

Tools and Equipment

One-inch micrometer and pieces of stock for measuring purposes.

PROCEDURE

1. Clean the ends of the spindle and anvil carefully, because dirt is an enemy of accuracy.

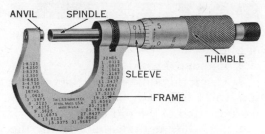

Parts of the micrometer. Courtesy L. S. Starrett Company.

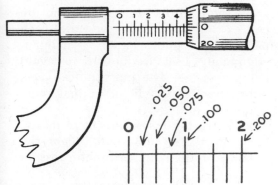

A micrometer open to 0.475 inch. Courtesy Bohn Aluminum & Brass Corporation.

2. Turn the thimble until the spindle and anvil meet. **Caution:** *Do not force them together, or you will spring the micrometer out of shape.*

3. Notice that the thimble is graduated at its edge into 25 divisions. Also notice that the "0" division on the thimble and the index mark on the sleeve come together when the micrometer is closed.

4. Turn the thimble one of these 25 divisions. Squint through the contacts — you are now looking at one thousandth of an inch (0.001 inch).

5. Turn the thimble one revolution (25 divisions) and notice that a cross line appears on the sleeve. Turn it another complete turn and notice that a second cross line appears. Each cross line means 25 thousandths of an inch (0.025 inch) or a total of 0.050 inch for the two turns.

6. Now, rotate it two more turns, and you will uncover two more cross lines. The last one is marked "1." The "1" stands for 100 thousandths of an inch (0.100 inch), and so on, with 2, 3, 4, etc., standing for 0.200 inch, 0.300 inch, and 0.400 inch respectively.

7. Notice how far the micrometer in the illustration shown above is open. The No. 4 line is visible, which accounts for 400 thousandths of an inch (0.400 inch). Then there are three more cross lines. (You will have to look closely for the third.) They represent 25 thousandths (0.025 inch) each or 0.075 inch together. Now add them up: 0.400 inch plus 0.075 inch equals 0.475 inch. That's the reading, 0.475 inch.

8. Practice on several pieces of stock until you become proficient at reading a micrometer.

Fitting Piston Pins

Piston pins wear slightly but need replacement every time new rings are installed to avoid undesirable noises. Pins come in various oversizes so that it is only necessary to ream out the piston and rod bushing to fit the larger pin. In unusual cases, it may be necessary to replace the rod bushing.

The hole in the bushing may be enlarged with an expansion reamer or a hone, depending on the shop equipment.

Tools and Equipment

Set of expansion reamers; pin-fitting hone; connecting rod and piston assembly with loose pin; set of oversize pins for fitting purposes.

LOCK RING

Removing the piston pin spring locks.

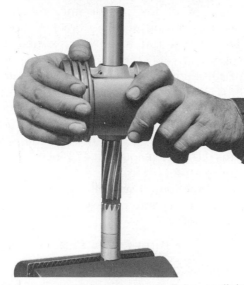

Using a reamer to fit a piston pin. Take very light cuts to avoid gouging out the surface and going oversize. Courtesy Chevrolet Division, General Motors Corporation.

Using a hone to finish the pin hole in a piston. Note the use of a tapered jig to keep the two holes in alignment. Courtesy Ammco Tools, Inc.

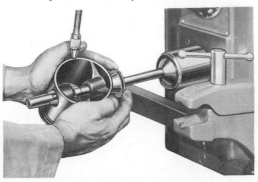

1. Remove the pin locks with a pair of pliers.

2. Remove the old pin.

3. Use a micrometer to select a new pin which is slightly larger than the unworn portion of the old pin.

4. Try the new piston pin in the piston and the rod to make sure that it does not enter.

5. Mount a reamer in a vise and revolve the piston around it. Expand the cutters slightly for a larger cut at each pass. Use a pilot sleeve to maintain alignment. Test frequently to avoid going oversize. The pin should have a light, thumb-press fit at normal room temperature.

6. Check the piston pin fit in its rod bushing. Using light cuts, ream the bushing until a light, thumb-press fit

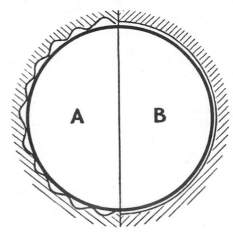

The actual pressure required to move a piston pin in the rod bushing depends on how accurately the hole was bored. In a hole made with a reamer (A), the fit should feel tighter so that it will wear into the proper clearance. The hole at (B) is bored very accurately and so the fit must feel looser. A bored hole should allow the pin to drop through of its own weight when tried dry. Courtesy Sunnen Products Company.

is obtained. To avoid bell-mouthed holes, use an extension handle on each rod to equalize pressure.

7. Install the piston pin into the fitted rod and piston assembly, making sure that the parts are assembled correctly.

8. Install new retainers at each end of the pin to hold it in place. Make sure that they seat in their grooves; otherwise, cylinder wall scoring will result.

The piston pin should move in the rod with a light thumb pressure in most cases. Many late-model cars specify an interference fit of 0.0009 inch to lock the pin to the rod, and so need no spring locks in the piston to hold the pin in place. Courtesy Plymouth Division, Chrysler Corporation.

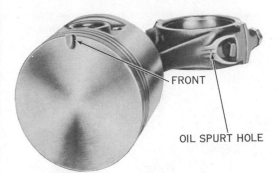

FRONT

OIL SPURT HOLE

Each car model has specific instructions for assembling the piston and rod correctly. Be sure to check the specification book. Courtesy Ford Motor Company.

Some late-model engines use piston pins that are installed with an *interference fit*. The hole in the rod is slightly smaller than the diameter of the pin. It takes special tools to force the pin into place. Courtesy Ford Motor Company.

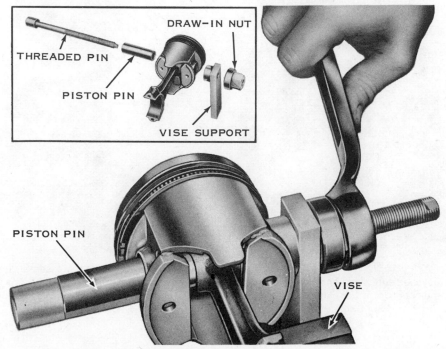

THREADED PIN

DRAW-IN NUT

PISTON PIN

VISE SUPPORT

PISTON PIN

VISE

Aligning a Connecting Rod

Constant power impulses tend to spring and twist the connecting rod. Installation of new piston pins and bushings also affects alignment. In order to make sure that the piston and rings are going to run true with the cylinder bore, the connecting rod must be aligned.

Tools and Equipment

Connecting rod and piston assembly; alignment gauge; bending and twisting tools.

PROCEDURE

TESTING FOR BEND

1. Mount the connecting rod on the mandrel.

2. To test for bend, position the piston straight up and down.

BEARING WEAR

This is what happens to the bearing when the rod is bent. Courtesy Ford Motor Company.

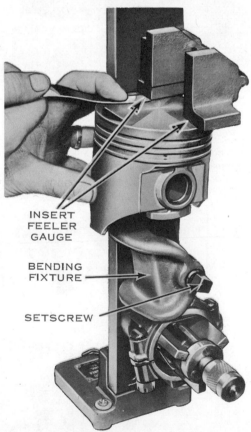

INSERT
FEELER
GAUGE

BENDING
FIXTURE

SETSCREW

Measuring the piston and rod assembly for bend. Note the bending fixture with a set screw (simple machines). Courtesy Plymouth Division, Chrysler Corporation.

PISTON WEAR

Such a polished surface on one side of a piston is a sure indication of a bent rod. Courtesy Ford Motor Company.

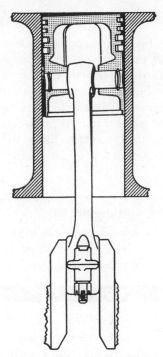

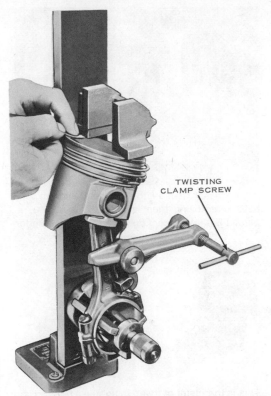

TWISTING
CLAMP SCREW

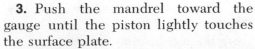

A twisted rod will cause the piston to cock each time it moves up and down, causing abnormal cylinder wall wear.

Testing the rod assembly for twist. Note the use of the *screw* and two first class *levers* combined into a piece of equipment to apply a twisting force to the rod. Courtesy Plymouth Division, Chrysler Corporation.

3. Push the mandrel toward the gauge until the piston lightly touches the surface plate.

4. The piston must touch at both the top and bottom of the skirt. If it touches only at the top or the bottom, then the rod must be straightened with the bending tool so as to align the piston with the surface plate.

TESTING FOR TWIST

5. To check the rod for twist, allow the piston to turn on the piston pin as far to one side as possible. Align the piston face against the plate. Turn the piston to the other end of its pin

travel and, if the faces of both piston and gauge are still parallel, then the rod is not twisted. If space appears at either the top or bottom of the piston, at either position, then the rod is twisted and correction should be made with the twisting tool.

6. On all alignment gauges, "V" blocks are furnished which must be used with cam-ground pistons because they are not finished true on the piston pin sides.

139

It is necessary to mark the block and bearing caps before removing them so that they will be replaced in their correct positions. Courtesy Dodge Division, Chrysler Corporation.

This is the result of trying to tighten a bearing cap when it was reversed during installation.

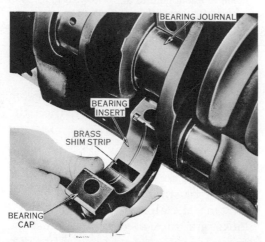

Using a piece of shim stock to measure bearing clearance. Courtesy Dodge Division, Chrysler Corporation.

Installing Main Bearing Inserts

Main bearings support the crankshaft and provide a surface in which it can turn. After many thousands of miles, the main bearings wear enough to lower the oil pressure. Because main bearings do not wear as much as connecting rod bearings, they usually have to be replaced only every other engine overhaul.

Tools and Equipment

$\frac{3}{4}$, $\frac{13}{16}$ and $\frac{7}{8}$ inch sockets; hinge handle; pry bar; torque wrench; 0.002 inch shim stock; "Plastigage."

PROCEDURE

SHIM STOCK METHOD

1. For identification purposes, mark the bearing cap and block with punch marks.

2. To determine the amount of wear, install several pieces of $\frac{1}{2}$ inch square, 0.002 inch thick shim stock between the bearing and journal, and then tighten the cap.

3. Rock the shaft slightly each way. **Caution:** *Do not turn it or you will score the soft bearing material.*

4. If the shaft locks, remove one piece of shim stock and try again. Continue testing and removing one piece of shim stock at a time until the shaft turns with a slight drag.

5. Remove the bearing cap and note the number of pieces of shim stock remaining. As each piece is 0.002 inch thick, the number of pieces multiplied by 2 is the clearance in thousandths of an inch.

6. After determining the clearance, remove the test pieces, as the engine

140

This tool is inserted into the oil hole in the crankshaft, which is then revolved to turn the top bearing insert out or in. Courtesy Dodge Division, Chrysler Corporation.

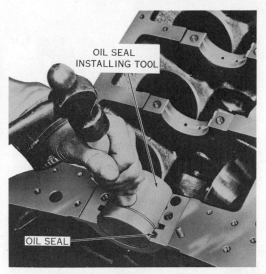

Some rear main-bearing oil seals must be installed in this fashion. Courtesy Cadillac Motor Car Division, General Motors Corporation.

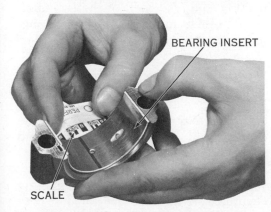

Using "Plastigage" to measure bearing clearance.

is never assembled with shim stock between the bearing and journal.

"PLASTIGAGE" METHOD

7. Use a piece of "Plastigage" to test the clearance again by inserting the "Plastigage" between the journal and bearing. Tighten the cap and then remove; compare the width of the plastic against the scale on the package to determine the clearance. If the bearing has over 0.004 inch clearance, replace it.

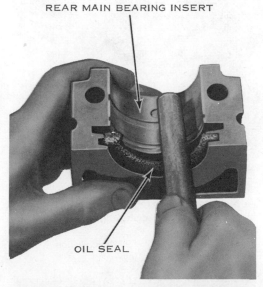

Some rear main oil seals must be rolled into place as shown. The new seal should be prelubricated so that the initial start-up does not destroy it before normal engine lubrication is established. Soak the seal in engine oil for at least 20 minutes before installation.

TESTING END PLAY

8. To test the end play, use a pry bar to move the crankshaft as far forward as possible.

9. Insert a feeler gauge blade between the shaft shoulder and the side of the main bearing to measure the clearance. Note that only one bearing has babbitted sides for end thrust. The bearing must be replaced if the clearance is over 0.008 inch.

10. Use a torque wrench to tighten the main bearing bolts to the factory recommended specifications.

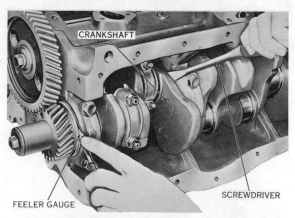

A feeler gauge is inserted between the main bearing thrust surface and the crankshaft shoulder in order to measure the crankshaft end play, which should be between 0.002″ and 0.007″.

Use a tension wrench to tighten the main-bearing caps, to avoid distorting the block.

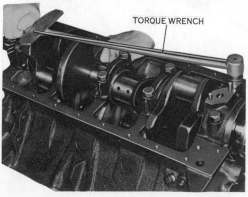

Installing Connecting Rod Bearing Inserts

Inserts are steel shims with a thin overlay of babbitt for the bearing surface. After many thousands of miles of service, bearings wear slightly and allow excessive quantities of lubricant to be thrown off the sides of the connecting rods and onto the cylinder walls, where even the best set of piston rings cannot control it, resulting in burning oil. When replacing rings, it is always necessary to replace the bearing inserts at the same time.

Tools and Equipment

Crankshaft with worn throw; connecting rod; $\frac{9}{16}$ inch socket; ratchet; 2- to 3-inch micrometer; connecting-rod inserts in various undersizes; "Plastigage"; torque wrench.

PROCEDURE

1. Remove the connecting rod nuts and cap. Note the markings on the camshaft side for an in-line engine and away from the camshaft for a V-8 engine.

2. Inspect the insert. A light grey surface indicates proper operating clearance. A dark surface, or one with broken-out areas, is a sure sign that the bearing is operating with too much clearance and needs to be replaced.

3. Check the specifications for the correct journal size.

4. Measure the crankshaft journal at four points: *sideways front; sideways rear; up-and-down front;* and *up-and-down rear.*

5. To find how flat the journal is, subtract the *up-and-down front* from the *sideways front; up-and-down rear* from *sideways rear.* To find the taper, subtract the front from the rear di-

142

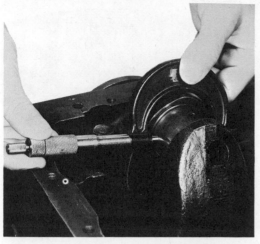
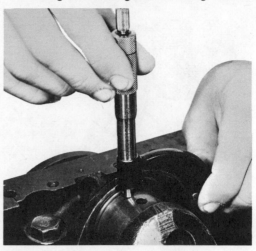

Measuring the crankshaft throw sideways (left) and up and down (right).

These students in an engine rebuilding class are measuring a crankshaft throw to determine whether it must be reground. Note the use of safety glasses; some form of eye protection is required at all times.

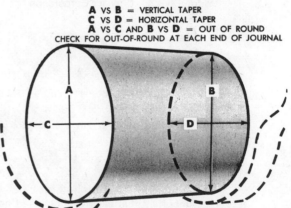

A VS **B** = VERTICAL TAPER
C VS **D** = HORIZONTAL TAPER
A VS **C** AND **B** VS **D** = OUT OF ROUND
CHECK FOR OUT-OF-ROUND AT EACH END OF JOURNAL

The taper is obtained by subtracting B from A and D from C. Courtesy Ford Motor Company.

mensions. New bearing inserts may be ordered if the journal is not over 0.002 inch flat or tapered. If it exceeds this limit, the journal must be reground.

6. Inserts come in various undersizes and should be ordered by subtracting the *sideways* dimension from the *original journal size*.

7. To test the correctness of your measurements, use a piece of "Plastigage" between the new bearing insert and the crankshaft journal before assembling the thoroughly cleaned parts. Remove the cap and compare the squeezed-out piece of "Plastigage" with the scale on the envelope. The clearance should be between 0.001 inch and and 0.002 inch.

143

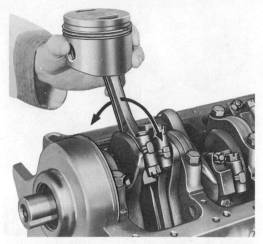

A correctly fitted rod will move back and forth freely, yet have no feelable side play. Courtesy Dodge Division, Chrysler Corporation.

It is most important that each bearing insert be absolutely clean before it is installed. Courtesy Federal-Mogul Service, Inc.

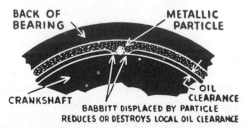

BACK OF BEARING METALLIC PARTICLE

CRANKSHAFT OIL CLEARANCE

BABBITT DISPLACED BY PARTICLE REDUCES OR DESTROYS LOCAL OIL CLEARANCE

This is the way in which a metallic particle displaces the bearing metal, destroying the oil clearance around it. Courtesy Bohn Aluminum & Brass Corporation.

This is a bearing insert that was scored by dirt particles from the oil holes in the crankshaft. Just think of what it was doing to the crankshaft journal. Courtesy McQuay-Norris Manufacturing Co.

8. For the final assembly, clean out the cap, bearing inserts, and journal. **Caution:** *Particles of dirt left in the cap will keep the insert from making a full surface contact and local hot spots will develop which will melt out small sections of the bearing.*

9. Lubricate the bearing, install the cap, and tighten the nut. Be sure that the markings are on the correct side of the journal. Torque the nuts to 45-50 foot-pounds.

Installing Piston Rings

Rings seal the space between the side of the piston and the cylinder wall. They keep the compression and combustion gases from leaking down and the oil from going up into the combustion chamber. They also pass the heat of combustion from the piston to the cylinder walls.

Tools and Equipment

Ring groove scraper; ring compressor; feeler gauge; mill file; ballpeen hammer; $9/16$ inch socket; ratchet handle; torque wrench; piston and ring assembly; engine.

Filing the end clearance of a piston ring. Keep your fingers up very close to the ends to avoid breaking the ring.

1. To check the piston ring end clearance, push the ring to the bottom of the cylinder, using a piston held upside down. The piston keeps the ring square with the cylinder wall. The bottom of the cylinder has the smallest diameter. The ring should have 0.003 inch end clearance for each 1 inch of piston diameter.

2. To check the ring side clearance, install it on the piston. Use a feeler gauge to measure the clearance, which must be 0.0015 inch for the top ring and 0.001 inch for each of the others.

3. To test the piston fit in the cylinder, use a feeler gauge between the piston and the wall at the bottom of the cylinder. The clearance should not be over 0.003 inch; otherwise, the piston must be expanded.

4. Fit new piston pins and align the connecting rods.

Measuring the end clearance of piston rings. Courtesy Dodge Division, Chrysler Corporation.

FEELER GAUGE

Measuring the side clearance of a ring. Courtesy Dodge Division, Chrysler Corporation.

Dressing down the side clearance of a piston ring.

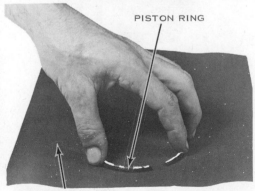

PISTON RING

ABRASIVE CLOTH

145

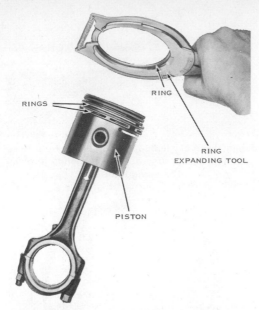

Installing a piston ring. This tool will prevent over-stretching the ring, which would distort it.

The completed piston and rod assembly. Note the indent mark on top of the piston and the "V" slot in the bearing cap, which must be assembled in this manner. For each car model, a different method of assembling the piston to the rod is required. Check the manufacturer's specifications before doing this job. Courtesy Dodge Division, Chrysler Corporation.

5. Install the new rings on the piston, with the oil ring in the bottom groove. The scraper ring is installed in the next higher groove and the compression ring in the top groove. Turn the top two rings so that the gaps line up with opposite ends of the piston pin. Position the oil ring gap away from the spurt hole. **Caution:** *No two consecutive gaps should be in line.*

6. Oil the rings and clamp a ring compressor over the piston and ring assembly. Make sure that all the rings and segments enter their grooves properly.

7. Insert the piston into its proper cylinder. Check that the connecting rod markings are on the camshaft side of an in-line engine or facing down on a V-8 engine. Check to make sure that the aluminum piston skirt slit is on the left side of the block. Check cam ground pistons for some mark or dot indicating the front of the piston which is to be installed toward the front of the engine.

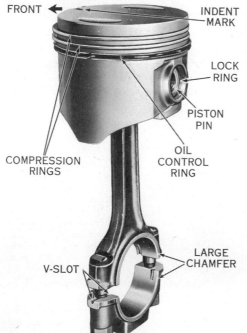

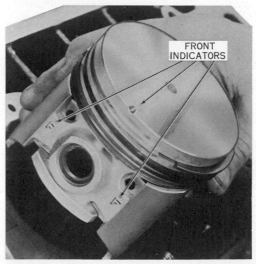

This engine has an "F" mark in the piston to identify the front. Courtesy American Motors Corporation.

146

The last chance to check things before the pan is installed. Note that the numbers on the caps agree, that there are "Pal" nuts on each rod nut, and that the main bearing bolts are locked with wires.

8. Push the piston down with the back of a hammer handle. Be careful that the rings do not slip out of the ring clamp. Use a steady push so that you can stop in the event something catches. **Caution:** *Do not force the piston down with hammer blows or you may break a ring.*

9. Reinstall the bearing inserts and the connecting rod bearing cap. Make sure the markings are together and that the assembled parts are thoroughly clean to avoid excess wear. Torque the nuts to 45-50 foot-pounds.

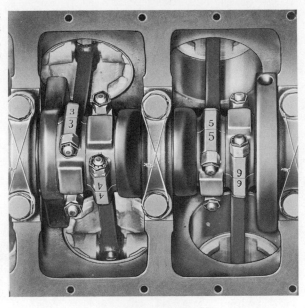

RING COMPRESSOR

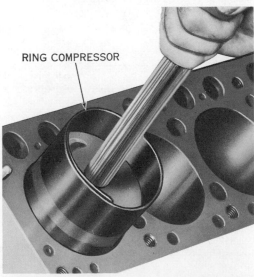

Installing the piston and rod assembly. Use a steady push so that you can stop before something breaks in case you feel resistance. Courtesy Dodge Division, Chrysler Corporation.

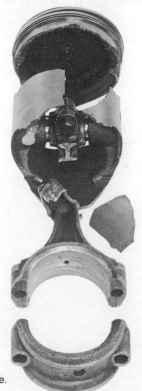

This is the result of not taking time to be sure. Courtesy Federal-Mogul Service, Inc.

CHECK YOUR KNOWLEDGE

1. What is the purpose of the piston?
2. Why must pistons be light in weight?
3. How does cam grinding a piston provide for heat expansion?
4. Why are some piston pins offset from the centerline of the piston?
5. What is the purpose of the horizontal slot in a piston? The vertical slot?
6. What three duties do piston rings perform?
7. Why is a spring expander never used behind the top ring?
8. Why is the oil ring inner spacer slotted?
9. What is the purpose of the crankshaft?
10. What is the purpose of an impulse neutralizer?
11. What are the two purposes of the flywheel?
12. What is the purpose of the connecting rod?
13. How is the piston pin lubricated?
14. What is the purpose of the spurt hole in the connecting rod?

Self-Check Tests

TRUE-FALSE

1. The crankshaft changes the sliding motion of the piston to a rotary motion.
2. The top compression ring is always installed without an expander under it in order to minimize cylinder wall pressure.
3. The scraper ring is basically a compression ring.
4. No lubricant is permitted to pass a good oil control ring.
5. The flow of power from an internal combustion engine is a smooth one.
6. Long crankshafts tend to wind and twist in operation.
7. The top end of the connecting rod moves in a straight line and the lower end moves in a circle.
8. Bearing metal is very soft.
9. Only one main bearing is designed to take end thrust.
10. Worn connecting rod bearings have no effect on oil consumption.
11. Engine noises are very easy to locate and identify.

MULTIPLE CHOICE

1. Which of the following terms does *not* apply to a piston: a) cam ground; b) strut; c) ring groove; d) spurt hole?
2. Which of the following terms does *not* apply to piston rings: a) combustion; b) scraper; c) oil control; d) expander?
3. Which of the following is *not* a part of the crankshaft assembly: a) impulse neutralizer; b) ring gear; c) drive shaft; d) bearing journal?
4. Which of the following terms does *not* apply to the connecting rod assembly: a) piston pin; b) spurt hole; c) main bearing; d) big end?
5. End play of the crankshaft is controlled by: a) one; b) two; c) three; d) four main bearings.

COMPLETION

1. The piston is secured to the connecting rod by a _____ _____.
2. Usually three _____ are used to seal the space between the piston and cylinder wall.
3. The _____ changes the sliding movement of the piston to a rotary motion.
4. A small flywheel or _____ _____ is always installed on the front end of a long crankshaft.
5. The connecting rod joins the _____ with the crankshaft.
6. The spurt hole is always installed *up* on a _____ engine.
7. The crankshaft rotates in _____ _____ set in the webbings of the crankcase.

MATCHING

1. Piston   a. Babbitt
2. Oil control ring   b. Spurt hole
3. Crankshaft   c. Cam ground
4. Connecting rod   d. Expander
5. Bearing   e. Impulse neutralizer

Chapter 6

The Fuel System

The fuel system is designed to store and distribute gasoline to each cylinder in the form of an exactly metered mist of fuel and air mixture. The fuel is stored in the *gas tank*, usually suspended from the rear of the chassis. A fuel line runs from the tank to a fuel pump attached to the engine. The fuel pump delivers gasoline to the carburetor under pressure. The *carburetor* mixes and atomizes the liquid gasoline. The *intake manifold* warms the mixture while conducting it to each cylinder.

Within the cylinder, the atomized air-fuel mixture is vaporized by the heat of the engine.

The Fuel Pump

A pump draws liquid fuel from the gas tank by "suction" and delivers it under pressure to the carburetor. The pump is operated by a cam on the camshaft. The eccentric movement of the cam is transmitted to levers, which pull a flexible diaphragm down. A calibrated spring pushes the diaphragm up, forcing the fuel out of the pump.

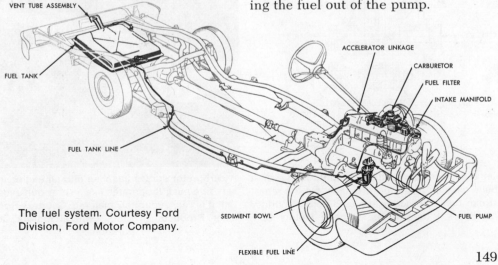

VENT TUBE ASSEMBLY

FUEL TANK

FUEL TANK LINE

ACCELERATOR LINKAGE

CARBURETOR

FUEL FILTER

INTAKE MANIFOLD

SEDIMENT BOWL

FUEL PUMP

FLEXIBLE FUEL LINE

The fuel system. Courtesy Ford Division, Ford Motor Company.

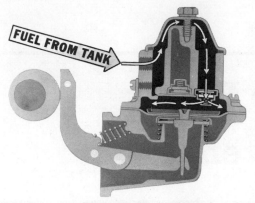

FUEL FROM TANK

The fuel pump draws the gasoline from the tank and forces it to the carburetor under pressure. Note the use of an *inclined plane* (camshaft) to operate the rocker arm (first class *lever*). Courtesy AC Spark Plug Division, General Motors Corporation.

Fuel Pump Operation

Power is applied to the rocker arm by an eccentric on the camshaft. Rocker arm movement, through the link and rod, pulls the diaphragm down. Vacuum

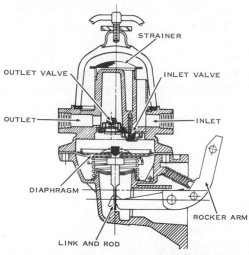

STRAINER

OUTLET VALVE

INLET VALVE

OUTLET

INLET

DIAPHRAGM

ROCKER ARM

LINK AND ROD

On the down stroke of the diaphragm, vacuum pulls gasoline from the fuel tank. On the return stroke fuel is forced to the carburetor. Courtesy AC Spark Plug Division, General Motors Corporation.

created by the diaphragm movement pulls gasoline from the supply tank through the inlet valve and into the fuel chamber. The return stroke releases the compressed diaphragm spring, pushing fuel through the outlet valve and into the carburetor. When the engine is idling, the pump fills the carburetor bowl, thus raising the float and closing the fuel entrance to the carburetor. Pressure builds up in the line and in the pump chamber, forcing the diaphragm to make shorter and shorter strokes, until the pump output matches the fuel needs of the engine.

The Carburetor

Liquid gasoline will not burn. It takes about 15 pounds of air, mixed with each pound of gasoline, to make an ideal flammable mixture. The carburetor meters and atomizes the liquid fuel and sprays it into the air stream so that it can be vaporized quickly by the manifold and engine heat.

The story of carburetion starts with the intake stroke of the engine. The

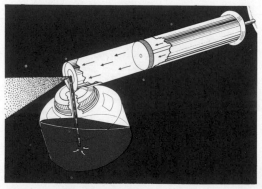

A carburetor sprays gasoline into an engine in a very fine mist. It operates like a spray gun except that it is very accurately metered. Courtesy Rochester Products Division, General Motors Corporation.

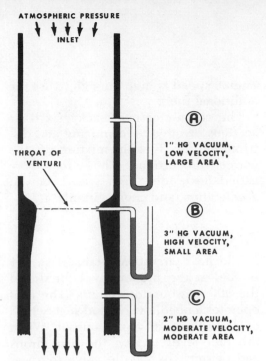

ATMOSPHERIC PRESSURE

INLET

THROAT OF VENTURI

A 1" HG VACUUM, LOW VELOCITY, LARGE AREA

B 3" HG VACUUM, HIGH VELOCITY, SMALL AREA

C 2" HG VACUUM, MODERATE VELOCITY, MODERATE AREA

A venturi tube reduces the pressure at the point of greatest restriction. This principle was first stated by Daniel Bernoulli. Courtesy Rochester Products Division, General Motors Corporation.

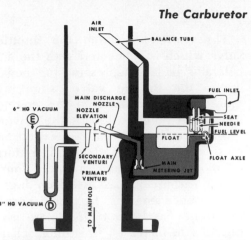

The Carburetor

AIR INLET — BALANCE TUBE

FUEL INLET

MAIN DISCHARGE NOZZLE
NOZZLE ELEVATION
6" HG VACUUM
E
SEAT
NEEDLE
FUEL LEVEL
FLOAT
SECONDARY VENTURI
PRIMARY VENTURI
FLOAT AXLE
MAIN METERING JET
3" HG VACUUM **D**
TO MANIFOLD

This is how the venturi is used in a carburetor. A second venturi is placed so that its exit is at the entrance of the primary venturi, thus providing a boost in the vacuum. Courtesy Rochester Products Division, General Motors Corporation.

piston moves to the bottom of the cylinder, drawing in the mixture past the opened intake valve. The fuel-air mixture enters the manifold from the carburetor, which contains a restriction in the air stream, called a *venturi*, which reduces the pressure around the fuel delivery nozzle so that liquid gasoline sprays out in the form of a fine mist.

The venturi effect was discovered by Daniel Bernoulli (Switzerland) who stated that: "If a liquid or gas is made to flow through a tube with a restricted area *(venturi)*, the pressure drops and the speed of the fluid or gas reaches maximum at the point of greatest restriction." An analogy of water rushing past rocks in a mountain stream may help in understanding this phenomenon. The rocks restrict the flow of water which increases speed accordingly. In areas where the stream widens, the water flows more slowly.

A four-barrel carburetor uses only the two primary barrels until the increased air flow of high speed indicates a need for more fuel. Below 70 mph, the counterweighted throttle plates (d) are closed. Courtesy Buick Motor Division, General Motors Corporation.

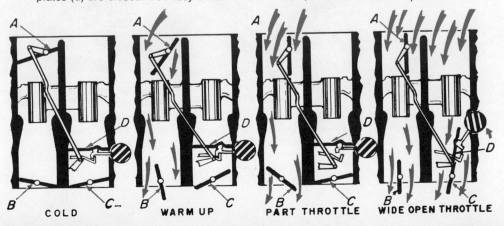

COLD   WARM UP   PART THROTTLE   WIDE OPEN THROTTLE

151

The carburetor contains a throttle valve which is connected with the accelerator pedal. Depressing the pedal opens the throttle valve, admitting more fuel-air mixture so the engine speed can be increased by the driver.

Single carburetor units are used on most small engines; dual carburetors on most eight-cylinder engines. Four-barrel carburetors are used on high-performance engines. In recent years, the trend has been to use more carburetors to increase "breathing" characteristics. On some engines, as many as three dual carburetors, or two four-barrel carburetors, are used. One dual carburetor, of a triple installation, or two barrels of a four-barrel carburetor, carries the load for average driving conditions. When high speed or extreme acceleration is required, depression of the accelerator pedal to the floorboard opens the throttles of the additional carburetors to provide a free-flowing induction charge (when engine speed is high enough to use the additional fuel).

The carburetor consists of six basic sections or circuits for mixing and distributing the fuel-air mixture in the correct proportions. The circuits are called float, idle, high speed, power, acceleration, and choke circuits.

Float Circuit

The float circuit maintains a supply of fuel at the proper level for use of the other carburetor circuits. The float operates a needle valve and seat, which controls the fuel pump output. When the fuel level is low, the float drops and permits the needle valve to open. Gasoline then is forced into the carburetor by fuel pump pressure. When the fuel level rises, the float moves up and shuts off the needle valve. In operation, the needle valve is open just enough to admit fuel equal to that being consumed by the engine.

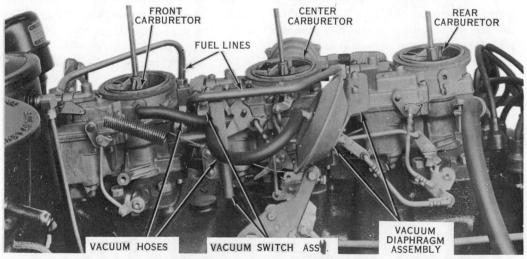

Some engines are equipped with three dual carburetors; the center one delivers the fuel-air mixture until very high speeds are reached. Courtesy Cadillac Motor Car Division, General Motors Corporation.

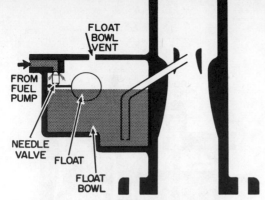

The float circuit contains a reservoir to store fuel for the other circuits. Courtesy Rochester Product Division, General Motors Corporation.

Some float chambers contain multiple floats so that the fuel level does not rise excessively when making sharp turns or climbing steep hills. Some float chambers are designed to surround the discharge nozzle. This maintains the same fuel level regardless of the angle of the carburetor.

The bowl is vented to the inside of the carburetor air horn to provide proper air pressure above the liquid fuel at all times. Internal venting compensates for a partial restriction of a dirty air cleaner by providing a similarly restricted pressure to the fuel in the float chamber.

Low Speed Circuit

When the engine is idling, only a small amount of air flows past the closed throttle valve. A slotted hole in the carburetor bore, opposite the closed valve,

The idle circuit supplies the fuel when the throttle is closed. Courtesy Rochester Products Division, General Motors Corporation.

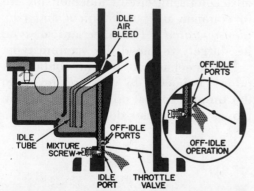

permits the high manifold vacuum below it to draw fuel from the float chamber through a low speed jet. Air enters the idle air bleed and mixes with the fuel as it travels to the idle port.

The idle port is slot shaped. As the throttle valve is opened, more of the idle port is uncovered, allowing a greater quantity of fuel to enter the carburetor bore to balance the increased air flow past the partially opened throttle valve.

The idle mixture is adjustable. By turning the idle adjustment screw in toward its seat, the mixture is made lean. By turning the screw out, the mixture is enriched.

High Speed Circuit

Fuel for part or full throttle is supplied through the high speed circuit. As the throttle is advanced, the idle port opening in the side of the carburetor bore receives less vacuum and

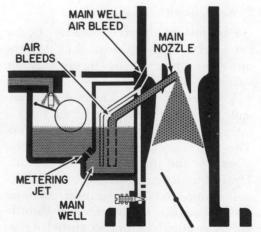

The high-speed circuit (or main metering system) controls the economy range of the carburetor. Courtesy Rochester Products Division, General Motors Corporation.

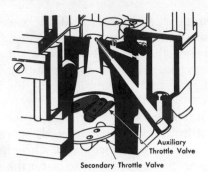

Secondary Throttle Valve

Auxiliary
Throttle Valve

The auxiliary throttle valves do not open until the air velocity is high enough for the engine to use the extra fuel-air mixture. Courtesy Cadillac Motor Car Division, General Motors Corporation.

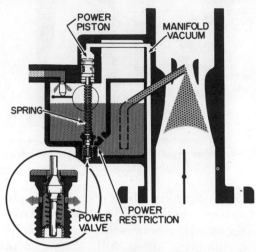

POWER PISTON

MANIFOLD VACUUM

SPRING

POWER VALVE

POWER RESTRICTION

The power circuit adds fuel to the main metering system in order to enrich the mixture for power or top speed. The power piston is actuated by vacuum from the intake manifold. When the engine is under a load, vacuum drops, and the piston spring forces a rod down to open the power valve. Courtesy Rochester Products Division, General Motors Corporation.

thus delivers less fuel. On the other hand, more air is admitted, which speeds up the air stream so that venturi action becomes more effective. The partial vacuum created by the venturi draws liquid fuel from the nozzle, spraying it into the air stream. An *air bleed* injects air bubbles into the stream of liquid fuel before it leaves the nozzle. In this way, the liquid is turned into a fine spray or mist.

Power Circuit

For pulling up steep grades, or for extremely high speeds, the mixture must be enriched by mechanical or vacuum-operated devices.

A metering rod, connected mechanically to the throttle, is lifted from a jet when a richer mixture is required. The rod may also be controlled by means of the intake manifold vacuum. During high speed driving or when accelerating, intake manifold vacuum drops because of the opened throttle valve. A small calibrated spring forces a piston to lift the metering rod from the high speed jet or open an additional jet to provide more fuel. When

the manifold vacuum increases again, it pulls the vacuum piston up against the spring to close the jet, which stops the flow of extra fuel.

Accelerating Circuit

When the throttle is opened suddenly, large amounts of air enter the intake manifold and, to compensate, a pump discharges additional fuel which balances the mixture. Two types of accelerating circuit mechanisms are in common use: *mechanical* and *vacuum-operated*. The mechanical type has largely replaced the vacuum type.

The mechanical system contains a pump connected by rods and levers to the throttle so that opening the throttle moves the plunger down the cylinder.

154

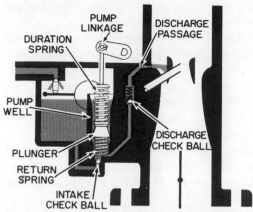

The accelerating circuit contains a pump which discharges a measured quantity of fuel into the air stream when the throttle is opened suddenly. The duration spring spreads the discharge over a short period of time. Courtesy Rochester Products Division, General Motors Corporation.

This forces a jet of liquid gasoline into the air stream.

The vacuum-operated system uses intake manifold vacuum to operate a piston-and-plunger mechanism to discharge the fuel. When the car is accelerated, intake manifold vacuum drops, and the spring forces the plunger

down the cylinder as in the first system.

Both systems contain intake and discharge valves as well as a discharge jet. Provision is made for venting the discharge nozzle to atmospheric pressure so that the reduced pressure of the air stream, within the carburetor bore, does not draw gasoline from this circuit when this system is not supposed to be in operation.

Stromberg carburetors use the pump piston to open an economizer valve when the throttle is in the wide-open position. This mechanism takes the place of the power circuit just described.

Choke Circuit

Because cold gasoline vaporizes slowly, more of it is required to obtain a flammable mixture during cold engine starts. To enrich the mixture, a valve is closed in the air horn of the carburetor to increase the vacuum within the carburetor bore, and thereby increase the flow of liquid fuel from the main nozzle.

Some four-barrel carburetors are equipped with a vacuum diaphragm control which opens the auxiliary throttle valves when the air velocity past the venturi tubes indicates that the engine is going fast enough to use the additional fuel-air mixture. Courtesy Lincoln-Mercury Division, Ford Motor Company.

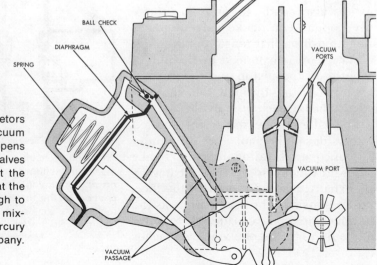

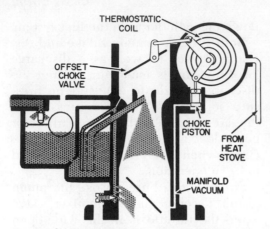

THERMOSTATIC
COIL

OFFSET
CHOKE
VALVE

CHOKE
PISTON

FROM
HEAT
STOVE

MANIFOLD
VACUUM

The automatic choke system contains a thermostatic coil which regulates the air-fuel mixture during warm-up. The actions of the offset choke valve and choke piston are referred to in the text. Most carburetors now use vacuum-kick diaphragm assemblies in place of the choke piston. Courtesy Rochester Products Division, General Motors Corporation.

The choke valve is closed by a thermostatic coil spring when the engine is cold. When the engine first starts, much air is needed immediately, and the air velocity against the offset choke valve causes the valve to open slightly against the thermostatic coil tension. Intake manifold vacuum, applied to a choke piston, also tends to pull the choke valve open. The choke valve assumes such a position that tension of the thermostatic coil is balanced by the pull of vacuum on the piston and the force of the air passing through the air horn against the offset choke valve.

When the engine starts, slots located in the sides of the choke piston cylinder are uncovered, allowing the intake manifold vacuum to draw air, heated by the exhaust manifold, through the thermostat housing. The warm air heats the thermostatic coil, causing it to relax gradually until the choke valve reaches

its wide-open position when the engine is thoroughly warmed.

On late-model carburetors, the choke thermostat is generally positioned in a well in the intake manifold casting, close to the exhaust passageway. In these systems, the choke piston is replaced by a diaphragm assembly which opens the choke valve partially when the engine starts and intake manifold vacuum increases. This new *vacuum-kick system* eliminates choke piston sticking. On the older systems this problem was caused by the passage of unfiltered air between the choke piston and the housing, causing a build-up of carbon and gum.

If the engine is accelerated during the warm-up period, the drop in intake manifold vacuum allows the vacuum-kick diaphragm spring to override diaphragm pressure, and the choke thermostatic coil momentarily becomes more effective, returning the choke valve to a closed position. This provides the richer mixture needed for acceleration when the engine is cold.

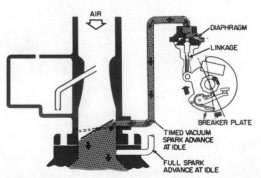

AIR

DIAPHRAGM

LINKAGE

BREAKER PLATE

TIMED VACUUM
SPARK ADVANCE
AT IDLE

FULL SPARK
ADVANCE AT IDLE

Provision is made in all carburetors for intake manifold vacuum to be supplied to advance the distributor timing. The position of the port with relation to the throttle valve is critical in determining the action of this advance mechanism. Courtesy Rochester Products Division, General Motors Corporation.

During the warm-up period, the engine must be idled faster to prevent engine stalling. This is accomplished by a fast idle cam connected to the choke shaft.

If, during the starting period, the engine becomes overchoked, the choke valve may be opened manually by depressing the accelerator pedal to the floorboard while engaging the starter. This opens the choke valve to admit more air.

Air-Valve Type Carburetors

A recent approach to four-barrel, two-stage carburetion is the air-valve type carburetor. The primary side is conventional, having two small bores with a triple venturi set-up, using plain tube nozzles. Primary side fuel metering is accomplished with tapered metering rods positioned by a piston that is controlled by intake manifold vacuum.

The secondary side of the air-valve type carburetor has two very large bores in order to increase engine breathing efficiency (volumetric efficiency) when power and high engine speeds are desired. Secondary side fuel metering is controlled by the air valve which is opened by the rush of incoming air in direct proportion to the engine's speed. The air valve is mechanically linked to two tapered metering rods which control the flow of liquid fuel in proportion to the amount of air entering the carburetor.

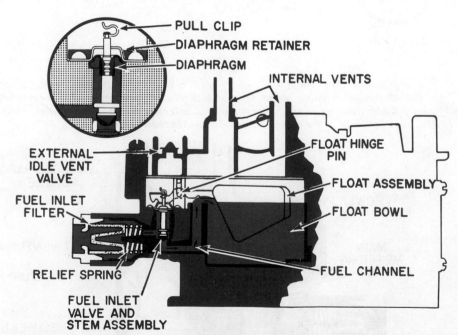

PULL CLIP
DIAPHRAGM RETAINER
DIAPHRAGM
INTERNAL VENTS
EXTERNAL IDLE VENT VALVE
FUEL INLET FILTER
RELIEF SPRING
FUEL INLET VALVE AND STEM ASSEMBLY
FLOAT HINGE PIN
FLOAT ASSEMBLY
FLOAT BOWL
FUEL CHANNEL

The float circuit of the new Rochester Quadrajet air-valve type carburetor is unique in that fuel pressure is directed against the float needle valve to assist in shutting it off. Courtesy Rochester Products Division, General Motors Corporation.

The idle system of the air-valve type carburetor is quite conventional but is built into the primary side only. It supplies the correct air-fuel mixture during idle and low engine speeds because there is not enough air flowing past the venturi area to make the main metering system effective. The hot-idle compensator valve admits additional air to the idle system whenever under-hood temperatures rise to the setting of the thermostat. Courtesy Rochester Products Division, General Motors Corporation.

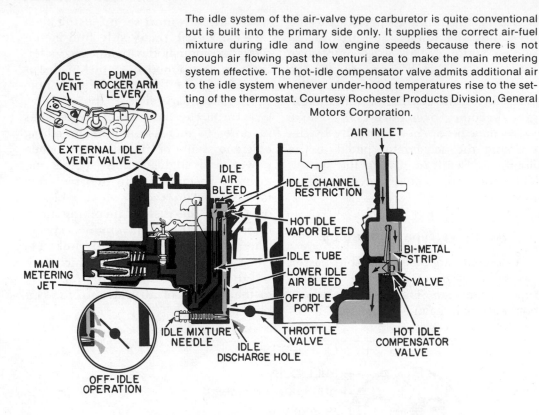

The main metering system furnishes the air-fuel mixture for the primary side of the carburetor through a double venturi system. Note how the fuel is metered on the primary side of the carburetor by means of a metering rod and main metering jet. Courtesy Rochester Products Division, General Motors Corporation.

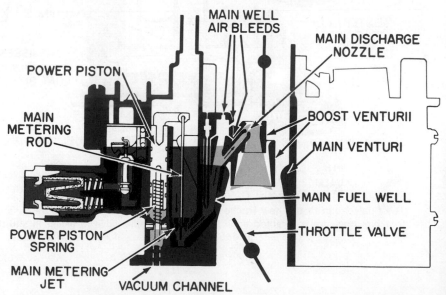

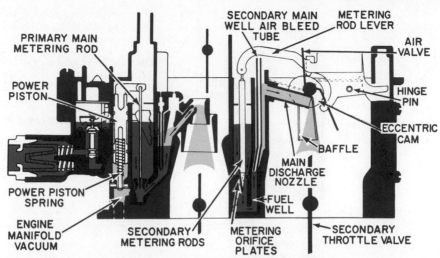

PRIMARY MAIN METERING ROD

POWER PISTON

SECONDARY MAIN WELL AIR BLEED TUBE

METERING ROD LEVER

AIR VALVE

HINGE PIN

ECCENTRIC CAM

BAFFLE

MAIN DISCHARGE NOZZLE

POWER PISTON SPRING

ENGINE MANIFOLD VACUUM

SECONDARY METERING RODS

METERING ORIFICE PLATES

FUEL WELL

SECONDARY THROTTLE VALVE

The high-speed circuit of the Quadrajet carburetor uses the air-valve metering principle. When engine speed reaches a point at which the primary bores cannot meet engine air and fuel demands, the secondary side throttle valves open. As the air flow increases through the secondary side, it forces the air valve to open against spring tension, rotating an eccentric cam which lifts the secondary side metering rods out of their metering orifice plates. This furnishes fuel to the secondary side of the carburetor in proportion to the incoming air. Courtesy Rochester Products Division, General Motors Corporation.

The power system furnishes an enriched mixture for heavy acceleration or high-speed operation. This system is controlled by engine intake manifold vacuum operating on the power piston, which changes the position of the primary side main metering rods in relation to their jets. On part throttle, manifold vacuum is high enough to hold the power piston down against spring tension so that the larger diameter of the metering rod tips is in the main metering jet orifices. As engine load increases, manifold vacuum decreases, so that spring tension lifts the metering rods upward. This presents the smaller diameter tips, and thus enriches the mixture flowing through the main metering jets. The secondary side has a dashpot piston which acts as a dampener to prevent oscillation of the air valve which can be caused by pulsations of the air flow. Courtesy Rochester Products Division, General Motors Corporation.

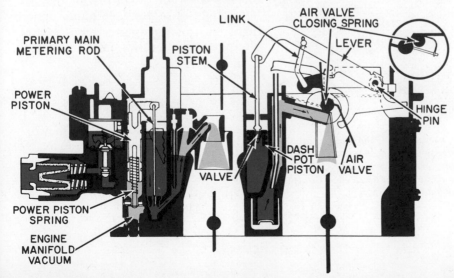

PRIMARY MAIN METERING ROD

LINK

AIR VALVE CLOSING SPRING

PISTON STEM

LEVER

POWER PISTON

HINGE PIN

POWER PISTON SPRING

ENGINE MANIFOLD VACUUM

VALVE

DASH POT PISTON

AIR VALVE

159

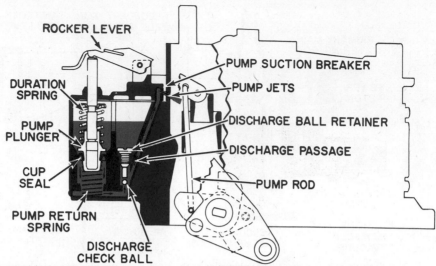

ROCKER LEVER

PUMP SUCTION BREAKER

PUMP JETS

DURATION SPRING

DISCHARGE BALL RETAINER

PUMP PLUNGER

DISCHARGE PASSAGE

CUP SEAL

PUMP ROD

PUMP RETURN SPRING

DISCHARGE CHECK BALL

The accelerating system is on the primary side of the carburetor only, and it contains the usual pump, check valves, and operating linkage. The pump plunger is a floating type which allows the intake of fuel past the two parts. The discharge check ball prevents entrance of air when the pump plunger is lifted, and the pump suction breaker orifice prevents vacuum from drawing fuel from the accelerating system during high-speed operation. Courtesy Rochester Products Division, General Motors Corporation.

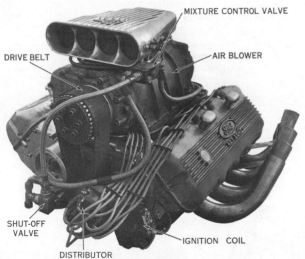

MIXTURE CONTROL VALVE

DRIVE BELT

AIR BLOWER

SHUT-OFF VALVE

IGNITION COIL

DISTRIBUTOR

A supercharger blows the air-fuel mixture into the engine. In this case, the fuel is injected into the air blower before being forced into the cylinders. This Ford engine is used on a dragster. Courtesy Ford Motor Company.

Superchargers

A supercharger is an air pump installed ahead of the carburetor or between the carburetor and intake manifold. It blows the fuel-air mixture into the combustion chamber rather than depending on suction to draw it in. In this way, larger quantities of fuel can be delivered at higher engine speeds than in an unsupercharged engine, whose power output falls off rapidly with speed.

Fuel Injector

A fuel injector takes the place of a conventional carburetor. It mixes fuel and air in the same proportions as the carburetor, but differs in that the fuel is sprayed directly into the intake

INJECTOR NOZZLE   TUNED INTAKE PIPES

SHUT-OFF VALVE

IGNITION COIL

FUEL PUMP

DISTRIBUTOR

This fuel-injected Ford engine is used on a dragster. Note the tuned intake pipes. When the throttle is suddenly closed, excess fuel is directed back into the fuel storage tank by means of the throttle-actuated fuel return valve. Courtesy Ford Motor Company.

manifold by eight spray nozzles instead of being mixed with the air stream as it passes through the venturi.

A fuel injector is composed of three main sections: a *fuel meter*, an *air meter*, and an *intake manifold* containing the *fuel nozzles*. The air meter section contains a conventional throttle valve to control the engine speed as determined by the driver. Air pressure inside the air meter section varies according to the position of the throttle valve and the speed of the incoming air. This information is sent to the fuel meter section to control the amount of fuel sprayed into the intake manifold.

Vapor Lock

Since fuel systems are designed to deliver liquid fuel, they fail to operate when the gasoline boils or vaporizes in the lines, fuel pump, or carburetor. In this case, insufficient liquid fuel is delivered to the carburetor; therefore the engine stalls. This is called vapor lock.

Automatic transmissions, high-output alternators, exhaust emission control systems, and air-conditioning pumps have added to engine compartment temperatures. In addition, higher octane fuels, required by the higher compression cars of today, vapor lock much more readily than earlier fuels.

Cars having the fuel pump mounted high above the fuel tank level or close to the hot exhaust pipe are more likely to experience this trouble. Vapor lock is aggravated by wear in the fuel pump parts, and especially by porous flexible lines. Air bubbles, entering the lines, cause the fuel to vaporize more quickly.

Hot-starting troubles may also be due to vaporizing of the fuel in the carburetor. When excessively heated, the fuel may boil and percolate over into the intake manifold to flood the engine with liquid gasoline. A panicky driver who pumps the accelerator pedal complicates the trouble. Usually, if a hot engine won't start, the best thing is to let it cool down. Then push the throttle to the floorboard to open the choke and admit more air. Do not pump the pedal; you only add more liquid fuel.

Air Cleaners and Silencers

The incoming air is full of dust and abrasive particles which could cause serious damage should they enter the engine. To prevent this an air cleaner is mounted on the carburetor air horn. In addition to removing foreign particles, the air cleaner is designed to silence the rush of air as it enters the carburetor.

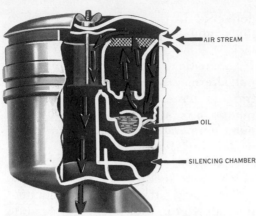

An oil-bath air cleaner contains a reservoir of oil which traps the heavier dirt particles as the air reverses direction above the surface of the oil. Courtesy Plymouth Division, Chrysler Corporation.

AIR CLEANER ELEMENT

A dry-type air filter element contains porous filter paper to trap the dirt. Courtesy Lincoln-Mercury Division, Ford Motor Company.

Air cleaners are of three types: oil wetted, oil bath, and dry-type filters.

The *oil-wetted* type has a wire mesh through which the incoming air passes. The mesh is coated with oil to which dust particles cling.

Some air-cleaner elements are made of polyurethane, which should be cleaned by washing in kerosene and squeezing out the excess solvent, after which it should be dipped in engine oil, the excess of which must be squeezed out. Courtesy General Motors Corporation.

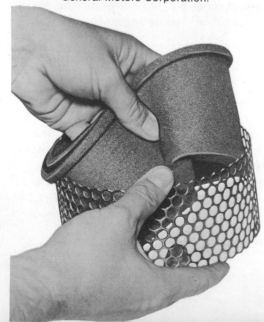

The *oil-bath cleaner* contains a reservoir of oil over which the direction of the air stream is reversed. The heavier particles of dust do not follow the swiftly moving air stream as it changes direction, so they are deposited in the oil.

The *dry-type filter* uses a band of filter paper through which the air passes before it reaches the carburetor. The filter paper is accordion pleated so as to present a greater surface for air to pass through.

Some late-model cars use a polyurethane, dry-type, plastic filter element. It is made of a highly porous material which allows air to pass through readily. The dust particles stick to the oily surface in a manner similar to the oil-wetted type cleaner. The element must be cleaned every 2,000 miles, dipped in light engine oil, and the excess squeezed out.

Service Procedures

Dirt and water are the greatest enemies of the fuel system. Preventive maintenance during an engine tune-up consists of cleaning the fuel and air filters on the fuel pump and carburetor.

Fuel pumps are relatively trouble free. But once or twice in the life of the car it may be necessary to rebuild the fuel pump. Carburetor troubles are more common. However, because the condition of the engine and the ignition system has a decided effect on carburetion, it is seldom possible to correct carburetor troubles unless the engine is tuned at the same time. Dirt, of course, may cause a specific carburetor complaint which can be remedied by cleaning the affected circuit. Generally, after about 50,000 miles of service, or about the time the engine requires overhauling, it is necessary to overhaul the carburetor to replace worn parts and to clean it thoroughly.

Troubleshooting

Fuel system troubles generally show up in three ways: the car won't start properly, the performance of the engine is unsatisfactory, or the gasoline mileage is poor. Before repairs are attempted, the trouble must be isolated.

When the car won't start, remove the air cleaner to check the accelerating pump discharge stream. If there is a full stream of liquid fuel discharged, it can be assumed that the fuel system is doing its job. If no stream appears, then the trouble must be traced back to the fuel pump, filter, gas lines, or fuel tank. Each part can be checked in turn by disconnecting the fuel line and checking its flow.

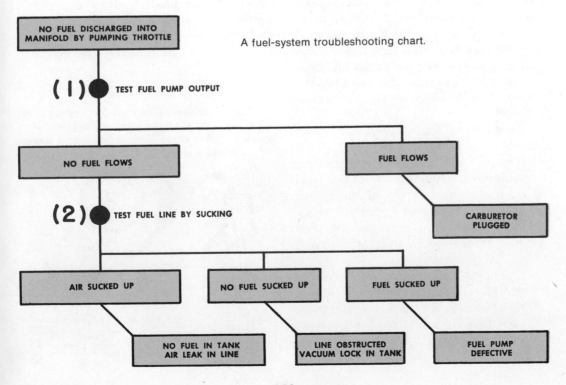

A fuel-system troubleshooting chart.

163

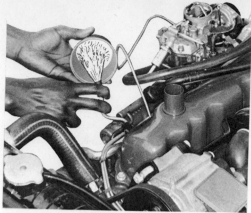

Testing the fuel pump output. The fuel should flow in strong pulses.

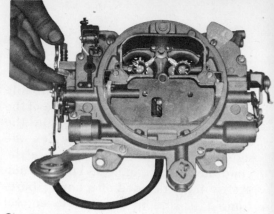

Checking the carburetor for fuel. The air cleaner must be removed in order to see into the throat so that the fuel discharge can be checked.

Unsatisfactory performance usually consists of: rough idling, stumbling on acceleration, or no high speed performance. Poor gas mileage accompanies such problems.

Rough idling may be due entirely to the mechanical condition of the engine, although the carburetor itself may be at fault. Sometimes atmospheric conditions change, which affect the idle mixture. A quick check can be made by turning the idle adjustment screw slightly to see whether or not an adjustment can eliminate the trouble. If it doesn't help, then an engine tune-up is necessary.

"Stumbling" on acceleration is generally due to dirt entering the accelerating system and affecting the check valve operation or plugging one of the small jets. It may also be due to an exhaust manifold thermostatic control valve which is stuck in the open position. If the trouble is in the carburetor, it must be cleaned.

Poor high speed performance can be caused by ignition or fuel pump trouble. If due to the fuel system, the fuel pump output pressure, flow rate, and vacuum should be tested by means of an accurate gauge. A partially plugged gas line, of course, will cause poor high speed performance.

Poor gas mileage can be caused by defects in the engine, carburetor, or bad driving habits of the owner. If the engine is sluggish, it probably needs an engine tune-up. If the car has about 50,000 miles of service, the carburetor needs an overhaul. If the mechanical parts of the engine are in good condition and poor gas mileage still exists, it frequently can be traced to the driver's habits.

The fuel pump pressure should be checked with the engine idling. A good pump will deliver about a pint of fuel in about one minute and the pump pressure should be from 3 to 5 psi.

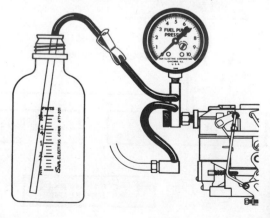

Repairing a Fuel Pump

Fuel pump troubles can be of two kinds; either the pump is supplying too little gasoline or, in rare cases, too much. If the pump is supplying too little fuel, either the engine will not run at all, or it will spit and sputter, especially at high speed. If the pump is supplying too much fuel, you will be able to see gasoline dripping from the carburetor, and the engine will be hard to start and will not idle smoothly.

Tools and Equipment

AC fuel pump; screwdriver; diaphragm alignment wrench; file; $^7/_{16}$, $^1/_2$, and $^9/_{16}$ inch combination-end wrenches; valve seat repair kit.

PROCEDURE

DISASSEMBLING

① Remove the pump. Use two wrenches on pipe fittings to prevent twisting the pipe which may split.

② File a mark across the diaphragm flanges to serve as a guide when reassembling the pump to make sure that the inlet and outlet holes will match the positions of the fuel lines. Remove the six screws (15) from the cover (14) and lift off the cover. To disassemble the cover, loosen the pulsator cover screw (19); remove the cover (17) and the pulsator (16). From the bottom of the cover, remove the two valve assemblies (13) and the gaskets (12). From the body (4), drive out the rocker arm pin (5) and push in on the diaphragm (11) to release the link (2). Now withdraw the link (2), the rocker arm (1), and the spring (3). Release pressure on the diaphragm and withdraw it from the body. Remove the spring (9), the oil seal (7), and the diaphragm (11).

165

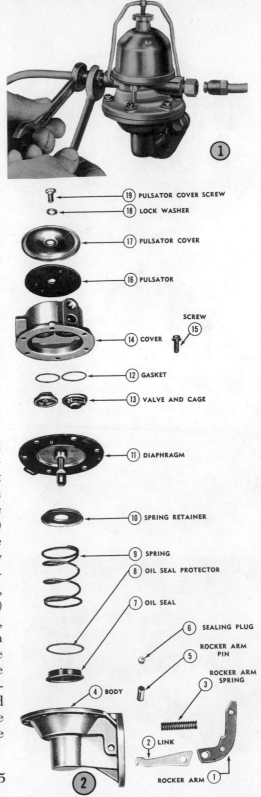

①
19 PULSATOR COVER SCREW
18 LOCK WASHER
17 PULSATOR COVER
16 PULSATOR
SCREW 15
14 COVER
12 GASKET
13 VALVE AND CAGE
11 DIAPHRAGM
10 SPRING RETAINER
9 SPRING
8 OIL SEAL PROTECTOR
7 OIL SEAL
6 SEALING PLUG
ROCKER ARM PIN
5
ROCKER ARM SPRING
3
4 BODY
2 LINK
ROCKER ARM 1
2

(3)

(4)

(5)

Cleaning and Inspecting

③ Wash all parts in clean solvent and blow dry. Replace worn parts with a kit of new parts. All kits contain a diaphragm, valves, linkage, and a set of gaskets. The diaphragm, which wears the most, generally cracks.

④ Replace any casting that shows evidence of water damage. The white oxide that forms will flake off continually and plug the jets of the carburetor.

⑤ Check the valve seats for pitting which would prevent proper seating of new valves.

⑥ The valve seats should be refaced with a tool containing an abrasive disc.

⑦ Or the valve seat can be replaced with a new one. To rivet the new seat in the casting, or to tighten an old one that has loosened, secure an anvil in a vise and place the installed seat over it.

⑧ Insert a tapered tool and tap it several light blows until the flange is spread in the casting. Then reface the valve seat as in step ⑥ .

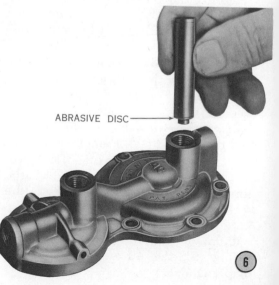

ABRASIVE DISC →

(6)

ASSEMBLING

⑨ Install new oil seal parts into the body recess.

⑩ Assemble the rocker arm and link and insert the two parts into the body. Hold them in place with a drift punch inserted through the rocker arm pin holes. Install the diaphragm return spring.

⑪ Invert the pump body so that the rocker arm link drops to its lowest position, and then install the diaphragm by hooking it over the end of the link.

⑫ Insert and stake the rocker arm pin to keep it in place.

OIL SEAL

⑨

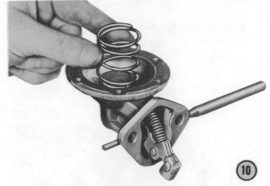

⑩

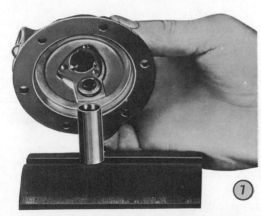

⑦

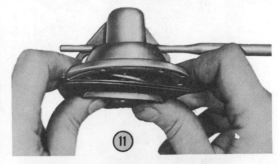

⑪

TAPER →

⑧

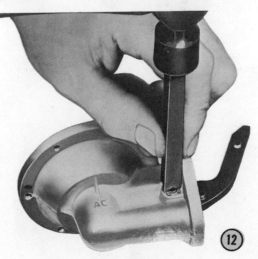

AC

⑫

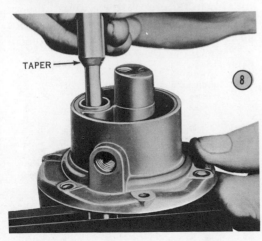

167

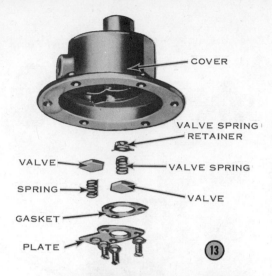

COVER

VALVE SPRING
RETAINER

VALVE

VALVE SPRING

SPRING

VALVE

GASKET

PLATE

⑬

⑬ Install the valves, spring, gaskets, and the retainer.

⑭ Replace the gasket, screen, and bowl. Secure the bowl with the bail.

⑮ Align the file marks on the body and cover. Press in on the rocker arm until the diaphragm is level across the body flange. Install and tighten the flange screws until the lockwashers just touch the screw heads. Then push the rocker arm in as far as possible and tighten the cover screws securely. If this procedure is not followed exactly, the diaphragm will be stretched excessively in operation, which will result in early failure.

Overhauling a Ford Single-Barrel Carburetor

APPLICATION: All Ford 6-cylinder engines

PROCEDURE

DISASSEMBLING

① Remove the automatic choke thermostatic spring housing clamp retaining screws, and then take off the clamp, housing, and gasket. Take out the choke housing retaining screws, and then remove the choke housing assembly and gasket. Take out the choke shaft retain-

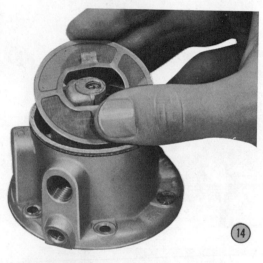

⑭

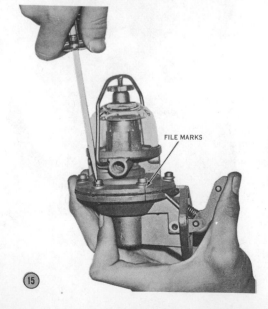

FILE MARKS

⑮

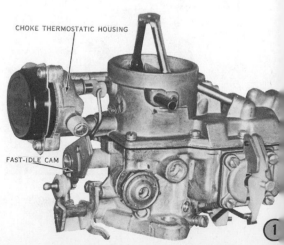

CHOKE THERMOSTATIC HOUSING

FAST-IDLE CAM

①

ing screw and washer. Remove the choke shaft and retainer assembly and the lever, link, and piston assembly from the choke housing. Remove the fast-idle cam lever retaining screw, and then take off the lever and choke control rod.

② Remove the air horn retaining screws and the carburetor identification tag. Tilt the upper body in order to provide clearance between the float assembly and the lower body. Separate the upper body from the lower body, using a twisting motion so as to disconnect the fuel vent rod from the actuating lever. Take off the body gasket. Hold the lower body over a pan and invert it to allow the three ball checks and one weight to fall into the pan.

③ To disassemble the air horn, take out the float shaft and the float assembly. Remove the fuel inlet needle valve. Take out the main metering jet. **Caution:** *The power valve assembly must not be disassembled.*

④ To remove the fuel vent valve rod, use a scraper to cut away the stake marks at the opening. Pull the vent valve rod assembly and spring out of the top casting.

POWER VALVE   MAIN METERING JET

FLOAT   FLOAT SHAFT

③

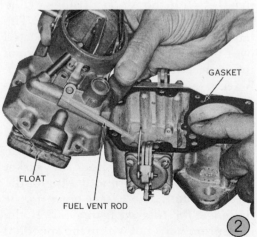

GASKET

FLOAT

FUEL VENT ROD

②

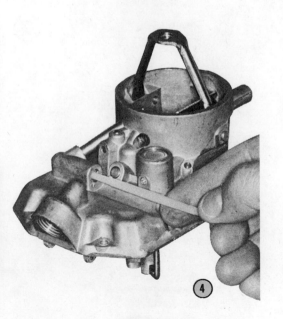

④

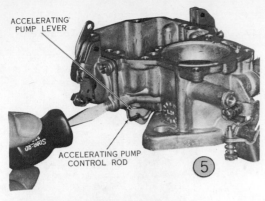

ACCELERATING
PUMP LEVER

ACCELERATING PUMP
CONTROL ROD

⑤

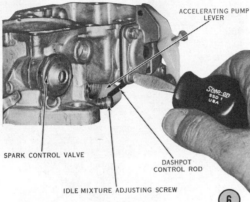

ACCELERATING PUMP
LEVER

SPARK CONTROL VALVE

DASHPOT
CONTROL ROD

IDLE MIXTURE ADJUSTING SCREW

⑥

POWER VALVE

MAIN METERING JET

⑦

FLOAT

FLOAT SHAFT

⑤ Remove the accelerating pump cover retaining screws, and then take off the cover. Separate the pump diaphragm and spring from the cover. Turn the assembly until the accelerating pump control rod can be slid out of the accelerating pump lever.

⑥ Take off the dashpot retaining screws (on cars with an automatic transmission), and then separate the diaphragm and spring from the cover. Turn the assembly until the dashpot control rod can be slid out of the accelerating pump lever. Take out the idle mixture adjusting screw and the spark control valve and gasket assembly.

ASSEMBLING

⑦ Insert the fuel vent valve return spring in the fuel vent passage, and then push the piston end of the fuel vent rod into the passage. Punch three indentations in the vent valve passage opening with a center punch and hammer. The indentations must distort the inside edge of the opening enough to act as a stop for the piston end of the vent rod. Turn over the air horn casting and replace the main metering jet, fuel inlet needle (with the Viton tip toward the valve seat), and the float assembly. The tab on the float arm should be located over the needle valve, and the hinge of the arm lined up between the hinge bracket holes in the upper body casting. Insert the float shaft through the holes in the upper body and the float assembly.

⑧ To make the float level adjustment, measure the distance from the gasket surface of the air horn to the top of the float. **Caution:** *The gasket must not be in place for this measurement.* If the measurement is not within the specified

170

limits, bend the float arm tab as required. **Caution:** *Don't apply pressure to the fuel inlet needle, as the Viton tip will be distorted and cause an improper fuel level setting.*

⑨ If the throttle shaft was removed, slide a new shaft into position, with the flat surface facing toward the bottom of the body, and then install the retaining pin. Insert the throttle plate through the slot in the shaft. **Note:** *The plate indentations must face the bottom of the body and point toward the accelerating pump side of the body.* Install the retaining screws snugly. Rotate the shaft while lightly tapping the plate in order to seat it in the bore. Hold the lower body up to the light. If the throttle plate is properly centralized in the bore, little or no light will show. When the plate is properly centralized, tighten and stake the retaining screws. **Caution:** *Support the shaft on a metal bar to keep from bending it when you stake the screws.* Position the over-travel spring on the accelerating pump lever, and then hook the tang of the spring onto the throttle shaft. Install the over-travel lever tension spring retaining pin in the throttle shaft. Pull the arm of the spring over the retaining pin to apply spring tension to the over-travel lever. Install the washer and retaining clip on the end of the throttle shaft. Position the small diameter of the dashpot diaphragm return spring onto the boss in the dashpot chamber, and then place the diaphragm in position with the plunger facing outward. Replace the cover, tightening the retaining screws finger-tight. Push the diaphragm lever inward, and then tighten the cover retaining screws securely. Replace the spark control valve and gasket. Tighten

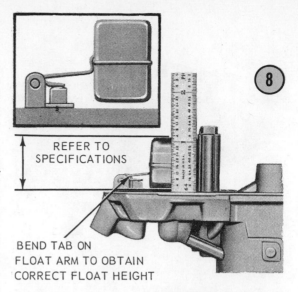

REFER TO SPECIFICATIONS

BEND TAB ON FLOAT ARM TO OBTAIN CORRECT FLOAT HEIGHT

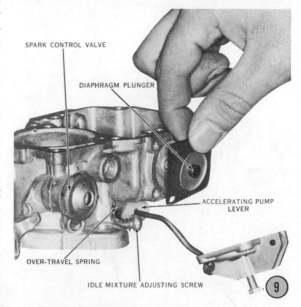

SPARK CONTROL VALVE

DIAPHRAGM PLUNGER

ACCELERATING PUMP LEVER

OVER-TRAVEL SPRING

IDLE MIXTURE ADJUSTING SCREW

the valve securely. **Caution:** *A loose valve will cause poor engine performance.* Install the idle mixture adjusting screw and spring, turn it in until it lightly touches its seat, and then back it out $1\frac{1}{2}$ turns for a preliminary adjustment. **Caution:** *Don't turn the needle tightly against the seat, or you will groove the tapered surface, which will make an idle adjustment impossible.*

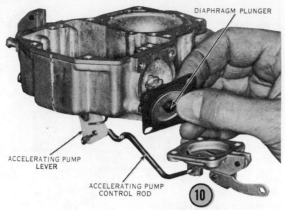

DIAPHRAGM PLUNGER

ACCELERATING PUMP LEVER

ACCELERATING PUMP CONTROL ROD

⑩ To assemble the accelerating pump, insert the keyed end of the accelerating pump control rod into the inboard side of the slotted hole in the accelerating pump lever. Position the small diameter of the accelerating pump diaphragm return spring onto the boss in the accelerating pump chamber, and then place the diaphragm into position, with the plunger facing outward. Replace the cover, tightening the retaining screws finger-tight. Push the diaphragm lever inward, and then tighten the cover retaining screws securely.

⑪ Install the accelerating pump circuit outlet ball check valve. **Note:** *The three ball check valves are equal in size.*

⑫ Install the accelerating pump circuit outlet check valve weight.

⑬ Install the accelerating pump circuit inlet ball check valve.

⑭ Install the dashpot ball check valve in the dashpot inlet passage.

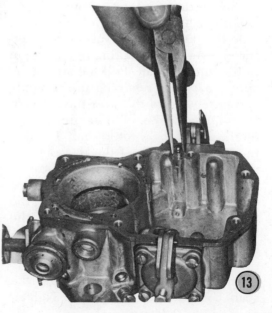

⑮ Position a new gasket onto the lower body, making sure that the word TOP faces upward. Insert the end of the fuel vent rod into the vent valve actuating lever at an angle, and then wind the rod into the lever. **Caution:** *Don't dislodge the gasket or the float shaft.* Install the air horn retaining screws and the carburetor identification tag. Tighten the screws securely.

⑯ Position the fast-idle cam on the main body and install the retaining screw. Install the choke control lever on the choke control rod. Make sure that the groove in the choke control lever fits over the flat end of the choke shaft properly. Insert the choke housing retaining screws, using a new gasket on the flange. Hold the choke plate closed, and then slide the choke control lever properly onto the choke shaft so that it operates smoothly. With the choke plate closed, install the choke housing and gasket assembly. Tighten the retaining screws. **Caution:** *Make sure that the gasket is properly installed.*

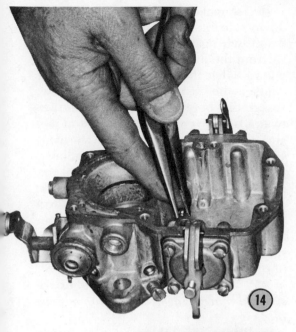

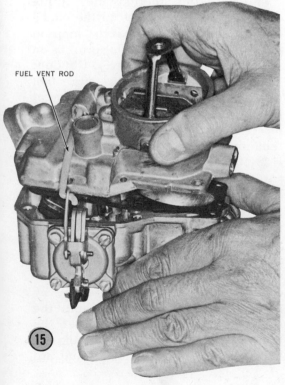

FUEL VENT ROD

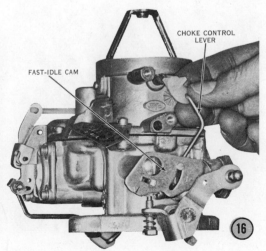

CHOKE CONTROL LEVER

FAST-IDLE CAM

Bench Adjustments

The following adjustments must be made in the order indicated below. **Caution:** *The following instructions contain specifications which may vary, depending on the model carburetor. Check these against the manufacturer's specifications before making the final adjustments.*

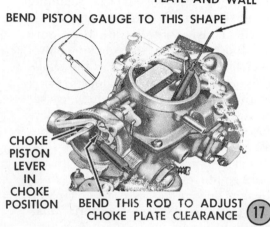

BEND PISTON GAUGE TO THIS SHAPE

PROPER SIZE GAUGE BETWEEN CHOKE PLATE AND WALL

CHOKE PISTON LEVER IN CHOKE POSITION

BEND THIS ROD TO ADJUST CHOKE PLATE CLEARANCE ⑰

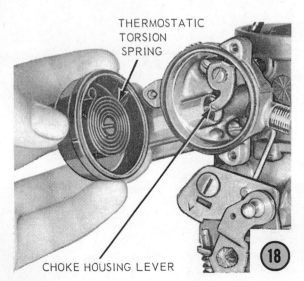

THERMOSTATIC TORSION SPRING

CHOKE HOUSING LEVER ⑱

⑰ To make the choke plate pull-down clearance adjustment, bend a 0.036″ wire gauge at a 90° angle, about ⅛″ from the end. Block the throttle half open so that the fast-idle cam does not contact the fast-idle adjusting screw. Insert the bent end of the gauge between the lower edge of the piston slot and the upper edge of the right-hand slot in the choke housing. Pull the choke piston lever counterclockwise until the gauge is held snugly in the piston slot. Make an "S" or "Z" bend in the rod between the choke piston and piston lever until the choke plate opens the specified distance. **Caution:** *The bend in the rod must be in the form of an "S" or "Z" to prevent interference or restricted movement of the piston assembly.*

⑱ Place the thermostatic spring housing and new gasket on the choke housing, making sure that the loop on the end of the thermostatic spring is on the choke thermostatic lever. **Caution:** *The spring must wind clockwise when viewed from the choke housing side of the carburetor.* Loosely install the thermostatic spring housing clamp and the retaining screws.

⑲ Rotate the thermostatic choke spring housing counterclockwise until the index on the choke housing aligns with the index mark on the spring housing, and then an additional ¼ turn toward the rich side. Tighten the retaining screws. Position the fast-idle adjusting screw on the index mark of the fast-idle cam. Adjust the fast-idle linkage by bending the choke control rod until the specified clearance exists between the front of the choke plate and the air horn. Bend the choke control rod inward

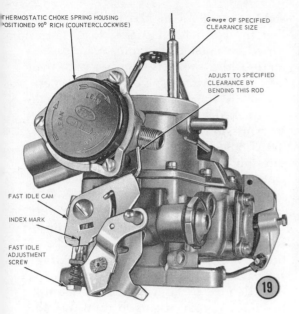

THERMOSTATIC CHOKE SPRING HOUSING POSITIONED 90° RICH (COUNTERCLOCKWISE)

Gauge OF SPECIFIED CLEARANCE SIZE

ADJUST TO SPECIFIED CLEARANCE BY BENDING THIS ROD

FAST IDLE CAM

INDEX MARK

FAST IDLE ADJUSTMENT SCREW

19

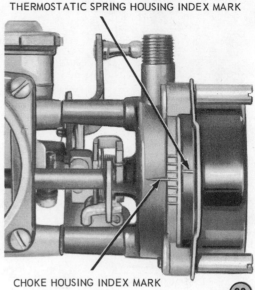

THERMOSTATIC SPRING HOUSING INDEX MARK

CHOKE HOUSING INDEX MARK

20

to decrease the clearance. **Caution:** *Make sure that the fast-idle screw remains on the index mark of the fast-idle cam during the adjusting procedure.*

20 Release the automatic choke cover retaining screws, and then rotate the housing to align the index mark on the housing with the specified mark on the choke housing. Tighten the retaining screws.

21 To make the accelerating pump clearance adjustment, insert the roll pin in the lower (HI) hole position in the lever. Back out the throttle idle speed adjusting screw until the throttle plate is seated in the throttle bore. Holding the throttle fully closed, position a gauge of the specified width between the roll pin and the cover surface. Bend the accelerating pump actuating rod to obtain the specified gauge clearance between the pump cover and the roll pin in the pump lever.

WITH THROTTLE PLATE FULLY CLOSED, INSERT A *Gauge* THAT EQUALS THE SPECIFIED CLEARANCE BETWEEN THE PIN AND COVER

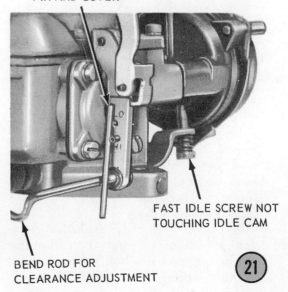

FAST IDLE SCREW NOT TOUCHING IDLE CAM

BEND ROD FOR CLEARANCE ADJUSTMENT

21

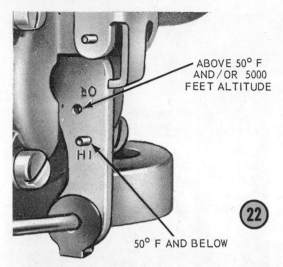

ABOVE 50° F
AND/OR 5000
FEET ALTITUDE

HI

50° F AND BELOW

22

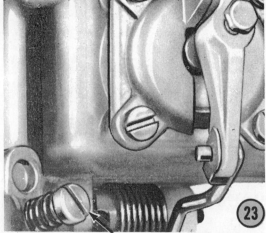

IDLE-FUEL MIXTURE ADJUSTING SCREW (NEEDLE)

23

stabilizes). Turn on the headlamps so that the alternator is under load. On a car with a manual-shift transmission, the engine idle speed is adjusted with the gear shift lever in NEUTRAL. With an automatic transmission, the idle speed is checked and adjusted first with the transmission selector lever in NEUTRAL and then checked with the transmission selector lever in DRIVE. **Caution:** *Make sure that the dashpot is not interfering with the throttle lever or that the fast-idle screw is not contacting the fast-idle cam.* Adjust the engine idle speed to specifications by turning the idle speed adjusting screw in to increase idle speed. Turn the idle mixture adjusting screw in until the engine rpm begins to drop due to the lean mixture. Back it out until the engine rpm increases and then just starts to drop. Now, turn the idle mixture needle inward for maximum rpm and engine smoothness. Always favor a slightly rich mixture for smooth idling and less tendency to stall during sudden stops. **Note:** *On cars with a Thermactor exhaust emission system, the outward adjustment of the idle mixture needle is the final adjustment required.* Because of the lean carburetor calibration, it is necessary to run these engines slightly on the rich side.

㉔ After having made the idle speed and mixture adjustments, the fast-idle speed adjustment can be made by rotating the fast-idle cam manually until the fast-idle adjusting screw rests next to the shoulder of the highest step on the cam. **Note:** *The adjusting screw should be aligned with the index mark on the cam.* Start the engine and turn the fast-idle adjusting screw to obtain the specified engine rpm.

㉒ For operation in temperatures below 50° F., place the roll pin in the lever hole marked HI (lower hole). For best performance at normal temperatures, position the roll pin in the LO (upper hole) of the lever.

㉓ To make the idle speed and mixture adjustments, install the carburetor on the engine. Attach a tachometer and set the parking brake. Start the engine and normalize it (until the temperature

IDLE SPEED (HOT ENGINE) ADJUSTMENT SCREW

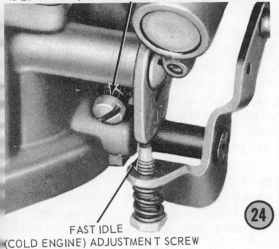

FAST IDLE
(COLD ENGINE) ADJUSTMENT SCREW

(24)

DASHPOT
ADJUSTING
SCREW

(25)

ADJUST THROTTLE
TO HOT IDLE POSITION
PRIOR TO ADJUSTING DASHPOT

㉕ To make the dashpot adjustment, turn the dashpot adjusting screw out until it just clears the dashpot plunger, and then turn it back in the specified number of turns against the dashpot diaphragm plunger assembly.

㉖ To make the vent valve adjustment, set the throttle linkage to the hot-idle position. The groove in the vent valve rod should be even with the open end of the vent. Bend the arm on the vent valve rod actuating lever (where it contacts the accelerating pump lever) to align the groove with the edge of the bore.

Overhauling Carter BBS & BBD Carburetors

Note: *These carburetors are basically alike in construction details and adjustments, with the exception that the BBD carburetor has dual throats.*

APPLICATION: Standard equipment on Chrysler product engines

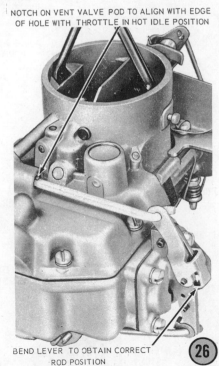

NOTCH ON VENT VALVE ROD TO ALIGN WITH EDGE
OF HOLE WITH THROTTLE IN HOT IDLE POSITION

BEND LEVER TO OBTAIN CORRECT
ROD POSITION

(26)

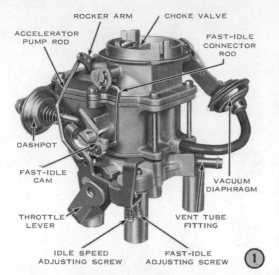

ROCKER ARM CHOKE VALVE

ACCELERATOR
PUMP ROD

FAST-IDLE
CONNECTOR
ROD

DASHPOT

FAST-IDLE
CAM

VACUUM
DIAPHRAGM

THROTTLE
LEVER

VENT TUBE
FITTING

IDLE SPEED
ADJUSTING SCREW

FAST-IDLE
ADJUSTING SCREW

①

CHOKE LEVER

ACCELERATOR PUMP
PLUNGER STEM

BOWL
VENT VALVE

CHOKE
OPERATING LINK

CAS
IDENTIFICATION
TAG

PLUNGER

VACUUM
DIAPHRAGM

MODEL
IDENTIFICATION
TAG

DISTRIBUTOR
VACUUM FITTING

VACUUM
DIAPHRAGM
HOSE

IDLE MIXTURE
ADJUSTING SCREW

GASKET

②

SPRING

ACCELERATOR
PUMP PLUNGER

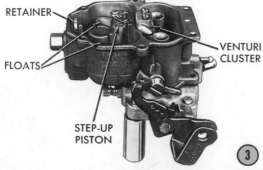

RETAINER

FLOATS

VENTURI
CLUSTER

STEP-UP
PISTON

③

DISASSEMBLING

① Place the carburetor assembly on repair blocks to prevent damaging the throttle valves. Remove the hairpin clips and disengage the accelerator pump operating rod. Remove the clips and disengage the fast-idle connector rod from the fast-idle cam and the choke lever. Remove the vacuum hose between the carburetor main body and the choke vacuum diaphragm.

② Remove the clip from the choke operating link, and then disengage the link from the diaphragm plunger and choke lever. Remove the choke vacuum diaphragm and bracket assembly and place it to one side to be cleaned as a special item. **Caution:** *A carburetor cleaner may damage the diaphragm material.*

③ Remove the air horn retaining screws, and then lift the air horn straight up and away from the main body. Discard the gasket. Remove the dashpot and bracket. Disengage the accelerator pump plunger from the rocker arm by pushing up on the bottom of the plunger, and then sliding the plunger shaft off the hook. Slide the plunger out of the air horn, and then remove the bowl vent valve, spring seat, and spring. If the old plunger can be used again, place it in a jar of clean gasoline or kerosene to prevent the leather from drying out. Remove the fuel inlet needle valve, seat, and gasket from the main body. Lift out the float fulcrum pin retainer and then take out the floats and fulcrum pin.

④ Remove the step-up piston retaining screw, and then slide the step-up piston and rods from the well. Now, lift out the step-up piston spring. Remove

178

the step-up piston gasket from the bottom of the well.

⑤ Remove the two main metering jets.

⑥ Remove the venturi cluster screws, and then lift the venturi cluster and gaskets up and away from the main body. Discard the gaskets. **Caution:** *Do not remove the idle orifice tubes or main vent tubes from the cluster.* Invert the carburetor and catch the accelerator pump discharge and intake check balls.

⑦ Remove the screws that attach the throttle body to the main body. Separate the bodies. **Caution:** *On CAS (Cleaner Air System) carburetors, do not remove the idle mixture adjusting screws from the throttle body. These screws have limited travel and will break if removed.* It is usually not advisable to remove the throttle shaft or valves from the throttle body, unless wear or damage necessitates the installation of new parts.

Cleaning and Inspecting

Clean all parts in carburetor cleaner. Follow with a solvent bath and blow dry. The diaphragms should be cleaned only in solvent—never in carburetor cleaner. Blow compressed air through all passageways and jets to make sure that they are open.

Shake the floats to check for leaks. Replace the float assembly if it contains liquid. Check the float arm needle contacting surface, and replace the float assembly if it is grooved.

Check the throttle shaft for wear in the throttle body. If wear is extreme, it is recommended that the throttle body assembly be replaced rather than installing a new shaft in the old body.

179

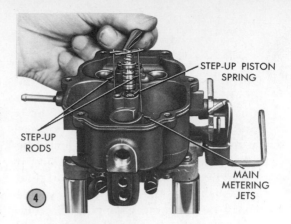

STEP-UP PISTON SPRING
STEP-UP RODS
MAIN METERING JETS
④

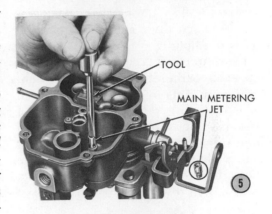

TOOL
MAIN METERING JET
⑤

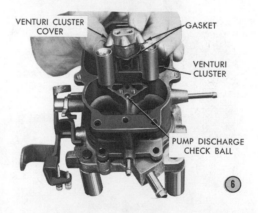

VENTURI CLUSTER COVER
GASKET
VENTURI CLUSTER
PUMP DISCHARGE CHECK BALL
⑥

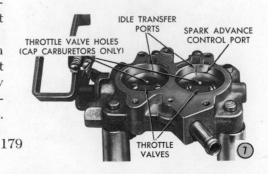

IDLE TRANSFER PORTS
SPARK ADVANCE CONTROL PORT
THROTTLE VALVE HOLES (CAP CARBURETORS ONLY)
THROTTLE VALVES
⑦

During manufacture, the location of the idle transfer port and the spark advance control ports to the throttle valve is carefully established for each particular assembly. If a new shaft should be installed in an old, worn throttle body, it would be very unlikely that the original relationship of the ports to the valves would be retained. Changing the relationship of the valves to the ports would adversely affect normal vehicle operation between the speeds of 15 and 30 miles per hour.

A carburetor kit is generally purchased for each carburetor overhaul. It contains new parts to replace those which wear the most, plus a complete set of gaskets. Each kit contains a matched fuel inlet needle and seat assembly, which should be replaced each time the carburetor is taken apart; otherwise, leaking will result.

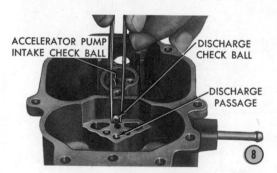

ACCELERATOR PUMP INTAKE CHECK BALL — DISCHARGE CHECK BALL — DISCHARGE PASSAGE — 8

ASSEMBLING

8 Invert the main body, position the gasket, and then place the throttle body on the main body. Install the screws and tighten them securely. Install the accelerator pump discharge check ball ($^5\!/_{32}''$ diameter) in the discharge passage. Drop the accelerator pump intake check ball ($^3\!/_{16}''$ diameter) into the bottom of the pump cylinder.

9 To check the accelerator pump system, pour clean solvent into the carburetor bowl. Slide the pump plunger down into the pump cylinder. Raise the plunger and press lightly on the shaft to expel the air from the pump passage. Using a small, clean brass rod, hold the discharge check ball down firmly on its seat. Again raise the plunger and press downward. No fuel should be emitted from either the intake or discharge passages. If fuel does flow from either passage, it indicates the presence of dirt or a damaged check ball or seat. Clean the passage again and repeat the test. If leakage is still evident, install new check balls. Remove the fuel from the bowl.

10 Place new gaskets on the venturi cluster, then install the assembly in position in the main body. Install the cluster screws and tighten them securely.

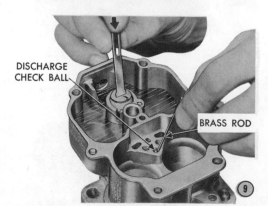

DISCHARGE CHECK BALL — BRASS ROD — 9

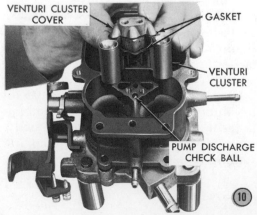

VENTURI CLUSTER COVER — GASKET — VENTURI CLUSTER — PUMP DISCHARGE CHECK BALL — 10

⑪ Install the main metering jets and tighten them securely.

⑫ Before installing the step-up piston, make sure that the step-up rods are able to move freely to each side of the vertical position as shown. The step-up rods must be straight and smooth.

⑬ Slide the step-up piston gasket down into position in the piston well, and then install the step-up piston spring and step-up piston and rods. Carefully guide the step-up rods into the main metering jets. Install the retaining screw and tighten it securely. A step-up piston stuck in the UP position will cause a rich mixture at part throttle, whereas a piston stuck in the DOWN position will cause a lean mixture at wide-open throttle and poor acceleration.

⑭ The carburetors are equipped with a synthetic rubber-tipped fuel inlet needle. The needle tip is a special rubber material which is not affected by gasoline and is flexible enough to make a good seal on the needle seat which provides increased resistance to flooding. The use of the new inlet needle requires a special procedure in adjusting the float setting. Care should be taken to perform this accurately in order to secure the best performance and fuel economy. To set the float height correctly, install the floats, fulcrum pin, and pin retainer in the main body. Install a new needle, seat, and gasket in the body. Tighten it securely.

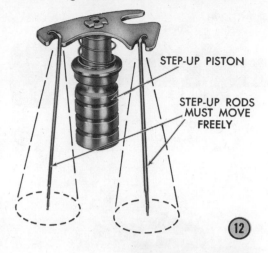

STEP-UP PISTON

STEP-UP RODS MUST MOVE FREELY

⑫

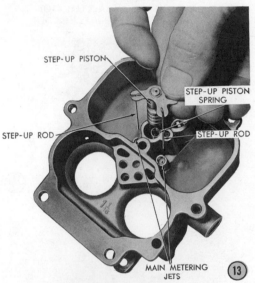

STEP-UP PISTON

STEP-UP PISTON SPRING

STEP-UP ROD

STEP-UP ROD

MAIN METERING JETS

⑬

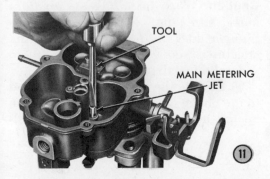

TOOL

MAIN METERING JET

⑪

FUEL INLET NEEDLE VALVE, SEAT AND GASKET

FLOAT FULCRUM PIN RETAINER

CROWN OF FLOATS

⑭

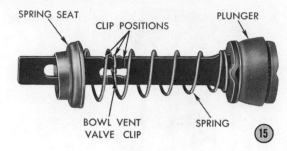

SPRING SEAT · CLIP POSITIONS · PLUNGER · BOWL VENT VALVE CLIP · SPRING ⑮

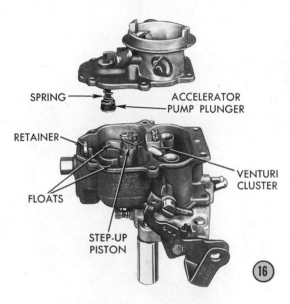

SPRING · ACCELERATOR PUMP PLUNGER · RETAINER · VENTURI CLUSTER · FLOATS · STEP-UP PISTON ⑯

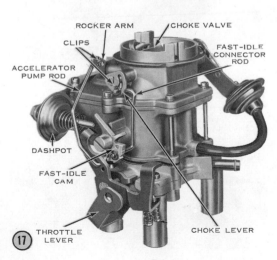

ROCKER ARM · CHOKE VALVE · CLIPS · FAST-IDLE CONNECTOR ROD · ACCELERATOR PUMP ROD · DASHPOT · FAST-IDLE CAM · THROTTLE LEVER · CHOKE LEVER ⑰

Invert the main body so that only the weight of the floats is forcing the needle against the seat. **Caution:** *Catch the pump intake check ball.* Hold your finger against the retainer to seat the fulcrum pin fully. Check the float as shown. There should be $\frac{1}{4}''$ from the surface of the fuel bowl to the crown of each float at the center. If an adjustment is necessary, hold the floats on the bottom of the bowl and bend the float lip toward or away from the needle as necessary. Recheck the $\frac{1}{4}''$ setting again, and then repeat the lip-bending operation as required. **Caution:** *When bending the float lip, do not allow the lip to push against the needle as the synthetic rubber tip can be compressed sufficiently to cause a false setting, which will affect the correct level of the fuel in the bowl.* After being compressed, the tip is very slow to recover its original shape. It is very important that the float lip be perpendicular to the needle, or slanted not more than ten degrees away from the needle, when the float is set correctly in its final position. Replace the pump intake ball check.

⑮ Assemble the pump plunger, spring, and spring seat as shown. Slide the plunger shaft through the opening in the air horn. Install the bowl vent valve over the plunger shaft, and then engage it with the pump rocker arm.

⑯ Place a new gasket on the main body, and then install the air horn. **Caution:** *When installing the air horn make sure that the leather on the plunger does not fold back.* Install the attaching screws and tighten them securely. Install the dashpot.

⑰ Engage the fast-idle connector rod in the choke lever and the fast-idle cam. Secure it with clips. Engage the accelerator pump operating rod in the outer hole in the rocker arm on cars with a manual transmission, or in the inner hole on cars with an automatic transmission, and in the center hole in the throttle lever. Install the clips to secure it.

⑱ Inspect the diaphragm vacuum fitting to insure that the passage is not plugged with foreign material. Leak-check the diaphragm by depressing the diaphragm stem, and then placing a finger over the vacuum fitting to seal the opening. Release the diaphragm stem. If the stem moves more than $1/16''$ in 10 seconds, the leakage is excessive, and the assembly must be replaced. Install the diaphragm assembly on the air horn. Tighten the attaching screws securely. Install the choke operating link in position between the diaphragm plunger and the choke lever. Install the clip to secure it. Inspect the rubber hose for cracks before installing it. **Caution:** *Make sure it is on the correct carburetor fitting.*

Bench Adjustments

Note: *It is very important that the following adjustments be made in the sequence listed below.* **Caution:** *The following instructions contain specifications which may vary, depending on the model carburetor. Check these against the manufacturer's specifications before making the final adjustments.*

⑲ When assembling the accelerator pump to the air horn, note that the hairpin clip (which opens the bowl vent) can be placed in any one of three positioning notches. These notches correspond to the long, medium, and short pump stroke holes in the throttle lever.

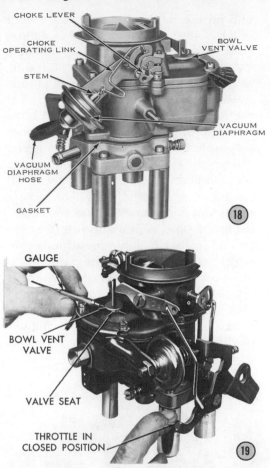

Normally, the bowl vent clip on the pump stem should be in the middle notch and the pump operating rod in the medium-stroke hole. The proper procedure is to adjust the amount of bowl vent opening instead of measuring and setting the height of the pump plunger. To adjust the bowl vent opening, back off the idle-speed adjusting screw. Open the choke valve so that the fast-idle cam allows the throttle valves to be completely seated in their bores. Be sure that the pump operating rod is in the medium-stroke hole in the throttle lever and that the bowl vent clip on the pump stem is in the center notch. Close the throttle valves tightly. It should be just possible to insert a $1/16''$ drill between the bowl vent and its seat as shown. If an adjustment is necessary, bend the pump operating rod at the lower angle, until the correct bowl vent opening is obtained. On CAS model carburetors, bend the pump operating rod so that the height of the pump plunger stem above the bowl cover will be between $1''$ and $1^1/_{32}''$. This is a very important adjustment since too much lift at the bowl vent will result in a considerable loss in low-speed fuel economy. Remember that if the pump operating rod is moved to either the short- or long-stroke position, a corresponding change must be made in the location of the bowl vent clip, and the amount of lift of the bowl vent rechecked and adjusted.

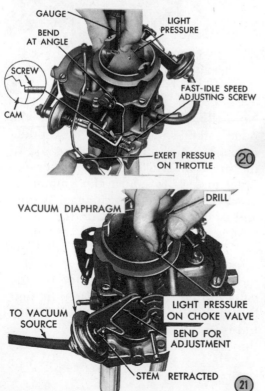

GAUGE
BEND AT ANGLE
LIGHT PRESSURE
SCREW
CAM
FAST-IDLE SPEED ADJUSTING SCREW
EXERT PRESSUR ON THROTTLE
⑳

VACUUM DIAPHRAGM
DRILL
TO VACUUM SOURCE
LIGHT PRESSURE ON CHOKE VALVE
BEND FOR ADJUSTMENT
STEM RETRACTED
㉑

⑳ The fast-idle adjustment should now be made. This adjustment is important to assure that timing of each cam step occurs properly during engine warm-up. With the fast-idle speed adjusting screw contacting the step on the fast-idle cam as shown, move the choke valve toward the closed position with light pressure. Use a No. 41 drill (0.095″) as a gauge between the choke valve and wall of the air horn. A slight drag should be obtained as the gauge is removed. If an adjustment is necessary, bend the fast-idle connector rod at the angle until the correct valve opening is obtained.

㉑ The choke diaphragm adjustment controls the fuel delivery after the cold engine starts. It positions the choke valve within the air horn by action of the linkage between the choke shaft and the diaphragm. The diaphragm must be energized to measure the vacuum kick adjustment. Use a distributor test machine with a vacuum source to adjust. Open the throttle valves enough to allow the choke valve to move to the closed position. Disconnect the vacuum hose from the diaphragm and connect a hose from the vacuum supply as shown. A minimum of 10″ Hg is necessary. Insert a No. 16 drill (manual transmission) or a No. 30 drill (automatic transmission) between the choke valve and the wall of the air horn. Apply sufficient closing pressure on the choke shaft lever to provide the smallest choke valve opening possible without distorting the diaphragm link. Note that the cylindrical stem of the diaphragm will extent as the internal spring is compressed. The spring must be fully compressed for proper measurement of the kick adjustment. A slight drag should be obtained as the gauge is removed. The adjustment of this opening

184

requires the removal of the choke operating link. **Caution:** *Damage to the diaphragm and the choke lever slot can result if the link is not removed for the bending operation.*

㉒ Remove the clip and disengage the choke operating link from the diaphragm stem, and then disengage the link from the choke lever. The best bending results are obtained by using a vise and a pair of pliers. Bend the choke operating link at an angle to provide the correct choke valve opening. **Caution:** *A correction in the length of the link of 0.010″ will result in a change of 0.015″ in the choke valve opening.* In other words, if the choke valve opening is 0.015″ in error, correction of the link length should be 0.010″. A 2″ micrometer is helpful in establishing the original and corrected length of the link. Reinstall the choke operating link and recheck the choke valve opening.

㉓ Install the vacuum hose to the diaphragm and make the following check: With no vacuum applied to the diaphragm, some clearance should exist between the choke operating link and the choke lever slot, in both the open and closed choke valve positions as shown. **Caution:** *This clearance is necessary to allow the choke valve to close for starting as well as to open fully after the engine reaches normal operating temperature.* If clearance does not exist in both of these positions, recheck the operating link adjustment. **Caution:** *Free movement of the choke valve between the closed and open positions is very necessary.* This free movement should also exist between the kick and the open choke valve positions with the engine running. If binding exists, the choke operating link has been improperly bent and should be corrected.

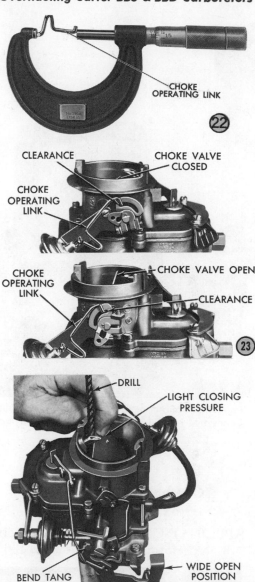

㉔ Hold the throttle valves in the wide-open position. Insert a ¼″ drill shank between the upper edge of the choke valve and the inner wall of the air horn as shown. Bend the unloader tang on the throttle lever until a slight drag is obtained.

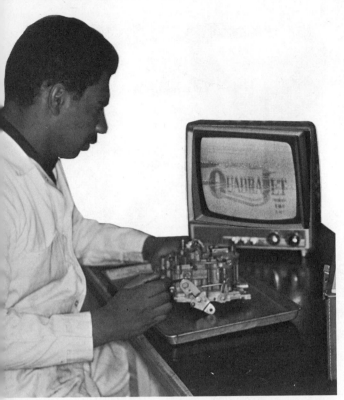

Taped instructions can be used for learning about automotive equipment. This student is studying the fuel system.

Overhauling a Rochester 4MV/4MC Carburetor

APPLICATION: All General Motors high-performance engines since 1966

DISASSEMBLING

① Place the carburetor on the proper holding fixture. Remove the idle vent valve attaching screw, and then take out the idle vent valve assembly. Remove the clips from the upper end of the choke rod, disconnect the choke rod from the upper choke shaft lever, and

then remove the choke rod from the bowl. Remove the spring clip from the upper end of the pump rod, and then disconnect the pump rod from the pump lever. Remove the nine air-horn-to-bowl attaching screws. **Note:** *Two attaching screws are located next to the primary venturi.* Remove the air horn by lifting it straight up. **Note:** *The air horn gasket should remain on the bowl for removal later.* **Caution:** *Care must be taken not to bend the accelerating well and air bleed tubes protruding from the air horn.*

② Remove the secondary metering rods by holding the air valve wide open and then tilting and sliding the rods from the holes in the hanger. Remove the dashpot piston from the air valve link by rotating the bend through the hole, and then remove the dashpot from the air horn by rotating the bend through the air horn. Further disassembly of the air horn is not required. **Caution:** *The air valves, air valve shaft, and secondary metering rod hangers are calibrated and*

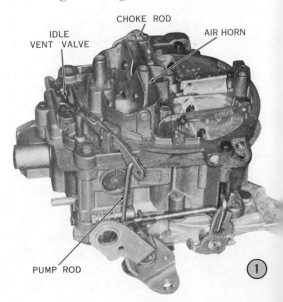

186

should not be removed. **Caution:** *The secondary high-speed air bleeds and accelerating well tubes are pressed in and must not be removed.*

③ Remove the accelerating pump piston from the pump well. Release the air horn gasket from the dowels on the secondary side of the bowl, and then pry the gasket from around the power piston and primary metering rods. Remove the pump return spring from the pump well.

④ Take out the plastic filler over the float valve. Remove the power piston and primary metering rods, using needle-nosed pliers to pull straight up on the metering rod hanger directly over the power piston. Remove the power piston spring from the well. Remove the metering rods from the power piston by disconnecting the tension spring from the top of each rod, and then rotating the rod to remove it from the hanger. Remove the float assembly by pulling up slightly on the hinge pin until the pin can be removed by sliding it toward the pump well. After the pin is removed, slide the float assembly toward the front of the bowl to disengage the needle valve pull clip. **Caution:** *Be careful not to distort the pull clip.*

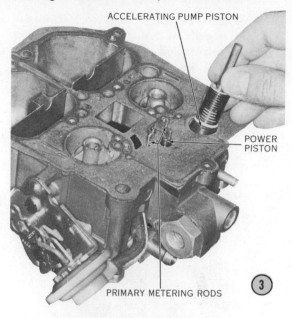

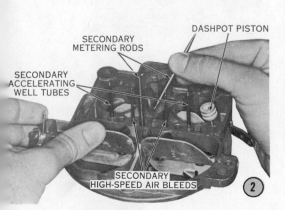

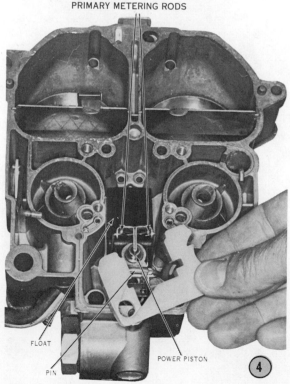

187

⑤ Remove the two screws from the float needle retainer, and then lift out the retainer and needle assembly. **Caution:** *The needle seat is factory staked and tested. Do not attempt to remove or restake it. If damaged, replace the float bowl assembly.* Remove both primary metering rod jets. Remove the pump discharge check ball retainer and the check ball. Remove the baffle plates from the secondary side of the bowl. Disconnect the vacuum hose from the vacuum break assembly and from the tube connection on the bowl. Remove the retaining screw and then lift the assembly from the float bowl.

⑥ On 4MC models, remove the choke coil retaining screws and clips, and then remove the choke coil assembly and baffle. Remove the retaining screw from the choke housing assembly, and then lift the assembly from the float bowl. Remove the fast-idle cam from the choke assembly and the lower choke rod and actuating lever from inside of the float bowl well.

⑦ Remove the two screws from the hot-idle compensator cover, and then remove the hot-idle compensator and O-ring from the float bowl. Remove the fuel inlet filter retaining nut, gasket, filter, and spring. Remove the throttle body by taking out the throttle-body-to-bowl attaching screws, and then lift off the throttle-body-to-bowl-insulator gasket. Remove the idle mixture screws and springs. **Caution:** *Extreme care must be taken to avoid damaging the secondary throttle valves.*

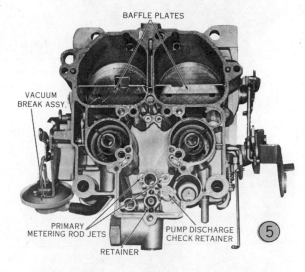

BAFFLE PLATES

VACUUM BREAK ASSY.

PRIMARY METERING ROD JETS

RETAINER

PUMP DISCHARGE CHECK RETAINER

⑤

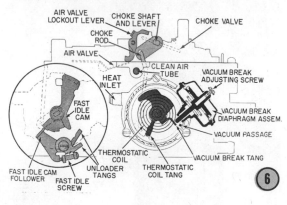

AIR VALVE LOCKOUT LEVER

CHOKE SHAFT AND LEVER

CHOKE VALVE

CHOKE ROD

AIR VALVE

CLEAN AIR TUBE

HEAT INLET

VACUUM BREAK ADJUSTING SCREW

VACUUM BREAK DIAPHRAGM ASSEM.

VACUUM PASSAGE

FAST IDLE CAM

THERMOSTATIC COIL

UNLOADER TANGS

THERMOSTATIC COIL TANG

VACUUM BREAK TANG

FAST IDLE CAM FOLLOWER

FAST IDLE SCREW

⑥

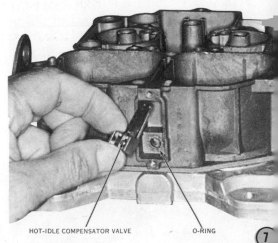

HOT-IDLE COMPENSATOR VALVE

O-RING

⑦

188

ASSEMBLING

8 Turn in the idle mixture adjusting screws until seated, and then back them out two turns for a preliminary adjustment. Install the pump rod in the lower hole of the throttle lever by rotating the rod. Position a new throttle-body-to-bowl-insulator gasket on the bowl, making certain that the gasket is properly located over the two dowels. Install the throttle body, making certain that it is properly located over the dowels on the float bowl. Install the throttle-body-to-bowl screws; tighten them evenly and securely. Install the fuel inlet filter spring, filter, new gasket, and the inlet nut. Tighten the nut securely. Place a new hot-idle compensator O-ring seal in the recess in the bowl, and then install the hot-idle compensator.

9 Install the vacuum break rod (U-bend end) in the diaphragm link, with the end toward the bracket, and then install the grooved end of the rod in the hole of the actuating lever. Retain it to the vacuum break lever with the spring clip. Install the fast-idle cam on the vacuum break or choke housing assembly. Be sure that the fast-idle cam actuating pin on the intermediate choke shaft is located in the cut-out area of the fast-idle cam. Connect the choke rod to the choke rod actuating lever (plain end) and then, holding the choke rod with the grooved end pointing inward, position the choke rod actuating lever in the well of the float bowl. Then install the choke assembly, engaging the shaft with the hole in the actuating lever. Install the retaining screw, and then tighten it securely. Remove the choke rod from the lever for later installation. Install and connect the vacuum hose (Model 4MV only).

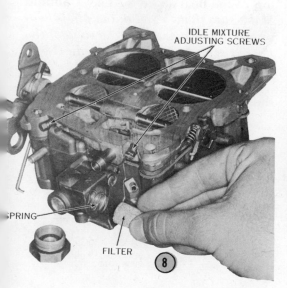

IDLE MIXTURE ADJUSTING SCREWS

SPRING

FILTER

8

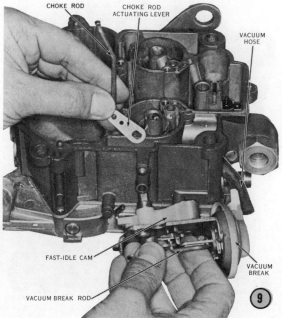

CHOKE ROD

CHOKE ROD ACTUATING LEVER

VACUUM HOSE

FAST-IDLE CAM

VACUUM BREAK ROD

VACUUM BREAK

9

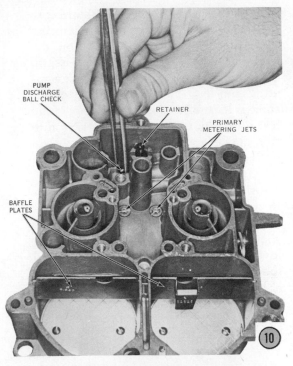

PUMP
DISCHARGE
BALL CHECK

RETAINER

PRIMARY
METERING JETS

BAFFLE
PLATES

10

⑩ Install the baffle plates in the secondary side of the bowl, with the notches facing up. Install the primary main metering jets. Install a new float needle and diaphragm assembly. Make certain that the diaphragm is properly positioned, and then install the retainer and two screws, tightening them securely. Install the pump discharge ball check and retainer in the passage next to the pump well.

⑪ Use needle-nosed pliers to install the pull clip on the needle. **Note:** *The pull clip is properly positioned with the open end toward the front of the bowl.* Install the float by sliding the float lever under the pull clip, from the front to the back. With the float lever in the pull clip, hold the float assembly by the toe, and then install the retaining pin from the pump well side. Be careful not to distort the pull clip.

⑫ To adjust the float level, measure from the top of the float bowl gasket surface (with the gasket removed) to the top of the float at the toe end. **Caution:** *Make sure that the retaining pin is held firmly in place and that the tang of the float is seated on the float needle.* Bend the float up or down to adjust.

⑬ Install the power piston spring in the power piston well. If the primary

FLOAT

PULL CLIP

11

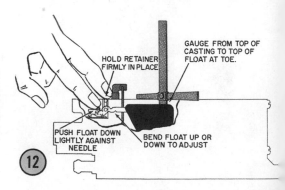

GAUGE FROM TOP OF
CASTING TO TOP OF
FLOAT AT TOE.

HOLD RETAINER
FIRMLY IN PLACE

PUSH FLOAT DOWN
LIGHTLY AGAINST
NEEDLE

BEND FLOAT UP OR
DOWN TO ADJUST

12

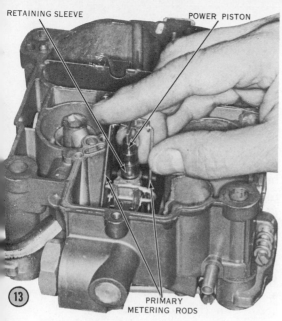

RETAINING SLEEVE   POWER PISTON

(13)

PRIMARY
METERING RODS

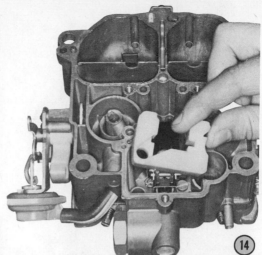

(14)

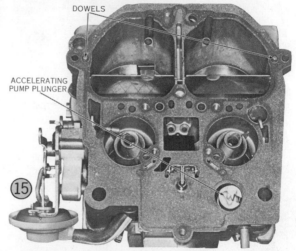

DOWELS

ACCELERATING
PUMP PLUNGER

(15)

(16)

main metering rods were removed from the hanger, re-install them, making sure that the tension spring is connected to the top of each metering rod. Install the power piston assembly in the well with the metering rods properly located in the metering jets. Press down firmly on the power piston to insure engagement of the retaining pin with the hole in the throttle body gasket on early models. A sleeve around the piston holds the later model pistons in place during assembly.

(14) Install the plastic filler over the float needle, pressing down firmly until seated.

(15) Position the pump return spring in the pump well. Install the air horn gasket around the primary metering rods and piston. Position the gasket over the two dowels on the secondary side of the bowl. Install the accelerating pump plunger in the pump well.

(16) Install the secondary metering rods. With the air valve held wide open, the rods should be positioned with their upper ends through the hanger holes and pointing toward each other.

(17)

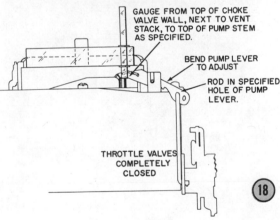

GAUGE FROM TOP OF CHOKE VALVE WALL, NEXT TO VENT STACK, TO TOP OF PUMP STEM AS SPECIFIED.

BEND PUMP LEVER TO ADJUST

ROD IN SPECIFIED HOLE OF PUMP LEVER.

THROTTLE VALVES COMPLETELY CLOSED

(18)

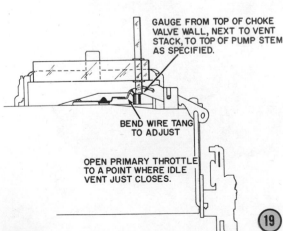

GAUGE FROM TOP OF CHOKE VALVE WALL, NEXT TO VENT STACK, TO TOP OF PUMP STEM AS SPECIFIED.

BEND WIRE TANG TO ADJUST

OPEN PRIMARY THROTTLE TO A POINT WHERE IDLE VENT JUST CLOSES.

(19)

⑰ Place the air horn assembly on the bowl carefully locating the secondary metering rods, high-speed air bleeds, and accelerating well tubes through the holes of the air horn gasket. Make sure that the dashpot and pump plunger are positioned properly through the holes in the air horn. **Caution:** *Do not force the air horn assembly onto the float bowl as distortion of the secondary metering plates will result.* A slight sideward movement will center the metering rods in the metering plates. Install the four long air horn screws around the secondary side, two short screws in the center section, and one short screw above the fuel inlet. The two counter-sunk screws are installed in the primary venturi area. All screws must be tightened evenly and securely. Install the idle vent actuating rod in the pump lever. Connect the pump rod in the pump lever and retain it with the spring clip. Connect the choke rod in the lower choke lever and retain it with the spring clip. Install the idle vent valve, engaging the actuating rod, and then tighten the attaching screw.

Bench Adjustments

The following bench adjustments must be made in the order below. **Caution:** *The following instructions contain specifications which may vary, depending on the model carburetor. Check against manufacturer's specifications before making final adjustments.*

⑱ To make the pump rod adjustment, measure from the top of the choke valve wall, next to the vent stack, to the top of the pump stem, with the throttle valves completely closed and the pump rod in the specified hole of the pump lever. Bend the pump lever to adjust.

192

19 - To make the idle vent adjustment, open the primary throttle to a point where the idle vent just closes. Measure the distance from the top of the choke valve wall, next to the vent stack, to the top of the pump plunger stem. Bend the wire tang on the pump lever to adjust.

20 - To make the air valve adjustment, measure the distance between the upper inside edge of the air valve and the back of the choke valve wall, at the torsion spring end. Bend the stop tang on the dashpot lever to adjust.

21 - To make the fast-idle adjustment, turn the fast-idle screw in 3 turns after the screw makes contact with the lever, with the primary throttle valves completely closed and the cam follower over the high step of the fast-idle cam.

22 - To make the choke rod adjustment, rotate the choke valve toward the closed position by pushing down on the vacuum break lever (Model 4MV) or the thermostatic coil tang (Model 4MC). With the cam follower on the second step of the fast-idle cam, and against the high step, the dimension between the lower edge of the choke valve and the air horn wall should be as specified. Bend the choke rod to adjust.

23 - To make the vacuum break adjustment on the 4MV model carburetor (with the choke spring pick-up located in the specified notch), hold the choke valve in the closed position using a rubber band on the vacuum break lever. Hold the vacuum break diaphragm stem against its seat so that the vacuum link is at the end of the slot. The dimension between the lower edge of the choke valve and the air horn, at the choke lever end, should be as specified. Bend the vacuum link to adjust.

193

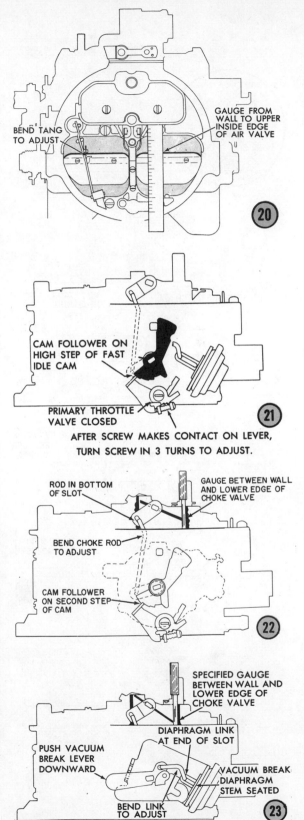

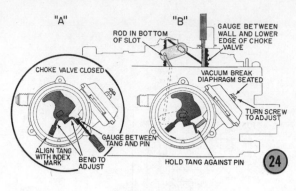

"A"
CHOKE VALVE CLOSED
ALIGN TANG WITH INDEX MARK
BEND TO ADJUST
GAUGE BETWEEN TANG AND PIN
ROD IN BOTTOM OF SLOT
"B"
GAUGE BETWEEN WALL AND LOWER EDGE OF CHOKE VALVE
VACUUM BREAK DIAPHRAGM SEATED
TURN SCREW TO ADJUST
HOLD TANG AGAINST PIN
(24)

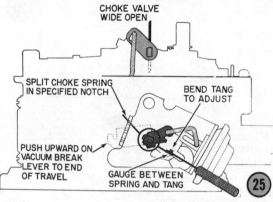

CHOKE VALVE WIDE OPEN
SPLIT CHOKE SPRING IN SPECIFIED NOTCH
BEND TANG TO ADJUST
PUSH UPWARD ON VACUUM BREAK LEVER TO END OF TRAVEL
GAUGE BETWEEN SPRING AND TANG
(25)

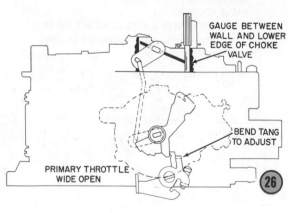

GAUGE BETWEEN WALL AND LOWER EDGE OF CHOKE VALVE
BEND TANG TO ADJUST
PRIMARY THROTTLE WIDE OPEN
(26)

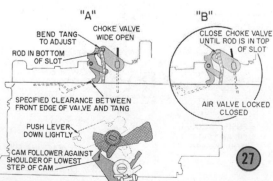

"A"
BEND TANG TO ADJUST
CHOKE VALVE WIDE OPEN
ROD IN BOTTOM OF SLOT
SPECIFIED CLEARANCE BETWEEN FRONT EDGE OF VALVE AND TANG
PUSH LEVER DOWN LIGHTLY
CAM FOLLOWER AGAINST SHOULDER OF LOWEST STEP OF CAM
"B"
CLOSE CHOKE VALVE UNTIL ROD IS IN TOP OF SLOT
AIR VALVE LOCKED CLOSED
(27)

㉔ To make the vacuum break adjustment on the 4MC model carburetor, hold the choke valve closed and the choke rod in the bottom of the slot in the upper choke lever. Align the thermostatic spring pick-up tang directly over the index tab on the inside of the choke housing. With the tang aligned, adjust the vacuum break tang to the specified dimension between the tang and vacuum break pin as shown at "A." Now, with the vacuum break diaphragm seated and the tang against the vacuum break pin, adjust the choke rod to give the specified dimension between the wall and the lower edge of the choke valve as shown at "B." Make sure that the choke rod is in the bottom of the slot in the choke lever when gauging. Turn the screw on the vacuum break cover to adjust. Install the baffle plate and thermostatic cover. Adjust the cover to the specified mark on the choke housing.

㉕ To make the split choke spring adjustment, open the choke valve by pushing up on the vacuum break lever to the end of its travel, making sure that the choke rod is in the upper end of the slot in the choke lever and that the split choke spring is in the specified notch. The dimension between the end of the torsion spring and the tang should be as specified. Bend the tang to adjust.

㉖ To make the unloader adjustment, hold the choke valve in the closed position with a rubber band on the vacuum break lever, and then open the primary throttle to the wide-open position. The dimension between the lower edge of the choke valve and the air horn wall should be as specified. Bend the tang on the fast-idle lever to adjust.

㉗ To make the Oldsmobile air valve lockout adjustment (opening clearance),

194

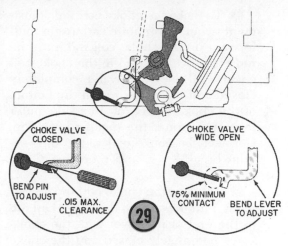

apply a light force to the vacuum break lever in the direction of a closed choke with the cam follower positioned against the rise of the lowest step of the fast-idle cam. Rotate the choke valve to its wide-open position by applying force to the under side of the choke valve. Move the air valves toward the open position. Bend the upper end of the air valve lockout lever to provide 0.015"-0.035" clearance between the lockout tang and the front edge of the air valve as shown at "A." To make the lockout clearance adjustment, apply a light force to the vacuum break lever in the direction of closed choke. With the cam follower positioned against the rise of the lowest step of the fast-idle cam, rotate the choke valve in the direction of the closed choke by applying a light force to the underside of the choke valve as shown at "B" so that the choke link is at the upper end of the slot in the choke lever. Move the air valves toward the open position but they must remain locked. If not, the opening clearance must be rechecked.

28 To make the air valve lockout adjustment on Chevrolet, Buick, and Pontiac, apply sufficient force to the thermostatic spring tang to move the choke rod to the top of the slot in the

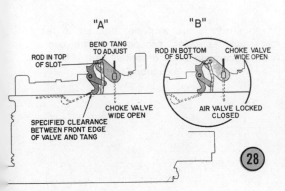

choke lever with the choke valve wide open. Move the air valve toward the open position. Bend the upper end of the air valve lockout lever to provide the specified opening between the lockout tang and the front edge of the air valve as shown at "A." Now, open the choke valve to its wide-open position by applying force to the underside of the choke valve. Making sure that the choke rod is in the bottom of the slot in the choke lever, the air valve lockout tang must hold the air valve closed as shown at "B."

29 To make the secondary lockout clearance adjustment, hold the choke valve and both primary and secondary throttle valves fully closed. The lockout lever should not contact the lockout pin but the clearance must not exceed 0.015" as shown in the left-hand insert. Bend the lockout pin to adjust. Hold the choke valve and primary throttle valves in the wide-open position and the secondary throttle valves fully closed. The lockout pin should have a minimum of 75 percent contact on the lockout lever as shown in the right-hand insert. To adjust, bend the lockout lever.

30 To make the choke coil rod adjustment on an Oldsmobile carburetor, pull forward on the choke coil rod until the rod is against the stop in the choke coil cover with the choke valve completely closed and the choke rod in the bottom of the choke lever slot. Bend the outer loop of the rod to the specified position. Connect the choke coil rod to the vacuum break lever, and then install the clip.

31 To make the choke coil rod adjustment, pull upward on the choke coil rod to the end of its travel with the choke valve completely closed and the choke rod in the bottom of the choke lever slot. The bottom of the choke coil rod must be even with the top of the hole in the vacuum break lever. Bend the choke coil rod to adjust. Connect the choke coil rod to the vacuum break lever, and then install the clip.

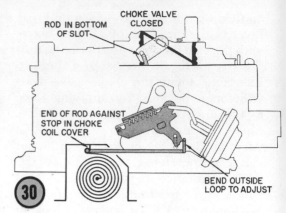

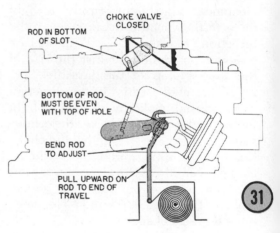

These students are working together to learn carburetor servicing procedures. The use of factory manuals is an essential part of this instruction.

196

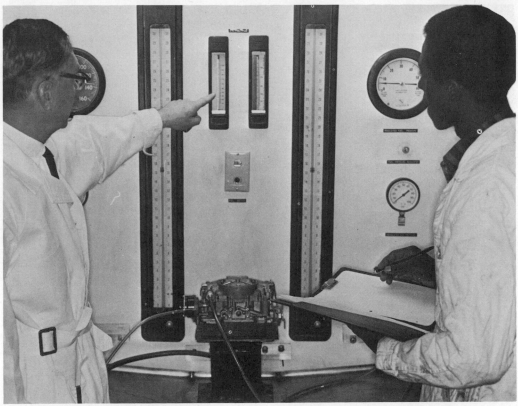

When a student in the fuel system class at Los Angeles Trade-Technical College rebuilds a carburetor, he must flow-test it and compare the results with factory specifications before the unit is allowed out of the shop.

CHECK YOUR KNOWLEDGE

1. What are the two purposes of the fuel system?
2. What is the purpose of the fuel pump?
3. What operates the fuel pump?
4. How does the fuel pump work?
5. Why won't liquid gasoline burn?
6. Where is the liquid gasoline vaporized?
7. What is the ideal fuel-air mixture?
8. What has the intake stroke of the engine to do with the action of the carburetor?
9. How is more fuel-air mixture carried to the cylinders?
10. Why are multiple carburetors used on modern engines?

11. Do all carburetors of a multiple installation work all the time? Explain.
12. How many circuits does a carburetor have? Name them.
13. What is the purpose of the float circuit?
14. How does it work?
15. What is the purpose of multiple floats?
16. What is the purpose of the bowl vent?
17. How does a balanced bowl vent operate?
18. Why is the idle port slot-shaped?
19. How is the idle mixture changed?
20. What has the venturi to do with the operation of a carburetor?
21. What is the purpose of an air bleed?

197

22. What circuit enriches the mixture for high speed or pulling up steep grades?
23. How does it enrich the mixture?
24. What two types of accelerating mechanisms are in common use?
25. What is the difference in their operation?
26. Why is it necessary to vent the accelerating circuit discharge jet?
27. Why is a choke necessary?
28. What closes the choke valve?
29. What two things tend to open the choke valve when the engine is first started?
30. What relaxes the thermostat when the engine warms to operating temperature?
31. How does the fast-idle mechanism operate?
32. What control does a driver have over an overchoked engine?
33. What is the difference in operation between fuel injection and carburetion?
34. What are the three major parts of the fuel-injection system?
35. How is fuel enrichment for acceleration provided?
36. What is the air throttle?
37. What is vapor lock? What causes it?
38. How can you start a car which has vapor locked?
39. How does each of the four types of air cleaners function?
40. What causes the most trouble in the fuel system?
41. What three general types of fuel system troubles are there?
42. What conditions may cause stumbling on acceleration?
43. What conditions may cause poor high-speed performance?
44. What conditions may cause poor gas mileage?

Self-Check Tests

1. The purpose of the fuel system is to deliver liquid gasoline to the cylinder where it is burned to propel the car.
2. The atomized fuel is vaporized thoroughly in the intake manifold.
3. The fuel pump draws the fuel from the tank by pressure.
4. The cam moves the fuel pump diaphragm up and down.
5. Liquid gasoline burns readily.
6. It takes 15 pounds of air for each pound of gasoline for an ideal mixture.
7. A venturi lowers the air pressure at its point of greatest restriction.
8. Using more carburetors increases the free-breathing characteristics of an engine.
9. The carburetor consists of five basic circuits.
10. Gasoline is sucked into the carburetor by intake manifold vacuum.
11. Multiple floats are useful to increase the amount of gasoline entering the manifold.
12. A balanced vent increases the pressure in the float bowl with a partially clogged air filter.
13. Turning the idle mixture adjusting screw *in* enriches the mixture.
14. A vacuum-operated piston opens the power jet when the intake manifold vacuum is high.
15. Fuel-injection nozzles spray fuel directly into each cylinder.
16. Vapor lock will cause a carburetor to run out of liquid fuel.
17. The oil-wetted type of air cleaner is the most efficient.
18. The oil-wetted type air cleaner contains a reservoir of oil.
19. Dirt and water are the greatest enemies of the fuel system.
20. Carburetors usually have to be overhauled after 50,000 miles of service.
21. The best test for a lack of fuel in the carburetor is to see if there is any in the gas tank.
22. Rough idling can only be caused by a poor carburetor mixture.
23. Stumbling on acceleration can only be caused by dirt entering the accelerating system check valves or the discharge jet.
24. Poor gas mileage may be due to poor driving habits of the owner.

1. Which of the following is *not* part of the fuel pump: a) rocker arm; b) diaphragm; c) filter; d) intake manifold pipe?
2. The liquid fuel is vaporized in the: a) fuel pump; b) carburetor; c) intake manifold; d) exhaust pipe.
3. Which of the following is *not* a part of the carburetor: a) venturi; b) accelerator pedal; c) high speed nozzles; d) air bleed?

4. Which of the following is *not* a carburetor circuit: a) ignition circuit; b) float circuit; c) idle circuit; d) power circuit?

5. Which of the following is *not* a part of the low speed system: a) venturi; b) air bleed; c) idle port; d) throttle plate?

6. Which of the following is *not* a part of the high speed circuit: a) power jet; b) metering rod; c) air bleed; d) venturi?

7. Which of the following is *not* a part of the accelerating system: a) pump; b) intake valve; c) discharge valve; d) metering rod?

8. Which of the following is *not* a part of the choke: a) piston; b) thermostat; c) offset air valve; d) metering rod?

9. Which of the following is *not* a part of a fuel-injection system: a) pump; b) throttle plate; c) high-speed nozzle; d) spray nozzles?

10. Which of the following is *not* a type of air cleaner: a) oil-wetted; b) wire gauze; c) oil-bath; d) dry-type?

COMPLETION

1. The _____ mixes and atomizes the liquid gasoline.

2. Power to operate the fuel pump is supplied by an eccentric on the _____.

3. The carburetor contains a restriction in the air stream called a _____.

4. Depressing the accelerator pedal opens the _____ _____ admitting more fuel-air mixture to the engine.

5. The _____ _____ purpose is to maintain a supply of fuel in the carburetor bowl for use of the other circuits.

6. The idle port is _____ shaped.

7. The _____ _____ enriches the mixture for high speed.

8. The _____ _____ regulates the fuel-air mixture during engine warm up.

9. The formation of air bubbles in the gas line frequently leads to _____ _____.

10. Poor high speed performance can be caused by _____ or fuel pump trouble.

MATCHING

1. Fuel pump
2. Supercharger
3. Carburetor
4. Manifold heat control
5. Air stream restriction
6. Float circuit
7. Fuel injection
8. Air cleaner

a. Dries out gas mixture
b. Spray nozzles
c. Hydraulic pump
d. Atomizes fuel
e. Air pump
f. Oil-bath
g. Venturi
h. Needle valve and seat

7

Fundamentals of Electricity

Magnetism

Magnetism is the basis of electricity. Experiments have shown that an electric current can produce magnetism, and magnetism can produce electricity. Many electrical effects are explained in magnetic terms. Therefore a knowledge of magnetism is important to understand electricity.

Magnetism was first noted by a man of ancient times, who found that a certain kind of rock always pointed in the same direction when suspended on a string. This natural magnetic substance was called *loadstone*. It was used as the first crude compass. Later investigation proved that the earth itself is a gigantic magnet; and its attraction for the loadstone caused the first inquiries into magnetic properties.

The present theory of magnetism is based on the idea that each molecule of a piece of certain materials is in itself a small magnet. In an unmagnetized piece of iron, the molecules are freely arranged. Magnetization consists of turning all these small magnets in the same direction, so that they combine to produce a powerful force.

Magnets are either of the permanent or temporary types. Once the molecules of hard steel are forced to line up in the same direction, they tend to maintain this position. Such a magnet is called a permanent magnet. When a piece of soft steel is placed in a magnetic field, the molecules line up as in hard steel but return to their original positions as soon as the external force is removed. Hence soft steel is used to make a temporary magnet.

In a magnetized piece of steel, the molecules align themselves in the same direction and combine their forces into a single magnet. The molecules of an unmagnetized piece of steel point in every direction.

Magnetic Poles and Fields

When magnetized, a piece of steel has a field of force around the ends, which are called *poles*. Because a freely suspended magnet rotates until it lines up with the earth's geographic poles, the end pointed toward the earth's North Pole is called a north-seeking pole or, more commonly, the *north pole* of the magnet. The opposite end of the magnet is called a *south pole* because it points toward the South Pole of the earth.

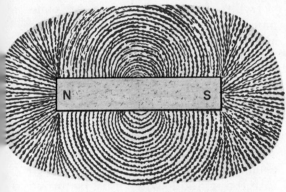

The field of force extends out from each pole of a magnet in circular lines.

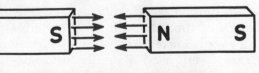

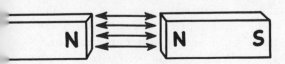

If two freely suspended magnets are brought close together, they will swing until a north pole of one is opposite a south pole of the other. Then the magnets will attract each other. Should you turn one magnet so that similar poles are facing each other, the magnets will be repelled. From these facts the *law of magnetism* is derived: namely, *like poles repel*, and *unlike poles attract*.

The region around the poles of a magnet is called a *field of force*. If a piece of steel is placed within this field, it will be attracted to the pole. If a compass needle is placed near the pole, the needle will swing toward it. While we cannot see a field of force, its effects can be shown by the compass.

Batteries

A single-cell battery is a container of acid in which two dissimilar metals are submerged. The chemical action of the acid on the metals sets up a flow of electricity. *Dry cells* contain the acid in the form of a paste or jelly.

When two plates of a single cell battery are connected together, a complete circuit is made, and electrons flow. The two plates of the battery are called poles. The electrons, being negative particles of matter, flow from the negative pole to the positive pole.

Electrons will flow along a circuit only when they are pushed by pressure. It is the action of the acid on the metals within the battery which creates this pressure, called *potential difference* or *volts*. The pressure of a fully charged wet cell battery is 2 volts, while that of a dry cell is $1\frac{1}{2}$ volts.

The physical size of a dry or wet cell has no effect on the pressure or voltage.

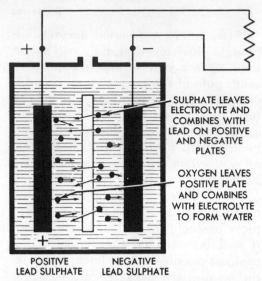

SULPHATE LEAVES ELECTROLYTE AND COMBINES WITH LEAD ON POSITIVE AND NEGATIVE PLATES

OXYGEN LEAVES POSITIVE PLATE AND COMBINES WITH ELECTROLYTE TO FORM WATER

POSITIVE LEAD SULPHATE   NEGATIVE LEAD SULPHATE

A wet cell battery contains two dissimilar metals submerged in an acid solution. Courtesy Lincoln Division, Ford Motor Company.

However, a large cell contains much more active material and will last longer under similar service. In other words, a large cell, wet or dry, supplies a larger number of electrons before the cell is exhausted.

The quantity of electrons flowing in a circuit is called *amperage*. This is discussed later.

Circuits

Electricity can flow only when there is a complete circuit. That is, there must be an uninterrupted path from the electrical source to the device being

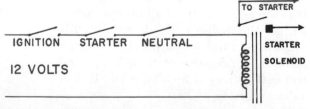

In a series circuit, the current must flow through each switch in turn.

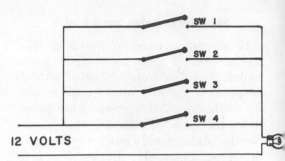

In a parallel circuit, the current can select any one of several paths.

operated and back to the source. Otherwise the circuit is said to be *open*.

Two types of wiring circuits are commonly used in the automobile—*series* and *parallel circuits*. In a series circuit, *all* the current leaving the battery must pass through *all* the electrical devices in that circuit. In a parallel circuit, there may be several branches so that only a part of the electricity flows through any one branch.

The starter and ignition switches are usually connected in series, in which case the ignition switch must be turned on before the starting motor switch will work. Some four-door cars are equipped with four door switches in parallel. Opening any one door lights the interior light.

Batteries are frequently connected in series to increase the total voltage. The length of time that two such batteries can supply current is the same as if one battery were used. Batteries are sometimes connected in parallel to increase service life. The voltage of batteries hooked in parallel remains the same as for one battery.

The automotive storage battery contains both series and parallel connections. Within each cell several plates are connected together in a parallel

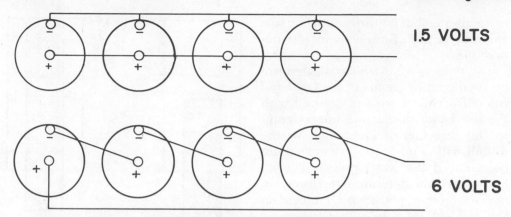

1.5 VOLTS

6 VOLTS

Dry cells are connected in parallel to increase the amperage or capacity. They are hooked in series to increase the voltage.

circuit to furnish enough current for the starting motor. Each of the six cells (2 volts each) is connected in series to furnish twelve volts to energize the other electrical equipment.

Electromagnetism

An electromagnet consists of a coil of wire wound around a soft iron core and connected to a source of current. Electromagnets depend on the flow of electrons in the coil of wire for their force and can be "turned off" by shutting off the electricity. Electromagnetism is used in automobiles, boats, aircraft, space missiles, and home equipment to operate electric motors, relays, and solenoids. An electromagnet can exist without the iron core but it will be weaker. The core concentrates the lines of force in the center of the magnet. The strength of an electromagnet depends on the amount of current flowing in the coil and the size and kind of core material; the strength is classified according to the number of *ampere turns* it contains. For example, an electromagnet of a 100 turns of wire, allowing one ampere to flow, is equal in strength

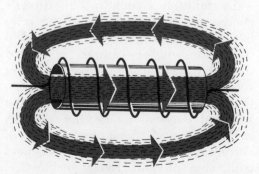

An electromagnet is a coil of wire with a soft iron core which, when energized with electricity, exhibits the same properties as a permanent magnet.

By holding a solenoid with your left hand, your thumb pointing in the direction of the north pole, your fingers will show the direction in which electrons flow.

to another coil of 50 turns allowing two amperes to pass. Both contain *100 ampere turns.*

The polarity of an electromagnet can be predicted by means of the *left-hand rule.* If a coil of wire is grasped with the left hand, so that the fingers point in the direction of electron flow, the thumb will point to the magnet's north pole. Or, if the north pole is known, but you wish to determine the direction of electron flow, place your left hand on the coil so that your thumb points in that direction; then the electrons flow in the direction in which your fingers point.

Solenoids and Relays

A *solenoid* is an electromagnet with a movable soft iron core. When the coil is energized, the iron core moves to the center. This movement is used to operate switches and levers.

In the starting motor, a solenoid moves the starter gear into mesh with the flywheel, and then closes the switch which sends electricity to the starting motor. In an overdrive transmission, a solenoid is used to control the shift mechanism.

A *relay* is an electromagnetic switch. It contains a coil of wire and a soft iron core to form the magnet; above this is a hinged piece of flat metal called the armature, which is attracted toward the core when energized. The end opposite the hinge contains a set of contact points used to control another electrical circuit.

Turning the ignition switch in the driver's compartment past the IGN position directs electricity to the relay coil, making it a magnet. It, in turn,

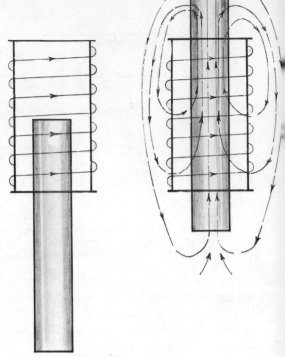

The iron core will move to the center of a solenoid when the coil is energized.

energizes the solenoid coil, which shifts the starter gear into mesh with the flywheel ring gear and completes the starting motor circuit to crank the engine.

You might wonder why it takes three switches to operate the starting motor —the ignition switch in the driver's compartment, the relay, and the solenoid. The high amperage required to crank the engine cannot be carried through the small switch that the driver activates, so it is used only to operate the relay. The relay controls the solenoid because its heavier contacts can safely carry the larger amounts of current needed to energize the solenoid coil. The solenoid, by its mechanical movement of the plunger, completes the starting motor circuit through very large contacts.

Circuit Breaker

A circuit breaker is a combination relay and solenoid. Used in place of a fuse, it has the advantage of not having to be replaced when a short circuit occurs.

Some circuit breakers contain a movable iron core which centers itself within the solenoid coil when an excessive amount of current passes through the unit. The core moves up and forces the armature above it to separate a set of normally closed points, thus breaking the overloaded circuit. This eliminates the trouble temporarily because no current flows in the damaged circuit, and so the circuit breaker resumes its normal position, allowing the contacts to close. If the short circuit remains, the cycle repeats itself continuously.

Some circuit breakers contain a *resistance wire* connected across the contact points so that, when the points are open, some current flows through the resistance wire, causing it to heat. The heated resistance wire is wound around a bimetallic armature which bends and keeps the points separated as long as the wiring defect exists.

Some circuit breakers are designed around a bimetallic switch instead of a solenoid. An abnormal flow of current through this type heats the bimetallic blade sufficiently to bend it and separate the points. This reduces the flow of current, which protects the wiring against overheating and burning. Removal of the excess load cools the thermostat, and the points resume their normally closed position. In action, the armature vibrates, causing the headlights to flicker, warning the driver of trouble.

Measurements of Electricity

Voltage is electrical pressure. It is what "pushes" electrons along a wire. Electrons flow only when there is a difference in pressure. Just as water flows from a point of high pressure to one of low pressure, so do electrons.

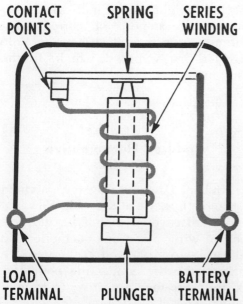

CONTACT POINTS   SPRING   SERIES WINDING

LOAD TERMINAL   PLUNGER   BATTERY TERMINAL

Wiring diagram of a circuit breaker. Note that the contact points are in series with the relay winding. Courtesy Delco-Remy Division, General Motors Corporation.

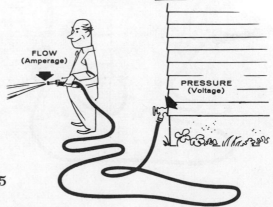

Voltage is pressure. Courtesy Delco-Remy Division, General Motors Coporation.

FLOW (Amperage)

PRESSURE (Voltage)

The unit for measuring electrical pressure is the *volt* and the unit for measuring the quantity of electrons flowing is the *ampere*.

Resistance is electrical friction. It hinders the free movement of electrons in a circuit. The more resistance, the fewer electrons flow. The unit for measuring electrical resistance is the *ohm*. One ohm is the amount of resistance in a circuit which allows one ampere of current to flow under a pressure of one volt.

Resistance depends on the length, size, kind of material, and temperature of a wire. The longer the wire, the more resistance it has; also, the thinner the wire, the more resistance and, when the temperature is increased, the resistance rises rapidly.

Some materials are far better conductors of electricity than are others. Metals like copper and silver are good conductors; therefore their resistance is low. Materials which do not conduct electricity at all are called insulators. Naturally, their resistance is extremely high.

Resistance retards the flow of amperage. Courtesy Delco Remy Division, General Motors Corporation.

Ohm's Law

The flow of electrical current is retarded by resistance and increased by voltage. This simple relationship is the basis for Ohm's law discovered by G. S. Ohm (Germany) in the early 19th century. One volt forces one ampere through a circuit with one ohm resistance, and two volts force two amperes through the same circuit of one ohm resistance. This can be expressed by the formulas:

Amperes = volts divided by the resistance
Resistance = volts divided by the amperes, OR
Volts = resistance times the amperes

For example, suppose you want to calculate the resistance of a circuit in which a 1.5 volt dry cell battery is connected to light a small bulb which consumes .25 ampere of current. The formula to use is Resistance = Volts divided by Amperes, which, in this case, is:

$$\text{Resistance} = \frac{1.5}{.25}, \text{ or 6 ohms.}$$

Induced Electromotive Forces

Michael Faraday (England), a chemist and physicist of the 18th-19th centuries, discovered that if he moved a coil of wire in a strong magnetic field, electric current flowed in the wire. He proved this by connecting both ends of the coil to a sensitive instrument which we call a *galvanometer.*

The current is produced by movement. It makes no difference whether the coil or the magnetic field is moved

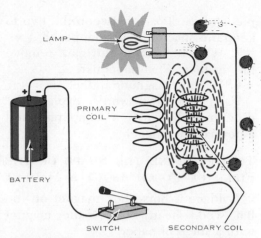

LAMP

PRIMARY COIL

BATTERY

SWITCH   SECONDARY COIL

When the switch is closed or opened, a surge of current is induced in the secondary coil. With a soft iron core, the surge is greatest when the switch is opened. This is because of the increased speed of movement of the magnetic lines of force back to the soft iron core. Courtesy Ford Division, Ford Motor Company.

—but movement must occur. The process by which electric currents are generated in a wire, through its movement in a magnetic field, is called *induction*.

The amount of induced electricity is dependent on the number of turns of wire in the coil, the strength of the magnetic field, and the speed of the movement. A stronger current is induced by increasing any one of these items.

Mutual and Self-Induction

Joseph Henry (America), a 19th century physicist, discovered *mutual induction*. He found that if two coils of wire are wound around a piece of soft iron, and one of them is connected to a battery, a strong magnetic field is produced. The lines of force created by the magnetism of the first coil (called the *primary*) move rapidly across the wires of the second coil (called the *secondary*), causing an induced current to flow. This process is called *mutual induction*. However, the secondary current makes the secondary coil a magnet, causing it to induce a second flow of current in the primary coil which is in a direction opposite to the initial flow. The generation of this reverse current is called *self-induction*.

A *transformer* is made up of two such coils wound around a soft iron core. By doubling the number of turns of wire on the secondary coil, twice the voltage is produced. By increasing the turn ratio ten times, ten times the voltage is produced across the secondary coil. However, the amperage will be *one tenth* so the total power remains the same.

Experiments

The following experiments are laid out in a progressive order to help you get a good basic background of knowledge in electrical work.

Magnetism

As you have learned, magnetism can exist in either temporary or permanent form. The temporary form is employed in most industrial uses, as it can be turned on and off at will. A knowledge of magnetism is essential to an understanding of the operation of motors, relays, generators, controls, starters, and ignition coils.

Tools and Equipment

Hacksaw blade; iron filings; two bar magnets; horseshoe magnet; soft iron nail; string; chalk; sheet of paper; small flat wood board.

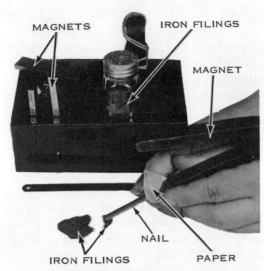

MAGNETS   IRON FILINGS

MAGNET

NAIL

IRON FILINGS   PAPER

Magnetic induction. Note the folded paper to keep the spacing between the magnet and nail.

PROCEDURE

TO DEMONSTRATE THE DIFFERENCE BETWEEN TEMPORARY AND PERMANENT MAGNETS

Note: *Answer the following questions in your notebook or on scratch paper as directed by your instructor. Do not write in this book.*

1. Magnetize a hacksaw blade by stroking one end of it with one pole of a strong bar magnet.

2. Dip the magnetized blade into the box of iron filings. What happens?

3. Tap the blade several times on a steel object, and then dip it into the iron filings. What happens?

4. Explain the different results according to the molecular theory.

5. Dip the tip of the soft iron nail into the filings. What happens?

6. Hold the tip of the nail about ⅛ inch over the filings. Bring one pole of a strong bar magnet close to, *but not touching*, the head of the nail. Hold a

piece of cardboard between the two to keep the spacing. What happens?

7. Without moving the nail, remove the magnet. What happens?

8. Explain magnetic induction.

9. In your own words, explain the difference between a temporary and a permanent magnet.

TO DETERMINE THE SHAPE OF THE FIELD OF FORCE ABOUT A MAGNET

1. Place a horseshoe magnet on the flat wood board. Cover the magnet with a sheet of paper.

2. Sprinkle iron filings on the paper. In your notebook, make a pencil sketch of the field of force which is revealed.

3. Place two bar magnets on the wood, with the north pole of one facing the south pole of the other, about ½ inch apart.

4. Cover with paper and sprinkle with iron filings. Make a sketch of the field.

5. Place two bar magnets so that the north poles face each other.

6. Cover with paper and sprinkle with iron filings as before. Make a sketch of the field of force.

A field of force exists between the poles of a magnet.

The law of magnetic attraction states that like poles repel each other.

To Demonstrate the Law of Magnetic Attraction

1. Hang a bar magnet on a string so that it swings freely. It will come to rest in a north-south position. The end pointing to the North Pole of the earth is called the *north pole*. Whiten this end with a piece of chalk.

2. Bring one end of a second bar magnet toward the whitened (north pole) end of the hanging magnet, which either will be attracted or repelled.

• If the hanging magnet is repelled, whiten the end of the magnet (held in your hand) which is closest to the north pole of the hanging magnet.

• If the hanging magnet is attracted, whiten the end of the magnet which is farthest from the north pole of the hanging magnet.

• Now, both magnets have their north poles whitened and the south poles unmarked.

3. Bring the north pole of the magnet toward the north pole of the hanging magnet. What happens?

4. Bring the south pole of the magnet toward the south pole of the hanging magnet. What happens?

5. Bring the north pole of the magnet toward the south pole of the hanging magnet. What happens?

6. Bring the south pole of the magnet toward the north pole of the hanging magnet. What happens?

7. Explain the law of magnetic attraction.

Electromagnetism

In this section you will find that both permanent and electric magnets produce the same force. It requires three things to make an electric magnet: a coil of wire, a soft-iron core, and an electric current. By turning the electric current on and off, you will be able to control the magnetic force.

Tools and Equipment

Storage battery; $\frac{1}{2} \times 1\frac{1}{2}$ inch bolt; $\frac{1}{4} \times 1\frac{1}{2}$ inch bolt; knife switch; O-10 ammater; $\frac{1}{2}$ inch brads; rheostat, O-10 ohms; compass; bell wire; No. 26 SCC wire; cardboard with a hole in the center; solenoid of two-inch diameter form; flat soft steel, $9 \times 1\frac{1}{2} \times \frac{3}{16}$ inch; welding rod, $\frac{1}{8} \times 6$ inch; iron filings.

PROCEDURE

To Demonstrate the Factors Affecting the Strength of an Electromagnet

1. Wind two coils around a piece of $\frac{5}{8}$ inch dowel or rod, one of forty turns and the other of eighty, using No. 26 SCC magnet wire.

2. Insert the large bolt into the forty-turn coil and connect it to a storage battery in series with an ammeter, rheostat, and switch.

3. Adjust the rheostat until the ammeter indicates a flow of two amperes.

4. Touch the end of the bolt to the pile of brads and record the number attracted. Open the switch while making notes, to minimize the drain on the battery.

5. Substitute the eighty-turn coil of wire for the smaller one.

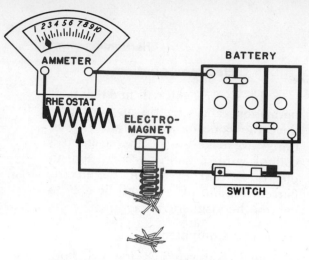

The strength of an electromagnet is dependent on the number of turns of wire, size of the core, and the amount of current flowing through the coil.

6. Close the switch and adjust the rheostat until the ammeter reads two amperes.

7. Touch the bolt to the pile of brads and record the number attracted.

8. Is the magnet weaker or stronger when the number of turns in the coil is increased?

9. Substitute a small bolt for the large one.

10. Readjust the rheostat until the ammeter reads two amperes.

11. Touch the bolt to the pile of brads and record the number attracted.

This is the equipment needed to show the difference between the strength of several types of electromagnets.

12. When the core size is increased, does the magnet become weaker or stronger?

13. Adjust the ammeter reading to one ampere and touch the bolt to the pile of brads.

14. Record the number attracted.

15. When the current flow is increased, does the magnet become weaker or stronger?

16. List the three factors which affect the strength of an electromagnet.

TO STUDY THE FIELDS OF FORCE ABOUT A WIRE, A SOLENOID, AND AN ELECTRO-MAGNET

WIRE

1. Pass a 15-inch length of bell wire through the hole in the cardboard.

2. Connect the bottom end of the bell wire to one post of the storage battery. **Note:** *Do not connect the wire to the other post of the battery.*

3. Place a compass directly north and 3 inches away from the wire.

4. *Flip* the free end of the wire across the first cell connector (two volts) of the battery. **Caution:** *Do not connect the wire to the battery post or it will become red hot.*

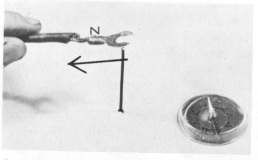

A circular field of force exists around a wire through which electricity flows.

5. Make a drawing of the cardboard and wire as the wire appears when looking down its length—it should appear as a dot in the center of the cardboard.

6. Draw an arrow on your paper, pointing in the same direction as the compass needle when electricity flows through the wire.

7. Place the compass to the east of the wire and repeat the experiment and drawing.

8. Place the compass to the south of the wire and repeat.

9. Place the compass to the west of the wire and repeat.

10. Grasp the wire with your left hand so that your fingers circle the wire in the direction which the four arrows point. Note how your thumb indicates the direction in which electrons flow in the wire (negative to positive).

11. In your own words, explain the left-hand rule.

12. Sprinkle iron filings on the cardboard around the wire.

13. *Flip* the free end of the wire across the battery post.

Sprinkling iron filings around a wire through which electricity is flowing indicates the circular field.

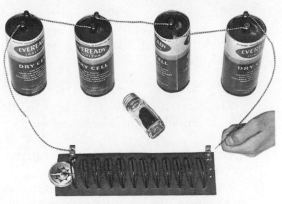

A solenoid exhibits the same characteristics as an electromagnet.

14. Make a diagram of the field of force about the wire.

SOLENOID

15. Connect the left end of the solenoid to the positive terminal of the storage battery. **Note:** *Do not connect the other end.*

16. Grasp the solenoid with your left hand so that your fingers follow the electron flow in the wires (negative to positive). Your thumb will point to the north pole.

17. Place a compass about 8 inches from the end of the solenoid, which your thumb indicated to be the north pole.

18. *Flip* the free end of the solenoid connecting wire across the negative post of the battery. If your prediction of the north pole was accurate, the south pole of the compass needle will be attracted to the solenoid's north pole.

19. Reverse the battery connections to the solenoid and again predict the north pole with the left-hand rule. Flip the wire across the free battery post to check your prediction.

20. Sprinkle iron filings on the solenoid and flip the other wire across the free battery post. Sketch the resulting field of force.

ELECTROMAGNET

21. Place a flat piece of iron inside the solenoid to make it an electromagnet.

22. Predict the north pole with the left-hand rule.

23. Place the compass about 8 inches away from the predicted north pole and flip the other wire across the free battery post to check your prediction.

24. Has the north pole been changed by the insertion of the iron core?

25. Insert a piece of cardboard, cut to fit over the iron core, inside the solenoid.

26. Sprinkle iron filings on the cardboard and flip the other wire across the free battery post.

27. In what two ways has the field of force been changed from that produced by the solenoid?

28. Remove the iron core and substitute a piece of welding rod, laying it loosely in one end of the solenoid.

29. Flip the other wire across the free battery post to energize the solenoid.

30. What happens to the welding rod?

31. Push the rod to the other end of the solenoid and repeat.

32. Explain the mechanical action of a solenoid.

Measuring Electricity

As previously mentioned, the *amount* or quantity of electricity flowing in a circuit is measured in amperes; electrical *pressure* is measured in volts. It is this pressure which forces current to flow from one point to another. The flow is hindered by *resistance;* the greater the resistance, the less electricity flows. The greater the pressure, the more flows.

Tools and Equipment

Four dry cells; bell wire; 0-10 ammeter; 0-10 volt meter; two-filament auto light bulb (32-32 CP); adjustable rheostat, 0-10 ohms; six-volt storage battery.

PROCEDURE

VOLTAGE

1. Measure the voltage of one dry cell. **Note:** *If the meter reads off scale, reverse the connections.*

2. Hook up two dry cells in *series* and measure the voltage. Record.

3. Hook up two dry cells in *parallel.* Record the voltage reading.

4. Hook up four dry cells in *series parallel* and record. **Hint:** *Hook up two dry cells in series; hook up the other two dry cells in series, and then connect both series sets in parallel.*

PROCEDURE

AMPERAGE

1. Hook up two dry cells in series. Connect this voltage source in series with an ammeter and one filament of a bulb. Record the amperage.

2. Hook up four dry cells in series. Connect this voltage source in series with an ammeter and one filament of the bulb. Record.

3. When you increase the voltage, do you increase or decrease the amperage flow?

212

Measuring the voltage of one dry cell. On a piece of scratch paper, make a sketch of the battery, meter, and the wiring you are going to make. Have this paper checked by your instructor before you wire the circuit. *Do not make any pencil marks in this book.*

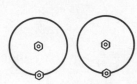 

Measuring the amperage of a headlight bulb under three volts pressure. Pencil the connections before you make the actual wiring connections.

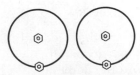

Measuring the voltage of two dry cells in series. In pencil, on scratch paper, make the necessary connections before connecting the actual wiring.

Measuring the amperage of a headlight bulb under six volts pressure. Pencil the connections before you make the actual wiring connections.

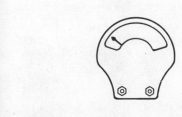

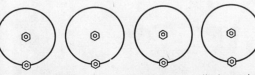

Measuring the voltage of four dry cells in series parallel. Pencil the connections on scratch paper before you make the actual wiring connections.

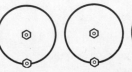

Measuring the amperage of two headlight bulbs in parallel under six volts pressure. Pencil the connections before you make the actual wiring connections.

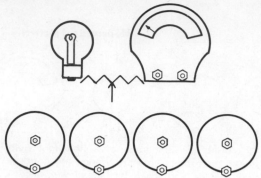

Connecting a variable resistance in series with a headlight bulb. The variable resistance regulates the flow of current to the light. Variable resistances are frequently used to control the speed of the heater motor and the intensity of the dash lights. Pencil the connections on scratch paper before you make the actual wiring connections.

PROCEDURE

RESISTANCE

1. Hook up four dry cells in series. Connect this voltage source in series with an ammeter, one filament of the bulb, and an adjustable rheostat.

2. Move the rheostat control arm to the right (maximum resistance) as far as it will go. Record the ammeter reading. How bright is the lamp?

3. Move the rheostat control arm to the center of the rheostat. Record the ammeter reading. Is the lamp bright, dim, or out?

4. Move the rheostat control arm to the extreme left (no resistance). Record the ammeter reading. Is the lamp bright, dim, or out?

5. When you increase the resistance, do you increase or decrease the amperage flow?

6. When does the lamp become brighter—when you increase or decrease the amperage?

7. When does the lamp become brighter—when you increase or decrease the resistance?

OHM'S LAW

1. Connect a six-volt storage battery in series with an ammeter and one filament of a bulb. Record the amperage.

2. To calculate the resistance of the lamp bulb, substitute the amperage reading in the following formula:

$$R \text{ (resistance)} = \frac{E \text{ (voltage)}}{I \text{ (amperage)}}$$

$$\text{as } R = \frac{E}{(\quad\quad)}$$

3. Measure the voltage of the storage battery you are using when the lamp is lit.

4. Substitute the value of "E" above in the formula:

$$R = \underline{\quad\quad\quad\quad}.$$

5. Divide the value of "I" into the value of "E" in order to get the value of "R." As:

$$I) \frac{E}{R} \text{ thus: } R = \underline{\quad\quad\quad} \text{ ohms}$$

6. Connect the second headlamp bulb filament in parallel with the first one. Record the amperage.

A handy wiring board to hold the headlamp wiring equipment. Note the diagram below the bulb mounting which shows how the filaments of the bulb are connected internally.

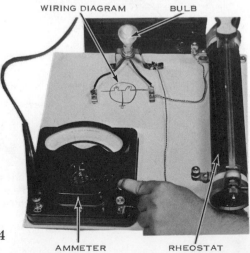

WIRING DIAGRAM   BULB

AMMETER   RHEOSTAT

7. Calculate the resistance of the circuit.

R = _____ ohms.

8. What is the relationship between the value of the first resistance and two similar resistances in parallel?

9. Hook up both filaments of the bulb in series. Record the amperage.

10. Record the voltage when the bulb is lit.

11. Calculate the resistance of two filaments in series.

R = _____ ohms.

Note: *The resistance of the two filaments in series is not twice that of the single filament.* This is due to the fact that the bulb is not as bright when the two filaments are hooked in series. Because the resistance increases with an increase in temperature, you would expect to find proportionally less resistance with the two filaments hooked in series because of the dimness of the bulb.

12. Is the resistance greater in a parallel or series circuit?

13. Explain step 12 in your own words.

Wiring Electrical Circuits

Electricity may be conducted to bells, lamps, heating devices, and motors by means of wires. These wires must be connected properly for the unit to work. In many cases, switches are installed in the circuit to control the flow.

Tools and Equipment

Two bells; one buzzer; one button; two single-pole knife switches; one double-pole, double-throw knife switch; one reversing switch; wire; four dry cells; screwdriver; pliers.

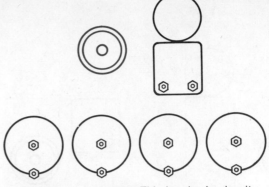

One button and one bell. This is a basic circuit used on all automotive electrical equipment such as ignition, starter, lights, and radio. Pencil the connections on scratch paper before you make the actual wiring connections.

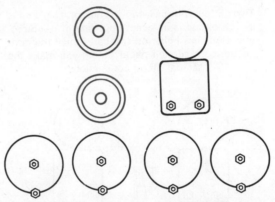

Two buttons and one bell. This switching arrangement is used to light the interior of a car when either door is opened. Pencil the connections on scratch paper before you make the actual wiring connections.

One button and two bells. This electrical circuit is basic when wiring any two lights or horns to a switch. Pencil the connections before you make the actual wiring connections.

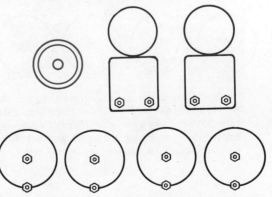

215

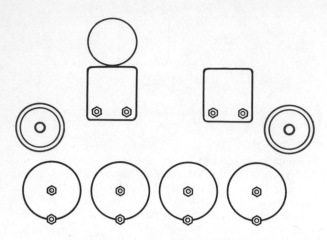

Two buttons, one bell, and one buzzer. This double switch circuit is an exact duplicate of the direction signaling lights on the car. Pencil the connections on scratch paper before you make the actual wiring connections.

The picture shows the construction of a board which will simplify the wiring of all bell experiments.

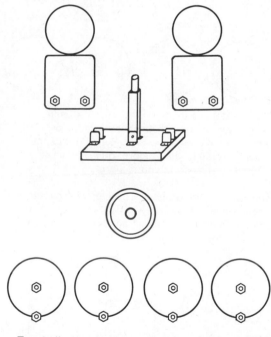

Two bells, one button, and one reversing switch. This reversing switch circuit is an exact duplicate of the high and low beam selector switch (tilt-ray) used on the car. Pencil the connections before you make the actual wiring connections.

PROCEDURE

1. Hook up four dry cells in series as a voltage source for the following experiments:

2. Study and apply the following three rules of wiring:

• a. Connect one pole of the battery to one pole of the bell or group of bells.

• b. Connect the other pole of the battery to one pole of the switch or switches.

• c. Connect the remaining pole of the switch to the remaining pole of the bell it is to control.

3. Connect one button to ring one bell. This type of connection is similar to that used to operate the horn.

4. Connect two buttons to ring one bell. This kind of circuit is used to turn on the interior body light of a car. Either car door will operate it.

5. Connect one button to ring two bells. This kind of circuit is used to connect the headlamps and tail lamps to a light switch.

6. Connect two buttons, one bell, and one buzzer so that one button will ring the bell and the other button will operate the buzzer. This type of connection is used whenever any two electrical units are operated by separate switches, such as the dash and interior lights of a car.

7. Connect one button and a reversing switch so that the button controls either of two bells selected by the reversing switch. The reversing switch used here is similar to the headlamp tilt-ray switch, which is used to select either the high or low bright lights.

Experiments in Electromagnetic Induction

Michael Faraday's discovery of the principle of electromagnetic induction in 1831 led to his producing electricity from magnetism. His success made possible the development of the generator. As previously mentioned, he noted that movement of a coil of wire, through a magnetic field of force, created enough electricity in the coil to move a galvanometer needle.

In this job you will study the principles of electromagnetic induction to aid in understanding the principles of the generator and induction coil.

Tools and Equipment

No. 10 copper wire, 3 feet long; twenty-turn coil of No. 10 copper wire wrapped about a 1-inch form; galvanometer; bar magnet; storage battery; bell wire; No. 20 SCC magnet wire;

laminations from an old radio power transformer; three 1-inch coil forms; two AC voltmeters, 0-15 volts; bell-ringing transformer; ignition board; horseshoe magnet.

TO DEMONSTRATE THE EFFECTS OF A COIL OF WIRE BEING PASSED THROUGH A MAGNETIC FIELD

1. Connect the ends of the 3-foot length of copper wire to a galvanometer.

2. Pass the loop of wire quickly between the poles of the horseshoe magnet, and then hold it stationary.

3. What happens to the galvanometer needle?

4. What has happened within the wire?

5. Lift the wire quickly between the poles of the magnet, and then hold it still.

Electromagnetic induction. The wire must be moved quickly across the magnetic lines of force to produce electricity.

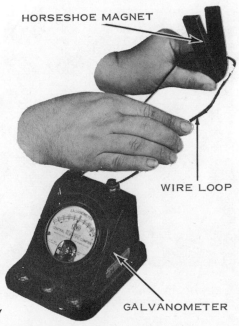

HORSESHOE MAGNET

WIRE LOOP

GALVANOMETER

217

6. What happened to the galvanometer needle?

7. Can you explain why the needle moved in a different direction in steps 3 and 6?

8. Connect the twenty-turn coil of No. 10 wire to the galvanometer. Remove the coil form so that the coil is air wound. It will support itself because of the size of the wire.

9. Thrust one end of a bar magnet into the coil and hold it motionless after it reaches the center.

10. What happens to the galvanometer needle?

11. Why does the needle return to zero after the magnet stops moving?

12. Quickly pull the magnet from the coil.

13. What happens to the galvanometer needle?

14. Hold the bar magnet stationary and move the coil back and forth over the magnet. Is there any difference between movement of the coil and movement of the magnet?

15. What is necessary to produce a constant flow of electricity?

PROCEDURE

To Demonstrate the Properties of a Transformer

1. Remove the laminations from an old radio power supply transformer. You will find them to be shaped like an "E."

2. Cut out the center section of the "E" so that it becomes "C" shaped.

3. Mount the laminations on a board with the two ends of the "C" pointed up so that you can place different coils over the ends for study.

4. Cut a piece of soft steel to cover the top gap so that the magnetic lines of force can pass completely around.

The transformer. While the efficiency of this unit is low, the ability to substitute coils of different sizes, while observing the voltage changes, makes it a very efficient learning tool.

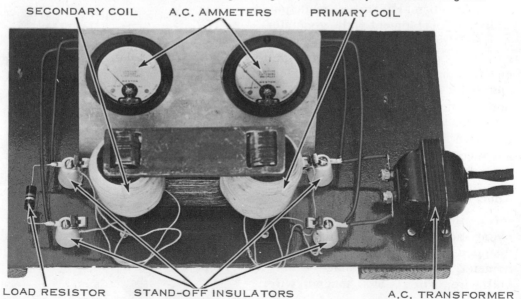

SECONDARY COIL   A.C. AMMETERS   PRIMARY COIL

LOAD RESISTOR   STAND-OFF INSULATORS   A.C. TRANSFORMER

5. For study, wind three coil forms with the No. 20 SCC wire. Wind two each of 200 turns and one of 400 turns.

6. Connect a bell-ringing transformer to the 110-volt AC line in order to reduce the working voltage to about 10 volts. This is a safety measure to prevent you from getting a strong shock.

7. Place the two 200-turn coils over the two upright ends of the laminations and install the top gap bar.

8. Connect one coil to the low voltage side (primary) of the transformer.

9. Connect the other coil (secondary) to the resistor load.

10. Connect a voltmeter across each coil to observe the working voltages.

11. Plug in the 110-volt AC line.

12. What is the voltage of the primary coil?

13. What is the voltage of the secondary coil?

14. The difference in voltage between the primary and secondary is due to the inefficiency of the transformer and not to any step-down ratio. To prove this, interchange the two coils and the voltages will remain constant.

15. How do you account for electricity being produced in the secondary coil even though there is no movement of either coil?

16. Hold a thin strip of steel such as a hacksaw blade close to the primary coil laminations. What happens to the blade?

17. What does this indicate is happening to the primary coil?

18. What causes the vibration? Is there a steady flow of magnetism, or is the flow pulsating?

19. Can you now account for the magnetic movement from an AC coil as compared with the mechanical movement of a bar magnet?

20. Substitute the 400-turn coil for the secondary and record the secondary voltage. This is a step-up transformer.

21. What is the ratio of the primary to secondary turns?

22. What is the difference between the voltages you found in the secondary in steps 13 and 20?

23. Change the primary and secondary coils so that you have a step-down transformer.

24. Measure the voltage of the secondary.

25. What is the ratio of the primary to secondary turns?

26. What is the ratio of the voltages in the secondary in steps 13 and 24?

PROCEDURE

TO DEMONSTRATE THE PROPERTIES OF AN INDUCTION COIL

1. Hook up the induction coil board as shown. Use the schematic symbols painted on the board to assist you in making connections.

2. Connect the two input terminals to a storage battery.

3. Adjust the high tension spark gap so that a spark occurs as you turn the cam which opens and closes the points.

4. Watch the points carefully and turn the cam to open and close the points just once.

5. Does the spark occur when the points open or when they close? The ignition coil is a step-up transformer, changing the voltage of the storage battery to about 15,000 volts, which is needed to jump the gap.

6. Disconnect the condenser wire from the circuit.

7. Open and close the points.

8. Do you get a high-voltage spark?

9. Adjust the high-tension spark gap closer until you do get a spark.

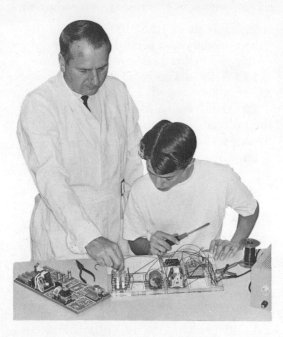

10. Turn the cam to open and close the points.

11. Watch the points carefully to note the arcing and burning which occur without a condenser.

12. Connect the condenser back in the circuit and repeat. Note the absence of the arcing and burning.

13. What effect has the condenser on the action of the points?

14. What effect has the condenser on the output of the coil?

The plug-in ignition components can be wired according to the diagram furnished with this kit of parts in order to further your understanding on how the ignition system functions. Courtesy DeVry Technical Institute.

CHECK YOUR KNOWLEDGE

1. Why is magnetism considered the basis of electricity?
2. What is loadstone?
3. What is the present theory of magnetism?
4. What is the difference between a permanent and temporary magnet?
5. Of what three things is a battery made?
6. What is an open circuit?
7. What is voltage?
8. What is amperage?
9. What is a complete circuit? Series circuit? Parallel circuit?
10. Explain how an automotive 12-volt battery is an example of series and parallel connections.
11. Describe an electromagnet.
12. What are ampere-turns?
13. What is the left-hand rule?
14. What is a solenoid? How does it work? Of what use is it?
15. What is a relay? How does it work? Of what use is it?
16. Why does it take three switches to operate the starting motor?
17. What is a circuit breaker? How does it work? Of what use is it?

18. What is resistance? How is it measured?
19. What is Ohm's law? Of what use is it?
20. What is induction?
21. On what three things does the strength of an induced current depend?
22. What is mutual induction? Self-induction?
23. What is the purpose of the primary coil of a transformer? Secondary coil?
24. What action does varying the turns ratio of a transformer have on its output voltage?

Self-Check Tests

TRUE-FALSE

1. Permanent magnets are made of soft steel.
2. The regions around the ends of a magnet are called the poles.
3. The law of magnetic attraction states that like poles repel each other.
4. The south pole of a magnet points toward the geographic North Pole.
5. A large dry cell contains more voltage than a small one.
6. A large dry cell contains more amperage than a small one.

7. Battery cells are connected in series to increase the total amperage.
8. The polarity of an electromagnet can be predicted by the right-hand rule.
9. A relay has a movable soft-iron core.
10. A circuit breaker is a form of solenoid.
11. An ohm is the amount of amperage which flows with a pressure of one volt.
12. Ohm's law states that the resistance is divided by the voltage to calculate the number of ohms in the circuit.
13. A galvanometer is necessary for induction.

MULTIPLE CHOICE

1. The first natural magnet was called: a) loadstone; b) temporary magnet; c) permanent magnet.
2. The difference in electrical pressure between two poles of a battery is called: a) amperes; b) ohms; c) volts.
3. A large dry cell furnishes more: a) amperes; b) ohms; c) volts than a small one.
4. A circuit in which all of the electrical energy must pass through all of the electrical devices is called a: a) series; b) parallel; c) open circuit.
5. A circuit which has many branches for electrical energy to pass is called a: a) series; b) parallel; c) open circuit.
6. Batteries are frequently connected in series to increase the: a) amperage; b) voltage; c) flux.
7. An electromagnet containing a soft-iron core is called a: a) relay; b) armature; c) solenoid.
8. A circuit breaker takes the place of: a) switch; b) fuse; c) open circuit.
9. The amount of resistance of a wire does *not* depend on the: a) size; b) length; c) temperature; d) cost.
10. Ohm's law states that the resistance of a circuit can be calculated by: a) voltage divided by the amperes; b) amperes times the voltage; c) amperes divided by the voltage.
11. The amount of electricity induced in a wire is *not* dependent on which of the following: a) number of turns of wire; b) strength of the magnetic field; c) speed of movement; d) size of wire.
12. By doubling the number of turns of wire of a transformer primary coil: a) one half; b) the same; c) twice the voltage will appear across the secondary coil.

COMPLETION

1. An _____ _____ can produce magnetism.
2. The first natural magnet was called _____.
3. A magnet made of _____ steel is called a temporary magnet.
4. A _____ is a container of acid in which two dissimilar metals are submerged.
5. The electrical pressure of a fully charged wet cell is always _____ volts.
6. The quantity of electrons flowing in a circuit is called _____.
7. The voltage of batteries hooked in _____ remains the same as for one battery.
8. The strength of an electromagnet is classified according to the number of _____ _____.
9. A _____ is an electromagnet with a movable soft-iron core.
10. A relay is an electromagnet with a hinged _____.
11. A circuit breaker takes the place of a _____.
12. Resistance is electrical friction and is measured in _____.
13. The process by which electric current is set in motion in a wire through movement in a magnetic field is called _____.
14. The _____ coil of a transformer is the one from which current is taken.

MATCHING

1. Loadstone	a. Region around poles
2. Soft steel magnet	b. Ampere turns
3. Hard steel magnet	c. Wet cell
4. Ends of a magnet	d. Temporary magnet
5. Field of force	e. Induction
6. Potential difference	f. Movable soft-iron core
7. Quantity of electricity	g. Poles
8. Storage battery	h. Permanent magnet
9. Electromagnet	i. Self-induction
10. Solenoid	j. Natural magnet
11. Circuit breaker	k. Amperage
12. Resistance	l. Ohm
13. Transformer	m. Takes the place of a fuse
14. Mutual induction	n. Voltage

Chapter 8

The Automotive Electrical System

Storage Battery

The standard 12-volt automotive storage battery consists of six cells of two volts each connected in series to provide a total of 12 volts. Each cell is made up of an acidproof compartment in which the battery element rests.

The storage battery. Courtesy Delco-Remy Division, General Motors Corporation.

The element within each cell is made up of two groups of plates—a positive plate group and a negative plate group nested together. Each plate is kept from contacting its neighboring plates by means of insulating separators made of wood, rubber, or glass mat. They have grooves which allow the *electrolyte* to contact the plates and release the gas formed by charging.

The plates are made of a lead-antimony metal grid into which a lead-oxide paste is pressed. They are assembled into groups and welded to a plate strap, the terminals of which are brought through the battery cover. Connectors are welded to the terminals to join the cells together.

The cover of each cell contains a filler plug which serves two purposes. (1) It can be removed to test the condition of the solution, and water can be added when necessary. (2) It contains a hole through which the gas, formed by charging, can escape.

Chemical Action

The *electrolyte* is added to each cell to start the chemical action. The solu-

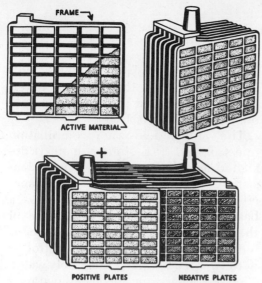

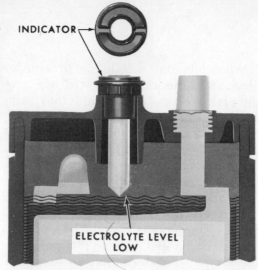

The plates are a network of metallic webbing into which are pressed the active chemicals. The plates are welded into groups and interlaced for each cell. Courtesy Pontiac Motor Division, General Motors Coporation.

The Delco Energizer has a special filler plug with a transparent rod extending through its center. The top of the indicator filler plug will remain dark as long as the tip of the rod is immersed in electrolyte, but it will glow brightly whenever the level falls below the tip, which indicates the need for water. Courtesy Chevrolet Motor Division, General Motors Corporation.

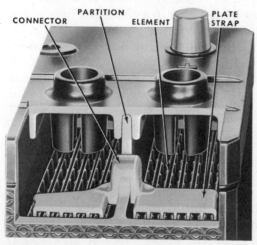

The plate groups are connected in series by means of cell connectors. Courtesy Chevrolet Motor Division, General Motors Corporation.

tion consists of about 40% sulphuric acid and 60% distilled water. When the battery is in a charged state, the active positive plate material is lead peroxide or PbO_2. The active negative plate material is spongy lead or Pb.

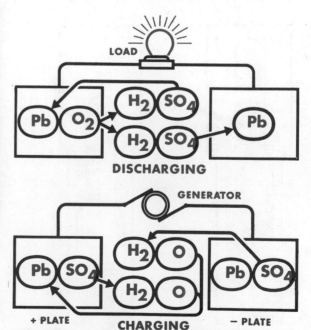

This is the chemical reaction during the charging and discharging cycles of the battery. Courtesy Delco-Remy Division, General Motors Corporation.

223

When a battery is called on to furnish electricity, the sulphuric acid acts on the plate material, changing it into lead sulphate. After most of the active material has been converted into lead sulphate, the positive and negative plates are then chemically similar, and no further chemical action is possible. Such a battery is said to be *discharged*.

If an electric current is sent into the battery, the process is reversed and the battery is charged. During this process, the chemicals of the battery are restored to their original form.

Specific Gravity

The specific gravity of a liquid is a number expressing *how many times a substance is heavier than an equal volume of water*, which is used as a stand-ard. For example, the weight of sulphuric acid is 1.8 times that of water, and so we say that the specific gravity of sulphuric acid is 1.800.

The proper acid-water combination (electrolyte) of a storage battery designed to deliver adequate power consistent with long life is one with a specific gravity of about 1.300. After a battery becomes discharged, some of the sulphuric acid chemically unites with the plates, leaving the electrolyte with a greater percentage of water. Thus, by measuring the specific gravity of the electrolyte, we are able to determine with accuracy the state of battery charge.

The *hydrometer* is the device used to measure specific gravity. It consists of a weighted float in a glass tube into which the liquid to be tested is drawn. It operates on the principle discovered by Archimedes (Greece): "The loss of weight of a body immersed in a liquid is equal to the weight of the displaced liquid." And because a body "loses" all of its weight when floating, the weight of the displaced liquid is equal to the weight of the floating object. Naturally, a floating body will displace more of a lighter liquid than it will of a heavier liquid, and so the height of the float in the liquid determines the specific gravity of the solution.

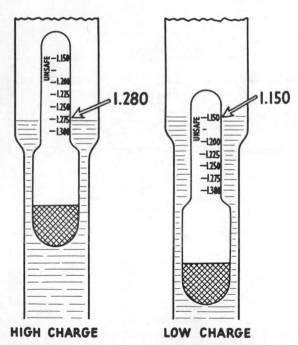

HIGH CHARGE **LOW CHARGE**

The heavier the specific gravity, the denser the solution. Courtesy Pontiac Motor Division, General Motors Corporation.

Battery Capacity

The amount of plate surface exposed to chemical action determines the capacity of the battery, which is expressed in ampere-hours. Twelve-volt, 60 ampere-hour capacity batteries usually contain nine plates in each cell, while 70 ampere-hour units contain eleven plates per cell.

The ampere-hour rating of a battery is derived from a 20-hour test which determines how much current it furnishes before the cell voltage drops below 1.75. Starting at a temperature of 80° F., a battery delivering three amperes for 20 hours would be rated as a 60 ampere-hour battery (3 × 20 = 60).

Battery troubles can often be traced to operating with too little solution, or to *overcharging*. Operating with part of the plates uncovered by the solution sulphates these areas and renders that part useless because sulphation is an insulator to chemical action. Loss of plate area lowers the capacity of the battery, which shows up in starting troubles during cold weather.

Overcharging heats the battery excessively and evaporates the water quickly. The surface of the positive plates of such a battery changes into powder, which drops to the bottom of the battery, eventually shorting the plates together. Also, the excessive

This is what the plates of an overcharged battery look like. Note the bowed plates and shedded material. Courtesy Delco-Remy Division, General Motors Corporation.

An overcharged battery lifts the cover because the plate material swells. Courtesy Delco-Remy Division, General Motors Corporation.

heat of overcharging causes the plates to swell, which buckles the separators, frequently shorting the cell.

Headlamps

Lights provide illumination for seeing and being seen at night.

Headlamps contain a filament, a reflecting surface, and a lens consisting of glass prisms molded together to blend the beam of light into an oval pattern and to bend it downward. A headlamp is made in one unit called a "sealed beam." The advantage is that the efficiency of the lamp's reflecting surface is not lost through dirt and corrosion.

Two filaments are usually incorporated in headlamps—one to provide a

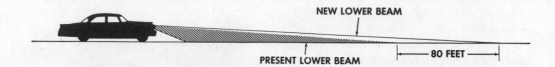

NEW LOWER BEAM

PRESENT LOWER BEAM

|← 80 FEET →|

**LOWER SEEING DISTANCE INCREASED
AS MUCH AS 80 FEET ON RIGHT SIDE OF THE ROAD**

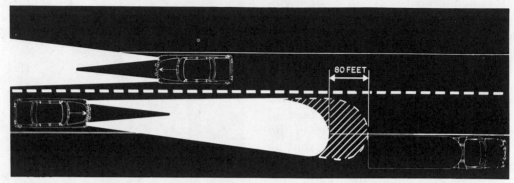

80 FEET

The capped filament bulb allows higher aiming because it cuts off the stray rays which blind drivers. Courtesy Chrysler Corporation.

The directional signal lamp circuit during a right turn. Courtesy Buick Motor Division, General Motors Corporation.

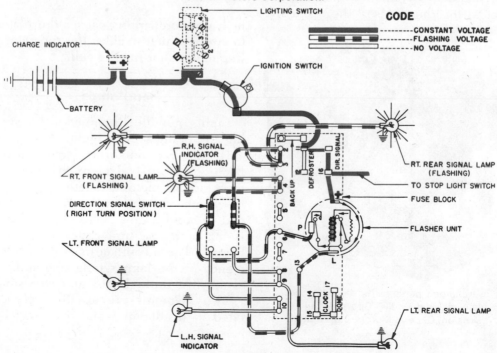

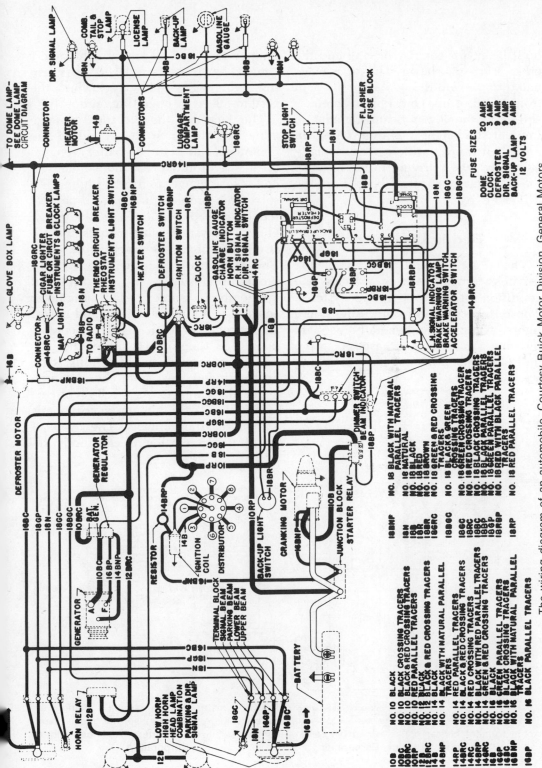

The wiring diagram of an automobile. Courtesy Buick Motor Division, General Motors Corporation.

227

high beam for country driving and the other a low city beam. The air is evacuated to prevent the white-hot filament from burning up. One improvement is shielding the lower beam filament to prevent stray light rays from being directed upward, which is especially annoying when driving in fog because the rays are reflected back into the driver's eyes.

Electrical Indicators

There are several devices in the driver's compartment to indicate the condition of vital operating systems. These take the form of gauges and lights. Gauges are generally used to indicate the amount of gasoline in the fuel tank, the generator charge, engine temperature, and oil pressure, but many gauges have been replaced by warning lights which glow red when the system is not operating properly.

The fact that the electrical voltage varies according to the speed of the generator and state of battery charge creates a problem. As the voltage increases, a gauge registers higher. To solve this problem, a *constant-voltage regulator* is incorporated in the gauge electrical system which holds the instrument voltage at exactly five volts. The regulator is placed in series with the ignition switch and the fuel and temperature gauges. The regulator consists of a bimetallic strip and heater acting together with a pair of contact points. As the contacts close, the current flows through the bimetallic strip, heating it and causing it to bend, which opens the contacts. As the flow of current is cut off, the bimetallic strip cools and closes the contacts. The cycle of opening and closing is constantly re-

An instrument cluster gauge wiring diagram. Courtesy American Motors Corporation.

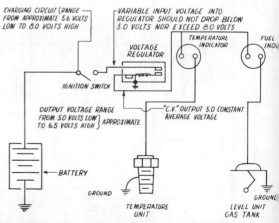

The CV (constant voltage) regulator changes the battery voltage to 5.0 volts so that gauge operation is stabilized. Courtesy American Motors Corporation.

228

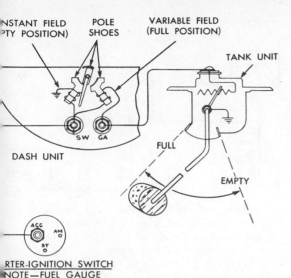

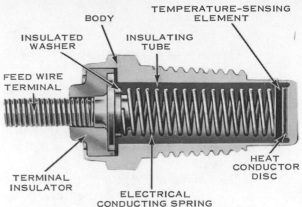

The coolant temperature gauge sender unit contains a metal which changes resistance with heat. Courtesy Mercury Division, Ford Motor Company.

The fuel gauge circuit. Courtesy Plymouth Division, Chrysler Corporation.

peated, providing a pulsating voltage at an average value of five volts.

Care must be taken when working around the CV regulator to avoid shorting it because of the delicate nature of its contacts. Disconnect the battery terminal before doing any work in that area.

The *gasoline indicating device* consists of two units: the dashboard gauge is an electrical indicator, while the tank unit provides a variable resistance. As the tank is filled with fuel, a cork float rises and, through levers, changes the amount of resistance in the circuit. The dash gauge then registers the electrical change in units of fuel gallons.

The *heat indicator* is essentially the same type of electrical device except that the "sender" changes resistance with a change in temperature. This changes the amount of current flowing to the dash gauge, which then registers as changes in coolant temperature.

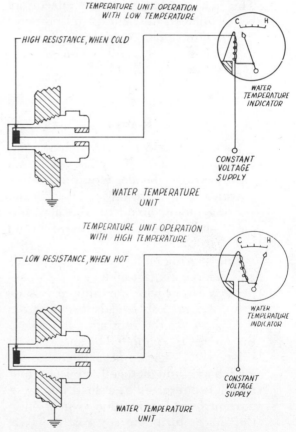

The electrical circuit of the temperature gauge when the engine is cold and when it is hot. Courtesy American Motors Corporation.

Oil pressure gauges are electrical recording devices controlled by a variable resistance which is changed in value according to the engine oil pressure. This changes the flow of current, which is recorded on the dash unit as a change in pounds per square inch pressure (psi).

The *ammeter* registers the amount of electrical energy passing through it. When the generator is operating, the ammeter registers "charge" and, when the generator is not operating, any electrical drain is registered as "discharge." The reason that some manufacturers have replaced this and the oil pressure gauge with signal lights is that a reading on a gauge is not nearly as conspicuous as a red warning light.

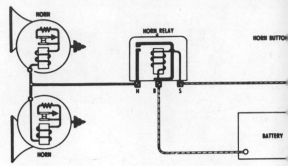

Horn relay connections. The horn button operates the relay which connects the horn directly to the battery. Courtesy Delco-Remy Division, General Motors Corporation.

Relays

Relays are electrical switches operated by a magnet. They are used with an electrical device requiring heavy current. Relays are always used in the starting motor circuit, in the horn circuit, and sometimes in the lighting circuit.

The starting motor needs large cables and a large contact area switch to pass heavy current with a minimum voltage drop. A large cable leads directly from the battery to the starting motor where the circuit is completed by an electrical relay switch. The points of the electrical switch are brought together by a magnet which is energized by a small amount of current from the ignition switch when the driver turns the key past the IGN position.

Horns and lights draw relatively heavy amperage, so, to have them work at maximum efficiency, a relay is installed in the circuit. The long wires leading to the switch are used to operate the relay which, in turn, connects the battery directly to the unit being operated. This results in maximum transfer of energy with minimum voltage loss caused by small wires and switching contacts.

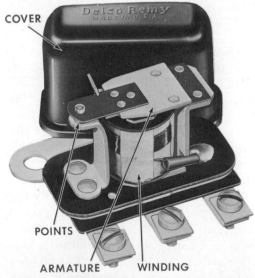

The horn relay. Courtesy Delco-Remy Division, General Motors Corporation.

230

A badly corroded cable connector will increase the resistance of the electrical circuit. Such a connector should be replaced.

Service Procedures

The battery requires regular servicing. Water must be added as needed, and the battery itself requires replacement each year or two. Occasionally, a battery may have to be charged if the radio or lights have been left on accidentally.

One frequently neglected operation is cleaning and tightening the battery cable connections. Any resistance at these points causes the generator to increase its operating voltage. The result is to place the entire electrical system under a heavy strain. High voltage from bad battery cable connections is frequently the cause of short bulb life and burned ignition points.

Other services are the replacement of light bulbs, fuses, the aiming of lights, and adjusting of horns. Infrequently, short and open circuits have to be checked out.

Troubleshooting

Most electrical troubles can be checked with a voltmeter. An increase in voltage can be traced to a bad connection and the defect isolated by measuring the voltage drop across each connection until the defective one is located.

A clear idea of what you are looking for, and an organized testing procedure, are essential.

Testing a Storage Battery

A storage battery is constantly being charged by the generator or discharged by electrical drains from the starter, lights, and ignition. It is important, therefore, to check the condition of the battery occasionally. First test the specific gravity (density) of the solution, using a hydrometer. Second, measure the voltage of each cell under load.

Tools and Equipment

Battery; hydrometer; expanded-scale voltmeter.

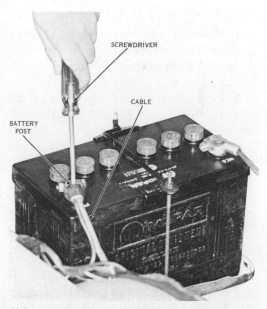

Using a screwdriver to test the connection between the cable and terminal. This is an emergency test to localize trouble.

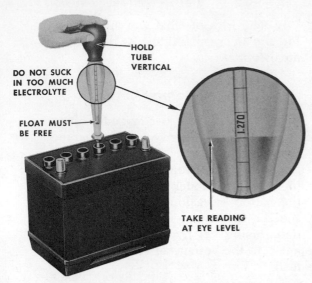

HOLD TUBE VERTICAL

DO NOT SUCK IN TOO MUCH ELECTROLYTE

FLOAT MUST BE FREE

TAKE READING AT EYE LEVEL

1.270

Testing a battery with a hydrometer. Courtesy Delco-Remy Division, General Motors Corporation.

HYDROMETER TEST

1. Remove the vent covers. Place them on the battery upside down to prevent dirt from collecting on the inside of the covers.

2. Compress the rubber bulb of the hydrometer. Insert the tip into the cell opening. Release pressure on the bulb until *just* enough solution is drawn into the glass cylinder to lift the float.

3. Hold the hydrometer straight. **Caution:** *Do not lift it from the cell because it may drip acid which will burn flesh and clothing.*

4. Read the float. The mark on the float which is in line with the liquid level is the gravity reading. Gravity is the density or thickness of the solution. The denser the solution, the higher the float will rise. As the cell becomes discharged through use, the acid is ab-

sorbed by the plates, and water which has a specific gravity of 1.000 remains. A reading of 1.280 indicates a fully charged cell; 1.210 half charged; and 1.150 a dead cell. Record the reading.

5. Return all of the electrolyte to the tested cell.

6. Repeat the test for each of the other cells.

7. Water must be added if the electrolyte is below the level of the plates. Add only enough water to bring it to the level of the split ring in the filler well. **Note:** *Never add acid, as it does not evaporate.* **Caution:** *Never add water before charging, except to cover exposed plates.* Charging causes the solution to bubble and, if the battery solution level is too high, the electrolyte will spill over.

8. If the cell readings are all over 1.225, proceed with the voltage test below; otherwise, charge the battery before making this test. **Caution:** *The voltage test must never be made on a discharged battery, or the plates will be damaged.*

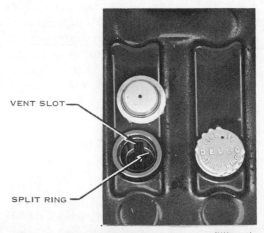

VENT SLOT

SPLIT RING

The split ring and vent slot prevent overfilling the cell with water. Courtesy Buick Motor Division, General Motors Corporation.

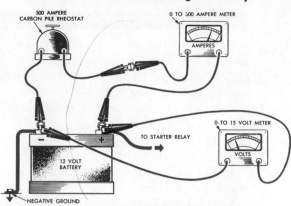

A load must be placed on the battery to make a capacity test. Be sure that the carbon pile is in its maximum resistance position before connecting it. Adjust it for 200 ampere draw and if the voltage reading is 9.5 or more, the battery is OK. Courtesy Chrysler Division, Chrysler Corporation.

One voltmeter prod must be pushed into the sealing compound to touch the cell connector. Courtesy Plymouth Division, Chrysler Corporation.

VOLTAGE LOAD TEST

9. With the ignition switch off, or the high tension wire removed from the coil, operate the starting motor.

10. Measure the voltage of each cell under load, using the 3-volt scale of the voltmeter. The voltmeter leads must be reversed for each cell test or the meter will read backward. A deflection of the needle to the left (off scale) indicates reversed polarity (positive where negative should be).

11. A reading of 1.5 volts or over indicates a good cell. The voltage difference between cells must not be over 0.2 volt. A cell in which the meter slowly drops to 0, or even reverses itself, is *shorted*. This condition is frequently due to the separators cracking and creating an electrical contact between the positive and negative plates. If the voltage reading is low, the battery should be charged and the test repeated before discarding it.

Installing a Battery

A new battery must be correctly installed or the electrical system will be damaged.

Tools and Equipment

Battery, ½ and 9/16 inch box, open-end wrenches; battery pliers; battery carrier; screwdriver.

Battery installation details.

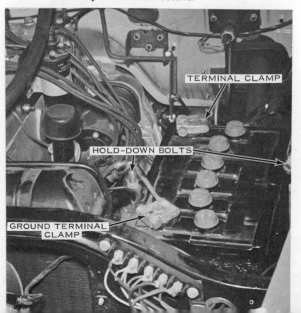

1. Loosen the ground cable terminal nut.

2. Spread the terminal with the pliers and remove it. **Caution:** *Always remove the ground terminal first to avoid shorting the cable to ground.*

3. Loosen and remove the hot battery cable terminal.

4. Loosen and remove the hold-down clamps.

5. Hook a battery carrier over the terminal posts and lift the battery from the case.

6. Before installing a new battery, clean the insides of the cable terminals and the outside of the battery posts with a knife or wire brush. **Caution:** *A bad connection will burn up the generator.*

7. Install the new battery and check for polarity by placing both battery cable terminals on the battery posts, but do not tighten. Turn on the light switch and note the ammeter reading. If the needle moves to the discharge side, the battery is correctly installed. If the needle moves to the charge side, the battery is in backward and must be turned around. In the absence of an ammeter, it is very important that you check the specifications to make sure you are installing the battery correctly; otherwise damage to the electrical system will result.

8. Tighten the battery hold-down clamps.

9. Tighten the cable terminal nuts.

10. Remove, clean, and tighten the ground strap where it is attached to the engine block.

Charging a Storage Battery

When a battery is discharged by accidentally leaving a switch turned on for a length of time, by a low-current drain in the car's electrical system, or by a malfunction of the generator, the battery must be recharged from an outside source of current. There are two basic types of chargers in common use: the slow and the fast charger.

The slow charger is used only in garages. The discharged battery must be removed from the car and connected to a source of DC current. It must remain on charge overnight. The fast charger is generally used in service stations. The current is sent through the battery at a high rate so that the charge can be completed in about an hour.

Slow Charging

1. Connect the positive (red) lead of the charger to the positive terminal post of the battery. Connect the negative (black) lead to the negative terminal post of the battery. The positive post of the battery is usually marked with a +, or "P," and it is slightly larger than the negative post. If several batteries are

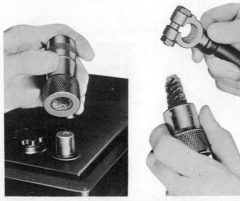

Using inside and outside steel brushes to clean the terminal and cable of corrosion. Courtesy Buick Motor Division, General Motors Corporation.

to be charged at the same time, they must be connected in series; that is, the positive post of one must be connected to the negative post of the next. When all of the batteries are connected in this manner, there will be one positive and one negative battery post free. These are then connected to the proper charger leads. Six- and twelve-volt batteries may be placed in series on the same line. Bring the electrolyte level to just above the top of the plates in each cell. Do not overfill. Leave the vent covers in place to exclude dirt but do not tighten them so that the gas can escape. Turn on the switch and adjust the charging rate to one ampere for each positive plate in a cell. For example, in a battery having 13 plates per cell, 6 of them would be positives; therefore the charging rate should be adjusted to 6 amperes. If batteries of several sizes are to be charged at the same time, the rate must be adjusted for the smallest battery.

2. Test the battery frequently with a hydrometer to determine its condition. It is fully charged when the specific gravity ceases to rise for three successive readings taken at hourly intervals. A freely gassing battery is another indication of a full charge. Most batteries can be recharged in about 24 hours; a badly sulphated one may take five times that long.

High-Rate Charging

3. Connect the positive charger lead to the battery positive terminal post and the negative charger lead to the battery negative terminal post. Set the *TIMER* to the desired charging time, depending on the state of charge. If the battery is dead, set the timer to 55 minutes; quarter charged, 45 minutes; and half

charged, 30 minutes. A battery that is ¾ charged should be charged at a slow rate. Turn the *SELECTOR* switch to 12 or 6 volts according to the battery size. Push the *RATE FINDER* switch in the direction indicated by the arrow, turn the *RATE* switch until the meter pointer rests as closely as possible to the dividing line between *normal* and *high* on the scale. Now, turn the *SELECTOR* switch to the *charge* position. The charging rate will automatically be reduced to the slow rate after a normal fast-charge according to the setting of the *TIMER*.

Replacing Light Bulbs

Electricity flows through the filament (resistance) of a light bulb, making it white hot which results in light rays. High voltage in the charging circuit is the enemy of bulb life. It causes the lights to flare up and burn out in which case the bulb must be replaced.

Tools and Equipment

8 inch screwdriver; test light; sealed-beam headlamp unit.

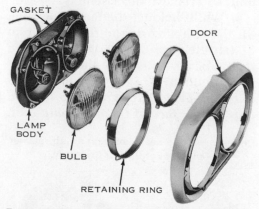

Exploded view of the headlamp retaining clamps. Courtesy Ford Division, Ford Motor Company.

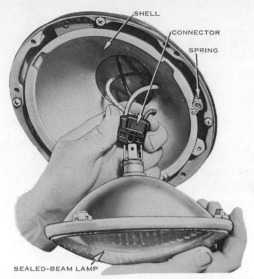

SHELL

CONNECTOR

SPRING

SEALED-BEAM LAMP

The socket makes it easy to take the connection apart. Courtesy Dodge Division, Chrysler Corporation.

PROCEDURE

1. Remove the headlamp door retaining screws and the door and gasket.

2. Unhook the spring from the retaining ring and, holding the sealed-beam unit, retaining ring, and mounting ring as an assembly, remove the mounting ring from the adjusting screws. **Caution:** *Do not disturb the adjusting screws.*

3. Pull the assembly forward, disconnect the plug from the sealed-beam unit, and remove the assembly.

4. While holding the mounting ring, lift the retaining ring to release it from its tab. Remove the retaining ring and sealed-beam unit from the mounting ring. **Caution:** *While lifting the retaining ring, avoid damage to the molded lugs on the face of the headlamp unit.*

Disassembly of a headlamp with a ring retainer. Courtesy Ford Motor Company.

ISOLATING THE TROUBLE

5. Test the filaments of the lamp by connecting it to a battery. Replace the lamp if it is defective.

6. Using the lamp tester, test the socket connections. If no electricity is present at the connector, test for an open circuit.

REPLACING THE LAMP

7. Slip a new sealed-beam unit into the mounting ring and position the unit so that the word "TOP" is to the right of the retaining ring tab. Line up the molded lugs on the back of the sealed-beam unit with the indentations in the mounting ring.

8. Match up the hole in the retaining ring with the tab on the mounting ring.

9. Connect the plug to the sealed-beam unit and engage the mounting ring adjusting screw tabs with the vertical and horizontal adjusting screws.

10. Engage the spring of the lamp body with the spring slot of the retaining ring.

11. Install the headlamp door with a gasket and tighten the retaining screws. You are now ready to aim the headlamps.

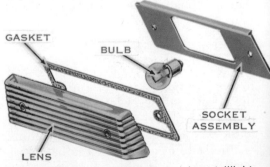

GASKET

BULB

SOCKET
ASSEMBLY

LENS

Disassembly of a screw-fastened lens taillight. Courtesy Ford Motor Company.

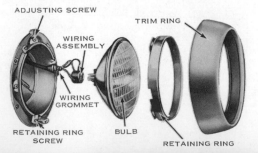

ADJUSTING SCREW

WIRING
ASSEMBLY

TRIM RING

WIRING
GROMMET

RETAINING RING
SCREW

BULB

RETAINING RING

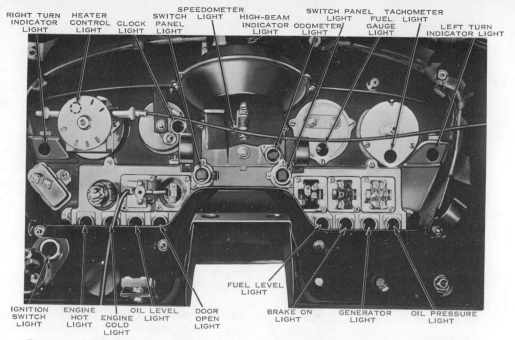

RIGHT TURN INDICATOR LIGHT · HEATER CONTROL LIGHT · CLOCK LIGHT · SWITCH PANEL LIGHT · SPEEDOMETER LIGHT · HIGH-BEAM INDICATOR LIGHT · ODOMETER LIGHT · SWITCH PANEL LIGHT · TACHOMETER LIGHT · FUEL GAUGE LIGHT · LEFT TURN INDICATOR LIGHT

FUEL LEVEL LIGHT

IGNITION SWITCH LIGHT · ENGINE HOT LIGHT · ENGINE COLD LIGHT · OIL LEVEL LIGHT · DOOR OPEN LIGHT · BRAKE ON LIGHT · GENERATOR LIGHT · OIL PRESSURE LIGHT

This rear view of a dash panel shows the placement of the various dash light bulbs and the rear of the instruments. Courtesy Ford Division, Ford Motor Company.

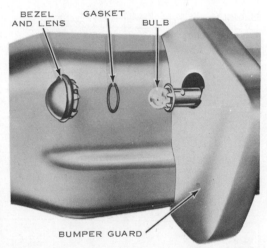

BEZEL AND LENS · GASKET · BULB

BUMPER GUARD

Disassembly of a bezel-type license plate light. Courtesy Ford Motor Company.

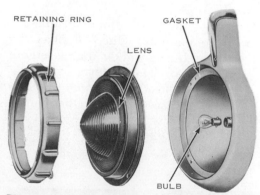

RETAINING RING · LENS · GASKET

BULB

Disassembly of a ring-type taillight. Courtesy Ford Motor Company.

Disassembly of dome light. Courtesy Ford Motor Company.

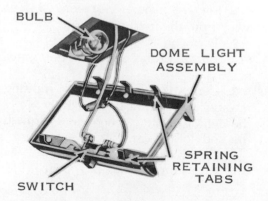

BULB

DOME LIGHT ASSEMBLY

SPRING RETAINING TABS

SWITCH

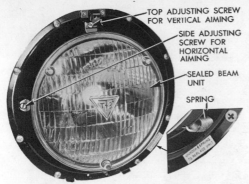

TOP ADJUSTING SCREW
FOR VERTICAL AIMING

SIDE ADJUSTING
SCREW FOR
HORIZONTAL
AIMING

SEALED BEAM
UNIT

SPRING

The vertical and horizontal adjusting screws.
Courtesy Buick Motor Division, General Motors
Corporation.

Aiming Headlamps

Headlamps must be aimed so that their beams point straight ahead to provide maximum illumination and must be tilted down slightly to avoid blinding an oncoming driver. Constant vibration tends to shake the lamps out of adjustment, therefore they should be checked yearly.

Two methods of aiming headlamps are in common use. One is to place the car 25 feet from a wall or aiming screen; another is to clamp a leveling attachment to each headlamp which can then be adjusted according to the gauge.

Tools and Equipment

8 inch screwdriver; focusing screen; T-3 Safety-Aimer.

PROCEDURE

AIMING HEADLAMPS WITH A SCREEN

1. Set the focusing screen 25 feet away from the front of the car.

2. Turn on the bright lights and position the tilt-ray switch to the upper beam.

3. Centralize the screen by sighting through the aiming device. Sight along the center of the car hood and through the body of the car.

4. Cover one lamp with a cloth. On cars with four headlamps, cover three.

5. Adjust the uncovered headlamp so that the light pattern is concentrated on the center cross-lines. The high beam pattern must be 2 inches below the center line of the bulb and directly in front of it. The vertical adjustment is made with the top screw and the horizontal adjustment with the side screw.

This is the pattern that can be expected with the single filament headlight of some Chrysler products (above) and the double filament headlight. Courtesy Plymouth Division, Chrysler Corporation.

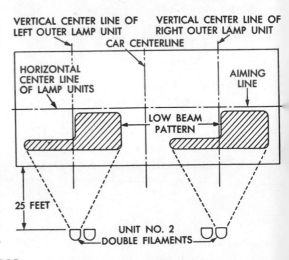

VERTICAL CENTER LINE OF
LEFT INNER LAMP UNIT

VERTICAL CENTER LINE OF
RIGHT INNER LAMP UNIT

CAR CENTERLINE

HORIZONTAL CENTER LINE OF LAMP UNITS

AIMING LINE   2 INCHES

25 FEET

UNIT NO. 1
SINGLE FILAMENT

VERTICAL CENTER LINE OF
LEFT OUTER LAMP UNIT

VERTICAL CENTER LINE OF
RIGHT OUTER LAMP UNIT

CAR CENTERLINE

HORIZONTAL
CENTER LINE
OF LAMP UNITS

AIMING
LINE

LOW BEAM
PATTERN

25 FEET

UNIT NO. 2
DOUBLE FILAMENTS

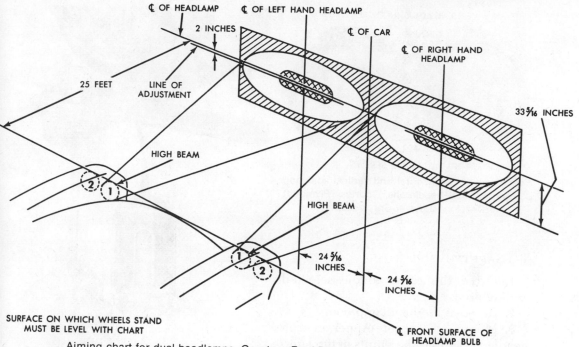

Aiming chart for dual headlamps. Courtesy Ford Division, Ford Motor Company.

Low beam aiming pattern. Courtesy Ford Division, Ford Motor Company.

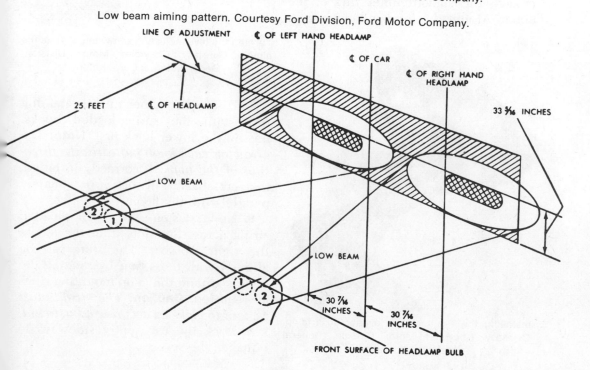

239

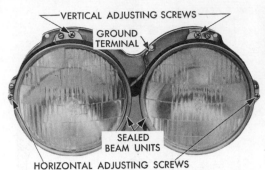

VERTICAL ADJUSTING SCREWS

GROUND
TERMINAL

SEALED
BEAM UNITS

HORIZONTAL ADJUSTING SCREWS

Position of the horizontal and vertical adjusting screws on dual headlamps. Courtesy Plymouth Division, Chrysler Corporation.

T-3 SAFETY-AIMER

1. Drive the car onto the selected aiming area.

2. Remove the headlamp doors.

3. Mount a T-3 Safety-Aimer on each headlamp so that the points of the lamp engage the smooth inner ring of the aimer. Mount the left-hand aimer first.

Turning the level adjusting screw to calibrate the aimer. Courtesy Chevrolet Motor Division, General Motors Corporation.

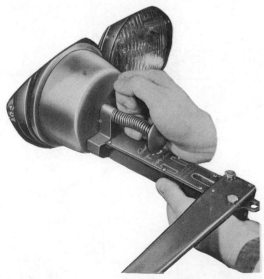

Installing the T-3 headlight aligner on a lamp. Courtesy Chevrolet Motor Division, General Motors Corporation.

4. Fasten the aimer to the retaining ring with the spring-loaded hooks. Fasten the lower hook first. **Note:** *The arrow on each knob indicates the direction of the hook.* If correctly installed, the crossbars will be approximately parallel with the floor.

5. Now, fasten the spring-loaded string across the slots from the left to the right crossbar. The slots can be aligned with the string by rotating the aimers around the lamp mounting rings as required. **Caution:** *The string must be taut to make an accurate adjustment.*

6. Rock the car gently sideways to equalize the springs.

RIGHT HEADLAMP AIMER   LEFT HEADLAMP AIMER

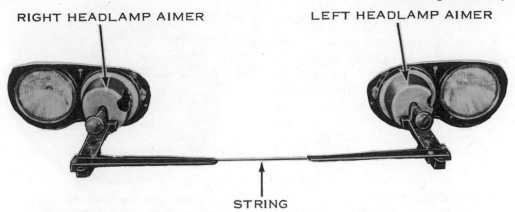

STRING

Correct installation of the aligners and the string on No. 1 headlamp units. Courtesy Chevrolet Motor Division, General Motors Corporation.

7. Rotate the aimer dial so that the number "2" is at the top and in line with the pointer.

8. To make the *horizontal adjustment:* (1) Rotate the aimers around the lamp ring until the notch in the arm is bisected by the string. Both arms must be horizontal. (2) Adjust the left headlamp by turning the horizontal adjusting screw in or out until the string just

Turn the headlamp horizontal adjusting screw until the string is centered on the aimer arm. Courtesy Chevrolet Motor Division, General Motors Corporation.

touches the arm. (3) Repeat the operation on the right side. (4) Recheck the contact points and make minor adjustments, if necessary.

9. To make the *vertical adjustment:* (1) Turn the vertical adjusting screw out until the bubble is at the end of the vial, and then turn the screw clockwise to center the bubble. (2) Repeat for the other headlamp. (3) Recheck the contact points to make sure that the string is still touching the arms and that both bubbles are centered. If necessary make small adjustments to correct.

10. Remove the aimers and install both headlamp doors.

Making the headlamp vertical adjustment. Courtesy Chevrolet Motor Division, General Motors Corporation.

HORIZONTAL AIMING SCREW

CENTER STRING ON AIMER ARM

VERTICAL ADJUSTMENT SCREW

241

Adjusting a Vibrator Horn

A horn is composed of an electro-magnet, attached to a diaphragm, which vibrates, setting a column of air in motion inside the projector. This air motion is transmitted to the diaphragm of your ear and is the sound you hear. You may disassemble a horn to study its operating principle and learn to make its adjustment.

Tools and Equipment

Screwdriver; ⅜ and ⁷⁄₁₆ inch box, open-end wrenches; vibrator horn.

PROCEDURE

1. Remove the horn from the car. Tape up the live lead to avoid a short.
2. Remove the retaining screw and back shell.
3. Remove the back shell bracket.
4. Remove the contact point adjusting locknut, but leave the adjusting nut in position.

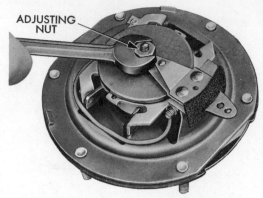

This type of horn requires movement of the armature itself to make the adjustment. Courtesy Plymouth Division, Chrysler Corporation.

5. Remove the diaphragm cover retaining nuts and bolts.
6. Remove the diaphragm cover and projector.
7. Remove the diaphragm locknut.
8. Remove the diaphragm and inspect for cracks.

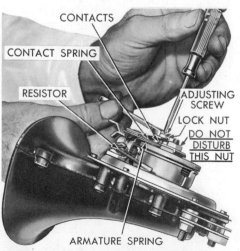

Adjusting a vibrator type horn. Courtesy Plymouth Division, Chrysler Corporation.

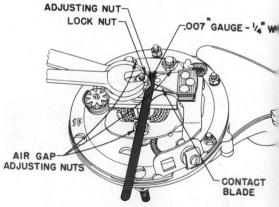

This specification calls for a .007″ feeler gauge blade inserted between the adjusting nut and the point lever. The adjustment is to screw the nut down just far enough to cause the horn to stop operating with the feeler gauge blade in place. When the blade is removed, the horn is correctly adjusted. Courtesy Oldsmobile Division, General Motors Corporation.

9. Inspect the field coil and armature for the principle of operation:
- Note how the field coil surrounds the laminated iron core.
- When current flows through the coil, it sets up a strong magnetic field which attracts the armature.
- Move the armature toward the field coil and note how the adjusting nut opens the contact points which breaks the electrical circuit. This causes the magnetic field to collapse and allows the spring to move the armature and diaphragm away from the coil, causing the contact points to close again. In operation, this cycle is constantly repeated.
- Assemble the diaphragm to the armature bolt and note how the back-and-forth movement of the armature is transmitted to the diaphragm by means of the bolt. The armature creates high notes by rapid vibration (smaller air gap) and a short air column projector; low notes by slower vibration (larger air gap) and a longer air column projector.

10. Unscrew the contact point adjusting nut about two turns until the full movement of the armature does not open the points.

11. Connect a battery to the two contact terminals and note what happens to the armature. Make and break the contact several times with the wires. **Caution:** *Do not leave the battery connected because the coil will overheat.* Note that the armature is attracted when you make the contact, and that it returns to its original position when you break it. Screw the point adjusting nut down two turns and connect the wire. Note that now the armature opens and closes the points and the vibrations continue.

12. Locate the resistor or condenser, which is connected across the points to minimize arcing.

13. Tighten the diaphragm locknut firmly to prevent its loosening.

14. Replace the diaphragm cover and projector.

15. Replace the diaphragm cover retaining nuts and screws.

16. Replace the contact point adjusting locknut.

17. Connect the horn to a battery and turn the contact point adjusting nut for the best tone. This adjustment is very critical, so move the nut only one sixth of a turn at a time. **Note:** *Be sure to tighten the locknut before making each test.*

18. Replace the back shell bracket and the shell.

19. Tighten the retaining screw.

20. Replace the horn on the car and connect up the wires.

Installing a Horn Relay

The single horn circuit consists of a "hot" wire from the junction block to the horn, and a return lead through the steering post up to the horn button, where it is grounded to complete the circuit. With dual horns, the current restriction of the long wires is enough to make the horns sound weak, so a relay is used to connect the horns directly to the battery. The horn button circuit operates the relay, which in turn connects the battery directly to the horns. Use number 10 wire on all horn connections, and solder lugs to the wires.

Tools and Equipment

Horn relay; dual horn set; single horn; number 10 wire; solder; soldering copper; soldering lugs.

SINGLE HORN

1. Connect one side of the horn to the junction block.

2. Connect the other horn terminal to the steering post ground wire.

3. Remove the horn button if it is necessary to install a new post wire.

DUAL HORNS

4. Connect one side of each horn to a good ground. Use number 10 wire, and solder lugs to each end of the wires.

5. Connect a number 10 wire from the starter solenoid switch to the center post of the horn relay marked "B."
Caution: *Be sure to use a soldered terminal lug under the starter switch cable retaining nut. Twisted wires here will cause generator trouble, as this is in the charging circuit.*

6. Connect the ground wire from the steering post to the relay terminal which operates the armature. A click can be heard when the correct post is grounded which is the armature being attracted to the relay core as it completes the battery-to-horn connection. (This wire can be No. 18 as it carries very little current.)

7. Connect the third relay terminal to the remaining terminal on each horn. Use number 10 wire and solder terminal lugs to each end.

HEADLAMPS

8. Light relays are installed in exactly the same way when brighter lights are desired. Install the relay close to the lamps and connect the regular headlight switch to operate the relay.

Tracing wiring and making repairs often requires work under the dash.

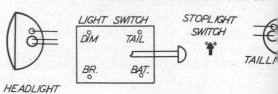

This is a basic wiring diagram. Copy these electrical symbols on scratch paper and make the necessary connections. Use the lighting circuit in the first part of this chapter as a guide. *Do not write in this book.*

Installing a Headlight Switch

A headlight switch receives electricity through the ammeter or from the junction block (where the main wires are connected) and, by means of sliding contacts, sends current to the lights selected by the driver. There are many different types of switches, but in all cases there is provision for both parking (dim) and bright lights. Also the tail light is connected so as to burn when

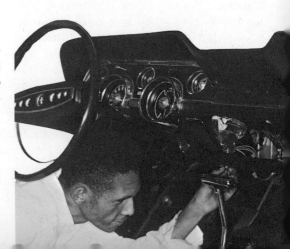

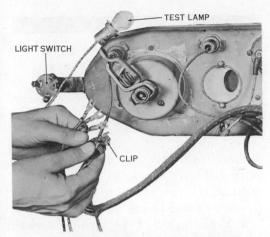

TEST LAMP

LIGHT SWITCH

CLIP

Using the test lamp to trace wiring. The lamp clip is fastened to any good ground and the other clip used to find the wire that conducts electricity. To probe through insulated wires, the clip is fastened to a knife blade that cuts through the insulation.

any other lights are on. The wire to the bright lights is connected through the tilt-ray switch on the floorboard, from where the driver can select either the high or low beam.

Tools and Equipment

Screwdriver; test light; auto-electric test stand.

PROCEDURE

1. It is best, when changing switches, to connect one wire from the old switch to the new one before disconnecting a second or third wire. This prevents confusion. In case this is not possible, proceed as below:

2. Locate the hot wire with the test light which is always connected to the terminal marked "B."

3. Touch each of the remaining wires to the hot post "B" until the tail lights come on. This wire, of course, is the tail light wire.

4. Connect your tester lead to each of the remaining prongs of the switch until the one is found which is "hot" on either side of the *off* position. In the case of a pull switch, the *in* position is *off*, the first notch *dim*, and the second notch *bright*.

5. Connect the tail light wire to the switch terminal which is "hot" on both *dim* and *bright* positions of the switch.

6. Locate the dim or parking light wire by touching each of the remaining wires to the hot post until the dim lights come on.

7. Connect this wire to the switch prong which is "hot" only on the *left notch* position of the switch handle, or the first notch in the case of a pull handle.

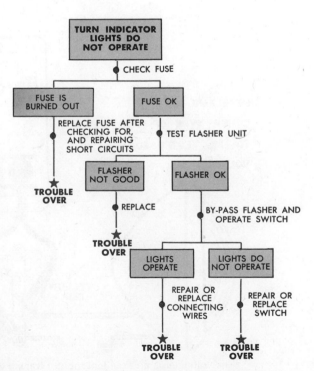

A routing chart shows the logical method of tracing troubles. Courtesy Ford Motor Company.

8. Locate the bright light wire in the same manner and connect it to the switch prong "hot" on the right side of the switch handle, or the second notch in case of a pull handle.

Testing for an Open Circuit

When a light does not work, or the horn does not blow, it means that one of two things has happened: either the unit is defective or the electrical circuit is incomplete. The latter is known as an *open circuit*.

Tools and Equipment

Screwdriver; test light; wiring diagram; auto-electric test stand.

1. Secure a car wiring diagram of the car on which you are working.

2. Turn the light switch to the *on* position of the circuit with the defective lamp.

3. Remove the bulb and test the socket for current with the test lamp. If there is current here, then the trouble is probably in the bulb. If there is no current, then you must trace back along the circuit and locate the *open*.

4. With the aid of the wiring diagram, locate the next unit in order—going back to the light switch—and test for current. If you find this unit *hot*, then the trouble is between the unit you just tested and the lamp you inspected.

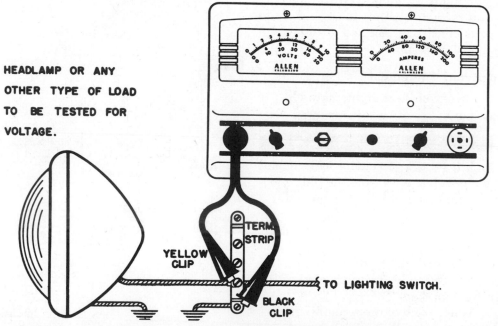

HEADLAMP OR ANY OTHER TYPE OF LOAD TO BE TESTED FOR VOLTAGE.

YELLOW CLIP

TERM STRIP

BLACK CLIP

TO LIGHTING SWITCH.

The voltmeter is an excellent tool for tracing electrical circuits. It is much better than the haphazard method of sparking the connection, which is likely to blow out the fuse. Courtesy Allen Electric and Equipment Company.

5. If the second unit has no current, test at the next unit in order, back toward the battery. Follow the wiring diagram back from the defective unit until you come to the one with current. Use the wiring diagram to follow the path. When you find the unit with current, the *open* is between it and the unit just before it. Further inspection and tests with the test lamp will reveal the *open* circuit.

6. The above method is the longest way to do the job but the most thorough. Several quick checks are listed below which will aid you in solving the average job more quickly:

• If all the lights are out, check for a burnt fuse or a defective circuit breaker.

• If all the bulbs are *burnt out*, a high voltage condition exists caused by a poor connection in the charging circuit. Replace the bulbs, but do not start the engine until the resistance connection is located.

• If both filaments of one bulb are out, check for a poor ground.

• If the lights, horn, and starter don't work, check the battery and its connections.

Testing for a Short Circuit

When a wire is properly insulated, it will conduct electricity to the proper device. When the insulation is chafed and worn off, the electricity returns to the battery directly through contact of the bare wire with the car frame. This direct path is known as a *short circuit*. When a short circuit occurs, the fuse burns out due to the overload. The fuse protects the wiring and electrically operated units from being destroyed, and may save the car from burning. **Note:** *A short in the generator circuit*

is especially dangerous because this circuit is not fused.

Tools and Equipment

Test light; screwdriver; auto-electric test stand; piece of round steel, $\frac{1}{4} \times 1\frac{1}{4}$ inch.

PROCEDURE

FUSED CIRCUIT

1. The entire fused light system must be imagined as five separate circuits: the high bright, the low bright, parking, stoplight, and interior lights. Locating the shorted circuit is by the process of elimination; that is, eliminate the good circuits until only the defective one is left.

2. Disconnect one side of the battery by disconnecting the ground cable.

3. Replace the fuse with a piece of steel $\frac{1}{4} \times 1\frac{1}{4}$ inch long. **Note:** *If a circuit breaker is used in place of a fuse, no change needs to be made.*

4. Pull or turn the light switch to its first position (parking).

5. *Lightly* touch the cable to its post while noting the ammeter reading. A normal circuit will cause the ammeter to read up to 20 amperes. A shorted circuit will cause the needle to deflect across the entire scale. **Caution:** *The cable must not be left on too long as a shorted circuit would damage the wiring and ammeter.* **Note:** *If the car is not equipped with an ammeter, the size of the spark at the battery post is a good indicator. A normal circuit will cause a small spark; a shorted one a large spark.*

6. Move the light switch to the second position (bright) and repeat the above test.

7. Step on the tilt-ray switch and repeat the test.

8. Step on the brake pedal (ignition switch turned on) and repeat the test.

9. Operate the dash lights and dome light and repeat the test.

10. By now, the short must have shown up in one of these circuits either by sparking or by showing a large ammeter discharge. Locate the defective circuit wire at the switch and disconnect it. Retest the other circuits once more to make sure that you have disconnected the correct wire.

11. After locating the shorted circuit, the exact spot can be isolated by tracing the smaller parts of the circuit. For example, if the short is in the high beam bright lights, disconnect the wires at the headlamp junction block and reconnect the wire at the headlight switch. Repeat the test, step 5. If the short is now eliminated, the trouble must be in the lamp itself. If the short still exists, it must be in the wiring because the lamp is disconnected.

12. If the short is traced to within the headlamps, then one lamp can be disconnected and the other tested. By this method of elimination, the defective spot can be located.

13. If the fuse blows in each of the three positions of the headlight switch the short must be in the tail light circuit. Can you explain this?

UNFUSED CIRCUIT

14. The unfused circuit consists of a wire to the starting motor switch, and then to the junction block or ammeter from where it leads to the regulator and generator. Disconnect the battery cable as before.

15. Disconnect the wire from the battery to the regulator and repeat the test, step 5.

16. Continue as before, working from the end of the circuit back to the battery, disconnecting one unit at a time until the short is eliminated. The last unit disconnected, before the short disappears, is the defective one.

17. Make the necessary repairs. **Note:** *Always solder connector lugs to the ends of new wires.*

18. Replace the battery cable after having cleaned the post and the inside of the cable connector.

CHECK YOUR KNOWLEDGE

1. Explain why it is said that a storage battery does not store electricity.

2. How many cells are required to make a 12-volt storage battery?

3. What are the three duties of the separators?

4. Of what materials are the positive plates made? Negative plates?

5. When is a battery said to be discharged chemically?

6. How is the ampere-hour rating of a battery determined?

7. What are two common causes of battery troubles?

8. Of what three things does a headlamp consist?

9. What is the advantage of capped filaments in the headlamps?

10. What two forms do driving compartment indicating gauges take?

11. Why is the generator varying voltage a problem in the gauge circuit?

12. How does a constant voltage regulator work?

13. What is the function of a relay?

14. How many switches does it take to operate the starting motor?

15. Why is it so important to service the battery cables periodically?

16. What is the result of a high resistance connection in the charging circuit?

17. What instrument is required for accurate troubleshooting?

Self-Check Tests

TRUE-FALSE

1. A storage battery stores electricity.

2. A standard 12-volt battery contains twelve cells.

3. Each cell contains a positive and a negative plate group.

4. The plates are made of a lead-antimony grid.

5. Oil pressure gauges are always of the hydraulic type.

6. The starting motor frequently is operated by a relay connected directly to the ignition switch.

7. High voltage from bad battery connections is frequently the cause of electrical breakdowns.

MULTIPLE CHOICE

1. Which of the following is *not* a part of the battery: a) sulphuric acid; b) hydrometer; c) separators; d) plates?

2. A fully charged battery shows a specific gravity reading of: a) 1.270; b) 12.70; c) 1.170; d) 11.70.

3. Which of the following is *not* a part of the headlamp: a) filament; b) reflector; c) lens; d) focus adjustment?

4. A constant voltage regulator of a 12-volt electrical system stabilizes the gauge operating voltage at: a) 12 volts; b) 8 volts; c) 5 volts; d) 3 volts.

5. Which of the following circuits *never* needs a relay: a) gauge; b) headlight; c) horn; d) starting circuit?

COMPLETION

1. Each battery wet cell delivers a voltage of _____ volts.

2. Each battery plate is separated from its neighbor by a _____.

3. The acid and water solution is called _____.

4. The amount of plate surface presented to chemical action determines the capacity of the battery which is expressed in _____ _____.

5. Dual horns draw relatively large amounts of current and, to have them operate at maximum efficiency, a _____ is installed in the circuit.

6. Most electrical troubles can be traced with a _____.

MATCHING

1. Storage battery	a. To stabilize gauge readings
2. Ampere-hours	b. Chemical action
3. Constant voltage regulator	c. Switching device
4. Relay	d. Battery rating

Chapter 9

Cranking Motors and Generators

Cranking Motor

The cranking motor consists of an armature, brushes, field windings, and drive mechanism. Some motors have a solenoid which shifts the starter gear into engagement and completes the battery-to-starter circuit at the same time.

The armature is supported on bushings which allow it to rotate. Brushes make contact with the commutator to carry current to the armature windings. This current is first passed through the field windings to create a strong magnetic field, which opposes the magnetic field set up in the armature in such a way that the armature is forced to rotate.

The drive mechanism, at one end of the armature shaft, has two jobs: (1) to transmit the cranking torque to the engine, and (2) to disconnect the cranking motor when the engine starts.

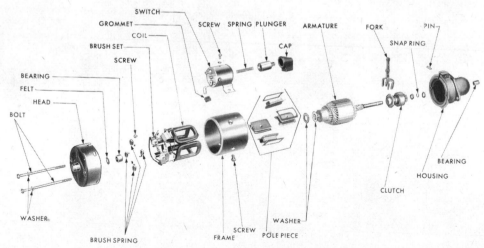

Exploded view of the cranking motor. Courtesy Chrysler Division, Chrysler Corporation.

BRUSH **COMMUTATOR**

SHUNT COIL

POLE SHOE

ERIES COILS

Electric current is first sent through the fields to energize them before being sent to the armature. Courtesy Delco-Remy Division, General Motors Corporation.

Overrunning Clutch Drive

The overrunning-clutch type drive is shifted into mesh with the flywheel by a solenoid which also closes the cranking motor switch after engagement is complete. The drive transmits torque in only one direction. It cranks the engine but slips when the engine starts and drives it faster than the armature.

BENDIX—OVERRUNNING CLUTCH DRIVE—CIRCUITS

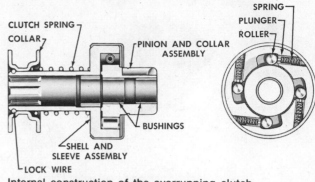

CLUTCH SPRING
COLLAR
PINION AND COLLAR ASSEMBLY
SPRING
PLUNGER
ROLLER
BUSHINGS
SHELL AND SLEEVE ASSEMBLY
LOCK WIRE

Internal construction of the overrunning clutch. Courtesy Delco-Remy Division, General Motors Corporation.

The overrunning clutch consists of a shell and sleeve, splined to the armature. Four notches, which taper inward slightly, are cut in the shell. When the pinion meshes with the flywheel gear, the rotating armature forces the rollers tightly into the smaller part of the notches where they jam and become a solid drive unit.

When the engine starts, the pinion is rotated at a high rate, moving the rollers back toward the larger part of the slot, so the pinion spins freely.

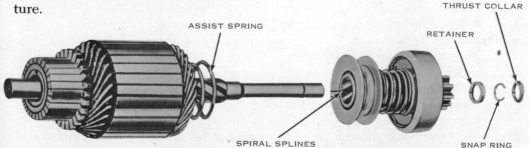

ASSIST SPRING
THRUST COLLAR
RETAINER
SPIRAL SPLINES
SNAP RING

Assembly of the overrunning clutch type of cranking motor drive. Courtesy Delco-Remy Division, General Motors Corporation.

251

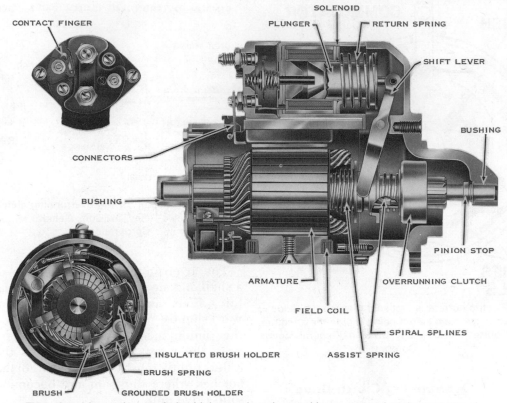

CONTACT FINGER

SOLENOID

PLUNGER — RETURN SPRING

SHIFT LEVER

BUSHING

CONNECTORS

BUSHING

PINION STOP

ARMATURE

OVERRUNNING CLUTCH

FIELD COIL

SPIRAL SPLINES

INSULATED BRUSH HOLDER

ASSIST SPRING

BRUSH SPRING

BRUSH

GROUNDED BRUSH HOLDER

The solenoid contains a switch which energizes the cranking motor and, at the same time, shifts the pinion gear into mesh with the flywheel. Courtesy Delco-Remy Division, General Motors Corporation.

Cranking Motor Control Circuits

Because a cranking motor draws heavy current, a solenoid switch must be used to handle the load. It is controlled from the driver's compartment by a small switch, which is part of the ignition switch.

Turning the key past the IGN position energizes the solenoid winding, which moves a disc across the switch contacts to complete the battery-to-cranking-motor circuit.

Solenoids that shift the pinion gear into mesh with the flywheel have two windings, a hold-in and a pull-in wind-

ing. It takes more energy to pull the plunger into the solenoid than to hold it. The pull-in winding is connected across the switch contacts and is shorted out of the circuit when the plunger closes the switch. Only the hold-in winding is energized during the cranking process, which reduces the battery drain.

Most 12-volt cranking motors have an ignition resistor by-pass switch in the solenoid, the purpose of which is to connect the primary of the ignition coil directly to system voltage (which is about 9 volts during the cranking

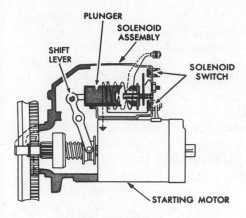

PLUNGER
SOLENOID ASSEMBLY
SHIFT LEVER
SOLENOID SWITCH
STARTING MOTOR

DISENGAGED

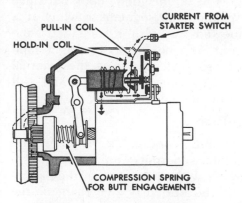

PULL-IN COIL
HOLD-IN COIL
CURRENT FROM STARTER SWITCH
COMPRESSION SPRING FOR BUTT ENGAGEMENTS

PINION PARTIALLY ENGAGED

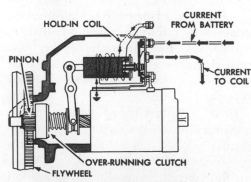

HOLD-IN COIL
CURRENT FROM BATTERY
PINION
CURRENT TO COIL
OVER-RUNNING CLUTCH
FLYWHEEL

PINION FULLY ENGAGED AND STARTING MOTOR CRANKING

Showing the action of the pull-in and hold-in windings during the operation of the solenoid. Courtesy Chevrolet Motor Division, General Motors Corporation.

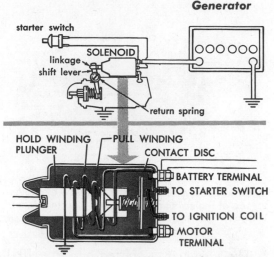

Generator

starter switch
SOLENOID
linkage shift lever
return spring
HOLD WINDING PLUNGER
PULL WINDING
CONTACT DISC
BATTERY TERMINAL
TO STARTER SWITCH
TO IGNITION COIL
MOTOR TERMINAL

Section through a cranking motor solenoid. The unit contains two coils: a hold-in and a pull-in winding. The pull-in winding is heavier and draws more current, but is shorted out of the circuit by the contact disc during the cranking period. Note that the contact disc makes contact with the ignition coil terminal to furnish system voltage during the cranking period. Courtesy Delco-Remy Division, General Motors Corporation.

process) so that the ignition circuit works at top efficiency during the starting cycle. After the engine starts, the cranking motor is disengaged and the ignition resistor by-pass switch is disconnected so that the ignition coil receives its current through the primary resistor.

Generator

The generator converts mechanical into electrical energy. It recharges the battery and supplies current for cranking, lighting, ignition, radio, etc. A generator is equipped with a fan to draw off the heat, which lowers its operating temperature, thereby allowing a higher output.

On new cars, generators have now been entirely superseded by alternators.

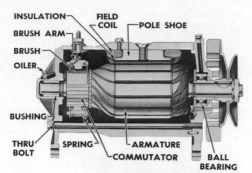

INSULATION — FIELD COIL — POLE SHOE
BRUSH ARM
BRUSH
OILER
BUSHING
THRU BOLT — SPRING — ARMATURE — COMMUTATOR — BALL BEARING

Cutaway view of a generator. Notice the *pulley,* one of the six simple machines. Courtesy Delco-Remy Division, General Motors Corporation.

The changeover started on some 1961 models and was completed by 1965. Alternators have been universally used on American-built passenger cars since that time. However, it is still necessary to understand the conventional generator in order to service older cars.

The generator consists of two main parts, an armature and a field. Two coils of wire create the magnetic field in which the armature revolves. The arma-ture consists of a number of coils of wire connected to each other and to a commutator on which the brushes ride so that current is removed while the armature is rotating.

The commutator segments keep the current flowing in the same direction regardless of the relative position of the two sides of the coil with respect to the north and south magnetic poles. When, for instance, the left-hand side of the coil has rotated 180°, it will be moving in the opposite direction with respect to the magnetic field, but since the commutator segment to which it is connected has also rotated 180°, the current will be fed to the right-hand brush, so that, as far as the external circuit is concerned, the current still flows in the same direction.

Regulator

Without control, a shunt-wound generator's output would continue to increase with speed so that the battery would be seriously overcharged, the generator damaged, and high voltage produced which would damage the electrical accessories. Regulation of the generator output is accomplished by controlling the strength of the field so that the generator just meets the requirements of the battery and electrical system.

In its simplest form, the regulator is nothing more than a switch which either connects a resistance in series with the generator field or shorts it out. When the field windings are directly grounded, the field strength and generator output are at maximum. When the resistance is inserted into the field circuit, the field strength and generator output are reduced. The regulator is composed of

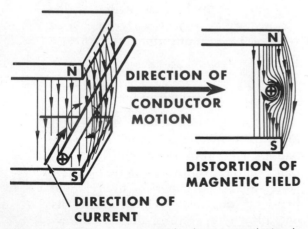

DIRECTION OF CONDUCTOR MOTION

DISTORTION OF MAGNETIC FIELD

DIRECTION OF CURRENT

Electricity is generated when a conductor is moved across magnetic lines of force. Courtesy Delco-Remy Division, General Motors Corporation.

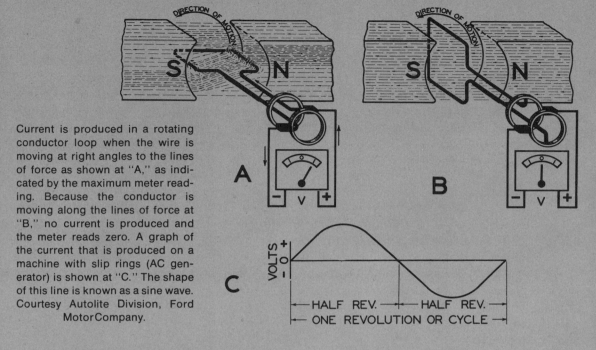

Current is produced in a rotating conductor loop when the wire is moving at right angles to the lines of force as shown at "A," as indicated by the maximum meter reading. Because the conductor is moving along the lines of force at "B," no current is produced and the meter reads zero. A graph of the current that is produced on a machine with slip rings (AC generator) is shown at "C." The shape of this line is known as a sine wave. Courtesy Autolite Division, Ford Motor Company.

Pulsating DC current is produced on the same type of machine when a segmented commutator is used to remove the generated current from the rotating conductor loop. As the loop turns, note that the commutator turns with it so that the same type of current (positive in these illustrations) is passed onto the right-hand brush. Each of the generated electrical pulses is above the graph line at "C." The shape of the line of current produced on a machine with a segmented commutator is pulsating DC. Courtesy Autolite Division, Ford Motor Company.

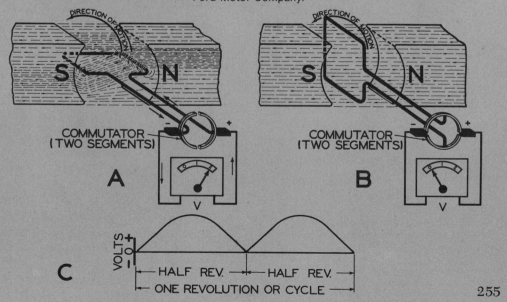

three switches: a cutout, a current regulator, and a voltage regulator.

The *cutout relay* closes the circuit between the generator and battery when the generator starts to operate. It opens the circuit when the generator slows or stops, thus preventing the battery from discharging back through the generator.

The *current regulator* acts as a current-limiting device and prevents the generator from producing more than its maximum rated output. It inserts a resistance in the generator field circuit when the output reaches the specified setting.

The *voltage regulator* operates to control the generator output in accordance with the condition of the battery charge and the electrical load. It is characteristic of a charging circuit that,

as a battery becomes charged, the generator increases its voltage. The voltage regulator prevents the voltage from increasing beyond a predetermined maximum by inserting a resistance in the generator field circuit when the output reaches the specified limit.

In operation, the contact points of the current and voltage regulators vibrate as they control the strength of the field and consequently the generator output. Actually only one of the two units is in operation at any time.

Alternating Current Generators

A current which periodically changes direction in a wire is called *alternating current;* that is, it alternates its direction of movement. *Direct current*, on the other hand, flows steadily in one direction.

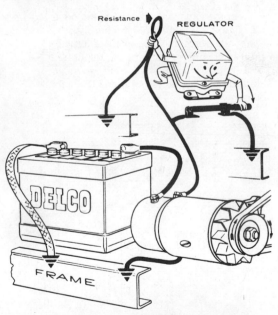

The regulator grounds the generator fields or inserts resistance in them to control the generator output. Courtesy Delco-Remy Division, General Motors Corporation.

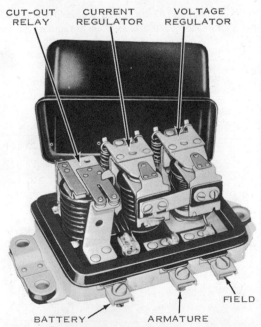

The regulator adjusts the output of the generator to the needs of the battery. Courtesy Delco-Remy Division, General Motors Corporation.

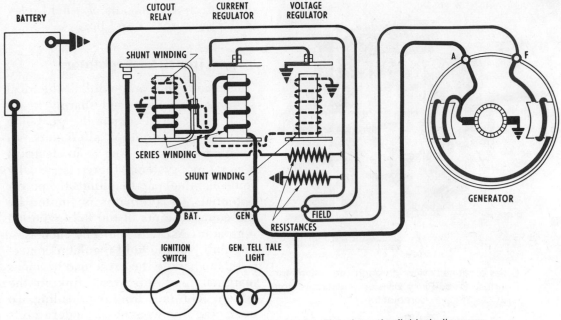

This is the wiring circuit of the regulator and generator. Note how the field windings are grounded through a resistor or through the current and voltage regulator points in series with the ground. Courtesy Buick Motor Division, General Motors Corporation.

Generators produce alternating current; batteries supply direct current. Inasmuch as all automotive electrical devices operate on direct current, it is necessary to convert the generator's alternating current output into direct current so as to be compatible with the rest of the system.

A generator consists of several coils of wire rotated within a strong magnetic field. As each coil moves past a field pole, an induced current is produced. At each half turn of the armature, the current is reversed in the coil because it passes an opposite pole. In a DC generator, a *commutator* revolves with the armature and always presents the same kind of current to the collector brush. In an AC generator, two *slip rings* remove the alternating current.

The slip rings *do not* reverse the current direction at each half revolution of the armature, and, therefore, such a generator supplies AC current.

Within the generator, coils of wire develop the required magnetic fields through which the armature coils pass. These electromagnets are called *field coils*.

The armature of a generator is made of thin strips of laminated metal, insulated from each other to decrease self-induced currents, which are called *eddy currents*. They overheat the armature and waste power.

Alternators

Some generators are designed to produce AC current which is changed

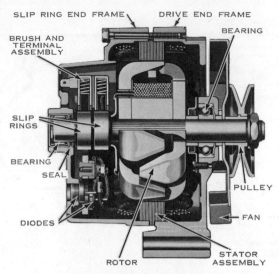

SLIP RING END FRAME

DRIVE END FRAME

BEARING

BRUSH AND
TERMINAL
ASSEMBLY

SLIP
RINGS

BEARING

SEAL

DIODES

PULLEY

FAN

ROTOR

STATOR
ASSEMBLY

Cross-sectioned view through an alternator.
Courtesy Delco-Remy Division, General Motors
Corporation.

into DC current by means of diodes (rectifiers), mounted internally. These are called *alternators*. The output of an alternator is greater than that of a conventional generator at low speeds, and the service problems are essentially fewer.

The diodes used to rectify the output have a high resistance to a reverse flow of current; therefore, no cutout is required to disconnect the battery when the system is not operating. A voltage regulator is required to vary the field strength in order to control the output. Because the field of an alternator does not retain enough residual magnetism to start it in operation (as does the generator), some external means must be used to excite the field. In the Chrysler system, the field winding is connected to the battery and disconnected from it through the ignition switch. In the General Motors, American Motors, and Ford systems, the field is connected and

disconnected by means of a field relay in the regulator control box.

Transistor Regulators

Demands on automobile electrical systems have increased sharply in recent years; these demands are being met by higher-output alternators. In raising the power rating of an electrical generating system, there is usually some marginal part that limits the power potential. An alternator is limited by the contact points of the field winding regulator. As field current increases, the ability of the field regulator contact points to handle the extra load becomes marginal, and this weak link in the system soon fails from overloading. To overcome this weakness, modern units make use of transistors to carry most of the current load that formerly passed through the vibrating regulator points, and this increases the reliability of the unit in spite of increased current load demands.

Many 1969 alternators utilize miniaturized electronic components for the regulator. This unit has become so small that it is now being mounted within the end frame of the alternator.

Transistors

Most materials can be classified as either electrical *conductors* or *insulators*, depending upon the structure of their atoms. Around the nucleus (core) of an atom is a ring of electrons. If there are fewer than four electrons, they are held to the nucleus somewhat loosely and can be made to leave the atom rather easily. It is this movement of electrons which carries electrical

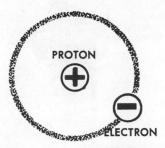

An atom consists of a core containing protons (+), with electrons (−) revolving around it. Courtesy Delco-Remy Division, General Motors Corporation.

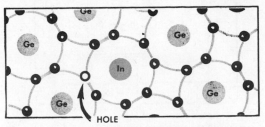

The element indium (In) has only three electrons in its outer ring. When added to germanium, there is a deficiency of one electron, which is called a "hole." Courtesy Delco-Remy Division, General Motors Corporation.

current through a material. Therefore materials with fewer than four electrons are usually conductors, while those with more are usually insulators.

However, some materials are neither conductors nor insulators. They are called *semi-conductors*. Scientists have recently learned quite a bit about these materials. For one thing, they have learned that unusual electron patterns will result when the atoms of certain elements combine.

For instance, an atom of the element germanium (Ge) has eight electrons; an atom of the element antimony (Sb) has five. When these elements join, the

eight electrons from the germanium join with four from the antimony, and there is one extra electron which is left free to move through the material. An electron carries a negative electrical charge; therefore a material which has an extra electron is known as a negative-type ("N" type) material.

The element indium has three electrons. When it joins with germanium, the resulting combination (called a *molecule*) has only eleven electrons. This is one too few (just as 13 was one too many in the previous example). The molecule formed by indium and germanium atoms is said to have a *hole* in its ring. This hole is free to move through the material, similar to the movement of a free electron. A hole in an electron ring represents a positive electrical charge, since it is the lack of a negative charge. Such material is called positive-type ("P" type) material.

A *transistor* consists of three sections of "P" type and "N" type materials joined together and enclosed in a container. If two of the sections are of "P" type material and the center section is "N" type, the unit is known as a PNP transistor. If two "N" type sections are combined with one of "P" type

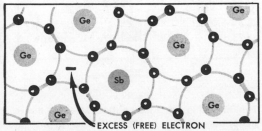

The element antimony (Sb) has five electrons in its outer ring. When combined with germanium (Ge), there is one electron left over, which can be made to move through the material rather easily. Courtesy Delco-Remy Division, General Motors Corporation.

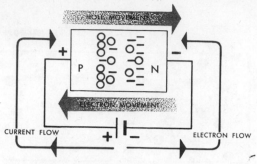

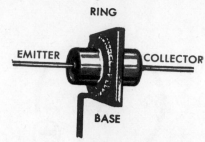

This diagram shows a diode hooked up to a battery with the positive pole connected to the "P" material and the negative pole to the "N" material. In such an arrangement, the negative polarity of the battery will repel the electrons in the "N" material, and the positive battery polarity will attract the electrons with such force that they move across the junction. The battery will supply the electrons to replace those which move across the junction. Courtesy Delco-Remy Division, General Motors Corporation.

material, the assembly is called an NPN transistor. If only two of the materials are joined together (one "P" and one "N" type), then the unit is called a *diode*.

To understand the action of a semiconductor, consider the way a diode works. If the diode were connected to a battery, as shown, the side of the battery with negative polarity would repel the electrons in the "N" material, and the side with positive polarity would attract the electrons with such force that they would move across the junction of the materials; this would result in a flow of electrons. Also, the positive holes in the "P" material would be repelled by the positive battery voltage and attracted by the negative battery voltage.

If we add another section of "P" material to the diode, then we have a transistor with three sections; two with "P" materials and one with "N" material (PNP). The parts of the transistor are named *emitter, collector,* and *base.*

The addition of a second section of "P" type material to a diode forms a complete transistor. The "P" type material on the left is called the *emitter,* and that on the right, the *collector.* The "N" type material in the center is called the *base.* Courtesy Delco-Remy Division, General Motors Corporation.

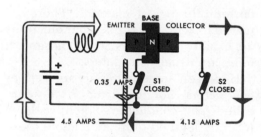

If a transistor is hooked into a circuit as shown, the total current flow of 4.50 amperes will be divided into two circuits, one of 4.15 amperes and one of 0.35 ampere. Courtesy Delco-Remy Division, General Motors Corporation.

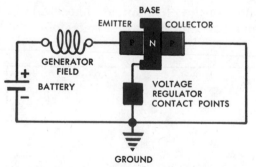

This circuit is designed so that the alternator (or generator) field is connected in series with the transistor. The contact points of the voltage regulator are connected into the base circuit in place of switch S_1. Thus the points will have to carry only 0.35 ampere, which is a relatively light load. Courtesy Delco-Remy Division, General Motors Corporation.

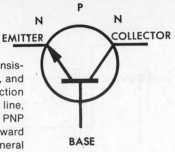

This is the way in which an NPN type of transistor is diagramed. The heavy line is the base, and the line with an arrow pointing in the direction of current flow is the emitter. The remaining line, which has no arrow, is the collector. In the PNP type of transistor, the arrow will point toward the base. Courtesy Delco-Remy Division, General Motors Corporation.

Note that the "N" type material is in the center and is the base.

If the transistor is hooked into a circuit, as shown, a division of current occurs. If, for example, a total current of 4.50 amperes flows through the circuit, the collector current will be 4.15 amperes and the base current will be 0.35 ampere. If the alternator regulator can be designed so that the vibrating contact points are inserted in the base circuit (in place of the S_1 switch), then the contact points will carry about $1/12$ of the total field current needed to control the alternator. This smaller load increases the reliability of the unit.

For greater reliability, two-transistor units have been developed which substitute another transistor for the vibrating voltage regulator contact points so that all moving parts are eliminated. Note that a second transistor, TR_2, is connected in the base circuit of TR_1 to take the place of the vibrating contact points used in the previously described transistor regulator.

This diagram shows the complete regulator circuit, with the divisions of current flow. Courtesy Delco-Remy Division, General Motors Corporation.

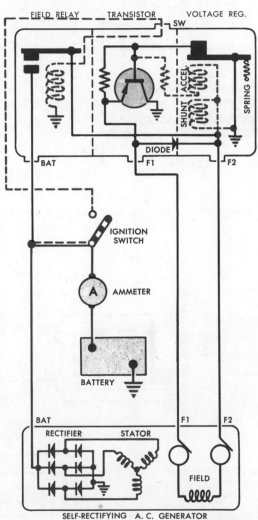

This is a diagram of a complete charging circuit with a transistor regulator taking some of the load from the vibrating voltage regulator contact points. Courtesy Delco-Remy Division, General Motors Corporation.

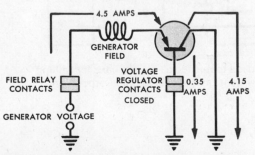

261

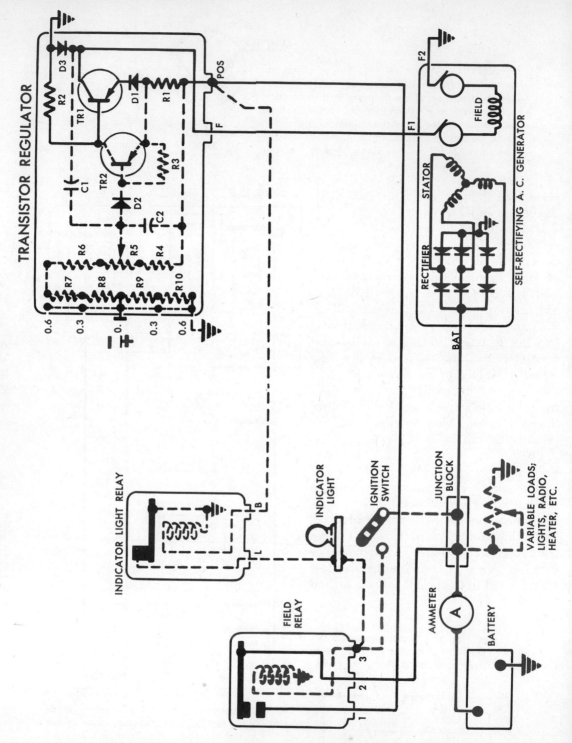

This is a diagram in which two transistors are used to replace all moving parts for limiting the alternator voltage. Courtesy Delco-Remy Division, General Motors Corporation.

262

Service Procedures

Generally, the cranking motor requires infrequent service. It must be reconditioned when it draws an excessive amount of current, caused by the armature rubbing over the pole pieces because of a worn drive-end bushing. This results in a hard-starting complaint because the working voltage of the entire system is reduced, which makes the ignition system work at lower efficiency. The heavy drain also runs the battery down.

As mentioned earlier, alternators require less service than do generators. Because alternator brushes carry only the field current, they work under a small load and are essentially trouble-free. Also, the current-producing wires of the alternator are part of the stator, which is the stationary part of the alternator (not the rotating armature as in the generator); thus the problems of centrifugal force are minimized.

The regulator requires service because its contact points are in constant

An overheated generator usually throws a thin band of solder on the generator cover band. The armature must come out to be tested. Courtesy Delco-Remy Division, General Motors Corporation.

operation. Eventually, they burn or oxidize, thereby opening the field circuit, which causes the output to drop sharply. Generally, the contact points can be cleaned and the regulator adjusted on the car.

Troubleshooting

Accurate troubleshooting requires a voltmeter and ammeter. Cranking motor troubles can be checked by noting the current draw. Excessive draw indicates an internal drag, which is usually due to a worn drive-end bushing. Insufficient draw is generally due to a dirty commutator which prevents good contact.

Brush wear is such that grooves are worn in one side so that sticking occurs, followed by arcing, and then burning of the commutator.

Using test equipment to determine a malfunctioning piece of electrical equipment. This is an essential part of automotive training, as demonstrated by these night-school students.

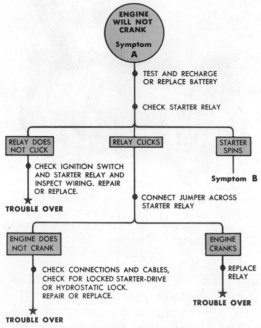

ENGINE WILL NOT CRANK
Symptom A

→ TEST AND RECHARGE OR REPLACE BATTERY

→ CHECK STARTER RELAY

RELAY DOES NOT CLICK
CHECK IGNITION SWITCH AND STARTER RELAY AND INSPECT WIRING. REPAIR OR REPLACE.
★ TROUBLE OVER

RELAY CLICKS

STARTER SPINS
Symptom B

CONNECT JUMPER ACROSS STARTER RELAY

ENGINE DOES NOT CRANK
CHECK CONNECTIONS AND CABLES, CHECK FOR LOCKED STARTER-DRIVE OR HYDROSTATIC LOCK. REPAIR OR REPLACE.
★ TROUBLE OVER

ENGINE CRANKS
REPLACE RELAY
★ TROUBLE OVER

It is important to troubleshoot logically, as shown in this chart. Courtesy Ford Motor Company.

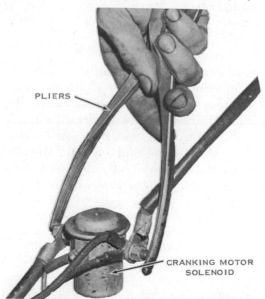

PLIERS

CRANKING MOTOR SOLENOID

A pair of pliers can be used to short across the terminals of a solenoid for a rough test. If the solenoid switch is defective, shorting across the terminals will activate the cranking motor.

The teeth can be worn flat (black arrow) causing engaging trouble, or the freewheeling unit can freeze up, causing the armature to throw its windings as shown in the next illustration.

Charging System

The first test of the generator charging system is to isolate the trouble to either the generator or regulator. To do this, ground the field terminal of the regulator externally. If the generator now charges, the trouble is in the regulator. If the generator does not charge, it is at fault. (The wiring of Ford generators is reversed, so the field terminal of the regulator must be externally connected to the generator output terminal to make the same test.) **Caution:** *Do not ground the field terminal of a heavy-duty, dual-point, Delco-Remy regulator, or you will burn the voltage regulator*

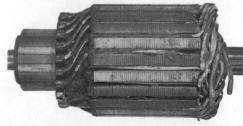

This is the result of a stuck freewheeling clutch on the cranking motor drive unit. Centrifugal force throws out the windings because the engine drives the unit at very high speeds. This is caused by the high gearing ratio (about 40:1) that exists between the engine and the unit.

264

contacts. To test a system with this type of regulator, disconnect the field wire at the regulator and hold it against a metallic part of the car.

To troubleshoot an alternator charging system, it is necessary to excite the field winding by connecting a jumper wire from the output terminal to the field terminal while the engine is idling. If the alternator now charges, the trouble is in the regulator.

Repairing a Cranking Motor

The cranking motor is used only three or four times a day, but these starts are generally with a cold engine. The thickened oil places a heavy strain on the motor bushings which, after a time, wear enough to allow the armature to drag on the field pole pieces. The extra internal drag slows the motor, thereby drawing more current.

Tools and Equipment

$7/16$, $9/16$ and $5/8$ inch combination end wrenches; screwdriver; bushing punch; hammer; lathe and equipment; growler; hacksaw blade.

PROCEDURE

1. Disconnect the grounded battery cable, and then remove the cable leading to the cranking motor.

2. Remove the motor.

3. Remove the cover and disconnect the two field-to-brush leads.

4. Remove the two long body screws holding the case together.

5. Separate the three castings.

6. Clean all parts, except the armature and the cranking motor drive, in clean solvent.

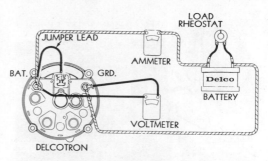

To troubleshoot an alternator charging circuit, connect a jumper wire from the battery terminal to the field. This shorts the regulator out of the circuit. Courtesy Delco-Remy Division, General Motors Corporation.

7. Rebush the drive-end housing, using a special punch.

8. Replace the four brushes. Tighten the ground brush screws.

9. Test the field for continuity and ground. There must be a continuous circuit between the two brushes or between the brush connectors. The fields must not be grounded.

10. Test the brush plate. Two brush holders must be grounded and two insulated from the plate.

11. Test the armature for shorted coils, open circuit, and ground. The open circuit and shorted coil tests are best determined by a visual inspection. For an open circuit, inspect the commutator where the wires are soldered. An open circuit is indicated by melted solder which will be found as a strip on the inside of the cover band. Resolder if necessary. Shorted armature coils are due to a foreign object wedging itself between the armature and case. A visual inspection will reveal this type of trouble. Sometimes the bars can be straightened but be sure to make the ground test after straightening.

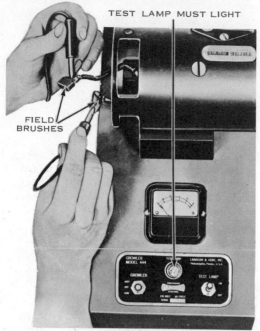

TEST LAMP MUST LIGHT

FIELD
BRUSHES

12. True the commutator in a lathe.

13. Lubricate the two bushings with cup grease and reassemble the cranking motor.

14. Test the assembled unit with a battery and two cables.

15. Install the cranking motor on the engine. Replace the battery cables.

Truing a Commutator

The brushes of the cranking motor and generator "ride" on the commutator of the armature. After long use, the commutator becomes pitted and grooved. When overhauling a generator or cranking motor, it is necessary to true the commutator in a lathe so that the new brushes will seat properly.

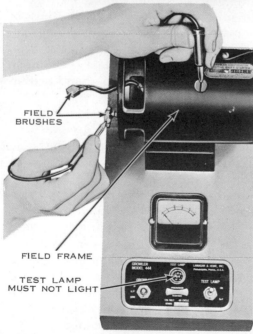

FIELD
BRUSHES

FIELD FRAME

TEST LAMP
MUST NOT LIGHT

Testing the fields for continuity (top) and ground (bottom). Courtesy Dodge Division, Chrysler Corporation.

INSULATED
BRUSH HOLDERS

BRUSH
PLATE

GROUNDED BRUSH HOLDERS

TEST LAMP

Testing the brush holders for ground. Courtesy Dodge Division, Chrysler Corporation.

Tools and Equipment

Lathe; armature; armature headstock and tailstock chucks.

PROCEDURE

1. Place the headstock drive belt on the small pulley (high speed).

2. Install the armature in the headstock chuck, with the commutator end to the right.

3. Tighten the chuck jaws.

4. Start the motor to test the armature trueness. **Caution:** *The commutator bearing must turn true without the tailstock supporting it.*

5. To true an armature:
• Loosen the chuck jaws.
• Turn the armature approximately ¼ turn.

• Tighten the chuck jaws and start the motor to recheck.
• If necessary, repeat until the armature turns true.

6. Position the tailstock chuck until the brass jaws encircle the shaft.

7. Tighten the chuck jaws and release slightly for turning clearance. Tighten the tailstock chuck lock.

8. Tighten the tailstock lock.

9. Lubricate the armature shaft where it revolves in the brass jaws.

10. Position the tip of the cutting tool at the center line of the shaft by adjusting the rocker arm under the tool holder.

11. Adjust the side of the tool against the end of the commutator. Leave a slight clearance so that only the tip of the tool touches the side.

The lathe is used to true a commutator. Note the use of the special tailstock chuck which supports the shaft exactly as it is when the armature is revolving in the cranking motor. How many simple machines can you identify in this picture?

HEADSTOCK CHUCK

CHUCK JAW ADJUSTER

COMMUTATOR

ARMATURE SHAFT

CUTTING TOOL

TOOL-POST BOLT

TRAVERSE-FEED HANDWHEEL

TAILSTOCK CHUCK LOCK

BRASS JAWS

TAILSTOCK CHUCK

TAILSTOCK LOCKS

TAILSTOCK-POSITIONING HANDWHEEL

TOOL HOLDER

ROCKER ARM

CROSS-FEED HANDLE

AUTOMATIC TRAVERSE FEED HANDLE

12. Tighten the tool-post bolt.

13. Turn on the motor.

14. Turn the cross-feed handle until the tool takes a light cut.

15. To engage the automatic traverse feed, lift up the handle.

16. To stop the automatic traverse feed at the end of the cut, push the feed handle down. Complete the cut by hand feed.

17. Undercut the mica from between the commutator bars.

18. Remove the armature and clean up the lathe.

19. Retest the armature in the growler to make sure that small brass cuttings have not shorted it.

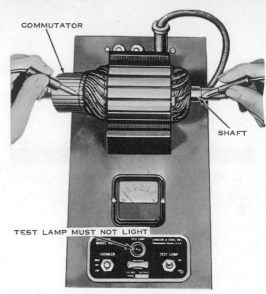

Testing for a ground. The commutator must not be grounded. Courtesy Dodge Division, Chrysler Corporation.

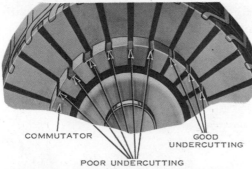

The correct and incorrect ways to undercut a commutator. Courtesy Ford Motor Company.

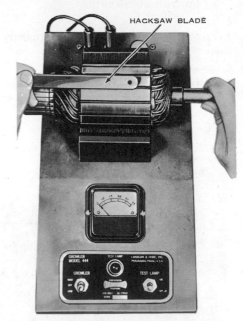

Testing the armature for shorted coils. The hacksaw blade will vibrate if the armature is bad. Courtesy Dodge Division, Chrysler Corporation.

Testing the armature coils for open circuits. The blade should spark each time contact between two segments is made. Some testers are equipped with special prods and a meter which takes readings of current induced in each coil.

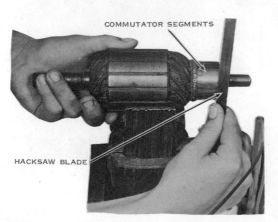

Repairing a Generator

The common causes of generator failure are overloading and worn brushes. Overloading is caused by improper adjustment of the regulator or high voltage (bad connections in the charging circuit). Worn brushes are the result of an out-of-round commutator, which causes arcing.

Tools and Equipment

Generator; ½ and 7⁄16 inch combination end wrenches; 13⁄16 inch socket and handle; screwdriver; growler; continuity tester; hacksaw blade.

PROCEDURE

1. Remove the generator from the engine.

2. Remove the cover band and disconnect the field-to-brush wires.

3. Remove the two long bolts holding the assembly together and separate the generator into three sections.

4. To disassemble the armature:

• Clamp it in a vise, across the laminations. **Caution:** *Never clamp a bearing surface in a vise or you will damage it.*

• Remove the pulley retaining nut and the pulley.

• Remove the Woodruff key.

• Slide the bearing end plate assembly from the shaft.

• Disassemble the end plate and remove the bearing.

5. Clean all parts in solvent, except the ball bearing and the armature.

6. Test the armature for shorted coils by placing a hacksaw blade over the windings while turning it in a growler. The hacksaw blade will vibrate if the armature is shorted.

7. Test the armature for open circuit by measuring the output of pairs of commutator segments while turning it.

8. Test the armature for ground. There shouldn't be any continuity between the commutator and the shaft.

9. Test the brush holders; one holder should be grounded and the other one insulated.

10. Test the fields for continuity and ground. There must be a continuous circuit through the fields but they must not be grounded.

11. Turn the commutator in a lathe.

12. Undercut the commutator so that the mica is below the copper.

13. Retest the armature to make sure that you did not short it during the turning process.

14. Assemble the end plate after lubricating the ball bearing.

BRUSH HOLDERS

Testing the brush holders for ground. Courtesy Dodge Division, Chrysler Corporation.

269

15. Assemble the drive mechanism to the armature.

16. Lubricate the brush holder plate bushing and assemble the three parts of the generator. **Caution:** *Do not overlubricate this bushing or the excess will run onto the commutator, forming an insulator.*

17. Install the main brush and connect it to the wire lead.

18. Install the ground brush and connect it to the ground lead.

19. Install the generator.

20. Cycle the generator by flashing the battery wire across the generator armature lead. This phases the generator polarity to the car battery so that it will charge correctly.

Adjusting a Cutout, Current Regulator, and Voltage Regulator

Because the voltage and current regulators are constantly vibrating, some arcing is unavoidably present. Eventually, the points become oxidized which opens the field circuit and stops the generator. Because the voltage regulator does most of the work, its points generally require the service. Clean the points with a fine file, and then pass a piece of tape, saturated with carbon tetrachloride, between them to remove any remaining particles of dirt and metal.

A simple electrical adjustment is all that is necessary to restore the unit to good working order. If the regulator has been taken apart for repairs, the air gaps must be adjusted before the electrical adjustments can be made.

Tools and Equipment

Screwdriver; long-nosed pliers; generator test bench; regulator; generator.

PROCEDURE

To Adjust the Cutout Relay

① Mount the generator and regulator on the test stand. Make the connections as shown. Tighten the *GEN-REG* control by turning it to the right until it is reasonably tight. Turn the *MOTOR* control gradually to the right to increase the generator speed until the contact points close. Take a *voltage* reading at this point. Decrease the motor speed until the cutout points open. Take an *ammeter* reading at this point.

② Adjust by bending the cutout return spring so that the points close between 12.0 to 12.5 volts. The points should open between one to four amperes discharge as the motor speed is decreased.

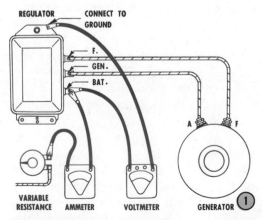

Connections for separate meters. The variable resistance is needed only when the voltage is low due to a discharged battery. Courtesy Delco-Remy Division, General Motors Corporation.

270

ture directly above the contacts. Measure the air gap between the armature and the center of the core. To adjust the air gap, loosen the two screws at the rear of the armature and raise or lower it as required. Check the point opening and adjust it to specifications by bending the upper armature stop as shown. Connect the battery lead, and then retest the cutout voltage setting.

To Adjust the Voltage Regulator

④ Turn the *MOTOR* control to the right and adjust the generator speed to 2,000 rpm. Gradually increase the resistance by turning the *GEN-REG* control to the left until the voltage regulator points vibrate. When the regulator is operating, the ammeter reading will gradually decrease as the resistance is increased, but the voltmeter reading must remain constant. Adjust the voltage setting by turning the adjusting screw.

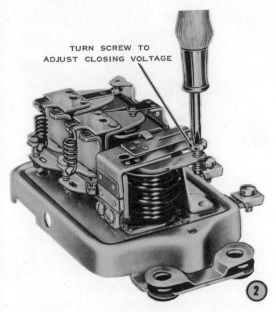

TURN SCREW TO ADJUST CLOSING VOLTAGE

②

③ If the cutout cannot be adjusted to specifications, it is because the air gap is incorrect. To adjust the air gap, first disconnect the battery lead from the regulator, and then press on the arma-

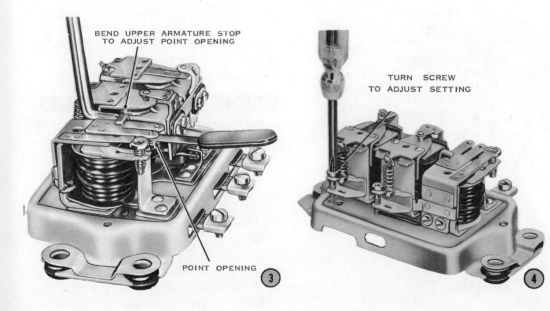

BEND UPPER ARMATURE STOP TO ADJUST POINT OPENING

POINT OPENING

③

TURN SCREW TO ADJUST SETTING

④

271

To Adjust the Current Regulator

⑤ Block the voltage regulator points into a closed position by inserting a piece of fiber insulator between the armature and the core. Adjust the drive motor speed until the current regulator points vibrate. (Ammeter reading does not increase.) Adjust the current setting by turning the current regulator adjusting screw.

⑥ If the regulator cannot be adjusted properly to specifications, it may be necessary to adjust the air gap. To do this, disconnect the battery lead to the regulator, and then push down on the armature until the contact points are just touching. Measure the air gap between the armature and the core. Adjust by loosening the contact bracket mounting screw as shown and then raising or lowering the contact mounting bracket as required. Connect the battery lead, and then retest the voltage setting as before.

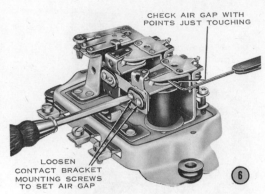

CHECK AIR GAP WITH POINTS JUST TOUCHING

LOOSEN CONTACT BRACKET MOUNTING SCREWS TO SET AIR GAP

⑥

Repairing an Alternator

Alternators are relatively troublefree, but they are still subject to some mechanical and electrical difficulties. Shorts and open circuits do occur, and bearings require replacement occasionally. In addition, alternators contain rectifying diodes which sometimes open or short, causing a lowered alternator output or a discharged battery.

Tools and Equipment

5.5" Delcotron; $^5/_{16}$" Allen wrench; $^3/_8$", $^7/_{16}$", and $^{15}/_{16}$" combination end wrenches; torque wrench with $^{15}/_{16}$" socket; Spin-tite with $^5/_{16}$" and $^{11}/_{32}$" sockets; pliers; screwdriver.

PROCEDURE

① Hold the alternator in a vise, clamping the mounting flange lengthwise. Keep the shaft from turning with a $^5/_{16}$" Allen wrench while you remove the pulley retaining nut. Take off the special washer, pulley and fan assembly, and the spacer.

② Remove the four through-bolts, and then break the end frames loose by prying at the bolt locations.

③ Remove the slip-ring end frame with the stator assembly. Remove the

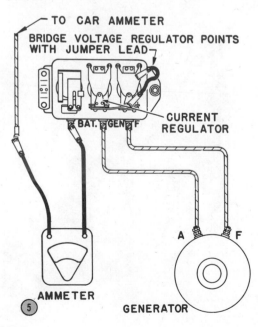

TO CAR AMMETER

BRIDGE VOLTAGE REGULATOR POINTS WITH JUMPER LEAD

BAT. GEN F

CURRENT REGULATOR

AMMETER

A   F

GENERATOR

⑤

PULLEY

ALLEN WRENCH

(1)

rotor assembly from the drive-end plate.

④ Remove the three stator lead attaching nuts, and then separate the stator from the end frame. Remove the two brush holder retaining screws, bend up the terminal lead, and then lift the brush holder assembly from the end frame.

⑤ Remove the heat sink from the end frame by first removing the "Bat" and "Gnd" terminals.

(2)

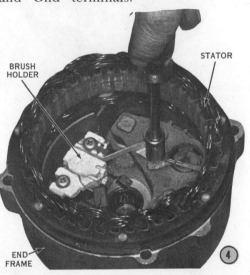

BRUSH HOLDER

STATOR

END FRAME

(4)

END FRAME

ROTOR

(3)

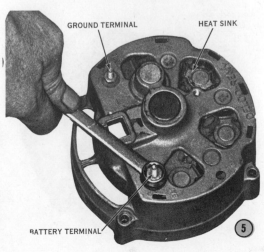

GROUND TERMINAL

HEAT SINK

BATTERY TERMINAL

(5)

HEAT SINK

(6)

(6) Turn the end frame over, and then remove the one heat sink retaining screw. Carefully lift out the heat sink. **Caution:** *Don't drop any of the washers and insulators.*

TESTING

(7) Test the rotor for a ground or open circuit by placing the ohmmeter leads on the two slip rings as shown at the bottom. The meter should register the specified field resistance of about 5 ohms. Position one ohmmeter lead on the shaft and one on a slip ring as shown at the top. The meter should read an open circuit; otherwise, the field winding is grounded. Replace the rotor if either of the tests is not up to specifications.

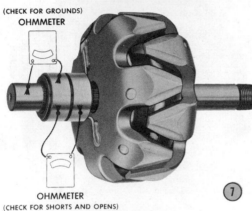

(CHECK FOR GROUNDS)
OHMMETER

OHMMETER
(CHECK FOR SHORTS AND OPENS)

(7)

(8) To test the stator for a ground, connect an ohmmeter test lead from any stator lead to the frame as shown at the lower right. The meter should read OPEN. If a reading is obtained, the winding is grounded and the stator is defective. Use an ohmmeter between each pair of stator leads as shown at the left. If the meter reads high in any one section, that one is open circuited. Because of the low resistance of the stator windings, it is extremely difficult to locate shorted coils. However, check each coil for visible heat discoloration, which would be an indication of such a defect.

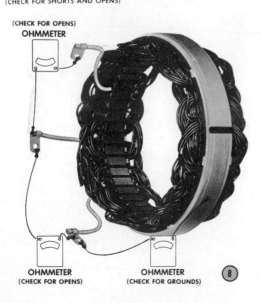

(CHECK FOR OPENS)
OHMMETER

OHMMETER
(CHECK FOR OPENS)

OHMMETER
(CHECK FOR GROUNDS)

(8)

(9) The diodes can be tested with a special diode tester, by using an ohmmeter, or by means of a 12-volt test lamp and a battery. **Caution:** *Don't use a 110-volt tester, or you will destroy the diodes.* To use an ohmmeter, adjust the meter to its lowest scale, and then make the test lead connections as described. To test the diodes, connect one test lead

274

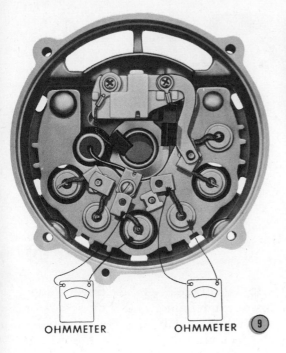

OHMMETER   OHMMETER   (9)

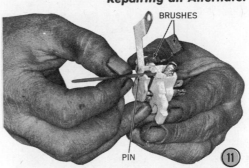

Repairing an Alternator

BRUSHES

PIN   (11)

ASSEMBLING

(10) To assemble the Delcotron, first install the heat sink in the end frame. Use this illustration to be sure that you have correctly positioned all of the insulators and spacers; otherwise, the heat sink will be grounded, and the alternator will not charge.

(11) Assemble the brush holder. **Caution:** *Make sure that the brushes are not contaminated by lubricant.* If so, they should be cleaned with trichlorethylene before assembly. To assist in assembly, install the plastic retaining pin as shown. The pin will hold the brushes in position, and it can be removed later through the end frame.

to the heat sink and the other to the diode lead. Observe the reading, reverse the test leads, and then observe the reading again. A good diode will allow electricity to pass in only one direction. If the reading is the same in both directions, the diode being tested is defective. Test each of the other diodes in a similar manner.

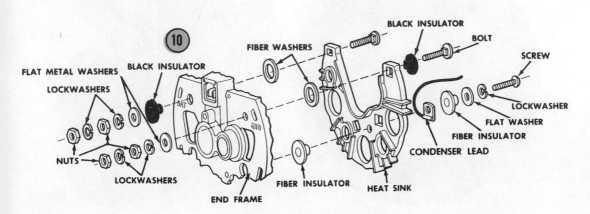

FLAT METAL WASHERS   BLACK INSULATOR   FIBER WASHERS   BLACK INSULATOR   BOLT   SCREW

LOCKWASHERS

NUTS

LOCKWASHERS   END FRAME   FIBER INSULATOR   HEAT SINK   CONDENSER LEAD   FIBER INSULATOR   FLAT WASHER   LOCKWASHER

(10)

PIN

12

ROTOR

14

⑫ Install the assembled brush holder in the end frame, and then secure it with the two retaining screws. Keep the plastic retaining pin in place until the alternator is completely assembled.

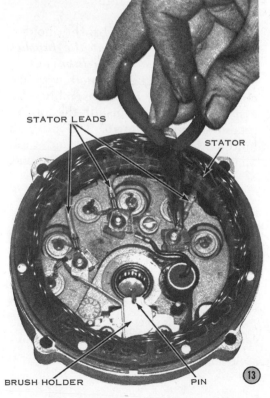

STATOR LEADS

STATOR

BRUSH HOLDER   PIN

13

SPACER

15

⑬ Install the stator, align each stator lead with its terminal screw, and then secure them in place with the retaining nuts.

⑭ Slip the rotor into the end frame.

⑮ Replace the spacer, and then install the drive-end plate.

⑯ Install and tighten the four through-bolts. Pull out the brush retaining pin which will allow the brushes to drop into their proper positions on the slip rings.

⑰ Install the spacer, fan and pulley assembly, special washer, and the retaining nut.

⑱ The retaining nut must be tightened to 40-50 ft-lbs. torque. This can be done by keeping the shaft from turning with the special adapter and Allen wrench as shown.

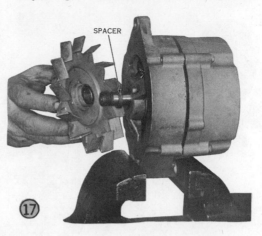

SPACER

⑰

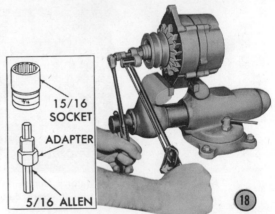

15/16 SOCKET

ADAPTER

5/16 ALLEN

⑱

Adjusting a Delcotron Two-Unit Regulator

Air gap adjustments must be made with the regulator removed from the car. Electrical settings must be checked and adjusted after making the mechanical adjustments, and these must be made on the car. It is normal for the contacts to be sooty or discolored after a relatively short period of operation. **Caution:** *Voltage regulating contacts must never be cleaned as they are made of special material that will be destroyed by an abrasive.*

PIN

⑯

After rebuilding, an alternator is bench-tested with its regulator to be sure that it is adjusted to factory specifications before the units are installed in a vehicle.

FEELER GAUGE

① To check the field relay contact point opening, insert the specified feeler gauge blade as shown. If an adjustment is required, bend the armature stop.

② Check the field relay air gap with the contact points just touching. If an adjustment is required, bend the flat contact spring. **Note:** *The air gap adjustment is not necessary if the opening and closing voltages are within specifications.*

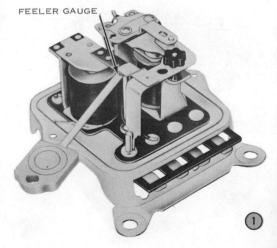

278

③ To check the voltage regulator contact point opening, measure the gap as shown with the lower contacts just touching. Adjust by bending the upper contact arm, being careful not to bend the hinge.

④ To check the air gap, measure it with a feeler gauge between the armature and core when the lower contacts are touching as shown. To adjust the air gap, turn the nylon nut on the contact support. **Note:** *Only an approximate setting can be made by the feeler gauge method.* The final air gap setting may have to be varied in order to obtain the specified voltage setting.

⑤ The field relay closing voltage adjustment must be made on the car with the engine not running. Connect a voltmeter and a 50-ohm variable resistance into the wiring harness as shown. **Note:** *This variable resistance in series from the battery to the field relay coil will enable you to change the voltage of the system.* Turn the ignition switch to OFF and the resistor to the OPEN position.

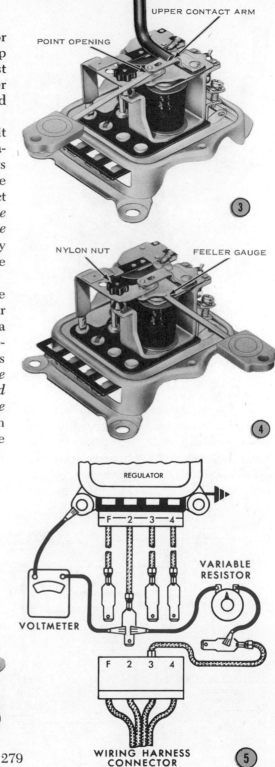

POINT OPENING

UPPER CONTACT ARM

③

NYLON NUT   FEELER GAUGE

④

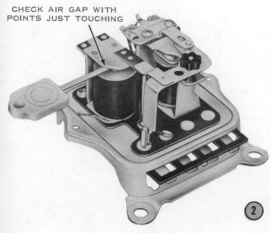

CHECK AIR GAP WITH POINTS JUST TOUCHING

②

REGULATOR

F — 2 — 3 — 4

VOLTMETER

VARIABLE RESISTOR

F   2   3   4

WIRING HARNESS CONNECTOR

⑤

279

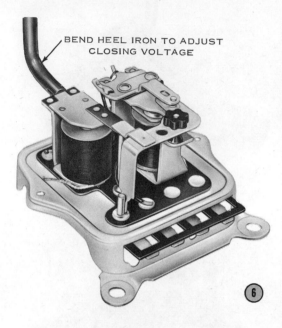

BEND HEEL IRON TO ADJUST CLOSING VOLTAGE

⑥

meter and a ¼ ohm resistor (25 watts) in series with the BATT terminal of the alternator as shown. Turn the high-beam headlights on and the heater blower motor to high speed in order to load the charging system, and then run the engine at 1,500 rpm for at least 15 minutes in order to warm the regulator to operating temperature. Cycle the regulator voltage control by disconnecting and reconnecting the four-terminal regulator connector. Read the voltage; if it is between 13.5 and 15.2 volts, the unit is operating properly and no adjustment is necessary.

⑧ If an adjustment is required, disconnect the four-terminal connector with the engine operating at 1,500 rpm, remove the regulator cover, and then reconnect the four-terminal connector. **Caution:** *The four-terminal connector must be disconnected before removing or installing the regulator cover to prevent damage by a short circuit.* Adjust the regulator to 14.2 to 14.6 volts by turning the adjusting screw at the rear of the regulator as shown. Disconnect the four-terminal connector, re-install the regulator cover, and then re-install

⑥ Slowly decrease the resistance and note the closing voltage of the field relay. Adjust by bending the heel iron as shown.

⑦ The final voltage regulator settings must be made on the car and, as the voltage varies with temperature, this must be measured ¼″ away from the regulator cover. To check the voltage setting of the system, connect an am-

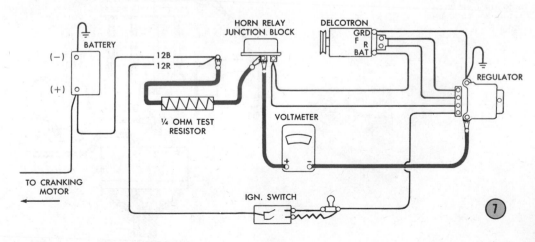

BATTERY   12B   12R   HORN RELAY JUNCTION BLOCK   DELCOTRON   GRD F R BAT   REGULATOR

(−)   (+)

¼ OHM TEST RESISTOR   VOLTMETER

TO CRANKING MOTOR   IGN. SWITCH   ⑦

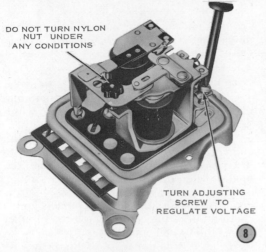

DO NOT TURN NYLON NUT UNDER ANY CONDITIONS

TURN ADJUSTING SCREW TO REGULATE VOLTAGE

⑧

⑨ To adjust the voltage setting on a transistor-type regulator, remove the pipe plug, insert a screwdriver into the slot as shown, and then turn it clockwise one or two notches to increase the setting or counterclockwise to decrease the setting. **Note:** *Each notch changes the voltage setting by approximately 0.3 volt.*

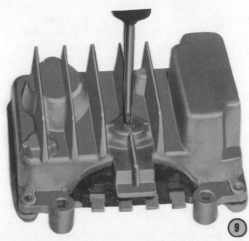

⑨

the four-terminal connector. Continue running the engine at 1,500 rpm for 10 minutes in order to re-establish the regulator internal temperature. Cycle the regulator by disconnecting and reconnecting the regulator four-terminal connector, and then recheck the operating voltage, which must be between 13.5 and 15.2 volts.

CHECK YOUR KNOWLEDGE

1. Of what four essential parts in the cranking motor composed?
2. What causes the cranking motor armature to rotate?
3. What are the two jobs of the drive mechanism?
4. What causes the overrunning-clutch type of cranking motor drive to mesh with the flywheel?
5. How is the engine prevented from spinning the armature with this type of drive?
6. Why are especially large switches required to operate the cranking motor?
7. What is the difference in function between the pull-in and hold-in windings of the cranking motor solenoid switch?
8. On what principle does a generator function?
9. What is the purpose of the brushes? Field coil? Commutator?
10. What is the difference between alternating and direct current?
11. What type of current does a generator produce?
12. What is the basic difference between an AC and a DC generator?
13. What are eddy currents?
14. How does an alternator change its current to DC?
15. Why does a generator need some sort of control device?
16. How is the modern generator controlled?
17. What three switches are part of the control unit?
18. What is the purpose of each of the three switches?
19. When does the cranking motor require service?
20. What are the operating results of a defective cranking motor?
21. What two instruments are necessary for accurate troubleshooting of the electrical system?

Self-Check Tests

TRUE-FALSE

1. The cranking motor brushes ride on the commutator so that they can pick up current to energize the fields.
2. The cranking motor armature is supported by ball bearings.
3. Only the solenoid pull-in winding is energized during the cranking process.
4. During the cranking process, the primary of the ignition coil operates on about 9 volts.
5. When the engine is being cranked, the primary of the ignition coil receives its current through the primary resistor.
6. The generator functions on the principle that electricity produces magnetic lines of force.
7. An AC generator is more efficient than a DC generator at low car speeds.
8. The AC generator requires a rectifier.
9. The cutout opens and closes the circuit between the battery and the generator.
10. The voltage regulator opens the field grounding circuit when the voltage increases to its setting.
11. Cranking motors require infrequent service.
12. To localize generator trouble, the field terminal of the regulator can be grounded externally on most charging systems.

MULTIPLE CHOICE

1. Which of the following is *not* a part of the cranking motor: a) brushes; b) fields; c) regulator; d) armature?
2. Which of the following is *not* a part of the cranking motor drive: a) flywheel; b) solenoid; c) shifting yoke; d) overrunning clutch?
3. Which of the following is *not* a part of the cranking motor control circuit: a) solenoid; b) transmission-neutral switch; c) ignition switch; d) overrunning clutch?
4. Which of the following is *not* a part of the generator: a) regulator; b) armature; c) fields?
5. Which of the following is *not* a part of an AC generator: a) armature; b) fields; c) commutator; d) slip rings?
6. Which of the following is *not* a part of the generator regulator: a) cutout relay; b) voltage regulator; c) current regulator; d) solenoid?
7. Which of the following requires the most service: a) cranking motor; b) cranking motor control switches; c) generator; d) generator regulator?

COMPLETION

1. _____ ride on the armature commutator and carry current to the armature windings of the cranking motor.
2. The _____ _____ has to transmit the cranking torque to the engine and has to disconnect the cranking motor from the engine when it starts.
3. The _____ winding of the solenoid is connected across the switch contacts and is shorted out of the circuit when the plunger closes the switch contacts.
4. A _____ is a machine which converts mechanical energy into electrical energy.
5. The _____ keeps the generator current flowing in the same direction.
6. An AC generator changes AC current into DC by means of a _____ _____ _____ _____.
7. _____ currents overheat the armature and waste power.
8. An _____ generator always contains slip rings.
9. Regulation or control of the generator output is accomplished by controlling the strength of the generator _____.
10. The _____ _____ closes the circuit between the generator and the battery when the generator is operating at a speed sufficient to charge the battery.
11. The _____ regulator serves to limit the maximum current that the generator can produce.
12. The regulator generally requires more service than does the generator itself because its _____ _____ are in constant operation.

MATCHING

1. Cranking motor drive	a. Generator
2. Cranking motor control	b. Cutout relay
	c. Solenoid
3. Manufactures electrical energy	d. Slip rings
4. Changes direction of current flow	e. Commutator
5. AC generator	f. Overrunning clutch
6. Generator regulator	

Chapter | 10

The Ignition System

The ignition system produces and delivers high-voltage surges to the spark plugs at the correct intervals and in "time" with the engine. Each surge produces a spark at the plug gap which ignites the fuel-air mixture in the cylinder.

The ignition system consists of the battery, ignition switch, ignition coil, resistor, distributor, spark plugs, and low- and high-tension wiring.

Ignition Coil

To change the storage battery voltage to one high enough to be able to jump the gap across the spark plug, a transformer, called an *ignition coil,* is used. It contains a *primary* and *secondary* winding, the latter is made of thousands of turns of very fine wire. Its high-turn ratio develops about 20,000 volts, enough to jump the spark plug gap with ease.

The voltage generated across the secondary is larger when the primary circuit is broken than when it is made because of the difference of speed of

the magnetic lines of force. When the primary circuit is first energized, the lines of force move away from the soft-iron core relatively slow because of

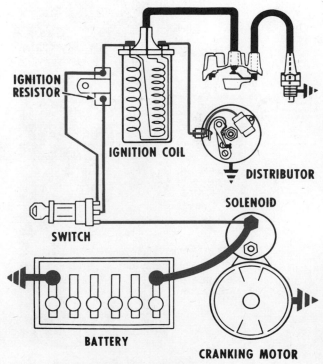

Parts of the ignition system.

283

their attraction for iron. When the primary circuit is broken, the rate of speed is increased by the attraction of the lines of force for the soft-iron core and because of the reversed current in the primary due to self induction.

In addition, a condenser is connected in the primary circuit to speed up the rate of change of the magnetic lines of force when the primary circuit is opened. Without a condenser, the primary current would arc across the contact points as they began to open; therefore the current flow in the primary circuit would decrease with relative slowness. With a condenser, the arc is minimized, and the primary current is shut off suddenly, increasing the secondary output sharply.

Resistor

A resistor, connected in the primary circuit, performs several important functions. During starting, the resistor is shorted out of the circuit to compensate for the lowered battery voltage, caused by the heavy drain of the starting motor. At low car speeds, the primary current flows through the resistor for a comparatively longer period of time causing it to heat, which raises its resistance and reduces current flow. This action keeps the coil cooler and reduces the load on the distributor contact points. At high engine speeds, the current flows through the primary circuit for a comparatively shorter period which lets the resistor cool, allowing more current to flow. This increases the generated secondary

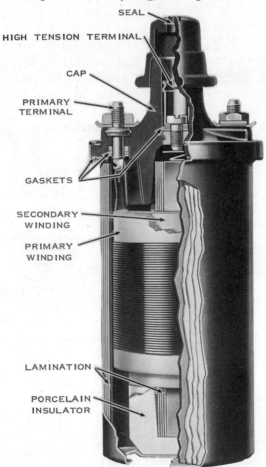

SEAL
HIGH TENSION TERMINAL
CAP
PRIMARY TERMINAL
GASKETS
SECONDARY WINDING
PRIMARY WINDING
LAMINATION
PORCELAIN INSULATOR

Parts of the ignition coil. Courtesy Delco-Remy Division, General Motors Corporation.

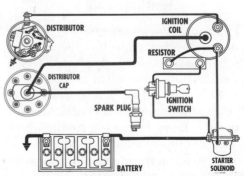

DISTRIBUTOR
IGNITION COIL
RESISTOR
DISTRIBUTOR CAP
SPARK PLUG
IGNITION SWITCH
BATTERY
STARTER SOLENOID

Typical ignition system. Note the resistor by-pass wire (red) from the starter solenoid to the primary of the ignition coil. This by-pass circuit is designed to supply the primary of the ignition coil with system voltage during the cranking cycle. Courtesy Allen Electric and Equipment Company.

voltage at high engine speeds where it is needed because the efficiency of the ignition coil falls off rapidly with speed.

Ignition Distributor

The distributor contains a set of contact points, a condenser, a cam (with eight lobes for a 8-cylinder engine), vacuum and centrifugal timing advance mechanisms, rotor, and distributor cap.

The contact points are separated by the rotating cam, "timed" to piston movement. The cam's position, relative to the piston's position, is advanced and

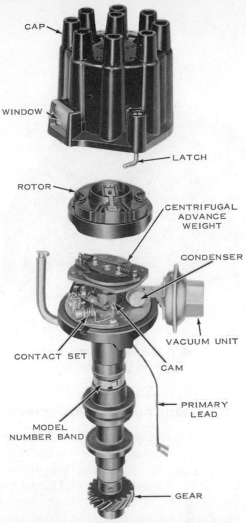

Exploded view of a distributor. Courtesy Delco-Remy Division, General Motors Corporation.

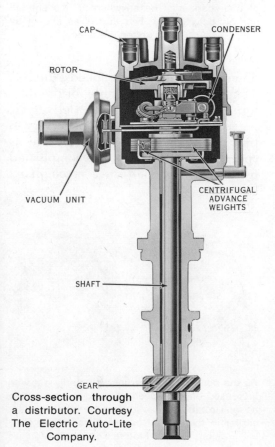

Cross-section through a distributor. Courtesy The Electric Auto-Lite Company.

retarded by two mechanisms: vacuum and mechanical. The distributor is driven at half engine speed so all the cylinders are fired during each two revolutions.

The ignition coil high-voltage surge is delivered to the center terminal of the distributor cap from where it passes through the metallic insert to the rotor, which revolves and distributes the voltage surge to the correct spark plug wire and thence to the plug.

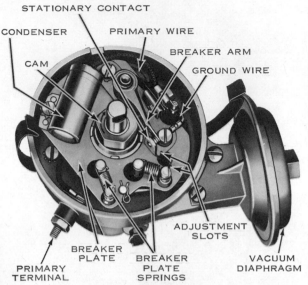

STATIONARY CONTACT
CONDENSER
PRIMARY WIRE
CAM
BREAKER ARM
GROUND WIRE
ADJUSTMENT SLOTS
BREAKER PLATE
BREAKER PLATE SPRINGS
PRIMARY TERMINAL
VACUUM DIAPHRAGM

Parts of the Ford breaker plate assembly. Courtesy Ford Motor Company.

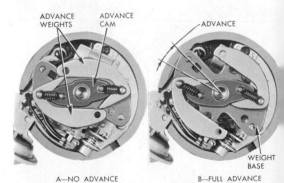

SPARK ADVANCE IN DEGREES ON FLYWHEEL BEFORE UPPER DEAD CENTER

PART THROTTLE-CAR DRIVE LOAD CURVE. SECURED BY VACUUM CONTROL.

FULL THROTTLE - MAX. POWER CURVE SECURED BY CENTRIFUGAL CONTROL

MILES PER HOUR
10 20 30 40 50 60 70

The total timing advance is dependent upon the mechanical and vacuum advance positions. As these vary considerably according to engine speed and throttle position, the actual position of the spark may be anywhere in the shaded portion between the two curves as shown by this dotted line.

Automatic Advance Mechanisms

Because it takes about $1/350$ of a second for complete combustion, it is necessary to time the spark to jump the gap just before the piston reaches TDC, so that the pressure of the expanding gas will be at a maximum when the piston starts down. At higher engine speeds, there is a shorter interval available for the mixture to ignite, burn, and deliver its power. Consequently, it is necessary to time the spark earlier in the cycle as speed increases. This is accomplished by a *centrifugal advance mechanism,*

CONTACT POINT ADJUSTING SLOT
CONTACT SET ATTACHING SCREW
VACUUM UNIT
CONDENSER
CONTACT SET
CIRCUIT BREAKER PLATE ASSEMBLY
PRIMARY LEAD

Parts of the Delco-Remy breaker plate assembly. Courtesy Delco-Remy Division, General Motors Corporation.

ADVANCE WEIGHTS
ADVANCE CAM
ADVANCE
WEIGHT BASE

A—NO ADVANCE   B—FULL ADVANCE

As the centrifugal governor weights fly out with increased engine speed, they advance the cam against rotation so as to time the ignition spark earlier in the cycle. Courtesy Buick Motor Division, General Motors Corporation.

286

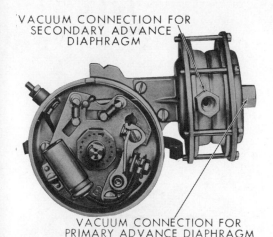

VACUUM CONNECTION FOR SECONDARY ADVANCE DIAPHRAGM

VACUUM CONNECTION FOR PRIMARY ADVANCE DIAPHRAGM

Some Ford distributors use two vacuum advance units, one of which takes the place of the mechanical advance mechanism of a conventional distributor. Courtesy Lincoln-Mercury Division, Ford Motor Company.

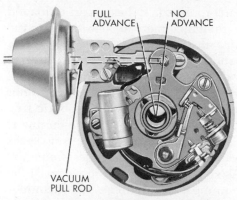

FULL ADVANCE   NO ADVANCE

VACUUM PULL ROD

A high vacuum below the throttle valve is used to turn the distributor point support plate in order to advance the ignition timing. Courtesy Allen Electric and Equipment Company.

containing two control arms which move out against spring tension with increased rpm. This motion is transmitted to the breaker cam so that it is advanced with regard to the distributor shaft.

Under part-throttle operation, there is a high vacuum in the intake manifold; consequently, a smaller amount of fuel-air mixture is delivered to the cylinders. The mixture is less highly compressed and, therefore, burns slower so additional spark advance is provided to increase fuel economy. To provide this, based on intake manifold vacuum conditions, a *vacuum advance mechanism*

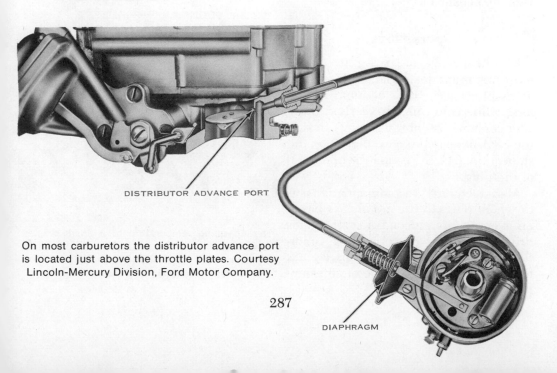

DISTRIBUTOR ADVANCE PORT

On most carburetors the distributor advance port is located just above the throttle plates. Courtesy Lincoln-Mercury Division, Ford Motor Company.

DIAPHRAGM

287

is incorporated. It has a spring-loaded diaphragm connected so as to rotate the entire distributor or the breaker plate assembly. The spring-loaded side of the diaphragm is airtight and connected to a vacuum passage in the carburetor bore, which is on the atmospheric side of the throttle plate when the engine is idling. In this position there is no spark advance, so the engine idles smoothly.

As soon as the throttle moves past the vacuum passage opening, the vacuum is applied to the airtight chamber so the diaphragm moves against spring tension. This moves the distributor or breaker plate to an advanced position.

As the engine is accelerated, intake manifold vacuum drops sharply, and the vacuum advance unit retards the spark to minimize detonation which would otherwise occur with advanced ignition timing and high combustion chamber pressures. The total timing advance of an engine, therefore, is regulated by the positions of both the vacuum advance and the centrifugal advance mechanisms.

Spark Plugs

The heat range of spark plugs is the most important design factor. Hot-operating plugs have long ceramic insulators, while cold plugs have short ones. The ceramic insulator passes its heat to the coolant chamber and, therefore, the shorter the path the cooler the operation of the plug.

Manufacturers' recommendations as to which plugs to use are always based on average driving conditions. Engines driven under severe operating conditions require cooler running spark plugs than those specified, while engines op-

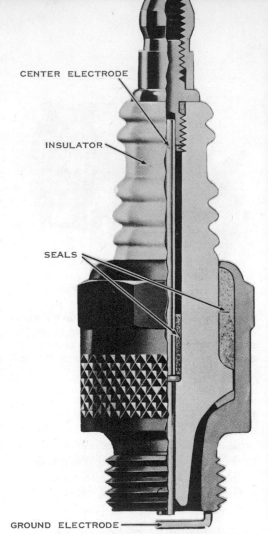

CENTER ELECTRODE

INSULATOR

SEALS

GROUND ELECTRODE

Parts of the spark plug. Courtesy Champion Spark Plug Company.

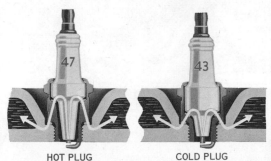

HOT PLUG   COLD PLUG

The operating temperature of a spark plug is determined by the length of the path the heat is required to travel. Courtesy AC Spark Plug Division, General Motors Corporation.

A normal operating spark plug shows a light gray color. Courtesy Champion Spark Plug Company.

Too hot a spark plug will blister and burn. Courtesy Champion Spark Plug Company.

erating at continuously slow speeds require hotter running plugs.

A spark plug that is too cool for an engine will foul with oil and eventually short out. A plug that is too hot will blister and ignite the mixture prematurely with its white-hot insulator. A properly operating plug will remain just hot enough to burn off the small amount of oil always present in the combustion chamber gases. The insulator is grayish tan.

The width of the gap between the electrodes determines the size of the spark passed through the compressed fuel-air mixture; the wider the gap, the larger the spark. At idle speeds, the compressed mixture contains relatively few fuel particles and, therefore, needs a larger spark for complete combustion. Wider gaps are desirable for smoother idling but cut down top engine speed. It takes a higher coil output to jump a wider gap and, therefore, at high speeds (where coil output drops off sharply) a wide gap causes engine misfiring. A closer gap makes the idle rougher but increases top engine speed.

Transistor-Controlled Ignition Systems

The performance of today's conventional ignition system is satisfactory for the average driver. The higher speeds used in racing, however, sorely overtax our present systems. Then, too, as engine improvements usually require additional ignition reserve, the time is approaching when the present system will not be able to carry the load. In general, the weakest link in the present system is the contact points. To raise the output

Too cool a spark plug will become sooted. Courtesy Champion Spark Plug Company.

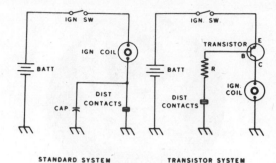

STANDARD SYSTEM   TRANSISTOR SYSTEM

These diagrams can be used to compare the parts which make up a conventional ignition system (left) with a contact-triggered, transistor-type ignition system.

voltage, is is necessary to raise the current passed through the contacts. Contact points presently carry approximately 4 amperes, and increasing this load one ampere dramatically reduces their service life. Then, too, at high speeds, the present contact points bounce, causing erratic operation and high-speed failure. The rubbing block of the contact point set is another weak point. As it wears, the point gap decreases, retarding the ignition timing.

To overcome the defects of the present ignition system, engineers have designed two types of transistor ignition systems: a contact-triggered and a magnetic-pulse type. The first advantage of the transistor systems over the standard contact-point type ignition system is that available output voltages can be increased substantially, because the contact points do not have to carry high currents. The second advantage is that service problems are minimized because of the lower current passing through the points. The magnetic-pulse type transistor system has a further advantage in that there are no contact points—this eliminates rubbing block wear and resulting ignition timing prob-

lems of the former system and should, therefore, eliminate most of the ignition service problems.

Since the natural temperature limitations of the germanium transistors involved must not exceed 160° F., the pulse amplifier is generally mounted ahead of the radiator or in the passenger compartment.

CONTACT-TRIGGERED TRANSISTOR IGNITION SYSTEM

The diagram shows a comparison of the standard ignition circuit (left) with that of the transistor circuit. Note that the distributor contacts trigger the transistor, but no condenser is required. The transistor circuit operates as follows: when the contacts are closed, current flows from the transistor emitter (E) through the base (B), rendering the transistor conductive. Under these conditions, current flows through the transistor from the emitter (E) to the collector (C), and then through the coil primary. Because the transistor can pass currents higher than a set of contact points, the system can be made to operate on about 6.5 amperes. This, of course, increases the magnetic field of the coil and the efficiency of the system. When the contact points break the circuit, the transistor emitter-to-base circuit is broken, making the transistor non-conductive. This breaks the coil primary circuit, causing a high voltage surge in the coil secondary circuit.

Ignition timing is accomplished by the cam and breaker points, as in the present system. In the transistor system, the contact points operate on currents of one ampere or less; therefore, their life is extended. This system uses only a single transistor; therefore, the initial

290

cost is lower than that of the magnetic-pulse type system.

MAGNETIC-PULSE TRANSISTOR IGNITION SYSTEM

The conventional contact point set is replaced by a magnetic-pulse type generator, the output of which is amplified by a transistor circuit, which is used to trigger another transistor circuit in series with the primary of the ignition coil.

The circuit diagram shows the magnetic-pulse type generator (magnetic pick-up), which is housed in the distributor, connected to the trigger transistor TR_1. TR_2 amplifies the trigger signal and turns TR_3 on and off in time with the magnetic pulses from the distributor.

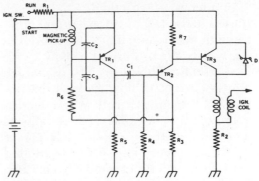

Schematic diagram of the magnetic-pulse type ignition system.

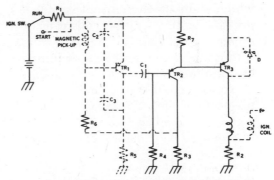

The solid lines show the path of current through a transistorized ignition circuit when the ignition switch is turned ON. The system is not firing in this diagram.

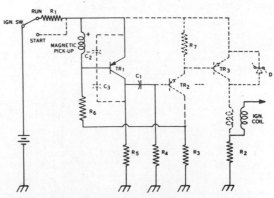

When the magnetic-pulse distributor generates an electric pulse, the current flow is as indicated by the solid lines, and the spark plug fires.

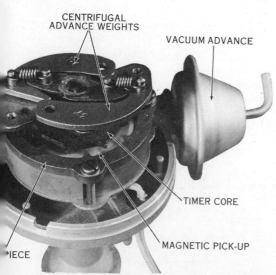

CENTRIFUGAL ADVANCE WEIGHTS

VACUUM ADVANCE

TIMER CORE

MAGNETIC PICK-UP

PIECE

A magnetic-pulse distributor looks quite conventional from the outside; however, a timer core and magnetic pick-up replace the conventional contact point set assembly. The pole piece is a steel plate having equally spaced internal teeth—one tooth for each cylinder. Courtesy Oldsmobile Division, General Motors Corporation.

In operation, with the ignition switch turned to the ON position, current flows through the base of TR_2. This turns TR_2 on, which allows current to flow in the base of TR_3. This turns TR_3 on, which allows current to flow through the primary of the ignition coil. When the distributor turns, a pulse of electricity is generated as the magnetic pole pieces pass each other. This pulse is applied to the base of TR_1, causing it to conduct, which then sends a reverse voltage to the base of TR_2, causing it to shut off. This interrupts the base current of TR_3, which shuts off the current flow in the primary of the ignition coil, causing a secondary discharge.

Ignition timing must be accomplished by a timing light, as the exact moment of spark generation cannot be noted precisely as with the separation of conventional contact points. However, ignition can be timed roughly by noting when the pole pieces of the pulse generator pass each other. Because there are no contact points, service problems should be less than the contact-triggered transistor system.

Capacitor-Discharge Ignition System

Since 1967, the magnetic-pulse, transistor ignition system has been further improved by new circuitry, and is now known as a C-D (capacitor-discharge) ignition system. In the new circuit, a charged capacitor is discharged into the primary of the output coil (ignition coil) to produce a more intense, high-voltage surge. The diagram is divided into four separate circuit blocks by means of dashed lines: timing, power supply, switching, and tachometer circuits.

The timing circuit receives the small

This is a diagram of the C-D ignition system. It differs from the older transistor ignition systems in that the energy stored in a capacitor is discharged into the primary of the output coil in order to intensify the spark. The thyristor is the switch which times the discharge of the capacitor.

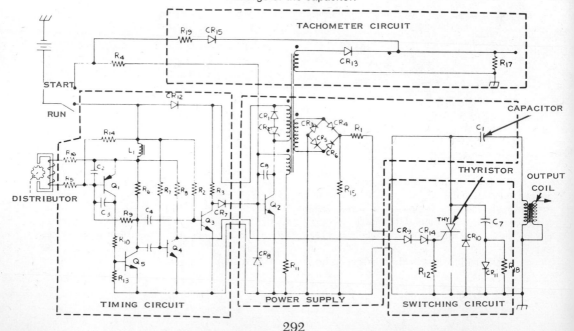

292

electric timing pulses produced by the magnetic-pulse generator mounted within the distributor. The power supply circuit develops about 300 volts DC to charge the capacitor for discharging into the output coil. The switching circuit stores energy in the capacitor C_1 and, on "command" from the timing circuit, discharges this stored energy into the primary of the output coil. The thyristor (THY) is an electric switch which "gates" the stored energy into the ignition coil. Peak currents as high as 30 amperes and voltages up to 450 are handled by this circuit. Because the pulse is of extremely short duration, most tachometers will not function when connected in the usual way. Therefore, a special tachometer circuit is provided which is pulsed from an added winding on the transformer.

Service Note

A very important service note to observe is that the dwell angle meter and rpm indicator you use must have a high enough internal resistance to keep the transistors from conducting. If the meter resistance is too low, enough current will flow through the meter to trigger the transistor into a semi-conducting state, which will cause excessive heating of the transistor and eventual self-destruction. A transistor is designed to operate either fully on or fully off. This is critical only when test instruments are connected across the distributor contacts.

Service Procedures

Ignition system adjustments are very critical and have a great deal to do with the efficient operation of the engine. Slight misadjustments show up as hard starting, poor acceleration, jerking, and poor gas mileage. Some troubles will begin to appear at 5,000 miles of operation and may be quite pronounced at 10,000 miles. Most car owners have an engine tune-up at 10,000 mile intervals.

An engine tune-up consists of testing, cleaning, adjusting, and, if necessary, overhauling each of the following units: battery and cables, generator charging circuit, fuel pump, carburetor, distributor, ignition coil, high-tension wiring, and spark plugs. Worn parts are either reconditioned or replaced; the distributor, spark plug, and carburetor adjustments are made; and the engine is balanced for smooth operation.

Troubleshooting

If the engine has been properly tuned, it is seldom necessary to do any troubleshooting because all parts have been reconditioned and accurately adjusted. However, an occasional engine will not function properly even after a good tune-up. Then it becomes necessary to isolate the trouble. To do this successfully, a mechanic must possess a thorough understanding of the function and operation of each part.

Many specialized types of troubleshooting equipment have been developed, and their use demands knowledge and skill on the part of the mechanic. However, there are several basic tests using minimum equipment with which all mechanics should be familiar. First, by logical procedures, he should be able to localize the trouble to the compression, fuel, or the ignition system. Further testing with accurate equipment will isolate the defective unit.

A student must learn how to adjust a distributor on a syncrograph. The distributor is the heart of the ignition system and it must function with precision if the engine is to run properly.

Portable type of tune-up equipment performs an important function in diagnosing trouble. Courtesy Allen Electric & Equipment Company.

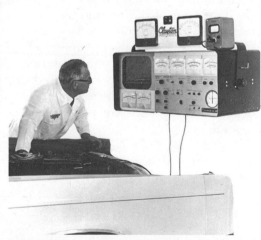

This tune-up equipment contains all the essential meters in a cabinet which can be wheeled up to the car.

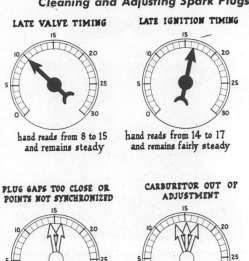

COMPRESSION GAUGE   RUBBER TIP

A compression gauge will isolate compression troubles to the defective cylinder. Courtesy Chevrolet Motor Division, General Motors Corporation.

A vacuum gauge is highly desirable for making carburetor adjustments and for troubleshooting. By connecting it to the intake manifold, the gauge will read the amount of vacuum that the engine is pulling, which is an indication of its efficiency. Several troubles can be traced by the readings, as illustrated.

Cleaning and Adjusting Spark Plugs

Spark plugs are subjected to the same high temperatures as is the combustion area. In normal operation the gap between the electrodes widens, due to wear caused by the electrical discharges and the constant heat of combustion. After 5,000 miles, the gap is widened enough to affect engine and starting performance. In many cases, a rich mixture from a defective carburetor or excessive oil from worn rings fouls a spark plug so that it does

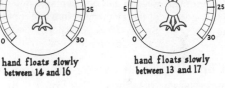

LATE VALVE TIMING

hand reads from 8 to 15 and remains steady

LATE IGNITION TIMING

hand reads from 14 to 17 and remains fairly steady

PLUG GAPS TOO CLOSE OR POINTS NOT SYNCHRONIZED

hand floats slowly between 14 and 16

CARBURETOR OUT OF ADJUSTMENT

hand floats slowly between 13 and 17

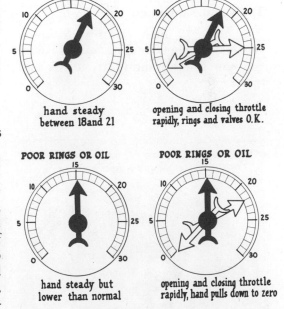

NORMAL MOTOR

hand steady between 18 and 21

NORMAL MOTOR

opening and closing throttle rapidly, rings and valves O.K.

POOR RINGS OR OIL

hand steady but lower than normal

POOR RINGS OR OIL

opening and closing throttle rapidly, hand pulls down to zero

Vacuum gauge readings and their interpretations.

The amount of mileage can be estimated according to the wear of the electrodes in a spark plug. Courtesy AC Spark Plug Division, General Motors Corporation.

not fire. Whenever tuning an engine, it is necessary to remove the spark plugs to clean and regap them.

Tools and Equipment

⅝ and ¹³⁄₁₆ inch deep spark plug sockets; ratchet; buffing wheel; wire gapping gauge; sand-blast cleaner and tester.

Heavy deposits of carbon are a sure indication of burning oil. Courtesy AC Spark Plug Division, General Motors Corporation.

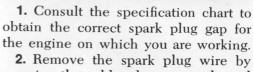
1. Consult the specification chart to obtain the correct spark plug gap for the engine on which you are working.

2. Remove the spark plug wire by grasping the rubber boot securely and twisting it to break the seal. Then remove the wire by pulling it by the boot. **Caution:** *Don't pull on the wire or you will break the carbonized conductor and cause engine misfiring.* Remove the spark plug with a deep socket and wrench. **Caution:** *Be careful not to tilt the socket or the top porcelain will crack.*

3. If the spark plug is not oil soaked, buff it on a wire brush. Make sure to buff the points and threads. If the spark plug is fouled with oil, wash it in solvent before sandblasting; otherwise, the sand will stick to the oil film.

4. To sandblast a spark plug, insert it into its correct-sized rubber adaptor. Lift the tester head and slip the spark plug and adaptor assembly into the ring

SPARK PLUG

Tilt the spark plug to direct the sand blast to all parts of the porcelain. Courtesy Champion Spark Plug Corporation.

296

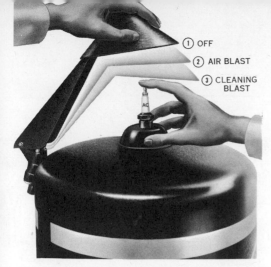

① OFF
② AIR BLAST
③ CLEANING BLAST

The handle of this spark plug cleaner has three positions. Courtesy AC Spark Plug Division, General Motors Corporation.

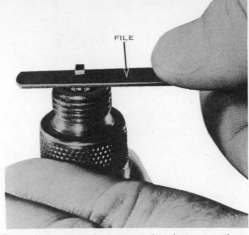

FILE

One of the most important cleaning operations is the removal of corrosion between the electrodes. Courtesy AC Spark Plug Division, General Motors Corporation.

over the sand blast nozzle. Turn on the air and turn the plug slowly until it is clean.

5. Clean the sand and dust from the plug by blowing it off with compressed air.

6. File the electrodes flat and then adjust them to the proper clearance. Make all adjustments by bending the side electrode. **Caution:** *Do not bend the center electrode or you will crack the porcelain.*

Measuring and correcting the spark plug gap. Never bend the center electrode or you will crack the porcelain. Courtesy AC Spark Plug Division, General Motors Corporation.

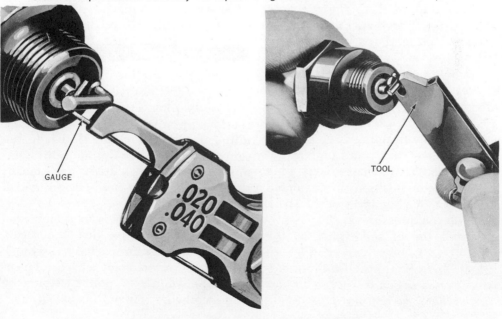

GAUGE

.020
.040

TOOL

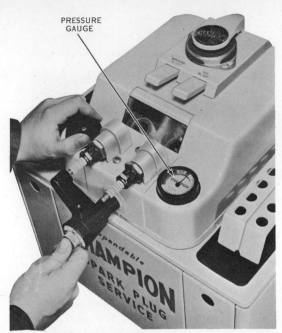

PRESSURE GAUGE

The insulated handle resting on top of the left-hand spark plug contains a high voltage contact. Courtesy Champion Spark Plug Company.

7. To test the spark plug, screw it into the correct-sized reducer. Thread the plug and reducer assembly into the left spark plug tester hole. Install a new spark plug in the right-side hole for comparison. Position the insulated arm on the cleaned spark plug terminal. Unscrew the air pressure needle valve to obtain the highest pressure.

8. Press the button on top of the insulated arm to produce an electric spark. Look in the polished metal mirror to see how the plug is firing. The spark should be strong and blue at 150 psi pressure. To compare your plug with a new one, position the insulated arm on the new plug and test the spark under different pressures.

9. Install the cleaned plug in the engine. Use a new gasket. Tighten to 20 ft.-lbs. of torque. **Caution:** *Excessive pressure bends the electrodes which changes the gap setting.*

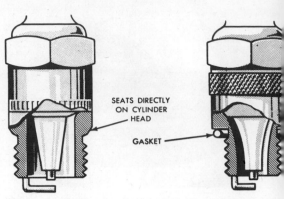

SEATS DIRECTLY ON CYLINDER HEAD

GASKET

Square shoulder spark plugs require a gasket; the taper-seated types do not. Courtesy Lincoln Division, Ford Motor Company.

Testing an Ignition Coil

There are three ways to test the output of a coil, two of which are quick but not accurate. A third method employs accurate testing equipment. The first two methods are generally used to locate the trouble, the third to verify it.

Tools and Equipment

Insulated screwdriver; Allen E-1403 Coil-Condenser Tester; assorted coils.

PROCEDURE

1. For the initial test, remove a spark plug wire and hold it $\frac{1}{2}$ inch from the base of the plug. Start the engine. If the spark jumps this gap with the engine idling, the coil is good. However, because this is a check on the entire ignition system, a weak spark here means ignition trouble but not necessarily coil trouble.

2. The second test is to remove the center wire from the distributor cap. Turn on the ignition switch. Remove the cap and rotor. Place a piece of insulation between the points. Hold the center coil wire $\frac{1}{2}$ inch from any ground.

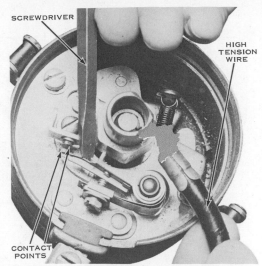

SCREWDRIVER

HIGH TENSION WIRE

CONTACT POINTS

Operating the points with a screwdriver.

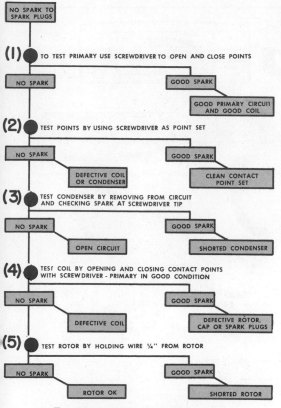

NO SPARK TO SPARK PLUGS

(1) TO TEST PRIMARY USE SCREWDRIVER TO OPEN AND CLOSE POINTS

NO SPARK

GOOD SPARK

GOOD PRIMARY CIRCUIT AND GOOD COIL

(2) TEST POINTS BY USING SCREWDRIVER AS POINT SET

NO SPARK

DEFECTIVE COIL OR CONDENSER

GOOD SPARK

CLEAN CONTACT POINT SET

(3) TEST CONDENSER BY REMOVING FROM CIRCUIT AND CHECKING SPARK AT SCREWDRIVER TIP

NO SPARK

OPEN CIRCUIT

GOOD SPARK

SHORTED CONDENSER

(4) TEST COIL BY OPENING AND CLOSING CONTACT POINTS WITH SCREWDRIVER - PRIMARY IN GOOD CONDITION

NO SPARK

DEFECTIVE COIL

GOOD SPARK

DEFECTIVE ROTOR, CAP OR SPARK PLUGS

(5) TEST ROTOR BY HOLDING WIRE ¼" FROM ROTOR

NO SPARK

ROTOR OK

GOOD SPARK

SHORTED ROTOR

Troubleshooting the ignition system.

A good spark should jump with the engine idling.

Slide a screwdriver up and down while making contact with the insulated point. The tip of your screwdriver is touching the base plate and you are using it as a set of points. A long high-tension spark means a good coil. A weak spark means ignition trouble but not necessarily coil trouble. This second test is valuable because it eliminates one of the most common possibilities—burned ignition points.

By insulating the points, a screwdriver can be used to take the place of a defective point set.

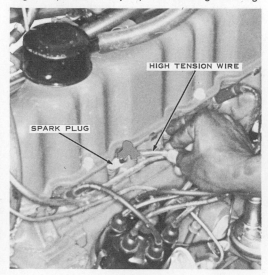

HIGH TENSION WIRE

SPARK PLUG

299

HIGH TENSION WIRE

INSULATOR

SCREWDRIVER

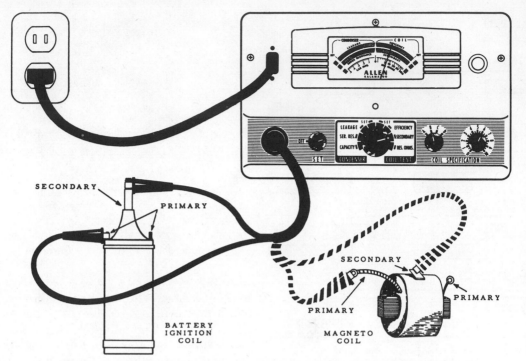

Connecting an ignition coil to a tester. Courtesy Allen Electric & Equipment Company.

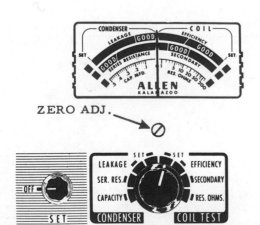

With the switch off, adjust the needle to the middle of the scale. Courtesy Allen Electric & Equipment Company.

3. To test the coil, remove it from the car and attach the test lead clips to both primary terminals.

4. Adjust the meter needle to *zero* with the *set control* turned to the *off* position.

5. Turn the *selector switch* to the *coil set* position and adjust the *set control* so that the meter needle rests on the *set* mark.

6. To make an efficiency test, adjust the *control knob* to the specifications given in the chart for the coil you are testing.

7. Note the meter reading on the upper right-hand scale. A reading in the *good* zone indicates that the coil is up to specifications.

With the switch on, turn the set control knob until the needle rests on the right end of the scale. Courtesy Allen Electric & Equipment Company.

With the control knobs set to the manufacturer's specifications, the needle should register in the *good* section for coil efficiency. Courtesy Allen Electric & Equipment Company.

With the control knob set to the *secondary* position, the needle should come to rest in the *good* section of the secondary scale. Courtesy Allen Electric & Equipment Company.

To test for a grounded condition, the control knob should be on the *res. ohms* position. Courtesy Allen Electric & Equipment Company.

8. To test the coil secondary, turn the *selector switch* to the *secondary* position and connect the test lead clips — one to the primary and the other to the secondary. Coils that do not register in the *good* zone should be replaced.

9. To test a coil for ground, where both ends of the primary are brought to outside terminals, connect one test lead to one primary terminal and the other to the case. The meter should read *zero* with the *selector switch* on the *res. ohms* position.

Testing a Condenser

A condenser is like a spring; it absorbs electrical energy when the points open to keep them from arcing and burning, and returns the energy to the coil which intensifies the spark. This process is known as charging and discharging. A condenser is always tested on a higher voltage than under which it operates. The condenser must be able to take a charge and hold it.

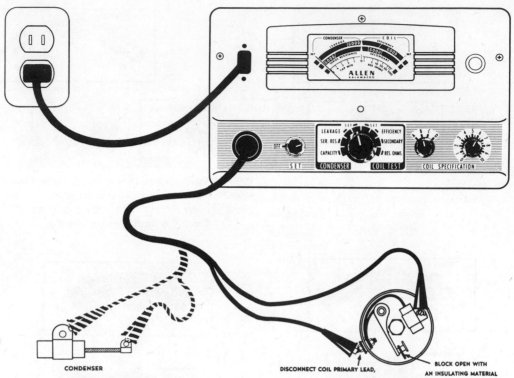

Connecting a condenser to the tester. Courtesy Allen Electric & Equipment Company.

Tools and Equipment

Allen E-1403 Coil-Condenser Tester; assorted condensers; screwdriver.

1. Remove the condenser from the car or disconnect the wire lead.

2. Attach the test lead clips to the condenser.

3. Adjust the meter needle to *zero* with the *set control* turned to the *off* position.

4. Turn the *selector switch* to the *condenser set* position and adjust the *set control* so that the meter needle rests on the *set* mark on the left side of the dial.

5. To make a leakage test, turn the *selector switch* to the *leakage* position and note the meter reading on the upper scale. A reading in the *good zone* indicates a condenser that is within recommended limits.

6. To make a series resistance test, turn the *selector switch* to the *ser. res.* position and note the meter reading on the middle scale. If the meter reads in the *red* zone, the condenser has excessive resistance and should be replaced.

7. To make a capacity test, turn the *selector switch* to the *capacity* position and note the meter reading on the lower scale. The reading should conform to the manufacturer's specifications, usually between 0.2 and 0.3 MFD.

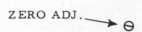

ZERO ADJ. ⟶

With the switch on, adjust the knob until the needle comes to rest at the left-hand side of the scale. Courtesy Allen Electric & Equipment Company.

With the switch off, adjust the screw until the needle comes to rest in the center of the scale. Courtesy Allen Electric & Equipment Company.

With the control knob set to *ser. res.*, the needle should come to rest in the *good* section of the middle scale. Courtesy Allen Electric & Equipment Company.

With the control knob set to *leakage,* the needle should come to rest in the *good* section of the top scale. Courtesy Allen Electric & Equipment Company.

With the control knob set to *capacity,* the needle should come to rest at the manufacturer's specified point. Courtesy Allen Electric & Equipment Company.

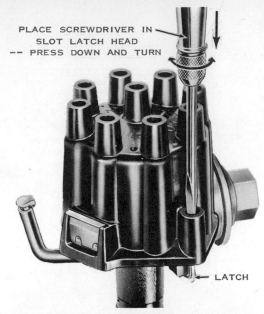

PLACE SCREWDRIVER IN SLOT LATCH HEAD -- PRESS DOWN AND TURN

LATCH

New distributor caps are retained by a latch which must be unseated with a screwdriver. Courtesy Delco-Remy Division, General Motors Corporation.

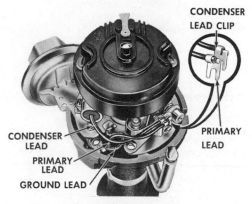

CONDENSER LEAD CLIP

CONDENSER LEAD

PRIMARY LEAD

PRIMARY LEAD

GROUND LEAD

The internal connections of the newer type distributor. Courtesy Delco-Remy Division, General Motors Corporation.

Cleaning Ignition Points

The ignition breaker points perform one of the most important duties for the automobile engine. They make and break the primary electrical circuit 8,000 times per minute when the car is traveling 40 mph. If they do not make a perfect electrical connection each time, the engine will miss and jerk. No wonder these points burn after 10,000 miles of service, causing such troubles as missing (jerking), hard starting, sluggishness, and poor gas mileage. To correct such conditions, the ignition points must be cleaned and respaced.

Tools and Equipment

Screwdriver; feeler gauges; emery wheel; engine in running condition.

PROCEDURE

1. Remove the distributor cap.
2. Turn the crankshaft until the rotor points to the front of the car. Mark its position with chalk or a scratch on the housing.
3. Loosen the clamp screw, vacuum connection line, and primary terminal.
4. Lift out the distributor.
5. Remove the screw holding the point spring in place.
6. Lift out the movable point.
7. Remove the retaining screw and the bottom point.
8. Face off both points squarely on the side of a fine emery wheel. **Caution:** *Be careful not to touch the face of the points with your fingers; otherwise, you will coat them with oil which is an insulator.*
9. Clean the remaining parts of the distributor in solvent.
10. Reinstall the points.
11. Measure and correct the point spring tension. It can be adjusted by either bending the spring or changing its position in the slotted hole.
12. Align the faces of the two points by bending the stationary point until they meet squarely and with full face contact.

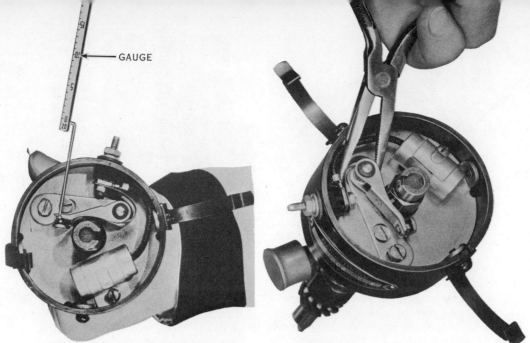

GAUGE

Measuring and adjusting breaker spring tension. Courtesy Delco-Remy Division, General Motors Corporation.

A frosted appearance indicates good operating conditions.

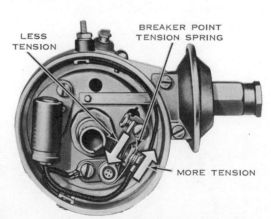

LESS TENSION

BREAKER POINT TENSION SPRING

MORE TENSION

Some springs have a slotted hole which can be moved to obtain the correct spring tension. Courtesy Ford Division, Ford Motor Company.

New points must be aligned to insure good electrical contacts. Courtesy Chevrolet Motor Division, General Motors Corporation.

A burned set of contact points which will cause hard starting and missing on acceleration.

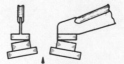

LATERAL MISALIGNMENT

PROPER LATERAL ALIGNMENT

CORRECT LATERAL MISALIGNMENT BY BENDING FIXED CONTACT SUPPORT NEVER BEND BREAKER LEVER

305

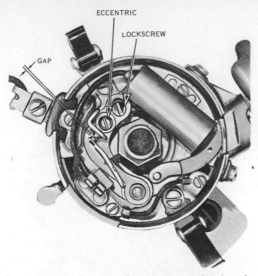

ECCENTRIC

LOCKSCREW

GAP

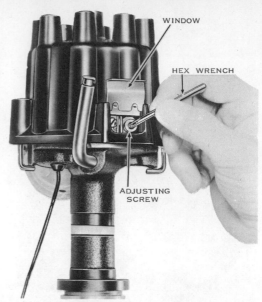

WINDOW

HEX WRENCH

ADJUSTING SCREW

On many distributors, the contact point gap is set to specifications by loosening the lockscrew and turning the eccentric until the gap is correct. Add an extra 0.003″ to the specification if you are installing new contact points. This will compensate for the initial rubbing block wear. Courtesy Plymouth Division, Chrysler Corporation.

The newer distributor provides for adjustment of the point gap with the engine idling. The gap is measured with a dwell meter. Courtesy Delco Remy Division, General Motors Corporation.

Some of the newer-type distributors have lubricating wicks, *which must never be oiled.* The end of the wick must just be touching the cam. Too much pressure will result in overlubrication and oxidation of the contact points. Replace the wick every 20,000 miles. Courtesy Chevrolet Motor Division, General Motors Corporation.

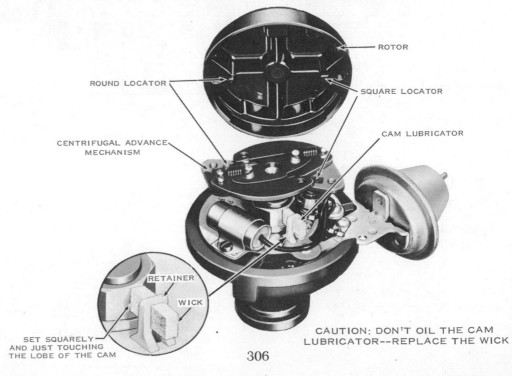

ROTOR

ROUND LOCATOR

SQUARE LOCATOR

CENTRIFUGAL ADVANCE MECHANISM

CAM LUBRICATOR

RETAINER

WICK

SET SQUARELY AND JUST TOUCHING THE LOBE OF THE CAM

CAUTION: DON'T OIL THE CAM LUBRICATOR--REPLACE THE WICK

13. Set the gap to specifications with a feeler gauge *which has been carefully wiped clean of grease and oil.*

14. Lubricate the automatic advance wick with a few drops of oil, and then install the rotor.

15. Lubricate the breaker cam with a light coating of cam lubricant. Turn the shaft until the lubricant rubs off on the back of the fiber rubbing block, where it acts as a reservoir and feeds lubricant as the fiber wears. Wipe the cam of excessive lubricant.

16. Reinstall the distributor in the engine with the rotor pointing to the front and in alignment with the scratch mark.

17. Set the ignition timing using a timing light.

Adjusting Points in a Dual-Point Distributor

The size of the high-tension spark depends on how much current is present in the primary of the coil the instant the points open. The longer the points remain closed, the greater the primary current buildup and the higher the induced voltage when the points open. On an 8-cylinder distributor with a single set of points, the length of time the points remain closed, when operating at high speed, is so short that the primary current does not increase to a high enough level for efficient operation.

On some V-8 engines, the build-up time is increased by using two sets of points. They are connected in parallel and are staggered about 8° in relation to each other. The over-lapping results in a longer dwell period. As they are wired in parallel, no spark occurs until both contact sets open.

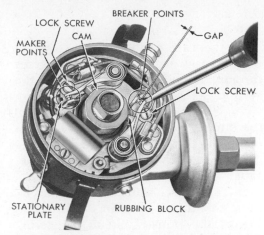

Point adjustments on a dual-point distributor. Courtesy Dodge Division, Chrysler Corporation.

Principle of operation of a dual-point set. Courtesy Dodge Division, Chrysler Corporation.

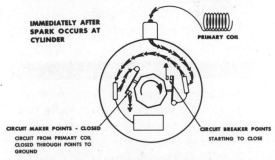

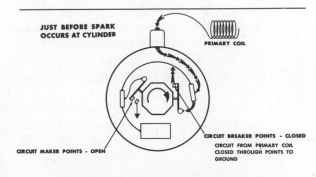

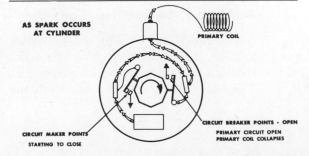

307

As the cam rotates, the first set of points closes, and primary current passes through the coil. As it rotates further, the second set closes, but since they are connected in parallel, it does not affect the circuit. Further rotation of the cam opens the first or "circuit maker" points. Again, the circuit is not interrupted because the second or "circuit breaker" points are still closed. Later in the cycle, the second set of points opens and breaks the primary circuit, triggering the secondary circuit. Thus, on a two-breaker distributor, one set of points closes the primary circuit and the other set opens it.

Cam angle determines the length of time the points remain closed. Courtesy Delco-Remy Division, General Motors Corporation.

Tools and Equipment

Screwdriver; feeler gauges; dual-point set distributor.

PROCEDURE

1. Clean the points or install new sets.
2. Rotate the distributor shaft until the rubbing block of one set of points is on the high spot of the cam.
3. Adjust the clearance to specifications, using a clean feeler gauge blade. **Note:** *The lock screw should be loosened just enough for the stationary point to move with a slight drag; otherwise, it will be difficult to set the points accurately.*
4. Turn the distributor shaft until the rubbing block of the second set of points is on the high spot of the cam. Adjust the second set of points in the same manner.

Adjusting the Ignition Cam Dwell

The length of the high-tension spark is dependent on the length of time the ignition points remain closed (dwell). The longer the dwell, the more time the primary has to build up magnetism. This is important at high speeds where the dwell period is very short due to the high rotating speed of the cam.

Without specialized equipment, points are spaced with a feeler gauge, which measures the distance the points open, rather than the more important consideration of the amount of time the circuit is energized. With a distributor analyzer, the dwell or cam angle is measured with meters and can, therefore, be more accurately set.

Tools and Equipment

Distributor analyzer; distributor; screwdriver.

PROCEDURE

1. Mount the distributor in the analyzer and attach the test lead to the primary terminal. Do not disconnect the condenser.
2. Adjust the chart so that the specifications of the distributor being tested are in view.

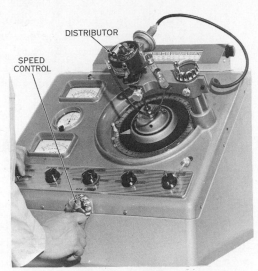

SPEED
CONTROL

DISTRIBUTOR

A distributor set in the analyzer for measuring point dwell and the advance mechanism operation. Courtesy Allen Electric & Equipment Company.

3. To test for breaker point resistance:
• Turn the *test selector switch* to the *point res.* position.
• Revolve the chuck by hand until the breaker points close.
• The cam angle meter should read in the OK zone. If it doesn't, there is excessive resistance caused by a faulty contact across the distributor points, primary leads, or a poorly grounded base plate; each of which may be checked by attaching the test lead first to the stationary contact, then to the movable contact, and finally to the low-tension distributor terminal for comparative checks.

4. To test the distributor insulation:
• Turn the *test selector switch* to the *cam angle* position.
• Revolve the chuck by hand until the contact points open.
• The cam angle meter should indicate zero reading, otherwise a short circuit to ground exists. This may be due to a poor primary terminal or lead insulation, a shorted condenser, poor insulation between the breaker spring and housing, or a short between the breaker arm and the breaker plate.

5. To test the mechanical operation:
• Turn the *test selector switch* to the *syncro.* position.
• Tighten the drive chuck securely on the distributor shaft.
• Turn the *motor control switch* to the *left* or *right* to correspond with the direction of rotation of the distributor being tested.
• Adjust the *rpm control* to vary the distributor speed between 400 and 4000 engine rpm. Erratic or faint flashes, preceding the regular flashes as the speed of rotation increases, can be caused by weak breaker arm spring tension or the breaker arm binding on its pivot pin.
• Operate the distributor at about 2500 engine rpm.
• Move the protractor scale so that the zero degree mark lines up with one of the neon flashes. The rest of the flashes should come within one degree of the cylinder indicating marks. A larger variation, erratic, or wandering flashes may be caused by a worn cam, a worn distributor shaft, or a bent shaft.

6. To adjust the cam angle:
• Turn the *cylinder selector switch* to the figure corresponding to the number of lobes on the cam of the distributor being tested.
• Turn the *test selector switch* to the *cam angle* position.
• Operate the distributor at about 1000 engine rpm.
• Adjust the distributor breaker point gap to the cam angle shown in the specifications.

Measuring the centrifugal advance by speeding up the drive motor and watching the number of degrees the arrows move along the scale as compared to the specified rpm. Courtesy Mercury Division, Ford Motor Company.

Bending the return spring to adjust the centrifugal advance mechanism. Courtesy Mercury Division, Ford Motor Company.

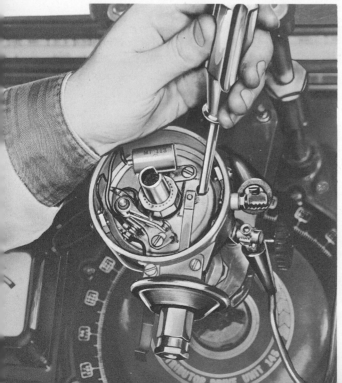

• If the distributor has dual breaker arms, block open one set with a piece of fiber while testing the other. Repeat the test for the first set of contacts.

7. To adjust the centrifugal advance mechanism:

• Turn the *test selector switch* to the *syncro.* position.

• Operate the distributor as slowly as possible, and move the protractor scale so that one of the flashes is at zero.

• Increase the distributor speed to correspond with the lowest speed shown in the specifications. Note the number of degrees the neon flash moved from the zero position and compare with specifications. If the advance does not conform to specifications, it should be adjusted, where possible, by bending the primary spring support (the one under tension) for the low rpm correction, and the secondary spring support (loose when the distributor is not rotating) for the high rpm correction.

8. To adjust the vacuum advance mechanism:

• Attach an adaptor fitting to the vacuum unit and connect the hose to it.

• Turn the *vacuum supply switch* to the *on* position.

• Adjust the *vacuum control knob* until the vacuum gauge registers the specified amount.

• Check the vacuum advance diaphragm for leakage by pinching the hose while observing the vacuum gauge. No change should occur if the unit is good.

• Operate the distributor at various speeds and compare the advance with specifications. If the readings do not agree at each test point, the vacuum control should be adjusted or replaced. Adjustment can be made by removing

310

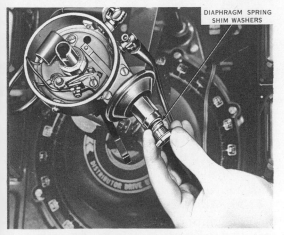

DIAPHRAGM SPRING
SHIM WASHERS

The vacuum advance can be adjusted by adding or removing shims. Courtesy Mercury Division, Ford Motor Company.

Sometimes the vacuum diaphragm tears. It can be tested by sucking on the fitting.

or installing washers behind the spring to change its tension.

• As a final check, reduce the distributor speed to 400 engine rpm. Remove all vacuum, and the spark advance should return to zero.

9. To test the distributor electrical circuit with the vacuum unit in operation:

• Turn the *test selector switch* to the *cam angle* position.

• Operate the distributor at about 2500 engine rpm.

• Vary the applied vacuum from zero to maximum and back again while watching the cam angle meter. Any change greater than 2 degrees may be caused by a worn breaker plate, worn breaker plate bushings or bearings, or worn bushings in the distributor housing.

Setting the Ignition Timing

For an engine to run at maximum efficiency, the combustion must occur precisely at the instant the fuel-air mixture is compressed to its highest point. The spark usually occurs a few degrees before top dead center on the compression stroke. To make sure of the exact setting, the specification chart must be consulted.

Tools and Equipment

Screwdriver; chalk; timing light; engine in running condition; spark plug socket and wrench.

PROCEDURE

1. Check the specification chart for the correct timing setting.

2. Turn the crankshaft and observe the flywheel or impulse neutralizer for timing marks. Stop when the pointer is at the ignition mark. Mark this point with a narrow band of white chalk or paint.

3. To install an overhauled distributor, turn the crankshaft until No. 1 piston is at top dead center of the firing position. This position can be checked by watching the valve action or holding

311

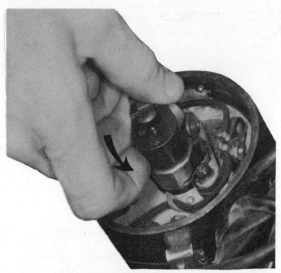

The rotor feels springy when turned in the direction of rotation. Courtesy Delco-Remy Division, General Motors Corporation.

a finger over the spark plug hole to feel the compression. The ignition spark must occur at the top of the compression stroke, and when the pointer is even with the white mark.

4. Note which direction the distributor turns by twisting the rotor while holding the shaft. The rotor will feel solid when twisted one way, and springy when twisted the other. **Note:** *The rotor turns in the springy direction (automatic advance springs).*

5. Adjust the distributor position so that the ignition points just start to open. Install the unit and tighten the clamp screw. **Caution:** *Check to see that you are working on the correct side of the cam by moving the rotor against its spring action. A slight movement of the rotor should open the points further,*

The firing order and placement of ignition wires on a Chevrolet V-8 engine. Courtesy Chevrolet Motor Division, General Motors Corporation.

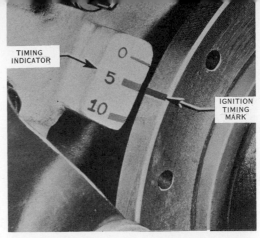

The timing marks are on a plate attached to the timing chain cover. An index mark is on the impulse neutralizer or a notch is cut into the flywheel pully. Courtesy Ford Motor Company.

not close them. If they close, you are working on the wrong side of the cam.

6. Install the distributor cap. Notice to which wire terminal the rotor points. Install No. 1 spark plug wire in this terminal.

7. Look up the specification chart for the firing order and install the high-tension wires in this order, after No. 1 wire, in the direction in which the rotor turns. For example, if the firing order of your engine is 1-5-3-6-2-4 and the rotor turns clockwise, No. 5 wire should follow No. 1 wire in a clockwise direction followed in order by 3-6-2-4, with No. 4 wire ending up next to No. 1 wire.

8. Install the coil high-tension wire in the center of the distributor cap.

9. Connect the low tension wires of the power timing light across the battery. Connect one high-tension wire to No. 1 spark plug terminal, the other to a good ground.

10. Disconnect the vacuum advance pipe at the carburetor or manifold to prevent the vacuum advance mechanism from operating, which would affect the timing. Tape up the hole to prevent the engine from drawing air into the manifold.

11. Start the engine and adjust it to idle at 500 rpm or less. (This is important to make sure that the mechanical advance unit is not operating.) Shine the light on the flywheel or impulse neutralizer and adjust the distributor so that the white chalk mark appears to be in line with the pointer. **Note:** *The impulse neutralizer is sometimes called the harmonic balancer.*

The neon flashes of the stroboscope make the impulse neutralizer appear to stand still.

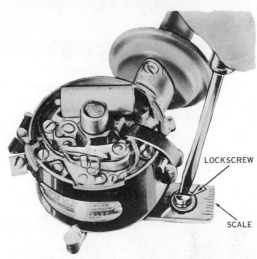

The ignition timing can be changed by loosening the retaining screw and turning the distributor the required number of degrees as noted on the degree scale or on the impulse neutralizer. Courtesy Dodge Division, Chrysler Corporation.

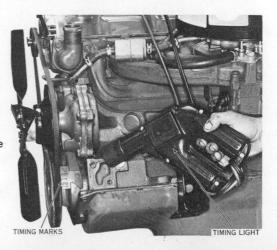

Testing the Engine for a Miss

An engine is composed of several cylinders constructed so as to fire successively, thus developing a smooth flow of power. If one cylinder does not operate properly, the engine jerks and loses power. A misfiring cylinder can be caused by a lack of spark, fuel, or compression.

Tools and Equipment

Engine; insulated screwdriver; testing wires; vacuum gauge; and spark plug wrench.

CARBON TRACKS

The carbon tracks at the bottom of the picture show a shorted distributor cap.

PROCEDURE

1. Accelerate the engine quickly and notice the stuttering sound of the exhaust. **Caution:** *Do not race the engine or you may damage it.* The stuttering can be felt only at low engine speeds on fast acceleration.

2. Connect a vacuum gauge and start the engine. Adjust the idle speed screw until the engine runs at about 2000 rpm.

3. Attach the main test clip to a *good* ground.

4. Short out all but the last two cylinders by attaching a wire test clip to each spark plug terminal. **Note:** *You will not get shocked if the main clip is properly grounded.* It may be necessary to advance the throttle as the cylinders are shorted out in order to keep the engine from stalling.

5. With the engine running on two cylinders, readjust the idle speed so that it runs as slowly as possible without stalling. Momentarily short out each of the operating cylinders in turn, so that the engine fires on a single cylinder. Uneven compression and ignition defects are immediately notice-

able. Accurate comparisons can be made by noting the vacuum gauge reading for each cylinder.

6. To run the engine on another pair of cylinders, change two shorting wires. Continue testing by operating the engine on each cylinder in turn. The cylinder with the defect is the one on which the engine does not run.

7. To stop the engine, back off the speed adjusting screw until the engine stalls. Remove the shorting wires.

The shorting wires are used to force the engine to operate on a single cylinder at a time. Naturally, it doesn't run on the defective one. Courtesy American Motors Corporation.

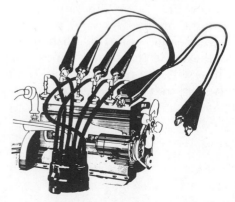

ISOLATING THE TROUBLE

8. Remove the spark plug wire from the defective cylinder and hold it ¼ inch away from the terminal. Start the engine and, if a spark jumps to the terminal, the trouble is either fuel, compression, or a defective spark plug.

9. If no spark jumps to the terminal, the trouble is in the ignition system.

10. Test the spark plug on a plug tester.

11. Check the compression with a compression gauge.

12. If the engine misses on adjacent cylinders, it may be caused by a blown cylinder head gasket or a leaking intake manifold gasket. A defective cylinder head gasket condition is indicated by a lack of compression in both cylinders. The leaky manifold gasket can be checked by wetting the suspected area with gasoline. If the gasket is leaking, the engine will smooth out as the gasoline is applied, and the leak area will dry quickly.

13. On an engine with a combination fuel pump having a cracked diaphragm, the two cylinders, receiving their fuel from the manifold port to which the vacuum line is connected, will fire weakly because of the air coming through the diaphragm and leaning out the fuel mixture. The spark plugs from these two cylinders may be fouled with oil from crankcase vapors on some engines.

The Oscilloscope

An oscilloscope is a device which provides a picture of the voltage in an electrical circuit. The picture is formed by a trace of light which appears on the screen of the oscilloscope. The trace makes wavelike patterns which indicate the voltage in the circuit. By studying these waveforms it is possible to see whether the voltage is correct and, if it is not, to get an indication of what is causing the trouble.

Scientific diagnostic equipment is becoming more sophisticated, as evidenced by this Autoscan, Model 5000. It is used in conjunction with a dynamometer to analyze ignition system operation. Courtesy Autoscan, Inc.

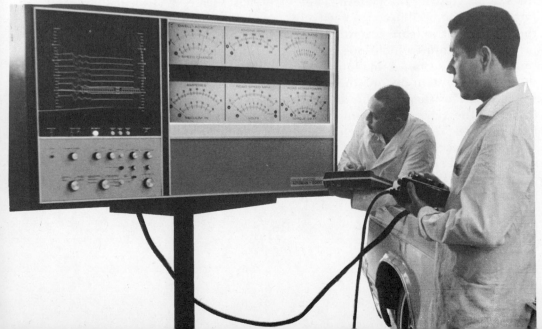

The oscilloscope can be used as an automotive ignition analyzer. It provides an easy-to-read picture of ignition system operation. All phases of the ignition cycle can be viewed at the instant they occur on an operating engine. To use a scope properly, the mechanic must be familiar with the basic principles of the ignition system and with the operation of the instrument.

Precision tuning with a scope gives the mechanic an unequaled opportunity for isolating troubles that are not found easily otherwise. The scope is a voltmeter that does not drain energy from an operating circuit; it always indicates true voltage. A moving-coil type of meter, on the other hand, drains some energy from the circuit and gives a false reading, the size of the error depending on the amount of current flowing in the circuit being tested and the internal resistance of the meter.

The scope looks formidable because of the large number of controls on the front panel, but most of them are pre-set and are not used each time the instrument is used. The few commonly used adjustments allow the operator to control his way of viewing the pattern. Therefore, to use the oscilloscope effectively, the main point to learn is how to interpret the waveforms which appear on the screen of the scope. A malfunction in the ignition system distorts the normal waveform. The shape of the distortion indicates the type of problem and the location.

The oscilloscope can be set to show voltage in either the primary or secondary circuit of the ignition system. The secondary waveform is more informa-

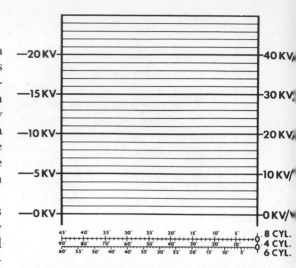

The screen of the scope is laid out in kilovolts to permit accurate reading of secondary voltages. The right side of this screen has a 40-volt scale for reading primary voltages. The scales on the bottom are for reading dwell. Courtesy Sun Electric Corp.

tive on overall ignition system operation. The screen of the scope is laid out in kilovolts to permit accurate voltage measurements of the secondary patterns. Each vertical division at the side of the screen represents 1 kilovolt (1,000 volts). For viewing primary waveform patterns, some scopes have two additional scales of 400 and of 40 volts. The 40-volt scale is especially useful in analyzing small voltage losses and malfunctions in the primary circuit.

Ignition system problems that affect either the intermediate or dwell sections will be indicated in both the primary and secondary waveform patterns. Primary patterns provide a good picture of contact point operating conditions, especially of the contact-triggered transistor types, and provide a waveform pattern of greater clarity for point dwell.

Each part of the waveform represents

a specific phase of ignition system operation. For the purpose of explaining the scope, we shall give individual instructions on the firing, intermediate, and dwell sections, first for the secondary and then for the primary waveform patterns.

VOLTAGE AND TIME RELATIONSHIPS

On a scope, a pattern waveform is a picture of voltage in relationship to time. All vertical movement of the trace represents voltage of one polarity when the trace is above the zero line and of the opposite polarity when the trace

moves below the zero line. Therefore, an oscillating pattern waveform, above and below the zero line, represents AC voltage. This vertical movement (voltage) can be measured by comparing it to the graduations (the graticule) on the scope screen.

Horizontal movement of the trace represents time. Time, on a scope, is not measured in minutes or seconds; rather, the scope screen is equipped for measuring it in distributor degrees of rotation. For example, when testing the ignition system of an eight-cylinder engine, it will be realized that the system will cycle eight times for each revolution of the distributor. Dividing 360

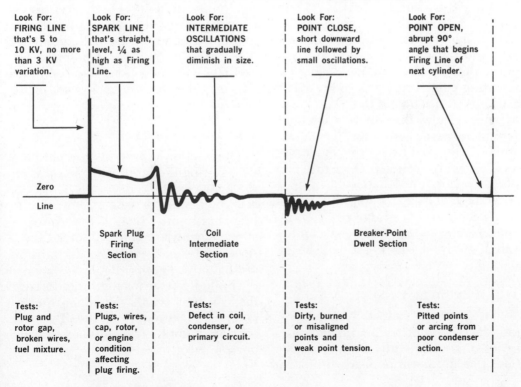

The secondary waveform is more informative than the primary for showing overall ignition system operation. This drawing shows the secondary waveform and some of the important tests that can be carried out with it. Courtesy Sun Electric Corp.

Look For:
FIRING LINE that's 5 to 10 KV, no more than 3 KV variation.

Look For:
SPARK LINE that's straight, level, ¼ as high as Firing Line.

Look For:
INTERMEDIATE OSCILLATIONS that gradually diminish in size.

Look For:
POINT CLOSE, short downward line followed by small oscillations.

Look For:
POINT OPEN, abrupt 90° angle that begins Firing Line of next cylinder.

Zero Line

Spark Plug Firing Section

Coil Intermediate Section

Breaker-Point Dwell Section

Tests:
Plug and rotor gap, broken wires, fuel mixture.

Tests:
Plugs, wires, cap, rotor, or engine condition affecting plug firing.

Tests:
Defect in coil, condenser, or primary circuit.

Tests:
Dirty, burned or misaligned points and weak point tension.

Tests:
Pitted points or arcing from poor condenser action.

Pull off plug wire—FIRING LINE should rise to 20 KV or more

(degrees) by eight results in 45 as the number of degrees of distributor rotation for each ignition cycle. If the scope trace is adjusted so that one complete ignition cycle starts at zero degrees and ends at 45 degrees on the dwell scale of the scope screen, any portion of the pattern can be accurately measured in distributor degrees of rotation.

Secondary Waveform Interpretations

THE FIRING SECTION

It is during this period that the actual firing of the spark plug takes place. This section of the pattern is composed of only two lines: the *Firing Line,* which is a vertical line indicating the voltage required to overcome the spark plug and rotor gaps, and the *Spark Line,* a horizontal line indicating the voltage required to maintain the spark.

Point A in the pattern represents the instant at which the breaker points separate, causing the magnetic field to collapse through the coil windings. The resulting high voltage is indicated by the vertical rise from A to B. The height at point B shows the voltage, sometimes referred to as the "firing" or "ionization" voltage, required to fire the spark plug and bridge the rotor gap. Once the spark plug fires, there is a noticeable drop in secondary voltage to point C. As the spark continues to bridge the gap, the voltage remains at a fairly constant low value until the spark extinguishes at point D.

THE INTERMEDIATE SECTION

This section, which immediately follows the firing section, is seen as a series of gradually diminishing oscillations that disappear or nearly disappear

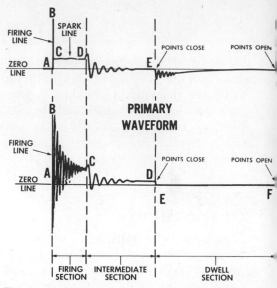

This is a comparison of the secondary waveform (top) with the primary waveform. The primary waveform shows a higher trace because of the more sensitive scale that is used. Courtesy Sun Electric Corp.

by the time the dwell section begins. Beginning at point D, the remaining energy in the coil dissipates itself as an oscillating current, which gradually dies out as it approaches point E. The oscillations result from the combined effects of the coil and condenser in dissipating this energy.

THE DWELL SECTION

This section represents the period of time during the ignition cycle in which the breaker points are closed. The dwell section begins at point E when the breaker points close. This causes a short downward line, followed by a series of small, rapidly diminishing oscillations. The oscillations represent the build-up of the magnetic field around the coil that occurs when the breaker points are closed. The dwell section continues until the points open at the beginning of the next waveform (point F).

Primary Waveform Interpretations

The scales on the scope screen indicate 400 or 40 volts when the CIRCUIT SELECTOR is in one of the PRIMARY positions. Although a resemblance exists between the primary and secondary patterns, it should be noted that the voltage values represented in the primary patterns are considerably lower than those in the secondary patterns, due to the ratio of the primary to the secondary windings of the coil.

THE FIRING SECTION

This section displays the series of rapid oscillations that take place in the ignition primary circuit during the period of time in which the spark plug fires. Point A represents the instant at which the breaker points separate. The vertical rise from A to B and the diminishing oscillations that follow represent the initial and repeated charging and discharging of the condenser and the induced voltage surges in the primary circuit while the spark plug is firing. As the spark bridges the gap and energy is being drained from the coil, the amplitude of these oscillations diminishes until the spark is extinguished, as indicated at point C.

THE INTERMEDIATE SECTION

The intermediate section is seen as a series of gradually diminishing oscillations that disappear or nearly disappear by the time the dwell section begins. Beginning at point C, whatever energy remains in the coil dissipates itself as an oscillating current, which gradually dies out as it approaches point D.

THE DWELL SECTION

The dwell section begins when the distributor contacts close and can be observed as a faint downward line from point D to point E. The dwell section is represented by the horizontal line that extends from point E to point F. During this period the points are closed.

This is the control panel of a Sun Tester. Courtesy Sun Electric Corp.

CONTROLS VERTICAL POSITION OF PATTERN

CONTROLS VERTICAL SPACING OF RASTER PATTERN

CONTROLS HORIZONTAL POSITION OF THE PATTERN

CONTROLS CLARITY OF PATTERN

CONTROLS BRILLIANCE OF PATTERN

CONTROLS HORIZONTAL SIZE OF PATTERN

CONTROLS VERTICAL SIZE OF PRIMARY PATTERN

CONTROLS VERTICAL SIZE OF SECONDARY PATTERN

SELECTS SUPERIMPOSED, RASTER OR DISPLAY PATTERNS

SELECTS PRIMARY OR SECONDARY PATTERNS

319

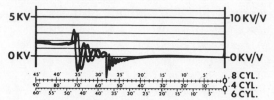

A superimposed pattern is obtained by simultaneously placing the patterns of all cylinders one on top of the other. Courtesy Sun Electric Corp.

Pattern Selector and Its Function

The PATTERN SELECTOR is the main operating control of the scope. As its name implies, it is used to select the type of pattern that is to be viewed. It also serves as an on-off switch. The selector has three positions: SUPERIMPOSED, RASTER, and DISPLAY.

SUPERIMPOSED

A superimposed pattern is one obtained by simultaneously placing the patterns of all cylinders one on top of the other. These patterns provide a convenient method of testing the ignition system for overall uniformity. By expanding the display horizontally to fill the space completely between the two vertical reference lines on the screen, any variation in the basic pattern can quickly be detected.

RASTER

The raster pattern makes use of the vertical height of the scope screen by stacking the patterns of each cylinder's ignition cycle one above the other so that all of the individual patterns are vertically distributed on the screen. This permits individual cylinder identification while viewing all cylinders simultaneously. Thus the mechanic can make detailed, close-up comparisons of all engine ignition cycles simultaneously. The raster pattern is especially helpful for individual cylinder identification of variations in the pattern waveform observed with a superimposed pattern.

With the Trigger Pick-up connected in the circuit of No. 1 spark plug, the pattern waveform, representing the ignition cycle of No. 1 cylinder, will be displayed at the bottom of the screen. The remainder of the pattern waveforms will appear in a normal firing order sequence, working up. This will position the pattern waveform of the last cylinder in the firing order at the top of the scope screen. It should be noted that with the raster pattern, like the superimposed pattern, the firing lines of the pattern waveforms cannot be viewed. The DISPLAY position of the PATTERN SELECTOR must be used for viewing the firing lines.

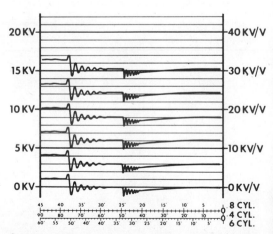

A raster pattern makes use of the vertical height of the screen by stacking the patterns of each cylinder's ignition cycle, one above the other. Courtesy Sun Electric Corp.

320

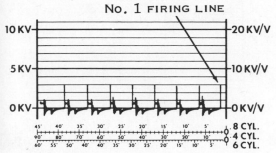

No. 1 FIRING LINE

The display waveform shows all ignition cycles alongside each other. Although the waveform for No. 1 cylinder is at the left side of the screen, the firing line for No. 1 cylinder is at the extreme right in most scopes. This is because the firing pulse of No. 1 cylinder is used to trigger the scope. Courtesy Sun Electric Corp.

DISPLAY

With the PATTERN SELECTOR in the DISPLAY position, the scope will trigger once for each complete ignition cycle for each cylinder. With the Trigger Pick-up connected in the circuit of No. 1 spark plug, the waveform viewed on the scope screen will begin on the left with the pattern for No. 1 cylinder. The trace moves from left to right, displaying ignition cycles in the engine's firing order until all the cylinder's ignition cycles have been completed.

It should be noted that the firing line of No. 1 cylinder will be at the extreme right, or at the end of the trace for most scopes. This is because it is necessary for the No. 1 spark plug to fire in order to trigger the scope and begin a new trace.

The display type of pattern allows the firing voltages of all cylinders to be measured individually or simultaneously. Whenever it is necessary to measure secondary voltages, the display type of pattern must be used. **Note:** *For accurate voltage measurements, the base of the pattern's firing line must be*

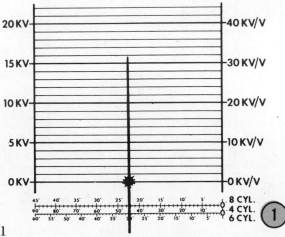

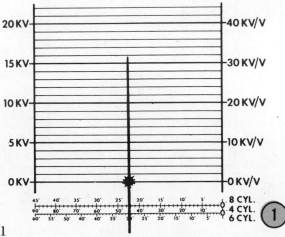

adjusted to the ZERO *line on the scope screen graticule.*

Using a Scope to Diagnose Ignition Troubles

The following section will show some basic scope patterns to give the student a background for reading the waveform that appears on the scope. This section is not intended to be a complete treatise on the subject but enough is shown to develop an interest in the serious student.

COIL OUTPUT TEST DURING CRANKING

① The height of the waveform seen while cranking the engine with the high-tension lead to the distributor disconnected is the measurement of the secondary voltage available to fire the spark plugs. In instances of hard starting or starting failure, it may be quickly determined whether the primary circuit or coil is at fault. Turn the PATTERN SELECTOR to the DISPLAY position. Align the pattern sweep to the ZERO line. Insert the Pattern Pick-up lead into the ignition coil tower. With the ignition switch ON, crank the engine.

321

Observe the waveform height, which should exceed 20 KV. A low voltage reading indicates a low battery, defective ignition circuit, failure of the ignition resistor by-pass circuit (not the resistor), insufficient dwell, excessive distributor resistance, or a defective coil or condenser. After completing this test, insert the coil lead from the distributor into the Pattern Pick-up to make the rest of the tests.

SECONDARY POLARITY

② Incorrect secondary polarity can require a 20–40% higher voltage to fire the spark plugs. To test the polarity, start the engine and allow it to idle. Turn the PATTERN SELECTOR to the SUPERIMPOSED position. Adjust the pattern length to align with the vertical lines on the scope screen. Observe the pattern, which should be right side up. An inverted pattern means that the battery polarity is reversed, that the coil is improperly connected, or that an incorrect coil is being used for the vehicle.

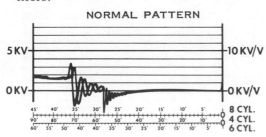

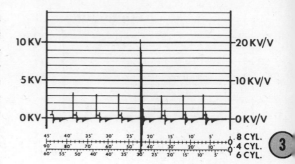

MAXIMUM COIL OUTPUT

③ "Maximum coil output" is a phrase used to indicate the maximum secondary voltage that an ignition system is able to produce under a given operating condition. Due to its operating characteristics, an ignition coil will produce its maximum secondary voltage whenever it attempts to fire an impossible gap, such as when a spark plug wire is removed from a spark plug and held away from ground. Set the CIRCUIT SELECTOR to the SECONDARY position and the PATTERN SELECTOR to the DISPLAY position. Adjust the engine speed to approximately 2,500 rpm. Use *insulated* pliers to disconnect a spark plug wire and hold the wire away from the ground. Observe the height of the pattern, which should be 20 KV or more. Reduce engine speed to 1,000 rpm. Insufficient coil output voltage indicates excessive resistance in the primary circuit, low primary input voltage, a defective coil, dwell less than specified, or defective secondary insulation.

SECONDARY CIRCUIT CONDITIONS

④ Spark line analysis reveals the condition of the secondary circuit. Excessive resistance uses up energy that

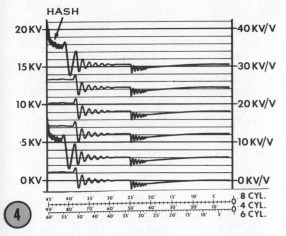

HASH

20KV- .... 40 KV/V

15KV- .... 30 KV/V

10KV- .... 20 KV/V

·5KV- .... 10 KV/V

0KV- .... 0 KV/V

8 CYL.
4 CYL.
6 CYL.

appears normal after grounding the spark plug wire, there is a defective spark plug or an engine condition that affects the spark plug. If the spark line shows high resistance with the spark plug wire grounded on each cylinder, there is a defect in the coil tower, coil wire, distributor cap towers, or rotor. High resistance on one or more cylinders indicates defective distributor cap towers or individual spark plug wires. Ground the distributor cap tower to determine if the cap or wire is defective.

COIL AND CONDENSER

⑤ The intermediate section, usually observed as a series of diminishing oscillations, represents the dissipation of the energy remaining in the coil after the spark plug has ceased firing. Ignition trouble can be analyzed by noting the rate at which the oscillations diminish. Normally, these oscillations should diminish gradually. If the intermediate section is incomplete and the dwell is normal, reduce engine speed to observe the complete intermediate waveform. Lack of oscillations in the intermediate section indicates a short in the coil or a leaky condenser.

④ is needed to maintain good ignition. The manufacturers build a reasonable amount of resistance into the secondary circuit for the purpose of controlling secondary current flow in order to extend spark plug electrode life and for minimizing interference with radio and television reception. Resistance of this nature is generally referred to as ignition suppression. Set the CIRCUIT SELECTOR to the SECONDARY position and observe the spark line for height, length, angle, and oscillations. For closer examination, turn the PATTERN SELECTOR to the RASTER position for individual cylinder identification. If abnormal spark lines, with "hash," are observed, the following detailed tests should be performed to determine the cause. Stop the engine and install the spark plug connectors between the spark plugs and the leads on all abnormal cylinders. Connect a jumper lead to the ground and to the large end of the resistance test contactor. With the engine running at 1,000 rpm, touch the spark plug connector with the point of the resistance test contactor. Observe the spark line and repeat the test on all cylinders with abnormal spark lines. If a spark line

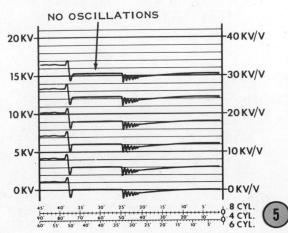

NO OSCILLATIONS

20KV- .... 40 KV/V

15KV- .... 30 KV/V

10KV- .... 20 KV/V

5KV- .... 10 KV/V

0KV- .... 0 KV/V

8 CYL.
4 CYL.
6 CYL.

⑤

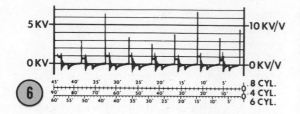

SPARK PLUG FIRING VOLTAGE

⑥ Spark plug firing voltage is the voltage required to overcome the rotor and spark plug gaps and to establish a spark across the spark plug electrodes. The condition of the spark plugs and/or secondary circuit, temperature, fuel mixture, and compression pressures also affect the required firing voltage. Set the PATTERN SELECTOR to the DISPLAY position. Observe the firing lines of all cylinders for height and uniformity. Normally, the lines should be from 5 to 10 KV, with no more than 3 KV variations between cylinders. Uneven firing voltages indicate worn spark plugs, breaks in the spark plug wires, a cocked or worn distributor cap, or an unbalanced fuel mixture.

SPARK PLUGS UNDER LOAD

⑦ When a load is applied to an engine, the required firing voltage rises. This rise will be slight and uniform if the plugs are in good condition and prop-

erly gapped. However, if any unusual firing characteristics are observed while the engine is operating under a load, it generally indicates a faulty spark plug. To be noted particularly are individual firing voltages that are considerably higher or lower than the firing requirements of the other cylinders. Momentarily load the engine by snapping the accelerator. Observe the rise of the firing voltages, which should be moderate and uniform. One or more lines higher than the others indicates a wide plug gap, an open spark plug resistor, or badly deteriorated electrodes. One or more lines lower than the others indicates spark plug fouling, flashover, or a cracked insulator.

DWELL TEST

⑧ Dwell is the period during which the distributor points remain closed for each ignition cycle. Either the sec-

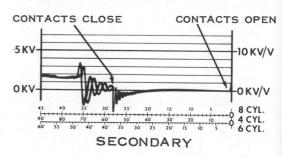

SECONDARY

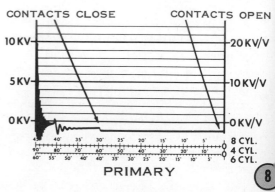

PRIMARY

324

ondary or the primary pattern can be used. Adjust the CIRCUIT SELECTOR for the desired pattern, secondary as shown at the top, primary as at the bottom. Lower the superimposed pattern until it rests on the dwell scale to permit the distributor contact point dwell to be measured. Compare the length of the dwell section with the dwell scale on the screen. The point-close signal will coincide with the contact point dwell reading. If the dwell reading is within specifications, the ignition points are spaced properly. If the dwell reading is not within specifications, there could be improper point spacing, a wrong point assembly, a defective point rubbing block, a misaligned point rubbing block, or a worn distributor cam.

POINT CONDITIONS

⑨ In analyzing the dwell section of the pattern, the point-close and point-open signals should be carefully observed. Normally, when the points close,

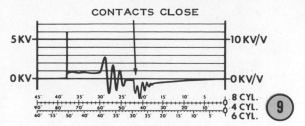

this action is seen as a short, downward line, followed by a series of diminishing oscillations. An unusual point-close signal indicates point bounce or weak point spring tension. This unusual point-close signal is evidence of dirty, burned, or misaligned points.

⑩ An unusual point-open signal indicates dirty or pitted points or point arcing caused by faulty condenser action.

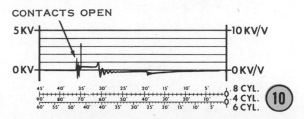

CHECK YOUR KNOWLEDGE

1. What is the function of the ignition system?
2. Of what parts is the ignition system composed?
3. What are the three parts which make up the ignition coil?
4. Which coil contains the fine wire?
5. Why is the secondary induced voltage greater when the primary circuit is broken than when it is energized?
6. What is the purpose of the ignition resistor?
7. What is the purpose of the condenser?
8. What seven parts does the distributor contain?
9. Why is it necessary for the spark to be delivered earlier in the cycle at higher speeds?

10. What is the purpose of the centrifugal advance mechanism?
11. What is the purpose of the vacuum advance mechanism?
12. How does the vacuum advance mechanism function at idle? Part throttle? Full throttle?
13. What is the purpose of the spark plug?
14. What is meant by the heat range of spark plugs?
15. How can you tell if a spark plug is operating too hot? Too cold?
16. What is the engine-operating result of a small spark plug gap? Large gap?
17. What operating condition indicates that an engine needs a tune-up?
18. Of what service procedures does an engine tune-up consist?

Self-Check Tests

TRUE-FALSE

1. The ignition coil generates an induced voltage when the ignition contacts make and break the primary circuit.
2. The induced voltage is greater on the break than on the make.
3. The rotor delivers primary voltage surges to each spark plug.
4. The vacuum advance mechanism varies the ignition timing according to intake manifold vacuum conditions.
5. Hot-operating spark plugs have short ceramic insulators.
6. Engines, driven under severe operating conditions, require a hot-running spark plug.
7. Larger spark plug gaps develop a larger spark and are, therefore, better for high speed.
8. An engine tune-up is necessary every 10,000 miles.

MULTIPLE CHOICE

1. Which of the following is *not* a part of the ignition system: a) battery; b) solenoid; c) coil; d) distributor?
2. Which of the following is *not* a part of the ignition coil: a) primary winding; b) secondary winding; c) core; d) condenser?
3. Which of the following is *not* a part of the ignition distributor: a) condenser; b) rotor; c) coil; d) cam?
4. The vacuum advance mechanism contains a: a) condenser; b) weights; c) cam; d) diaphragm.
5. Which of the following symptoms is caused by an engine needing a tune-up: a) poor acceleration; b) hard starting; c) poor gas mileage; d) jerking?

COMPLETION

1. The ignition system changes the battery voltage to _____ volts.
2. A _____ is connected in the primary circuit to speed up the rate of change of the magnetic lines of force when the primary circuit is broken.
3. The distributor is driven at _____ engine speed.
4. The _____ advance mechanism changes the timing according to engine speed.
5. The _____ advance mechanism changes the timing according to throttle pressure.

MATCHING

1. Ignition coil
2. Distributor
3. Spark plug
4. Tune-up

a. Engine balancing adjustment
b. Vacuum advance mechanism
c. Primary and secondary
d. Center electrode

11

Air Pollution Control

The Smog Problem

Air pollution is not new. Even before man appeared on earth, a great number of natural events affected the atmosphere. Organic materials decayed, airborne volcanic ash sifted over wide areas, and winds whipped up clouds of dust and sand. Today, air pollution can be found in varying degrees in most areas of the country, especially in and around large cities.

Visible pollution consists of smoke, mist, and dust. The burning of oil, natural gas, and coal adds to atmospheric contamination. In the Los Angeles basin, special atmospheric conditions exist to form a lid which seals in contaminated air. "Smog" was coined from the words fog and smoke to describe this eye-irritating mist, and it soon became a byword.

Studies into the causes, and attempts to control it, soon pointed up the fact that the problem was photochemical. It involved hydrocarbons and oxides of nitrogen. In the presence of sunlight, these chemicals unite to form the visible smog, which reduces visibility, causes eye smarting, and results in

crop damage. Initial attempts to minimize the smog problem in the Los Angeles area revolved about outlawing all forms of unrestricted combustion. Outdoor incinerators were banned, industrial plants were forced to control pollutants discharged into the atmosphere, and the companies in the petroleum industry were required to redesign their storage tanks in order to reduce evaporative losses. Even with

The blame for smog can be largely placed upon the rapidly increasing number of cars. This rush hour scene on the Harbor Freeway dramatically illustrates the problem. Courtesy Air Resources Board.

327

Los Angeles on a clear day. The tall building in the background is the City Hall. Courtesy Air Resources Board.

The same scene with polluted air obscuring the view. Note how the smog forms a layer of dirty air. When compressed by an inversion layer of warm air above it, the results are intensified. Courtesy Air Resources Board.

this highly controlled atmosphere, the smog problem grew worse. This pointed the finger of suspicion at the rapidly increasing number of motor cars as the prime cause of the eye irritants. One very important fact that must be remembered about the complexity of the smog problem is that our entire transportation system—air, road, rail, and water—depends almost entirely on burning hydrocarbon-type fuels.

The internal combustion engine is now known to be the major source of hydrocarbons, carbon monoxide, and oxides of nitrogen. On an individual basis, the concentrations of these internal combustion engine products are insignificant. But, when multiplied by millions of vehicles in city traffic, the emissions are measured in tons. Even these quantities are not irritatingly significant unless the air masses are stagnated by lack of wind or because they are trapped by an overlay of warm air, called an *inversion layer*.

Because the smog problem was unusually severe in the Los Angeles basin area, initial attempts to solve the air pollution problem started in this city. This was done by forming an administrative organization called the Motor Vehicle Pollution Control Board (which is now called the Air Resources Board) with power to enforce regulations designed to control atmospheric pollutants. In 1961, the Board enacted regulations which required all motor vehicles sold in the state of California to have crankcase emission control devices as factory-installed equipment. Similar regulations were enacted for used cars offered for sale in that state.

Despite an increase in vehicle registration in the Los Angeles area of about a million cars in the seven years from 1960-67, the daily atmospheric contamination level remained constant, rather than rising as would have been the case without controls. This progress was due entirely to the success of the crankcase emission control devices required since 1961. Because of this proven success, the same regulations were adopted nationwide in 1963.

While it is difficult to see how the small amounts of gases expelled from each vehicle could cause such problems, it has been calculated that each car emits about 1.25 pounds of pollutants per day. Had this been allowed to continue uncontrolled, the emissions would have reached the staggering total of 4,000 *tons per day* in the Los Angeles basin by 1980.

Much research is going on to find out exactly what happens when hydrocarbons are acted upon by sunlight. In this General Motors Research Laboratory, a 300-cubic-foot smog chamber is used to determine how changes in fuel composition, engine operation, vehicle operation, and engine design affect smog formation. The exhaust of a running engine is piped into this chamber for irradiation from these 247 special fluorescent lamps, which simulate Los Angeles noonday sunlight. Courtesy General Motors Corporation.

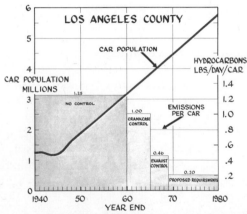

This chart shows the growth in number of cars in Los Angeles County, projected through the year of 1980. Before 1960 there were no controls, and the average car emitted 1.25 pounds of unburned hydrocarbons per day. With the introduction of crankcase controls, the level was reduced to 1.0 pound per car per day. Exhaust emission control systems further reduced the level to 0.46 pound per car per day. Future goals are to bring this level to 0.20 pound per car per day. Courtesy Air Resources Board.

One big problem of smog control is that engineers are dealing with microscopic measurements. Identifying one part per million is like locating one grain of sugar in a cup of salt.

With the introduction of the crank-case control devices in the mid-1960's, the individual vehicle hydrocarbon emission level dropped from 1.25 to 1.00 pounds per car per day. With this gain, the total vehicular hydrocarbon emission level ceased to rise. The peak of 2,040 tons per day was reached in 1963. Since that time, in spite of a rising motor vehicle registration, the trend has been reversed and a decrease in the total hydrocarbon content of the atmosphere has occurred. Up to model year 1966, all of this progress could be credited solely to the crankcase ventilation system devices.

Satisfactory exhaust emission control devices took longer to develop, but in 1966 all motor vehicles sold in California were required to have such devices installed at the factory. The exhaust controls had to be able to limit the unburned hydrocarbons to 275 parts per million (ppm) and the carbon monoxide to a 1.5% concentration by volume level. This, it was calculated, would reduce the total emissions per car from the uncontrolled 1.25 pounds to an average of 0.46 of a pound per car per day. Actually, the controls installed on the 1966–1967 model cars prevented a total of 470,000 gallons of unburned gasoline and 2,100 *tons* of carbon mon-

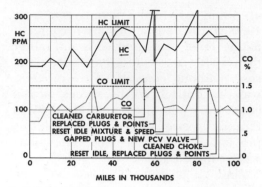

Emission control systems must have proper service to keep functioning correctly. This graph shows results of a test in which a car was driven 100,000 miles, with minimum maintenance, under conditions resembling city driving. The car, which had air injection equipment, did not exceed the California limits for hydrocarbon (HC) and carbon monoxide (CO), except when the engine developed trouble. When maintenance was provided, performance again became satisfactory. This chart shows the need for skilled personnel who know how to service cars with emission control systems. Courtesy General Motors Corporation.

oxide from entering the atmosphere *every day*.

Because mechanical devices deteriorate in service, the effects of controlling atmospheric contamination are soon nullified unless the equipment is maintained at designed efficiency. Every legislative body studying this problem is being advised that compulsory ve-

The need for service work must be emphasized to the average driver because he is not aware of the existence of these new control devices. Billboards are one of the ways to convey the message. Courtesy Air Resources Board.

hicular inspection is required to keep the devices operating properly. And when these regulations are enacted into law, it may be that a further legal step will require each mechanic to secure a license in order to service cars that are so equipped. That is why this subject is becoming so important to mechanics who want to upgrade their skills and to those who are planning on entering this field.

There are three sources of pollutants from the internal-combustion-engine propelled vehicle: (1) crankcase blow-by gases, (2) exhaust emissions, and (3) evaporative losses. These topics will be covered in this order.

New equipment is being designed to measure the hydrocarbon emission level of a running engine. Mechanics are going to have to learn a new set of skills in order to service the new engines properly.

Crankcase Emissions

Uncontrolled crankcase emissions result in about 25% of the total unburned hydrocarbons allowed to es-

Skill in the use of precision testing equipment is essential for troubleshooting engines which have emission control systems.

331

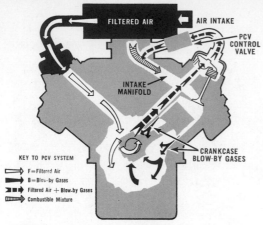

KEY TO PCV SYSTEM

⇨ F = Filtered Air
➡ B = Blow-by Gases
⬛➡ Filtered Air + Blow-by Gases
▭▭▭⇨ Combustible Mixture

This diagram shows how the PCV control valve is used to remove the blow-by gases from the crankcase and pass them into the combustion chamber for burning. Courtesy General Motors Corporation.

cape to the atmosphere. These gases result from blow-by which occurs when a small portion of the air-fuel mixture, inside the combustion chamber, is forced past the piston rings and into the crankcase. It happens just before and during the combustion cycles. In laboratory tests, it was established that the blow-by amounts to about 0.14 cubic inches per cylinder during each complete combustion cycle. The composition of these gases is about 80% unburned air-fuel mixture and about 20% combustion products, including water, carbon dioxide, and carbon monoxide.

These blow-by gases have always been a problem to automotive engineers. If they are allowed to remain in the crankcase, they condense to form varnish deposits, acids, and sludge, all of which lead to poor engine life and performance. Before 1960, these blow-by gases were allowed to flow uncontrolled into the atmosphere. Since that time, Positive Crankcase Ventilation (PCV) systems have been installed on all automobile engines. These devices route the blow-by gases back to the combustion chamber, where they are consumed in the normal combustion process.

In older engines, and during certain periods of operation, it is possible that the amount of blow-by will exceed the flow-rate of the valve. If this occurs, some of the blow-by gases will escape to the atmosphere through the breather vent. This condition also occurs when the PCV valve becomes clogged. To minimize this source of air pollution, engineers are now routing the breather vent to the inside of the air cleaner, so that the air entering the induction system will carry with it any of the excess.

The PCV valve bleeds the blow-by gases into the intake manifold. From there they are carried into the combustion chamber for burning. At idle, intake manifold vacuum is high, and the valve is pulled up against spring pressure which seats the valve. This limits the amount of fumes which can be drawn into the intake manifold through the calibrated opening. The crankcase pressure is low during idle and it requires very little venting. During acceleration, the vacuum is insufficient to overcome spring pressure, and the valve moves back to allow more fumes to pass. This is necessary because crankcase pressures are higher during acceleration, and more ventilation is needed to cleanse the crankcase. Courtesy AC Spark Plug Division, General Motors Corporation.

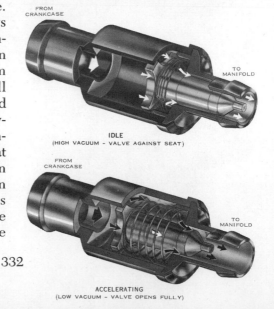

FROM CRANKCASE

TO MANIFOLD

IDLE
(HIGH VACUUM – VALVE AGAINST SEAT)

FROM CRANKCASE

TO MANIFOLD

ACCELERATING
(LOW VACUUM - VALVE OPENS FULLY)

This type of installation is called a *closed system.*

Exhaust Emissions

The exhaust emissions of an internal combustion engine contain a minute quantity of unburned hydrocarbons, about one-tenth of one per cent (0.1%).

High-speed pictures of the combustion process inside an engine itself reveal that the source of these unburned hydrocarbons is a thin boundary area around the walls of the combustion chamber. When the spark plug ignites the air-fuel mixture, a flame front sweeps across the combustion chamber. When it approaches the relatively cool

The source of unburned hydrocarbons is a thin boundary layer around the walls of the combustion chamber. These high-speed pictures of the combustion process, inside the engine itself, reveal that a quench area develops as the flame front approaches the relatively cold wall. This area is smaller under severe acceleration (4″ Hg) than during deceleration (20″ Hg), which accounts for the greater emissions during deceleration. Courtesy General Motors Corporation.

APPROACHING   CLOSEST APPROACH

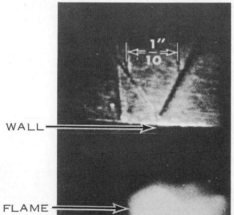
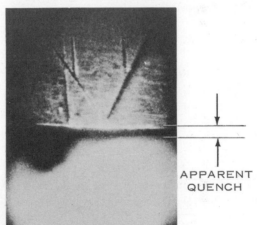

INTAKE VACUUM 20″ HG.

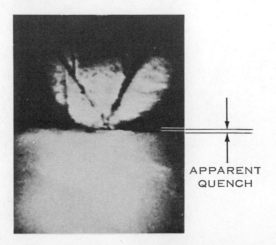

INTAKE VACUUM 4″ HG.

cylinder walls, a quenching action occurs, and the flame front is snuffed out. This leaves a very thin margin of partially unburned air-fuel mixture, which is discharged into the atmosphere through the exhaust pipe.

Although it may not be possible to eliminate all discharged hydrocarbons, current engineering efforts are directed at reducing them. Since 1968 (1966 in California), allowable exhaust emissions have been set at the levels mentioned earlier—that is, 275 ppm for hydrocarbons and 1.5% by volume for carbon monoxide. As more engineering efforts are directed toward this problem, it is hoped to reduce these levels

further. The 1970 goal is to reduce the exhaust level of hydrocarbons to 2.2 grams per mile and the carbon monoxide level to 23 grams per mile.

The control of exhaust emissions has taken two forms to date: (1) raising the combustion efficiency and (2) consuming the unburned hydrocarbons in the exhaust system.

Raising the Combustion Efficiency

Engineers are working on better control of the air-fuel mixture which, after all, is the source of the free hydrocarbons. Examination of the emission values studied during the various testing procedures showed that the cruising

The six-cylinder engine of the Maverick uses the IMCO system of exhaust emission control. Courtesy Ford Motor Company.

range was relatively free of unburned hydrocarbons, making it one of the more efficient carburetor circuits. However, the other circuits — warm-up, idle, acceleration, and especially deceleration — left much to be desired. A great deal of engineering effort is now going into methods of making these modes of operation more efficient.

COMBUSTION CHAMBER

Engineers have learned that cold surfaces within the combustion chamber tend to quench the flame front before all of the air-fuel mixture is consumed. Consequently, efforts are being directed at reducing such areas as much as possible. For example, the wedge-

Changes in the shape of the combustion chamber affect the emission levels of an engine. Changing the shape of the cylinder head gasket from a circular opening to a contoured opening eliminated a gap, the effect of which was to reduce the emission level. Courtesy Chrysler Corporation.

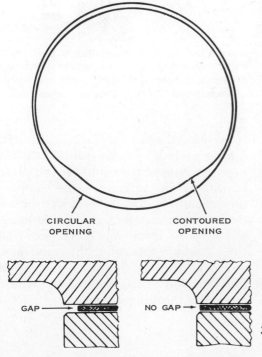

type combustion chamber has a "squish" area which presents a relatively large cooling surface to the flame front, and its design is being modified to minimize this effect.

COOLING SYSTEM

A significant hydrocarbon emission reduction can be achieved by increasing engine operating temperatures. In certain cases, the specified thermostat opening temperatures have been raised from 180° F. to 200° F.

In the systems where the excess hydrocarbons are consumed in the exhaust manifolds, under-hood temperatures have increased 20° F. over other models because of the extra heat generated in the exhaust manifolds. This requires greater cooling capacity and generally a thermostatic vent in the idle circuit to prevent fuel percolation.

CARBURETOR

To raise the efficiency of the idle circuit, engineers are specifying higher idle speeds. Several methods have been devised to keep mechanics from adjusting the idle mixture too rich. In some cases, the idle mixture adjusting needle is restricted in its travel by a lockscrew. Sometimes the idle port hole is so reduced in size that complete withdrawal of the needle will not cause an excessively rich mixture. In some designs, the taper of the adjusting needle is extended so that part of it always remains in the idle port as long as any threads are engaged. In many cases, plastic limiter caps are installed on the idle mixture adjusting screws to restrict the amount of available movement.

335

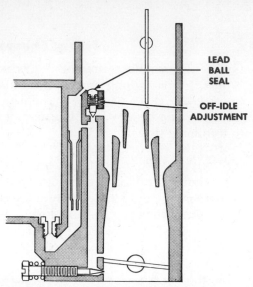

LEAD
BALL
SEAL

OFF-IDLE
ADJUSTMENT

Carburetion changes are now being made, with the intent of reducing air pollution. This illustration shows a method of adjusting the off-idle air-fuel mixture to closer tolerances on the carburetor final assembly line. Courtesy General Motors Corporation.

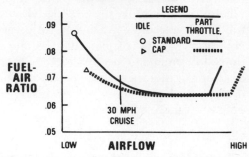

This graph shows the difference between the air-fuel ratio curve of a standard engine and one with the Chrysler Cleaner Air System (CAS). Courtesy Chrysler Corporation.

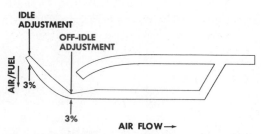

This graph of the air-fuel mixture shows how the off-idle adjustment is used to maintain a 3% tolerance band at this critical point of engine operation. Courtesy General Motors Corporation.

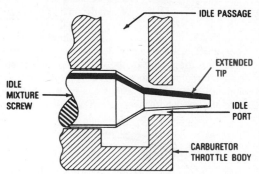

In some of the new-style carburetors, the taper of the idle adjusting needle is extended so that part of it remains in the idle port as long as any threads are engaged. Courtesy Chrysler Corporation.

IGNITION TIMING

Retarding the ignition timing at idle will reduce exhaust emissions. In all cases, the spark has been retarded to make this operating mode more efficient. To compensate, the mechanical advance curve has been redesigned to provide a greater advance so that the timing reaches the normal efficiency point during the range period of operation.

Additional spark advance is required during periods of deceleration to allow as much time as possible for complete burning of the mixture in the combustion chambers. This is achieved in the CAS and some AIR (Air Injection Reactor) systems through a special sensing valve, which provides the maximum spark advance at this time, instead of the retarded spark normally obtained when the throttle closes.

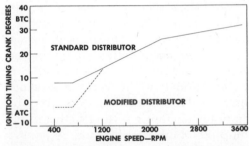

The method of connecting the ignition distributor vacuum advance unit to the vacuum source has changed considerably. This illustration shows a ported supply in which no vacuum is supplied during idle and deceleration. Other applications use ports below the throttle valve, and some use ports above and below the throttle valve in various combinations. Courtesy General Motors Corporation.

Additional timing retard is specified at idle, and the modified distributors are calibrated to restore normal ignition timing at engine speeds above 1,200 rpm. Courtesy General Motors Corporation.

COUPLINGS

Because the deceleration mode of engine operation is one of the worst offenders, much effort is going into methods of reducing the resulting exhaust emissions. One way is to reduce the coupling efficiency, and this can be done on an automatic-transmission equipped vehicle by designing more slip in the torque converter. The mechanical clutch presents more of a

problem, and this can only be overcome by engine modifications.

Raising Combustion Efficiency

There are several systems in general use which are designed to raise the combustion efficiency: (1) Cleaner Air System (CAS), (2) Combustion Control System (CCS), (3) Improved Combustion Exhaust Emission Control System (IMCO), and (4) "Engine Mod" System.

CLEANER AIR SYSTEM (CHRYSLER)

The CAS approach to exhaust emission control is designed about a modified carburetor, distributor, and a sensing vacuum control valve; this valve changes the ignition timing under varying conditions of engine operation.

The Chrysler Cleaner Air System is designed around a modified distributor and a carburetor which is calibrated on the lean side. A vacuum control valve modifies the distributor timing. Courtesy Chrysler Corporation.

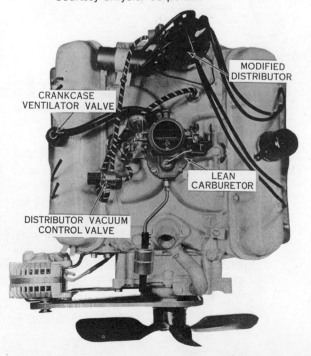

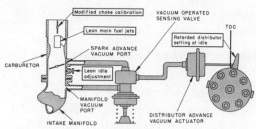

This diagram of the Cleaner Air System shows how the sensing valve receives vacuum from above and below the throttle valve in order to control the distributor vacuum advance unit. Courtesy Chrysler Corporation.

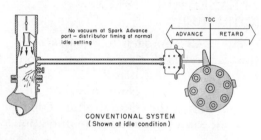

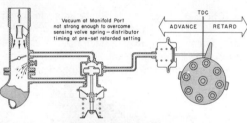

This diagram shows the action of the vacuum sensing valve at idle. A conventional system is also shown for comparison. Courtesy Chrysler Corporation.

The carburetor is specially calibrated to provide leaner mixtures for idle and low-speed operation. The distributor is designed to provide a retarded ignition timing at idle speed, and the vacuum advance control valve, in conjunction with the distributor, advances the ignition timing during deceleration.

The CAS static timing is retarded more than in a pre-controlled engine so that the idle speed can be increased for a higher air-flow through the carburetor. In this way, the combustion is more nearly that of cruising speeds. Ignition advance is required during deceleration to provide the most efficient combustion and thereby reduce exhaust emissions. The vacuum advance control valve provides this additional spark advance during deceleration.

VACUUM ADVANCE CONTROL UNIT

Carburetor vacuum and manifold vacuum act on the vacuum advance control valve so that it senses engine speed and load conditions. The unit then relays a vacuum signal to the distributor in order to vary the ignition timing as necessary. During idle, normal cruise, and acceleration, the unit has no affect on ignition timing. It is during deceleration that the vacuum advance control valve advances the ignition timing to its maximum setting so that more-complete combustion occurs.

CONTROLLED COMBUSTION SYSTEM (GENERAL MOTORS)

The CCS approach is designed about a special air cleaner and a modified carburetor and distributor. The distributor retards ignition timing at idle speed, and the centrifugal advance curve is modified to restore the normal operating spark advance at about 1,200 engine rpm. The carburetor is specially calibrated to provide leaner mixtures for idle and low-speed operation. A more precise calibration is obtained because of a new system of air inlet temperature control. The air passing through the special temperature-regu-

338

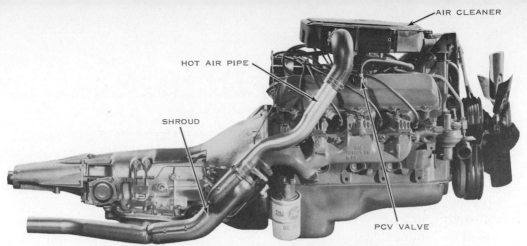

The Climatic Combustion Control (CCC) system is used on some G.M. engines. It incorporates a specially designed air cleaner which mixes cold air with preheated air. The CCC air intake system is used in conjunction with other engine design changes, and the complete exhaust emission control system is referred to as the Controlled Combustion System (CCS). Courtesy Oldsmobile Division, General Motors Corporation.

lating air cleaner is maintained at 100° F. This controlled induction system is called Climatic Combustion Control (CCC).

CLIMATIC COMBUSTION CONTROL (CCC)

The CCC system consists of a special air cleaner, shroud assembly, hot air pipe, and the necessary connectors. The air cleaner is equipped with vacuum motors, a temperature sensor, hose connectors, and a replaceable dry-type air filter element. The shroud assembly takes its heated air from around the right exhaust pipe and conducts it to the air cleaner.

OPERATION

During warm-up, with engine compartment temperatures below 120° F., the temperature sensor is closed. This allows engine vacuum to be directed to the vacuum motor which closes this valve plate to outside air. The cool air flows through the hoses in the left side of the shroud where it is heated and then flows up through the hot air pipe into the air cleaner.

The CCC system consists of a specially designed air cleaner assembly, warm air duct, and an exhaust pipe heater unit. Courtesy Oldsmobile Division, General Motors Corporation.

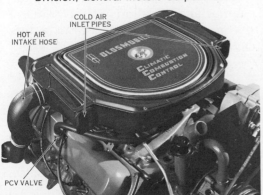

The temperature-sensing unit uses vacuum motors to control mixing doors in order to blend the warmed air with cold air so as to maintain an air intake temperature of about 100° F. Courtesy Oldsmobile Division, General Motors Corporation.

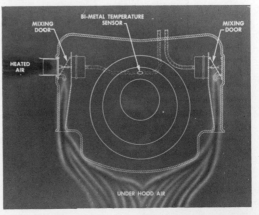

As the temperature inside of the air filter element reaches approximately 100° F., the bi-metallic temperature sensor bleeds off vacuum to the right vacuum motor, causing the valve to open. This allows under-hood air to mix with the heated air as needed to keep the air inlet temperature at approximately 100° F.

Under full throttle conditions (below 6-8″ Hg), the vacuum motor cannot hold the valve open for the hot air; therefore only under-hood air enters the air cleaner.

On the larger engines the vacuum motor and valve plate in the left air-intake tube (snorkel) are controlled only by intake manifold vacuum; therefore this tube is always closed until full throttle is approached. This allows maximum air to flow into the air cleaner during this operating mode.

IMPROVED COMBUSTION EXHAUST EMISSION CONTROL SYSTEM (FORD)

The IMCO approach to exhaust emission control is designed about a modified carburetor and distributor. In addition, some engine modifications include smaller intake ports and increased exhaust heat to the carburetor for better vaporization of the air-fuel mixture. The operating temperature of the cooling system is raised by using a thermostat that opens at about 200° F., and the radiator capacity is increased to compensate for the extra heat that is developed.

By increasing engine operating temperatures, the air-fuel mixture can be calibrated closer to the lean side. Generally, the IMCO system requires a retarded initial timing of the distributor to the engine.

"ENGINE MOD" SYSTEM (AMERICAN MOTORS)

The "Engine Mod" consists of a modified carburetor and distributor. The carburetor incorporates an "idle rich limiter" to prevent setting the mixture beyond the acceptable limit. The distributor provides a retarded ignition timing at idle, and the centrifugal advance curve is modified to restore normal spark advance during driving range operation. The conventional steel cylinder-head gasket has been replaced by a composition gasket on the 232 cu. in. engine, which has a compressed thickness of 0.045″.

Consuming Hydrocarbons in the Exhaust System

The previously discussed method of controlling exhaust emissions mainly involved engine modifications for more efficient burning of the air-fuel mixture within the combustion chamber. The second method of attacking this problem is to burn the discharged hydrocarbons after they leave the combustion chamber. The two systems which have been developed to date are: (1) afterburners and (2) Air Injection Reactor (AIR) systems. The latter is known as the Thermactor Exhaust Emission Control system when used on Ford product engines and is called the "Air Guard" system when used on American Motors' engines.

AFTERBURNERS

Afterburners are essentially furnaces which burn the small quantities of fuel that are not consumed in the combustion chamber. The greater the excess, the larger the furnace must be and the more often it must be replaced. At the present time, the problems of cost, service, finding the proper heat-resistant materials, space and location, and mechanical complexity indicate that additional work is required in all of these areas before afterburners can become commercial realities.

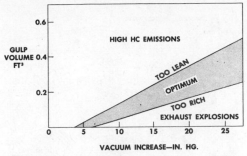

There is an optimum amount of air required for each degree of throttle closing. Too little air results in a backfire, and too much air can cause higher emission values. Courtesy General Motors Corporation.

AIR INJECTION REACTOR SYSTEM

The AIR system consists of an air pump which forces a constant flow of air into each exhaust port immediately beyond the exhaust valve. Since the exhaust gases at this point are above the kindling temperature and have an excess of hydrocarbons, the infusion of oxygen starts the mixture burning, thus consuming the hydrocarbons that would normally be expelled into the atmosphere.

The AIR system draws air from the air cleaner and forces it into two outlet hoses (one for each cylinder head on a V-8 engine), through a check valve, and into an air manifold, where it is delivered to stainless steel nozzles which project into the exhaust ports.

An exhaust check valve is located in the air inlet side of each air supply manifold. It prevents a reverse flow of exhaust gases into the air supply pump in the event that the exhaust pressure becomes greater than the air pump delivery pressure.

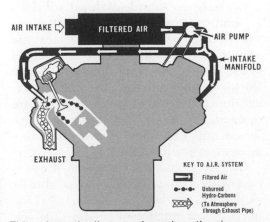

This schematic diagram shows how the air pump forces fresh air into the exhaust manifold in order to burn the hydrocarbons that escape from the combustion chamber. Courtesy General Motors Corporation.

Cross-sectioned view through an air-gulp type of backfire-suppressor valve. Courtesy Ford Motor Company.

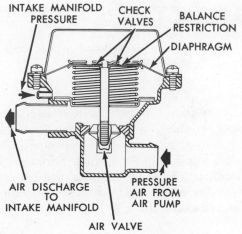

341

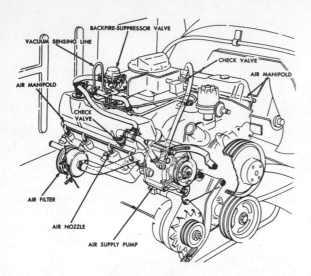

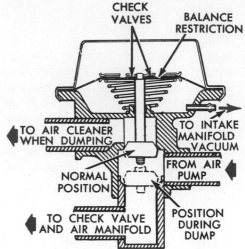

Cross-sectioned view through an air by-pass type of backfire-suppressor valve. Courtesy Ford Motor Company.

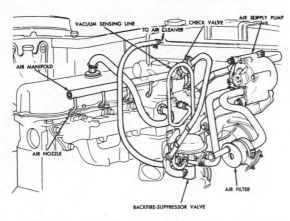

The top drawing shows an AIR system with an air gulp backfire-suppressor valve as used on a V-8 engine. The lower view shows the system with a by-pass type of backfire-suppressor valve as used on a 6-cylinder engine. Since 1968, the by-pass type backfire-suppressor valve has replaced the air-gulp type valve on almost all engines. Courtesy Ford Motor Company.

A by-pass type of valve is used on most engines to redirect the flow of air into the carburetor air cleaner for silencing purposes during periods of deceleration. At other times, the output from the air pump is directed into the exhaust manifold.

DOUBLE-ACTING DIAPHRAGM

On some engines, a double-acting diaphragm is used on the distributor. The vacuum-retard side is connected to intake manifold vacuum below the throttle valves. At idle speed, with the throttle valves closed, vacuum on this diaphragm retards the spark timing 10°. The opposite side of this diaphragm is connected to a spark port, just above the throttle valves. When the throttle valves are opened, vacuum is directed to this side of the diaphragm to advance the spark timing back to the initial static setting. After the throttle valves are opened, the double-acting vacuum advance unit functions exactly the same as any conventional unit.

On some manual-shift transmission cars with AIR, a sensing valve (similar to the one in the CAS arrangement) is used in conjunction with the dual-acting distributor control unit to provide additional spark advance during deceleration in order to reduce exhaust emissions to acceptable levels.

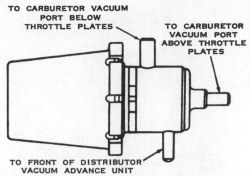

This special vacuum sensing valve is used on some G.M. engines in conjunction with the dual-acting distributor to provide additional spark advance during deceleration. Courtesy Pontiac Motor Division, General Motors Corporation.

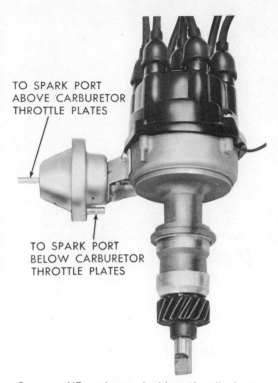

TO SPARK PORT ABOVE CARBURETOR THROTTLE PLATES

TO SPARK PORT BELOW CARBURETOR THROTTLE PLATES

On some AIR engines, a double-acting diaphragm is used on the distributor for better control of the timing. Courtesy Pontiac Motor Division, General Motors Corporation.

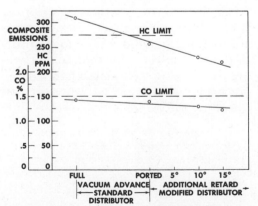

This graph shows how the additional retard provided by the double acting diaphragm unit reduces hydrocarbon emissions, with no significant loss in economy or performance. Courtesy General Motors Corporation.

THERMAL-SENSING DISTRIBUTOR CONTROL

On some models with an air conditioner, a special thermal-sensing unit is connected into the coolant outlet. It operates a vacuum switch to advance ignition timing at idle speed whenever excessively high coolant temperatures are encountered. The unit changes the ignition timing by switching the vacuum line from a ported one to full vacuum advance at idle. This improves engine cooling.

If a heating problem exists at idle speed only, disconnect the distributor vacuum hose at the thermostatic switch. When the engine temperature is above 230° F. and the engine is idling, there should be vacuum at the switch port "D" (distributor). Below 230° F., there should be no vacuum at this port.

Evaporative Losses

Much of the smog problem can be traced to mixing of nitrous oxides from from the exhausts of internal combus-

A thermal-sensing valve is used on some models with an air conditioner and with AIR in order to advance the ignition timing at idle whenever the coolant temperature reaches 230° F. This illustration shows the placement of the valve and the hose arrangement as used on Ford engines. The valve has three identifying letters "C", "D", and "M" stamped on it to identify the correct hose installation from the carburetor (C), distributor (D), and intake manifold (M). Be sure to disconnect and plug the distributor vacuum line when adjusting the ignition timing in order to avoid an error.

tion engines and hydrocarbons which evaporate from fuel tanks and carburetors. Evaporative losses have been estimated to be 10%-15% of the total hydrocarbons discharged into the atmosphere. The 1971 (1970 in California) regulations for limiting evaporative losses are 6 grams per vehicle per test.

Vapors are formed in the gas tank when the vehicle is allowed to stand in the sun. Vapors from the carburetor are caused by engine heat, and this is intensified when a hot engine is shut off, often causing the gasoline in the carburetor float chamber to boil. In the past, these vapors have been allowed to flow into the atmosphere through vents designed to relieve the pressure.

To reduce these emissions, it has been necessary to eliminate the external vents from the gas tank and the carburetor. One method of doing this is called the adsorption-regeneration system. In it a canister of activated carbon traps the vapors and stores them. Later, fresh air is passed over the carbon, stripping it of the trapped vapors. These vapors are then fed into the engine for burning in the combustion chamber. This burning takes place at times when engine operation would not be adversely affected by the enriched mixture.

Air pollution from exhaust and crankcase can now be controlled. Evaporative losses from the fuel tank and carburetor vent are still a major problem. However, control of these pollution sources by 1971 (1970 in California) is required by law. Courtesy General Motors Corporation.

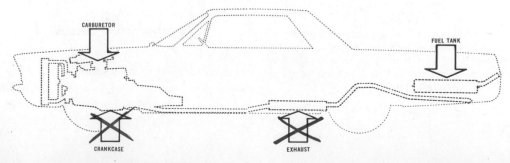

344

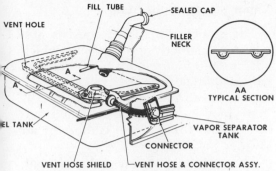

VENT HOLE
FILL TUBE
SEALED CAP
FILLER NECK
AA TYPICAL SECTION
VAPOR SEPARATOR TANK
EL TANK
CONNECTOR
VENT HOSE SHIELD
VENT HOSE & CONNECTOR ASSY.

The 1970 Maverick introduced the first workable evaporative emission control system. In the top of the fuel tank there is a polyethylene vapor-collection assembly. This routes vapors from the tank into the vapor separation subsystem. The fuel tank filler cap is unvented. Courtesy Ford Motor Company.

To say that the vapors are adsorbed means that they form a layer *on the surface* of the carbon. This is different from absorption. When a substance is absorbed it soaks into another substance, beyond the surface. To regenerate means to restore or renew. When the vapors are stripped away from the carbon, the canister is ready to adsorb more vapor. This is the regeneration phase.

The first functional system of this sort was introduced on the 1970 Maverick, a Ford product. This vehicle is equipped with an evaporative emission control system containing three subsystems: vapor collection, vapor separation, and vapor storage.

Vapor Collection Subsystem

The collection subsystem is a molded polyethylene unit in the top of the fuel tank. Vapors which enter this unit are carried from the tank through a vent hose to the vapor separator. The fuel tank filler cap is unvented and a specially designed fill pipe and vent assembly are employed to insure proper tank venting during fueling.

Vapor Separator Subsystem

The separation subsystem consists, in part, of a molded polyethylene tank and tubes. Fuel vapors pass through these. The tank is so designed that it prevents liquid fuel from entering the vapor line leading to the vapor storage system. Condensed vapors and liquid fuel return to the fuel tank through the return line, which is part of the connector assembly.

This subsystem also includes a three-way valve. During fueling, the valve acts as a stopper to prevent overfilling the tank. It does this by closing the vapor line, thus maintaining an expansion volume within the fuel tank. During a hot-soak period (after shutting off a hot engine), the valve opens under pressure to allow the expanded vapors to pass into the storage canister. The valve also permits air to enter the fuel tank to compensate for fuel which the engine consumed. Air also is allowed to enter whenever the fuel tank air pressure is reduced by a drop in temperature.

The vapor separation subsystem prevents liquid fuel from entering the vapor line leading to the vapor storage subsystem. The three-way control valve prevents the fuel tank from being overfilled and permits air to enter the tank to compensate for fuel which the engine consumes. Courtesy Ford Motor Company.

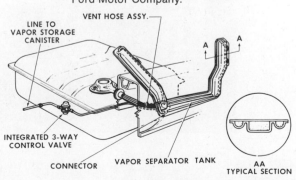

VENT HOSE ASSY.
LINE TO VAPOR STORAGE CANISTER
A A
INTEGRATED 3-WAY CONTROL VALVE
CONNECTOR
VAPOR SEPARATOR TANK
AA TYPICAL SECTION

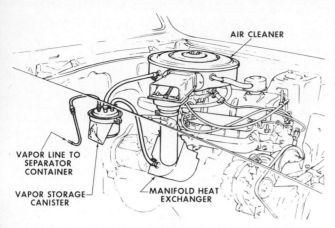

Vapor Storage Subsystem

The storage subsystem consists of a canister of activated carbon which adsorbs the fuel vapors. The saturated carbon particles are then purged of the vapors by air passing through the carbon granules and being inducted into the engine through the carburetor air cleaner.

The carburetor has no external vent. Fuel vapors from the carburetor float bowl are vented to the air cleaner during engine-off periods; they flow into the storage area through a hose.

In the vapor storage subsystem, a canister containing activated carbon adsorbs the fuel vapors. The carbon is purged of the vapors by air passing through the carbon granules and being carried into the engine through the air cleaner. Courtesy Ford Motor Company.

Service Procedures

Cleaning the filter elements and the PCV valve are the operations generally performed to service crankcase ventilating systems. They should be done every six months in order to keep the system operating efficiently.

Highly skilled personnel and accurate equipment are needed in order to keep smog-control devices and other complex items functioning properly. The days of the backyard mechanic are gone.

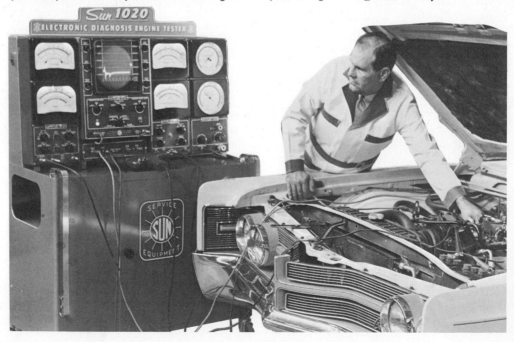

Good tune-up procedures are required to adjust an engine to designed specifications so that its exhaust emissions will be within acceptable legal limits. Troubleshooting is essential in servicing exhaust emission control systems, and it will be covered along with the service procedures that follow.

Servicing the Positive Crankcase Ventilating System

① If excessive sludging of the PCV valve occurs, the valve may stick closed. This will cause high crankcase pressures at highway speeds, which can force engine oil through the seals and gaskets. The efficiency of the PCV system can be checked in several ways, one of which is to hold a piece of cardboard over the filler tube. If the PCV valve is working properly, the negative pressure will suck the cardboard over the filler tube opening. This is a rough check, but it can be made quickly and without elaborate equipment.

② A plugged PCV system will cause a rough idle. A quick check to see if the idling condition is being caused by the PCV valve is to connect a tachometer to the engine, and then start it up. Clamp off the hose that goes from the valve to the base of the carburetor. If the valve is working properly, engine speed will drop about 50-60 rpm, and you should be able to hear the valve click when clamping and releasing the line several times. If the valve is stuck open, engine speed will drop off more than 60 rpm. If the valve is plugged, there will be no change in engine speed.

③ A much more accurate test can be made by using the AC tester on engines equipped with an AC system. It provides visual evidence of the need for service.

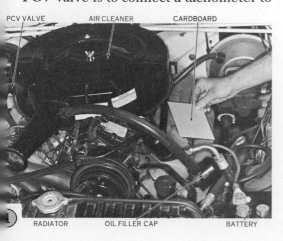

PCV VALVE   AIR CLEANER   CARDBOARD

RADIATOR   OIL FILLER CAP   BATTERY

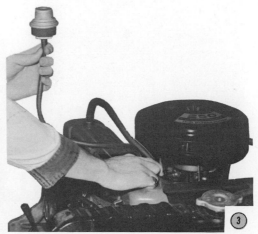

The first step is to seal all crankcase openings. Remove the dipstick and plug the tube with the blanking plugs furnished with the tester. If the engine has a breather on one rocker arm cover, remove it and plug the opening. On engines with a closed PCV system, remove the hose to the carburetor air cleaner and plug it to prevent the entrance of air. Now, set the selector knob on the bottom of the tester to match the car being tested, according to the information provided in the service manual for the tester. With the engine warm and running at idle speed, insert the tester adapter into the crankcase breather opening. Hold the tester upright and make sure that there are no kinks in the hose. Allow at least half a minute for vacuum to build up. Look directly into the tester viewing window to observe the color of the indicator. If it shows green, the system is operating at its designed efficiency. If it shows yellow, there is an air leak at the sealing adapters, at a broken gasket, or the PCV valve is stuck open and must be replaced. If the indicator shows red, the PCV valve is plugged and must be replaced.

Specialized testing equipment is being introduced for precision-tuning an engine so that exhaust emissions can be reduced to legal limits.

STANDARD AND CAP SPECIFICATIONS
1966 MODELS

ENGINE	CARBURETOR	TRANSMISSION	IGNITION TIMING AT IDLE		ENGINE SPEED* AT IDLE (RPM)	
			STANDARD	CAP	STANDARD	CAP
170	1	M	5° BTC	5° ATC	550	700
170	1	A	5° BTC	5° ATC	550	650
225	1	M	2.5° BTC	5° ATC	550	650
225	1	A	2.5° BTC	5° ATC	550	650
273	2	M	5° BTC	5° ATC	500	700
273	2	A	10° BTC	5 ATC	500	650
273	4	M	10° BTC	5° ATC	600	700
273	4	A	10° BTC	5° ATC	600	650
318	2	M	5° BTC	5° ATC	500	650
318	2	A	10° BTC	5° ATC	500	600
361	2	M	12.5° BTC	5° ATC	500	650
361	2	A	12.5° BTC	TDC	500	600
383	2	M	12.5° BTC	5° ATC	500	650
383	2	A	12.5° BTC	TDC	500	600
383	4	M	12.5° BTC	5° ATC	500	650
383	4	A	12.5° BTC	TDC	500	600
440	4	M	12.5° BTC	TDC	500	650
440	4	A	12.5° BTC	TDC	500	600

Standard idle mixture is set on lean side of maximum vacuum.
CAP idle mixture is set at 1% CO.
CAP off-idle mixtures leaner.
CAP 75° choke leaner part throttle.
CAP mixtures have narrower limits.

*—With transmission in neutral.

This chart shows the difference in specifications for CAS and conventional engines. Be sure to check the manufacturer's specifications before making any adjustment to the new controlled engines. Courtesy Chrysler Corporation.

Tuning a Cleaner Air System (Chrysler)

The usual ignition and carburetor tune-up service procedures apply, and these must be accurately performed first. The following points are emphasized as the engine must be balanced and operating within specifications for the CAS system to do its work properly.

PROCEDURE

① Check and adjust the ignition timing to specifications. **Note:** *The CAS arrangement carries a greater retarded static timing setting than a standard engine.* **Caution:** *The vacuum line between the vacuum control valve and the intake manifold must be clamped shut.*

CLAMP

TIMING LIGHT

①

② Check and adjust the warm-engine idle speed to specifications with a tachometer. The air cleaner must be in place, transmission in neutral (not in PARK), air conditioner off, and the headlights on high beam for cars with a 6-cylinder engine. Adjust the carburetor dashpot stem so that it doesn't contact the throttle lever. **Caution:** *The final idle speed must be within 25 rpm of specifications.* Using a combustion analyzer that has been properly balanced, adjust the air-fuel ratio to 14.0–14.2 by turning the idle mixture screws $\frac{1}{16}$ turn at a time. **Note:** *On some vehicles it is extremely difficult to adjust the mixture with the air cleaner in place. To solve this problem take two air-fuel analyzer readings while the engine is idling, one before and the other after removing the air cleaner. Make a note of the difference between the two readings and remember to compensate for it when making the adjustment.*

COMBUSTION EFFICIENCY ②

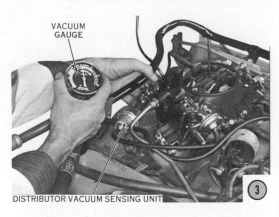

VACUUM
GAUGE

DISTRIBUTOR VACUUM SENSING UNIT

(3)

CLAMP

(4)

(3) Check the operation of the distributor vacuum sensing unit by connecting a vacuum gauge into the distributor vacuum line, using a "T" fitting. With the transmission in neutral, increase engine speed to 2,000 rpm, hold this speed for about 5 seconds, and then release the throttle. The vacuum gauge should read above 16″ Hg for a minimum of one second. **Caution:** *Use a stop watch to time it.* Within 3 seconds after releasing the throttle, the gauge should fall to 6″ Hg or below. **Note:** *If the gauge does not fall below 6″ Hg, the idle speed, mixture, or basic timing setting is not within specifications.* **Caution:** *Make sure that the carburetor dashpot rod is not contacting the throttle lever.* To adjust the timing of the distributor vacuum sensing unit, turn the adjusting screw on the spring end counterclockwise to increase the time that the distributor vacuum remains above 6″ Hg after releasing the throttle. **Note:** *One turn will change the setting about ½″ Hg.* If the valve cannot be properly adjusted, replace it.

(4) With the curb idle speed and mixture properly adjusted and a tachometer installed, position the throttle lever so that the actuating tab is contacting the

stem of the dashpot, *but not depressing it.* The tachometer should read 2,000 rpm. If necessary, adjust by screwing the dashpot in or out as required, and then tighten the locknut.

Tuning a Controlled Combustion System (General Motors)

Good tune-up procedures are essential in obtaining a smooth running engine consistent with reduced exhaust emissions. These engines are designed for ported spark advance (taken above the throttle plate) so that no vacuum reaches the distributor control diaphragm at idle speeds. The static spark setting is generally more retarded than on pre-controlled engines.

When setting the carburetor idle mixture, the following procedure should be followed: **(1)** With the engine at normal operating temperature and the automatic transmission in *drive,* adjust the engine idling speed to 625 rpm. **Note:** *If the car is air conditioned, the system must be in the OFF position and the idle port compensator valve held closed.* **(2)** Turn the idle mixture adjusting

350

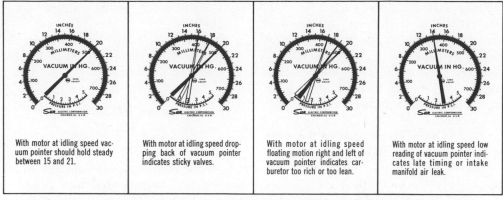

With motor at idling speed vacuum pointer should hold steady between 15 and 21.	With motor at idling speed dropping back of vacuum pointer indicates sticky valves.	With motor at idling speed floating motion right and left of vacuum pointer indicates carburetor too rich or too lean.	With motor at idling speed low reading of vacuum pointer indicates late timing or intake manifold air leak.

Good tune-up procedures and techniques are essential in obtaining a smooth running engine consistent with reduced exhaust emissions. The skilled technician must understand the use of the scientific testing equipment. This illustration shows the various engine conditions and resulting vacuum gauge readings. Engines with defects have excessively high emission values. Courtesy Sun Electric Corporation.

screws to obtain a smooth idle at 625 rpm. **Note:** *It may be necessary to readjust the idle speed to 625 rpm, and then turn the idle mixture screws for a smooth idle.* **(3)** Now, turn in the idle mixture adjusting screws *evenly* until the idle speed drops to 600 rpm. This procedure is designed to position the idle mixture slightly on the lean side in order to reduce exhaust emissions.

FUNCTIONAL CHECKS ON THE CCC SYSTEM

1. Vacuum motors and valve plates

With the engine shut off, the vacuum motors should be holding the valve plates open. Check by looking into the two snorkels. **Note:** *The left snorkel*

The Climatic Combustion Control (CCC) system uses a bi-metallic temperature sensing unit. It bleeds manifold vacuum to regulate the diaphragm controlling the amount of preheated air that is mixed with cold air entering the air cleaner. This is done to maintain an air inlet temperature of about 100° F. Courtesy Oldsmobile Division, General Motors Corporation.

will be blocked closed on some smaller engines.

1a. Start the engine. The left valve plate should close immediately, regardless of temperature.

1b. If the temperature in the air cleaner is below 90°-120° F., the right valve plate will also close to block the entrance of outside air.

1c. If the temperature is above 90°-120° F., the valve plate must remain open to admit outside air. Replace defective vacuum motor(s).

2. Temperature sensor

Remove the air cleaner and allow it to cool down. Re-install the air cleaner, attach the hoses, and then tape a thermometer alongside the temperature sensing unit in the air cleaner. Install the cover on the air cleaner, then start the engine.

2a. Observe the valve plate in the right snorkel to see when it begins to move toward the open position.

2b. Quickly remove the air cleaner cover and check the thermometer, which must read approximately 100° F.

2c. If the temperature reading is not within specifications, replace the temperature sensor.

Tuning an IMCO System (Ford)

The ignition timing must be accurately set with the vacuum line to the distributor disconnected and plugged. Be sure that the engine is idling slowly

This new Ford engine is equipped with a thermostatically controlled air mixing door in order to blend the hot air picked up from the shroud around the exhaust manifold with the cool outside air. The distributor has a dual-action vacuum unit to provide about 10° of retard at idle. Courtesy Ford Motor Company.

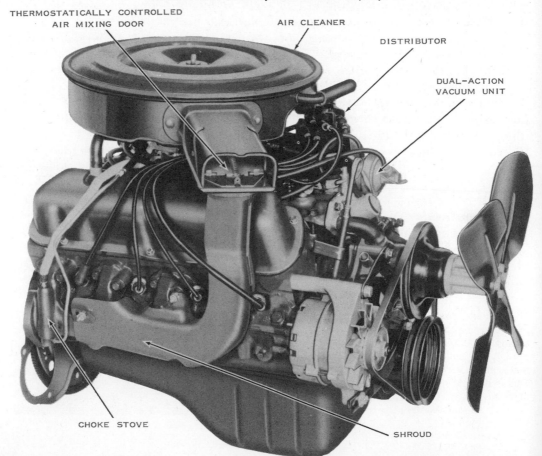

THERMOSTATICALLY CONTROLLED AIR MIXING DOOR

AIR CLEANER

DISTRIBUTOR

DUAL-ACTION VACUUM UNIT

CHOKE STOVE

SHROUD

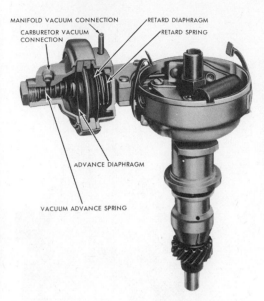

MANIFOLD VACUUM CONNECTION

CARBURETOR VACUUM CONNECTION

RETARD DIAPHRAGM

RETARD SPRING

ADVANCE DIAPHRAGM

VACUUM ADVANCE SPRING

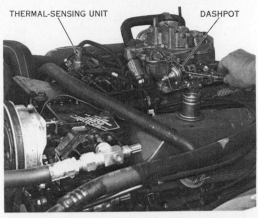

THERMAL-SENSING UNIT

DASHPOT

When tuning an IMCO (Ford) system, make sure that the choke plate is in the wide-open position and that the dashpot is not contacting the throttle lever.

This is a cutaway picture of the new dual-action vacuum unit on a distributor. This unit provides 10° additional retard at idle. Courtesy Ford Motor Company.

enough to prevent the centrifugal advance from operating, which would cause a retarded condition throughout the operating range.

The idle speed and mixture adjustments must be made with the engine temperature normalized. To do this, place the transmission selector lever in neutral and set the parking brake. Connect a tachometer. Operate the engine at least 15 minutes at 1,500 rpm to normalize the temperature. **Note:** *This increased idle speed can be obtained by positioning the fast-idle screw on the second step of the fast-idle cam.* Connect an exhaust gas analyzer to the tail pipe and adjust it to the SET position.

Turn the headlamp switch to high beam and the air conditioner switch ON to engage the compressor clutch

while adjusting the idle speed. Make sure that the choke plate is in the wide-open position, and then adjust the idle speed to specifications. On vehicles with an automatic transmission, place the selector lever in DRIVE, and then re-adjust the idle speed to specifications. **Note:** *The final speed and mixture adjustments must be made with the selector lever in DRIVE.*

Turn the idle mixture adjusting screw(s) in evenly, $\frac{1}{16}$ turn at a time, until the exhaust gas analyzer reads 14.2 (13.8 for the 200 cu. in. engine). Place the automatic transmission selector lever in neutral, increase engine speed to 2,000 rpm for 30 seconds, and then let the engine return to its normal idle speed. Place the selector lever in DRIVE and recheck the analyzer. **Caution:** *Wait at least 10 seconds for the reading to stabilize.* If necessary, re-adjust the air-fuel mixture.

Reconnect the distributor vacuum line. Turn off the headlamps and the air conditioner.

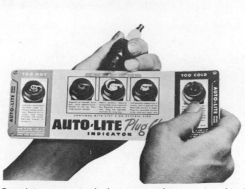

Good tune-up techniques require you to check the operating temperature of each spark plug as it is removed from the engine. This indicator can be used to compare the coloring of the removed plugs so that unusual operating conditions of the engine can be noted. Courtesy Autolite Division, Ford Motor Company.

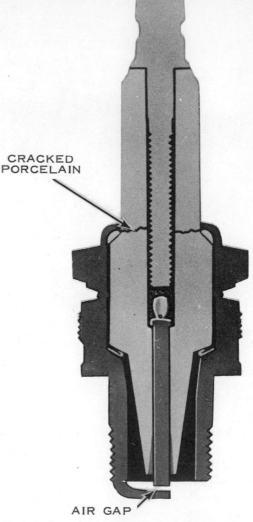

CRACKED PORCELAIN

AIR GAP

A cracked porcelain will result in misfire when accelerating. This will cause unburned hydrocarbons to be emitted from the exhaust system. Courtesy AC Division, General Motors Corporation.

If a spark plug has soft black soot over it, the air-fuel mixture is excessively rich. This results in a high level of unburned hydrocarbons. Courtesy Champion Spark Plug Company.

Tuning an "Engine Mod" System (American Motors)

Adjust the ignition timing to specifications with the engine idling at exactly 500 rpm for the 232 cu. in. engine. This is necessary to prevent some centrifugal advance in the distributor which would cause a retarded condition throughout the operating range. **Note:**

The idle speed will be increased before adjusting the mixture.

Adjust the engine idle speed to 600 rpm with the transmission selector lever in neutral, air conditioner on, and the air cleaner in place. Turn the idle mixture adjusting screw(s) out until no further increase in idle speed can be obtained, and then turn the adjusting screw(s) in until the idle speed drops 20 rpm. Now, turn the screw(s) out to the point where the original idle speed is regained, and then stop. At this point, the idle speed must be exactly 600 rpm. If not, repeat the adjustments.

Tuning an AIR System

In the AIR system, where the excess hydrocarbons are burned in the exhaust manifold, accurate engine tune-up procedures are required for efficient engine operation and control of exhaust emissions. The spark timing must be set accurately to specifications with the distributor vacuum line disconnected and taped shut. Generally, engine speeds are greater and the spark timing is retarded at idle over that specified for uncontrolled engines, but this is not so for all AIR engines. **Caution:** *Check the manufacturer's specifications to be sure.*

In order to obtain an accurate indication on the exhaust gas analyzer, it is necessary to disconnect the air pump; otherwise, the gauge will show a false, lean reading. The pump can be disconnected by removing the drive belt, or the outlet hose can be pulled off. With the air pump disconnected, the idle speed will drop slightly. **Caution:** *The final idle mixture adjustment must be made at this lower speed.*

With the air cleaner in place, turn in each mixture adjusting screw $1/16$ turn at a time until the exhaust gas analyzer reads 13.8. Wait at least 10 seconds for the meter to stabilize before changing any adjustment. **Caution:** *Any change in idling speed must be corrected immediately.* **Note:** *The final adjustments must be made in an inward direction.*

Contact points must be clean and make perfect contact each time they come together; otherwise, the spark plug will miss and unburned hydrocarbons will pass off through the exhaust. A burned set of contact points is shown at left, with a good one at right for comparison.

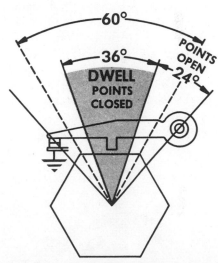

One of the very important specifications is the "dwell" or amount of time that the contact points remain together. Unless the contact point gap is adjusted to specifications, the tune-up will be unsatisfactory, especially in regard to emission levels. Courtesy Sun Electric Corporation.

Place the automatic transmission selector lever in neutral, increase engine speed to 2,000 rpm for 30 seconds, and then allow it to return to its normal idle speed. Position the selector lever in drive and recheck the analyzer reading.

355

Wait 10 seconds for the meter to stabilize itself before making any corrections.

Reconnect the distributor vacuum line. Turn off the headlamps and air conditioner, if the specifications indicated that they were to be on during the adjustment. Reconnect the air pump hose or replace the drive belt. Tighten the drive belt to 60 pounds, using the Borroughs' belt tension gauge. **Caution:** *Don't pry on the aluminum housing, or you will damage the pump.*

Troubleshooting an AIR System

In general, the tune-up procedures that were discussed will suffice unless there is some trouble that cannot be eliminated. In that event, it is necessary to troubleshoot the system in order to isolate the trouble to either conventional engine systems or to the AIR system.

To check out the Air Injection Reactor (AIR) system, it is first necessary

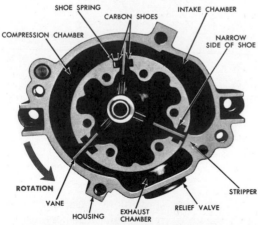

Cross-sectioned view through the air pump, which is self-lubricating. *CAUTION: Don't pry against the housing when adjusting the drive belt, or you will damage it.* Courtesy Ford Motor Company.

to disconnect the by-pass valve vacuum sensing hose and the air supply hose at the intake manifold so that the other engine components can be checked out as possible sources of the trouble. For best results and most efficient operation, the emission control system hoses, tubes, oil separator screen, fittings, and the carburetor spacer should be cleaned; and the emission control valve and the air pump filter element replaced every 12,000 miles.

If the trouble has been localized to the AIR system, use the following troubleshooting procedures as a guide.

AIR SUPPLY PUMP TEST

Connect a low-pressure gauge into the air supply hose at the check valve. On a V-8 engine with two hoses, the second one must be plugged. Start the engine and increase its speed to 1,500 rpm; at this point the pressure should be 2-6 psi. A lower pressure might indicate leaks at the by-pass valve, the hose of which should be plugged and the test repeated. If the pump is still below specifications, install a new air pump filter element and retest. Replace the air pump if it still does not reach the specified pressure.

EXHAUST CHECK VALVE TEST

Disconnect the air supply hose(s) at the air manifold(s) and visually inspect the position of the valve plate inside the valve body. It should be positioned lightly against the seat, and away from the air supply manifold. Depress the valve with a pencil to make sure that it is free and that it returns to its original position against its seat when released. Start the engine with the air manifold hose(s) disconnected and increase

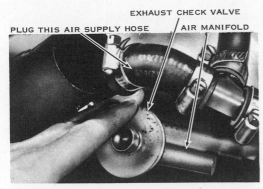

To test the exhaust check valve, disconnect the air supply hose and inspect the position of the valve plate inside the valve body. It should be positioned lightly against the seat and away from the air supply manifold. Courtesy Ford Motor Company.

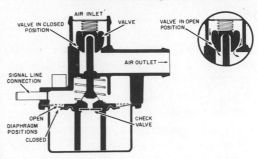

Cross-sectioned view through a backfire-suppressor valve. Courtesy Buick Motor Division, General Motors Corporation.

engine speed to 1,500 rpm. There must be no exhaust leakage at the check valve(s). **Note:** *The valve may flutter at idle speed, but this is a normal result of exhaust pulsations in the manifold.*

BY-PASS VALVE TEST
Air Leakage Test

With all parts of the AIR system connected, set the idle speed to specifica-tions and adjust the air-fuel mixture. If the idle is rough, or if it is not possible to reduce the idle speed to specifica-tions, disconnect the vacuum sensing tube at the valve and plug the tube end. If the idle can now be smoothed or the specified speed achieved, then the valve is defective and must be replaced. If there is no difference in idle quality or rpm, reconnect the hose and line and check out the rest of the engine for trouble.

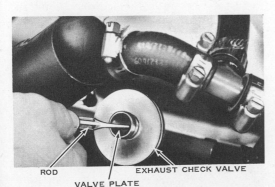

Depress the valve with a rod to make sure that it is free and that it returns to its position against the seat. Courtesy Ford Motor Company.

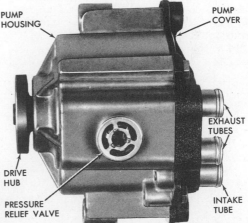

Details of the air pump used in the AIR system. The pressure relief valve is color-coded to indicate the pressure at which it operates. Courtesy Chevrolet Motor Division, General Motors Corporation.

357

FUNCTION TEST

Disconnect the rubber hose from the by-pass valve to the carburetor air cleaner or air supply pump air filter (at the valve end). Open and close the throttle rapidly. If the valve is functioning properly, an escaping compressed air noise should be heard from the valve on deceleration.

AIR TROUBLESHOOTING CHART

1. Excessive backfiring in the exhaust system

1a. Sensing hose damaged, plugged, or leaking

1b. Defective valve

2. Flat spot on acceleration after deceleration above 20 mph

2a. Leaking intake vacuum hose to valve

3. Baked or burned air-supply hoses

3a. Defective exhaust check valve(s) in the air supply manifold(s)

4. Engine surges at all speeds

4a. Defective by-pass valve

4b. Incorrect carburetor adjustments

5. Noisy air-pump drive belt

5a. Incorrect adjustment

5b. Seized or failing pump

5c. Misaligned pulleys

6. Rough engine idle

6a. Incorrect carburetor adjustments

6b. Incorrect static ignition timing

6c. Vacuum leak at the by-pass valve hoses

6d. Defective valve

CHECK YOUR KNOWLEDGE

1. The word "smog" was coined from which two words?

2. Which three atmospheric pollution gases are blamed on the internal combustion engine?

3. During which year were crankcase emission control devices required on cars sold in the state of California?

4. The exhaust emission control systems introduced in 1966–68 are required to limit unburned hydrocarbons to how many parts per million?

5. What are the three sources of pollutants from the internal combustion engine?

6. How do the blow-by gases get into the crankcase?

7. What is the purpose and operation of the PCV valve?

8. What is a closed system for controlling crankcase emissions?

9. What is the source of the unburned hydrocarbons in an internal combustion engine?

10. What are the 1970 goals for limiting hydrocarbon emissions? Carbon monoxide emissions?

11. What are the two methods of controlling exhaust emissions?

12. Which of the driving ranges is relatively free of unburned hydrocarbons?

13. What is being done to the cooling system to reduce hydrocarbon emissions?

14. What four methods are discussed for preventing a mechanic from adjusting the idle air-fuel mixture too rich?

15. What is done to the ignition timing at idle to reduce exhaust emissions?

16. What must be done to the ignition timing during deceleration to reduce exhaust emissions?

17. Which three units of the engine are modified for the CAS approach to exhaust emission control?

18. What is the purpose of the vacuum advance control unit in the CAS system?

19. Which three units of the engine are modified for the CCS system of exhaust emission control?

20. The CCC system consists of which three special devices?

21. What is the temperature of the air entering the carburetor in the CCC system?

22. Which manufacturer uses the IMCO approach to exhaust emission control?
23. Which two units of the engine are modified for the "Engine Mod" system of exhaust emission control?
24. Which two methods have been developed to consume the excess hydrocarbons in the exhaust system?
25. What is the AIR system?
26. What is the purpose of the double-acting diaphragm control unit for distributors?
27. What is the purpose of the thermal-sensing valve?
28. What are the 1970 goals for limiting evaporative losses?

Self-Check Tests

TRUE-FALSE

1. Smog is an atmospheric condition which exists exclusively in California.
2. The internal combustion engine is known to be the major source of hydrocarbons.
3. It is estimated that each uncontrolled car emits about 1.25 pounds of air pollutants per day.
4. The first exhaust emission control systems were designed to limit unburned hydrocarbons to a 1.5% concentration by volume.
5. Crankcase emissions result from blow-by gases.
6. The source of unburned hydrocarbons in the exhaust is the result of the quenching action that occurs when the flame front is snuffed out.
7. The 1970 goal is to limit carbon monoxide emissions to 23 grams per mile.
8. A "squish" area in the combustion chamber is most effective in reducing emissions.
9. Raising the temperature of the coolant is effective in reducing emissions.
10. Emissions during the idle mode of engine operation are relatively high in an uncontrolled engine.
11. To reduce emissions, the ignition timing must be advanced at idle speed.
12. To reduce emissions, the ignition timing must be advanced during deceleration.
13. The Cleaner Air System requires a special temperature-compensating air cleaner.

14. The Controlled Combustion System requires all of the parts of the Climatic Combustion Control system.
15. The air inlet temperature of the CCC system is regulated to about 100° F.
16. The two systems that have been developed to consume hydrocarbons in the exhaust system are afterburners and the Air Injection Reactor (AIR).
17. Afterburners are not used presently because they are not commercially feasible.
18. The AIR system requires an air pump.
19. The CAS arrangement requires a by-pass valve.
20. On some CAS engines, a double-acting diaphragm is used.
21. A thermal-sensing valve is required on all models with AIR and an air conditioner.
22. Evaporative losses have been effectively controlled since 1966.
23. The crankcase ventilating system should be serviced twice a year.
24. In each system, it is necessary for the distributor vacuum line to be disconnected and the opening taped shut before setting the ignition timing.
25. In order to obtain an accurate reading on an exhaust gas analyzer, used on an engine with AIR, it is imperative for the air pump to be disconnected.

MULTIPLE CHOICE

1. What is the chemical make-up of smog? a) hydrogen and carbon dioxide; b) hydrogen and carbon monoxide; c) hydrocarbons and nitrous oxide.
2. The PCV value means: a) Positive Crankcase Vacuum; b) Potential Carbon Values; c) Positive Crankcase Ventilation.
3. Initial exhaust emission limit levels of hydrocarbons were set at: a) 275 ppm; b) 180 ppm; c) 110 ppm.
4. Which engine operating mode emits the least unburned hydrocarbons from the exhaust system? a) idle; b) range; c) deceleration.
5. CAS means: a) Cleaner Afterburner System; b) Crankcase Air System; c) Cleaner Air System.
6. CCC means: a) Climatic Combustion Control; b) Cleaner Combustion Control; c) Calibrated Carburetor Control.

7. Which exhaust emission control system uses a by-pass valve? a) CCS; b) CAS; c) AIR.

8. What is the 1970 "hot soak" goal for limiting evaporative losses? a) 6 grams; b) 7.5 grams; c) 8 pounds.

9. To what air-fuel ratio should the idle mixture adjustment be set when tuning an engine with CAS? a) 14.2; b) 1.42; c) 0.142.

10. To what designed temperature is the inlet air controlled in the CCC system? a) 100°; b) 200°; c) 300°.

COMPLETION

1. The internal combustion engine is known to be the major source of _____, carbon monoxide, and oxides of nitrogen.

2. The three sources of pollutants from vehicles propelled by internal combustion engines are: crankcase blow-by gases, exhaust emissions, and _____ losses.

3. The PCV system routes the crankcase blow-by gases back to the _____ _____ through the intake manifold.

4. The control of exhaust emissions has taken two forms to date as follows: (1) raising the combustion efficiency and (2) consuming the unburned hydrocarbons in the _____ system.

5. To raise the efficiency of the idle circuit, engineers are specifying _____ idle speeds.

6. _____ the ignition timing at idle will reduce exhaust emissions.

7. _____ the ignition timing during periods of deceleration will reduce exhaust emissions.

MATCHING

1. Smog	a. Crankcase
2. Blow-by gases	b. Chrysler
3. CAS	c. Air pollution
4. CCS	d. American Motors
5. IMCO	e. Air pump
6. "Engine Mod"	f. General Motors
7. AIR	g. Ford

Chapter 12

The Clutch

The power produced by the engine must be transferred to the rear wheels of the car under the control of the driver. He has to be able to connect and disconnect the power and change the amount and direction of power flow. A clutch, transmission, and rear drive mechanism are provided to do these jobs.

The *clutch* is a coupling device positioned between the engine and transmission to disconnect the engine from the drive mechanism when the driver wants to stop the car of shift gears. *Automatic transmission equipped cars* have fluid couplings which perform the same functions. The clutch mechanism consists of four main parts: the flywheel, driven plate, pressure plate, and throwout mechanism.

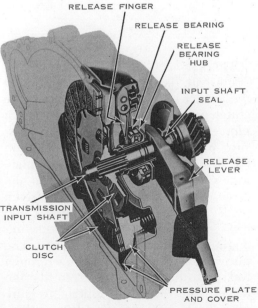

The power of the engine is transmitted to the rear axle through the clutch, transmission, and driveshaft. Courtesy Pontiac Motor Division, General Motors Corporation.

A phantom view of the clutch mechanism. Courtesy Ford Motor Company.

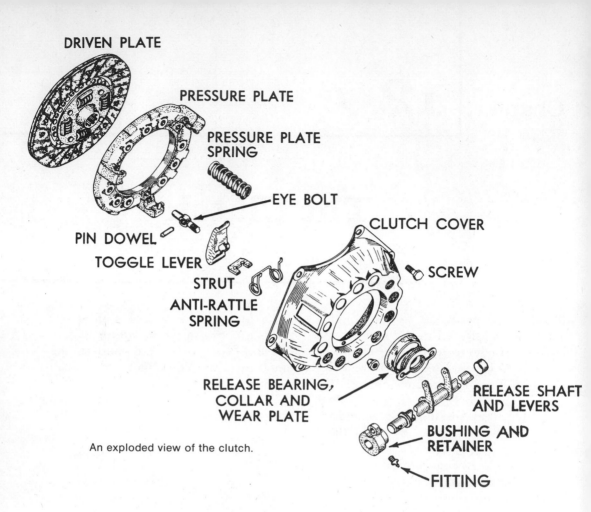

DRIVEN PLATE

PRESSURE PLATE

PRESSURE PLATE SPRING

EYE BOLT

PIN DOWEL

TOGGLE LEVER

STRUT

ANTI-RATTLE SPRING

CLUTCH COVER

SCREW

RELEASE BEARING, COLLAR AND WEAR PLATE

RELEASE SHAFT AND LEVERS

BUSHING AND RETAINER

FITTING

An exploded view of the clutch.

The *flywheel*, attached to the engine crankshaft, is the driving member of the clutch—to which is bolted the clutch pressure plate. The clutch *driven plate* is positioned between the pressure plate and the flywheel; when in the driving position, the pressure plate forces it against the flywheel so the three parts rotate as a unit. The driven plate is splined to the transmission drive pinion (clutch gear) to transmit engine power to the transmission. The throwout mechanism is coupled through linkage to the clutch pedal, so that the driver may move the clutch pressure plate back, releasing the driven plate, which can now coast freely.

The *friction disc* contains a wavy cushion spring between the two friction linings so that engagement is smooth. It also contains a series of coil springs arranged around the hub in a circular fashion to absorb the torsional vibration of the crankshaft caused by the pulsing flow of power.

The *pressure plate* contains a series of springs arranged around its circumference to force it against the driven disc. Some pressure plates are designed with a weight at the outer end of each throwout lever. As engine speed increases, centrifugal force on these weights causes the release levers to exert more pressure which forces the

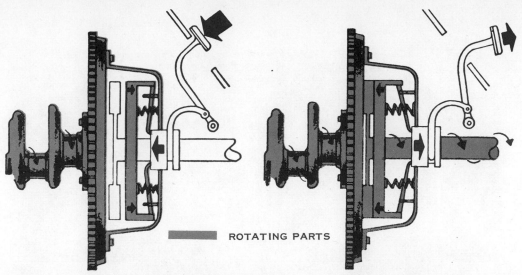

```
■         ■  ROTATING PARTS
```

PEDAL DOWN--CLUTCH DISENGAGED PEDAL UP--CLUTCH ENGAGED

Operation of the clutch. The driven plate is squeezed between the two pressure driving plates. The clutch pedal is a second class lever. Courtesy General Motors Corporation.

pressure plate into tighter contact with the driven disc to minimize slippage.

Some pressure plates use a diaphragm-type spring whose action is like the bottom of an oil can that snaps in and out. The tensed metal snaps over center on a pivot ring, "dishing" the diaphragm inward, which releases pressure on the driven disc.

Service Procedures

Clutch pedal adjustment and clutch rebuilding are the usual service jobs. A slipping clutch develops frictional heat which soon removes the temper from the springs. The relaxed springs do not hold the clutch assembly together with enough pressure, and so the slippage increases. Eventually, the clutch pressure plate, and sometimes the flywheel, are burned beyond further use.

If a slipping clutch is caused by too little play in the pedal linkage but is adjusted soon enough, its life may be prolonged.

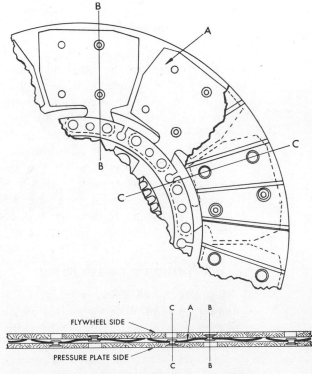

A wavy spring (A) cushions clutch engagement. This cross-section at BB shows its construction.

363

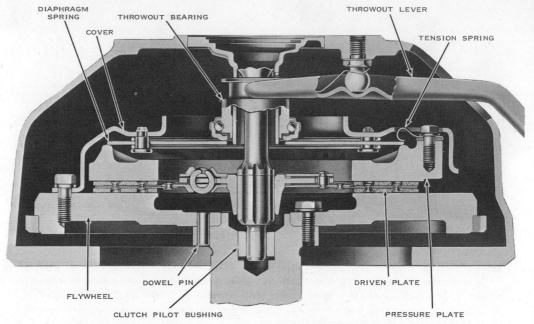

DIAPHRAGM SPRING
COVER
THROWOUT BEARING
THROWOUT LEVER
TENSION SPRING
FLYWHEEL
DOWEL PIN
CLUTCH PILOT BUSHING
DRIVEN PLATE
PRESSURE PLATE

The diaphragm-type spring pressure plate and the clutch assembly. Courtesy Chevrolet Motor Division, General Motors Corporation.

Troubleshooting

To test for a slipping clutch, apply the hand and foot brakes firmly. Shift the transmission into high gear. Start the engine and advance the throttle to an engine speed of about 30 mph. Take your foot off the clutch pedal and, if the engine stalls, the clutch is in a satisfactory condition; if the engine continues to run, the clutch is slipping and the pedal must be adjusted, if possible, or the clutch overhauled.

Adjusting a Clutch Pedal

Stepping on the clutch pedal separates the two clutch driving discs which releases the driven disc. When the clutch is in the driving position, the pedal must be fully released, otherwise a slight pressure would tend to release the discs and the clutch would slip.

Test the play by pressing on the clutch pedal by hand. There should be 1 inch free play before the clutch pressure plate spring tension is felt.

Clutch pedal adjustment of Chrysler products. Courtesy Dodge Division, Chrysler Corporation.

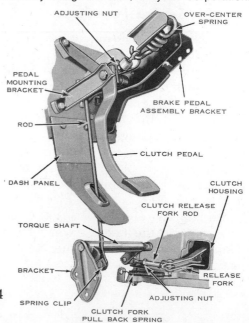

ADJUSTING NUT
OVER-CENTER SPRING
PEDAL MOUNTING BRACKET
BRAKE PEDAL ASSEMBLY BRACKET
ROD
CLUTCH PEDAL
DASH PANEL
CLUTCH HOUSING
CLUTCH RELEASE FORK ROD
TORQUE SHAFT
BRACKET
RELEASE FORK
SPRING CLIP
ADJUSTING NUT
CLUTCH FORK PULL BACK SPRING

364

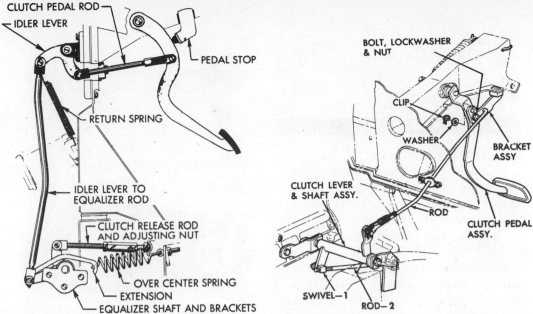

Buick clutch pedal adjustment. How many *levers* can you identify in this picture? Courtesy Buick Motor Division, General Motors Corporation.

Chevrolet clutch pedal adjustment. Swivel 1 is removed from the lever and threaded along rod 2. Courtesy Chevrolet Motor Division, General Motors Corporation.

Pontiac clutch adjustment. Courtesy Pontiac Motor Division, General Motors Corporation.

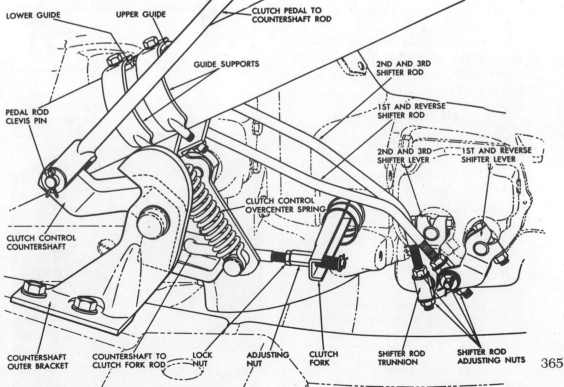

365

Tools and Equipment

$\frac{1}{2}$, $\frac{9}{16}$, and $\frac{5}{8}$ inch box, open-end wrenches; pliers.

PROCEDURE

1. Test the pedal play.

2. Every car has a different detailed adjustment but the method is similar. Have someone step on the pedal while you observe the linkage to determine which way the various levers and rods move.

3. On some cars, a yoked clevis joint can be taken apart and threaded onto the shaft or backed off to obtain the correct play.

4. Some cars have a threaded shaft with two positioning nuts passing through the throwout lever. The two nuts are moved up or down along the shaft to change the adjustment. Jamming the nuts together locks them against the throwout lever.

5. Some cars have the adjustment near the end of the clutch release fork. Loosen the locknut to turn the adjustment and tighten it after the adjustment is made.

Rebuilding a Clutch

The clutch is subjected to a good deal of abuse by a driver who slips the clutch or races the engine when starting. Some drivers "ride the clutch," which causes slipping and heating, eventually burning up the lining and taking the temper out of the clutch pressure plate springs.

It is always necessary to replace the clutch driven disc and the pressure plate springs at each overhaul. If the clutch driving surfaces are grooved, it is necessary to replace the clutch

366

This cross shaft is worn from lack of lubrication.

Worn linkage makes clutch pedal adjustment impossible.

A burned clutch pressure-plate assembly is caused by slipping the clutch or making jack-rabbit starts. Such an assembly must be replaced.

WORN AREA

A clutch fixture allows you to release the clutch spring pressure gradually. Note the method of using punch marks to assure correct assembly. How many simple machines can you identify in this picture? Courtesy Dodge Division, Chrysler Corporation.

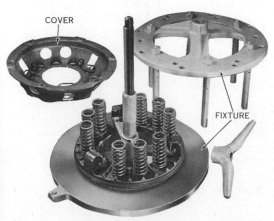

When the clutch fixture is removed, the clutch parts can be taken out for inspection and replacement. Courtesy Dodge Division, Chrysler Corporation.

pressure plate assembly and grind the flywheel surface.

Tools and Equipment

Plymouth power plant; alignment tool; adjustment gauge; $\frac{1}{2}$, $\frac{9}{16}$ and $\frac{5}{8}$ inch sockets; ratchet; extension.

REMOVING THE CLUTCH

1. Disconnect the speedometer cable and the propeller shaft.

2. Remove the transmission gearshift control rods and the back-up light.

3. Remove the four bolts holding the transmission to the clutch housing and pull it straight back until the pinion shaft clears the clutch disc before lowering the transmission.

4. Remove the clutch housing pan.

5. Remove the clutch release bearing by sliding the bearing assembly from the fork.

6. Punch mark the clutch cover and flywheel for correct positioning during installation.

7. Remove the clutch pressure plate by loosening each bolt a small amount at a time; otherwise the cover will be bent.

DISASSEMBLING

1. Mount the clutch assembly in a compressing fixture.

2. Mark the cover and pressure plate so that they can be reassembled in their original position in order to maintain balance.

3. With the clutch assembly under pressure, remove the clutch release lever eyebolt nuts, and back off the compressor tool nut slowly until all spring tension is relieved.

4. Remove the compressor nut and spider, and then lift off the clutch cover. Make a notation of the spring arrangement to insure proper assembly.

5. Remove the levers, struts, and eyebolts.

6. Test the springs for specified tension.

367

This broken spring caused clutch chatter.

A diaphragm type spring sometimes cracks in this fashion. It also wears flat spots at the points indicated by the arrows.

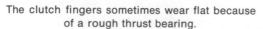

The clutch fingers sometimes wear flat because of a rough thrust bearing.

A scored thrust bearing surface indicates that the bearing is not operating smoothly and is the cause of the clutch fingers wearing flat as shown in the preceding picture.

THEORY OF OPERATION

To observe the operation of the clutch, assemble the fingers and struts to the pressure plate.

• Lift one eyebolt with the right hand until the pressure plate just leaves the bench top.

• Press on the end of the clutch lever with your left hand and note that the pressure plate lifts off the bench.

• Your right hand is taking the place of the clutch cover in the car. Pressing on the lever separates the pressure plate from the flywheel, releasing the driven disc.

ASSEMBLING

1. Coat the driving lug sides with a thin film of Lubriplate.

2. Assemble the lever pin-and-eyebolt to the release lever.

3. Hold the end of the lever and eyebolt in one hand, as close together as possible. Enter the lower end of the eyebolt in the pressure plate opening and, with your free hand, insert the strut into the slot of the pressure plate lug. Assemble the other two levers in the same manner.

368

CRACKS

BROKEN
FLANGE

A defective clutch driven disk. Note the arrows which point out defects.

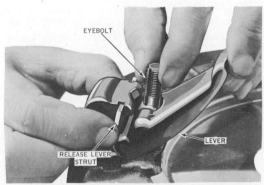

EYEBOLT

LEVER

RELEASE LEVER
STRUT

Assembling the eyebolt and lever. Which part of this picture is the fulcrum of a first class lever? Courtesy Dodge Division, Chrysler Corporation.

4. Install the pressure plate springs over the small bosses on the pressure plate in the same order as removed.

5. Install the clutch cover, lining up the punch marks. Also, guide the eyebolts and drive lugs through the holes in the cover while compressing the assembly.

6. With the clutch compressed in the fixture, thread the adjusting nuts onto the protruding eyebolts until they are flush with the tops.

7. Slowly release pressure by unscrewing the fixture compression nut. Tap the release levers several times to seat the parts.

ADJUSTING THE RELEASE LEVER HEIGHT

8. Place the specified spacer over the center screw of the fixture.

9. Install the compression plate on the center screw, resting it directly against the clutch release levers.

10. Install the self-aligning washer, flat washer, and the compression nut.

11. Tighten the nut until the compression plate comes into snug contact with the spacers.

12. Turn the eyebolt adjusting nuts until the three feeler blades have the

369

FEELER GAUGE

Adjusting the clutch lever height according to the gauge. The feeler gauge blade is used to check the clearance between each clutch lever and the tool. Courtesy Dodge Division, Chrysler Corporation.

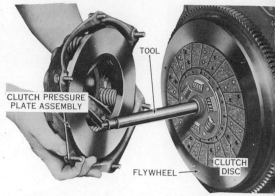

TOOL

CLUTCH PRESSURE PLATE ASSEMBLY

FLYWHEEL

CLUTCH DISC

An alignment tool is required to centralize the clutch disc when bolting the pressure plate to the engine so that the transmission can be installed properly.

same slight drag when they are moved in or out. Tighten the nuts to decrease drag.

13. Stake the eyebolt nuts to hold them in position and remove the clutch assembly from the fixture.

INSTALLING

1. Tighten the flywheel retaining bolts to 60 foot-pounds.

2. Lubricate the pilot bushing by placing a half teaspoon of short fiber grease in the radius at the back of the bushing.

3. Clean the flywheel and pressure plate surfaces, making certain that oil and grease have been entirely removed.

4. Hold the new clutch disc in the mounting position with the radially mounted springs away from the flywheel. **Caution:** *Do not touch the disc facings otherwise you are likely to get grease on the lining which would cause clutch chatter.*

5. Insert the clutch disc aligning tool through the hub and slip it into the pilot bushing.

6. Install the clutch pressure plate over the aligning tool and into position against the flywheel.

7. Align the punch marks and insert the cover attaching bolts finger-tight. To avoid clutch pressure plate distortion, the bolts should be tightened a few turns at a time, alternately, until all are tight.

8. Tighten the bolts to 15–20 foot-pounds torque. Remove the aligning tool, and install the clutch release bearing and collar, carefully engaging the springs over the clutch fork fingers.

9. Install the transmission. **Caution:** *Do not allow the transmission to hang or it will bend the clutch disc.* Support the transmission with a suitable jack, slide it into place, and bolt it securely.

10. Install the clutch housing cover.

11. Check and adjust the pedal free play.

12. Connect the gearshift control rods, the backup light, the speedometer cable, and the propeller shaft.

CHECK YOUR KNOWLEDGE

1. Name three things that a driver must be able to do with engine power.
2. Of what four main parts does the clutch mechanism consist?
3. What is the purpose of the series of coil springs arranged in a circular fashion around the hub of the driven disc?
4. What is the purpose of the weight at the outer end of some throwout levers?
5. What are the usual service jobs performed on a clutch?
6. What procedure is suggested to test for clutch slippage?

Self-Check Tests

TRUE-FALSE

1. The pressure plate contains a wavy cushion spring between the two friction linings.
2. Some pressure plates use a diaphragm-type spring.
3. Stepping on the clutch pedal separates two clutch driven discs.
4. If a slipping clutch is caused by too little pedal play, an adjustment is all that is necessary to restore it to good operating condition.

MULTIPLE CHOICE

1. Which of the following is *not* part of the clutch mechanism: a) flywheel; b) pressure plate; c) throwout mechanism; d) clutch shaft?
2. Which of the following is *not* a part of the clutch pressure plate: a) driven disc; b) springs; c) throwout lever; d) diaphragm-type spring?

COMPLETION

1. The _____ is the driving member of a clutch assembly.
2. The _____ _____ contains a series of springs around its circumference.
3. Clutch _____ _____ and clutch rebuilding are the usual service jobs performed on this unit.

MATCHING

1. Clutch
2. Pressure plate

a. Driving part
b. Mechanical coupling

371

Chapter 13

Manually Shifted Transmissions

The internal combustion engine is very inefficient at low speeds and, because it requires a great deal of power to start an automobile rolling, some type of torque multiplication device must be used to increase engine power at low car speeds. Transmissions increase engine leverage and power by stepping down the ratio between engine speed and road speed, which results in increased torque. Two kinds of transmissions are in common use—manually shifted and automatically shifted.

Gearing Fundamentals

Gears are levers that increase power or speed. An increase of speed always

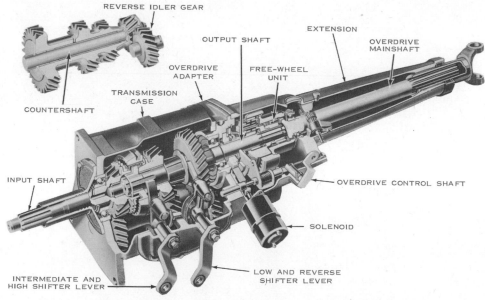

REVERSE IDLER GEAR

EXTENSION

OVERDRIVE MAINSHAFT

OUTPUT SHAFT

OVERDRIVE ADAPTER

FREE-WHEEL UNIT

TRANSMISSION CASE

COUNTERSHAFT

INPUT SHAFT

OVERDRIVE CONTROL SHAFT

SOLENOID

INTERMEDIATE AND HIGH SHIFTER LEVER

LOW AND REVERSE SHIFTER LEVER

Phantom view of a transmission and overdrive unit. Courtesy Ford Motor Company.

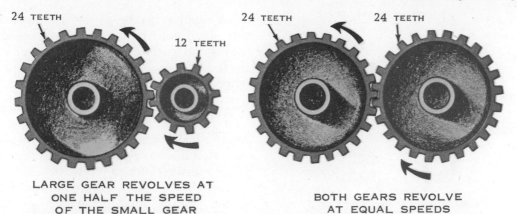

24 TEETH   12 TEETH   24 TEETH   24 TEETH

LARGE GEAR REVOLVES AT
ONE HALF THE SPEED
OF THE SMALL GEAR

BOTH GEARS REVOLVE
AT EQUAL SPEEDS

Gears are modified *levers* (six simple machines) and direction-changing devices. When the gears have an unequal number of teeth, a force or speed increase is possible. Notice that the gears are a non-slip form of the *wheel and axle*. Courtesy General Motors Corporation.

results in a corresponding decrease of power—and the reverse is also true. Two meshed gears with the same number of teeth turn at the same speed, transmit the same amount of torque, and rotate in *opposite* directions. When one of the two gears has fewer teeth than the other, the smaller one revolves faster, but the larger one has more power. Thus a gear of ten teeth, meshed with one of twenty teeth, turns twice as fast, but the larger gear has twice the turning torque.

Reverse gearing is obtained with the aid of an additional gear, called an idler, which is positioned between the drive and driven gears to change the direction of rotation.

A *dog clutch* is an internal and external gear arrangement which can be shifted into mesh with another gear to lock two shafts together.

A dog clutch is an internal and external gear which can be meshed for a direct drive. Courtesy General Motors Corporation.

Planetary Gearing

A planetary gearing unit consists of a sun gear, a set of planet gears assembled on a planet pinion carrier, and an internal gear meshed over the planet gears. Five gearing combinations are possible: neutral, direct drive, reverse, reduction, and overdrive.

Neutral results when the engine drives the sun gear, the planet pinion

FRICTION CLUTCH

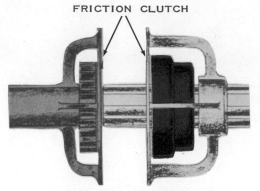

COMPLETELY DISENGAGED

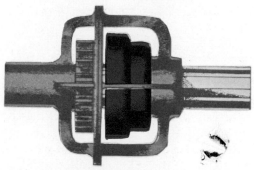

FRICTION CLUTCH ENGAGED, POSITIVE
CLUTCH STILL DISENGAGED

COMPLETELY ENGAGED

A syncromesh unit contains friction discs which engage before the gear teeth mesh in order to synchronize the speed of the gears so as to minimize clashing. Courtesy General Motors Corporation.

gears revolve on the planet pinion carrier shafts and drive the unrestrained internal gear. The rear wheels are connected to the planet pinion carrier which does not revolve.

Direct drive results when the entire unit is locked together by means of a hydraulically operated clutch. One set of clutch discs is splined to the internal gear, and the other to the planet pinion carrier. When oil pressure is applied to the pistons, forcing the two sets of discs together, the entire mechanism locks and rotates as a unit.

Reverse gear results if the power is applied to the sun gear while the planet pinion carrier is kept from turning. The internal gear revolves in a reversed direction.

Reduction results when the power is applied to the sun gear while the internal gear is kept from turning. The planet pinion gears are forced to "walk" around the internal gear, turning the planet pinion carrier at reduced speed. It could also be done by restraining the sun gear and applying the power to the internal gear.

Overdrive, the opposite of reduction, requires that the power be applied to the planet pinion carrier while restraining the sun or internal gear. The speeded-up power is taken from the unrestrained gear. Engagement of the unit for overdrive or gear reduction is accomplished in the transmission by the application of a brake band to the internal gear or to the gear to be restrained. This is done by directing oil pressure to a piston and cylinder assembly (servo) which applies the brake band smoothly.

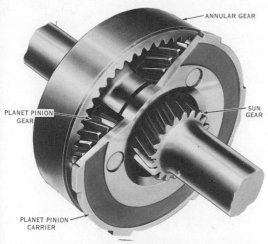

The parts of a planetary gear set. Courtesy Dodge Division, Chrysler Corporation.

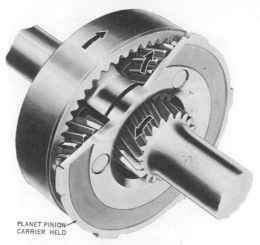

When the planet pinion is kept from turning, reverse gearing results. Courtesy Dodge Division, Chrysler Corporation.

When the parts are locked together, direct drive results. Courtesy Dodge Division, Chrysler Corporation.

When the power is applied to the ring gear, with the sun gear held stationary, reduction occurs. Courtesy Dodge Division, Chrysler Corporation.

Standard Geared Transmission

The standard geared transmission is designed so that about twelve revolutions of the engine turn the rear wheels once when in first gear. When the car is in motion, the gears are shifted to an intermediate gearing range, so that the engine turns about eight revolutions for each revolution of the wheels. For general driving, the transmission is shifted into high gear (direct drive), so that the engine turns approximately four revolutions for each turn of the rear wheels. This four-to-one reduction occurs in the *differential* unit.

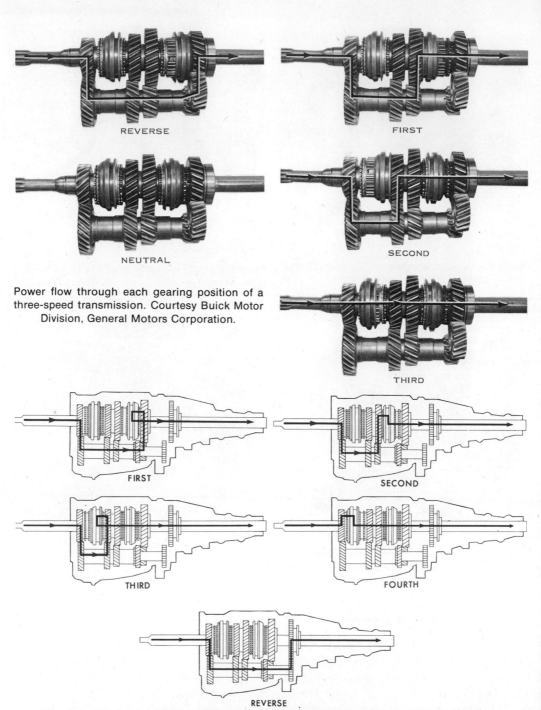

REVERSE

FIRST

NEUTRAL

SECOND

Power flow through each gearing position of a three-speed transmission. Courtesy Buick Motor Division, General Motors Corporation.

THIRD

FIRST

SECOND

THIRD

FOURTH

REVERSE

Power flow through each gearing position of a four-speed transmission. Courtesy Buick Motor Division, General Motors Corporation.

In addition to the three forward speeds, it is necessary to provide reverse gearing so that the car can move backward. Many sportscar models are equipped with transmissions having four forward speeds.

The standard transmission consists of a drive pinion (clutch) gear, splined to the clutch driven disc, which transmits engine power to the transmission countergear. These two gears are always turning regardless of which geared position the driver selects, as long as the clutch is engaged and the engine running.

Movement of the selector lever back or forth shifts the second-high sliding gear into mesh for second or high gear. A low-reverse sliding gear is moved backward or forward for either first or reverse gear. Reverse gear requires an idler gear to change the direction of rotation.

To minimize gear clashing when shifting, a synchronizing device is incorporated. It brings the two gears being shifted to equal rotating speed by means of two rotating cones that make contact before the gear teeth mesh.

Freewheeling Units

Units that permit power to be applied in one direction only, and disengage whenever the power flow is reversed, are called *freewheeling units*. They take two forms: overrunning clutch and sprag clutch.

An *overrunning clutch* (similar to the unit used in the cranking motor drive) consists of an outer race and an inner cam, connected by a series of rollers. When the power is applied in

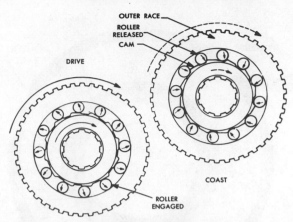

The overrunning clutch consists of an outer race and an inner cam, connected by a series of rollers. The rollers are engaged in the left view for drive and released in the right view for coast.

the coupling direction, the rollers are forced to ride toward the larger diameters of the cams, wedging the race and cam into a solid unit. When the power is applied in the opposite direction, the rollers are forced back into the smaller diameters of the cams, uncoupling the two parts of the drive; thus the unit "freewheels."

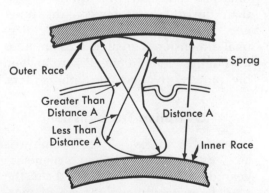

The sprags are machined so that the wedging dimension is larger than the coasting dimension. Note the use of the *wedge*, one of the six simple machines. Courtesy Cadillac Motor Division, General Motors Corporation.

377

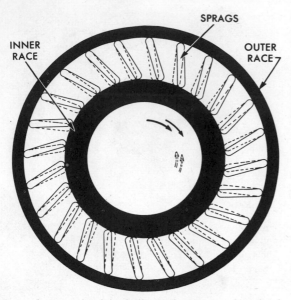

INNER RACE

SPRAGS

OUTER RACE

A sprag clutch is similar to the overrunning clutch in its action. It drives in one direction and freewheels in the other. Courtesy American Motors Corporation.

A *sprag clutch* is an overrunning clutch which permits rotation in only one direction. It consists of an inner race, an outer race, and a sprag assembly. The sprags are designed so that one diagonal dimension is less than the distance between the inner and outer races, while the other diagonal dimension is greater. This provides a wedging action in one direction when the sprags pivot about their centers.

Overdrive Transmission

Basically, an overdrive assembly is an automatic, two-speed, planetary geared transmission attached to the rear of a conventional three-speed transmission. When the overdrive control is in, the unit shifts automatically from direct drive to an overdrive ratio (7/10 to 1) at road speeds above 30 mph. As the road speed drops to about 20 mph, the assembly shifts automatically from overdrive to direct drive. The driver may shift (kickdown) from overdrive to direct drive at any speed by depressing the accelerator pedal to the floor. When the overdrive handle is out, all automatic operation stops.

Mechanically, the overdrive mechanism consists of a planetary unit and an overrunning clutch. There are three possible drives or power flows: direct drive, overdrive, and locked-out drive.

A *direct, free-wheeling drive* occurs when the control is in and the car is operated at speeds up to 30 mph. The power flows from the transmission output shaft, through the overrunning clutch, to the overdrive output shaft. The drive is freewheeling because the overrunning clutch permits the transmission output shaft to drive the overdrive output shaft, but it does not allow the driving action to reverse.

With constant accelerator pedal pressure, the overruning clutch cam rotation moves the rollers higher on the cam surfaces and wedges them against the outer race. This permits the cam, which is splined to the transmission output shaft, to drive the clutch outer race, which is splined to the overdrive output shaft. When the overdrive output shaft tries to drive the transmission output shaft, the outer race turns faster than the clutch cam. This moves the rollers lower on the cam surfaces and away from the outer race, unwedging them and permitting the outer race to overrun the clutch cam.

Overdrive gearing results when the sun gear is held from rotating by engagement of a pawl in the balk ring gear, which is splined to the sun gear.

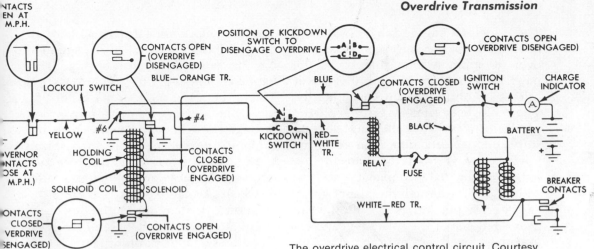

NTACTS
EN AT
M.P.H.

CONTACTS OPEN
(OVERDRIVE
DISENGAGED)

POSITION OF KICKDOWN
SWITCH TO
DISENGAGE OVERDRIVE

CONTACTS OPEN
(OVERDRIVE DISENGAGED)

LOCKOUT SWITCH

BLUE—ORANGE TR.

BLUE

CONTACTS CLOSED
(OVERDRIVE
ENGAGED)

IGNITION
SWITCH

CHARGE
INDICATOR

YELLOW

#6

#4

A B
C D
KICKDOWN
SWITCH

RED—
WHITE
TR.

BLACK

BATTERY

VERNOR
NTACTS
OSE AT
M.P.H.)

HOLDING
COIL

CONTACTS
CLOSED
(OVERDRIVE
ENGAGED)

RELAY

FUSE

SOLENOID COIL

SOLENOID

BREAKER
CONTACTS

ONTACTS
CLOSED
VERDRIVE
SENGAGED)

CONTACTS OPEN
(OVERDRIVE ENGAGED)

WHITE—RED TR.

The overdrive electrical control circuit. Courtesy
Ford Motor Company.

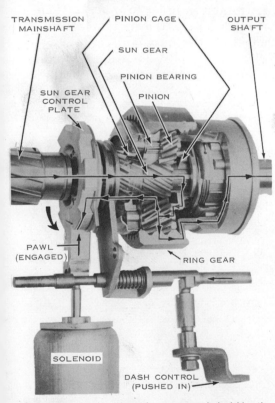

TRANSMISSION
MAINSHAFT

PINION CAGE

OUTPUT
SHAFT

SUN GEAR

PINION BEARING

SUN GEAR
CONTROL
PLATE

PINION

PAWL
(ENGAGED)

RING GEAR

SOLENOID

DASH CONTROL
(PUSHED IN)

Overdrive results when the sun gear is held by the
pawl, which is engaged in this illustration.

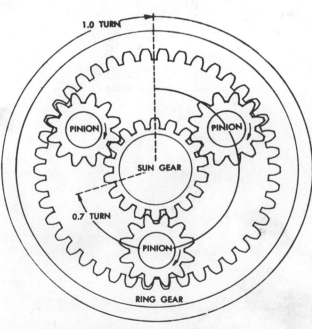

1.0 TURN

PINION

PINION

SUN GEAR

0.7 TURN

PINION

RING GEAR

When power is applied to the planet pinion
carrier, with the sun gear held stationary, the
pinions are forced to "walk" around the sun gear,
which drives the ring gear faster. Courtesy Warner
Gear Division, Borg-Warner Corporation.

The pawl is engaged by a solenoid energized by the governor at speeds over 30 mph. A balk ring keeps the pawl from engaging until the driver releases throttle pressure momentarily. Then the balk ring reverses, and the pawl engages the balk ring gear to stop sun gear rotation. The resulting power flow is from the transmission output shaft to the planet carrier— splined to it—through the planet gears, and then to the sun gear. With the sun gear stationary, the planet gears are forced to "walk around" the sun gear and drive the internal ring gear. The transmission output shaft drives the overdrive output shaft at a ratio of $\frac{7}{10}$ to 1.

A forced *kickdown drive* results when the pawl is pulled out of engagement by the solenoid return spring. This happens under two conditions: (1) When the car speed drops below 20 mph, the governor opens the circuit through the relay and de-energizes the solenoid, permitting the return spring to retract the pawl. (2) The driver may depress the accelerator pedal to the floorboard at any speed, and then the kickdown switch opens the governor circuit through the relay and de-energizes the solenoid, permitting the return spring to retract the pawl. At the same time, the ignition system is momentarily interrupted in order to release driving pressure on the transmission gears so that the pawl may slip out without difficulty. Usually about four cylinders misfire during the ignition interruption.

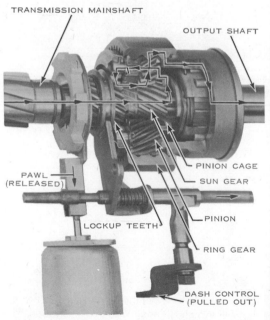

FREEWHEEL CLUTCH OUTER RACE

FREEWHEEL CLUTCH ROLLER

FREEWHEEL CLUTCH ROLLER CAGE

TRANSMISSION MAINSHAFT

OUTPUT SHAFT

PAWL (RELEASED)

FREEWHEEL CLUTCH CAM

DASH CONTROL (PUSHED IN)

TRANSMISSION MAINSHAFT

OUTPUT SHAFT

PAWL (RELEASED)

PINION CAGE

SUN GEAR

LOCKUP TEETH

PINION

RING GEAR

DASH CONTROL (PULLED OUT)

A forced kickdown results when the pawl is pulled out of engagement by the solenoid return spring.

Lock-out is achieved by pushing in the dash control, or by shifting into reverse gear.

When the pawl withdraws, the sun gear runs free. The overdrive gearing is now in neutral. As soon as the speed of the transmission output shaft comes up to the speed of the overdrive output shaft, the overrunning clutch automatically locks up, and direct drive is restored.

When the control handle is pulled out, the overdrive is *locked out*. This is accomplished by movement of the shift rail which meshes the sun gear with the lock-up teeth on the planet carrier, causing the entire mechanism to revolve as a unit.

This lock-out is necessary in reverse gear because the transmission output shaft reverses its rotation and, therefore, cannot drive the overdrive output shaft through the overrunning clutch. The lock-up is accomplished in reverse gear by the transmission shifter rod, which moves the overdrive shift rail to the rear (locked-out position).

Service Procedures

Transmissions which require major repairs must be removed from the car, disassembled, and rebuilt.

Troubleshooting

Transmission noises should be traced before the unit is disassembled to assist in pinpointing the trouble. With the engine idling, step on the clutch pedal to determine whether the noise is in the transmission itself. Transmission parts stop revolving when the clutch is disengaged. If the noise is in the transmission, it can be localized by driving the car in each gearing position.

Failure of the gears to stay in mesh is frequently caused by worn parts or misalignment, which must be checked when the transmission is disassembled. The clashing of gears, when shifting between second and high, is caused by a worn synchronizing unit.

Overdrive troubles are usually due to improper operation of the electrical control system. However, it saves time to determine whether the trouble is electrical or mechanical in nature. If the relay and solenoid click as road speed comes up through about 28 mph, and click again as the speed drops through about 22 mph, but the overdrive does not engage, the trouble is probably mechanical.

Synchromesh Transmission

For quieter operation, the modern transmission uses helical gears (teeth cut at an angle), which are in constant mesh. Shifting is done by moving a dog clutch into engagement. However, before the teeth actually engage, two friction elements move into contact so that the gears are forced to rotate at the same speed for a noiseless shift.

Some transmissions are synchronized in 2nd and 3rd (direct drive) speeds; others are synchronized in 1st speed also. Transmissions with four forward speeds are generally synchronized in all four.

Tools and Equipment

Dodge (or Chrysler) three-speed transmission; $\frac{1}{2}''$ and $\frac{5}{8}''$ end wrenches; $\frac{1}{2}''$ socket, ratchet, and 6″ extension; snap ring pliers; screwdriver; feeler gauge; dummy shaft; hammer.

381

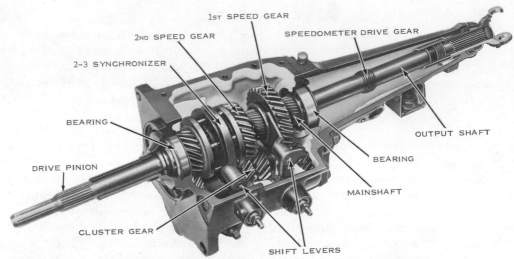

1ST SPEED GEAR

2ND SPEED GEAR

SPEEDOMETER DRIVE GEAR

2-3 SYNCHRONIZER

BEARING

OUTPUT SHAFT

DRIVE PINION

BEARING

MAINSHAFT

CLUSTER GEAR

SHIFT LEVERS

Three-speed, synchromesh transmission used on Chrysler products. Courtesy Chrysler Corporation.

DISASSEMBLING

① Drain the lubricant. Remove the bolts that attach the cover to the case. Remove the cover and discard the gasket.

② Use feeler gauges to measure the synchronizer float, which must be 0.050″–0.090″ when measured between the synchronizer outer ring pin and the opposite synchronizer outer ring. This measurement must be made on two pins, 180° apart with equal gap on both ends for float determination.

③ To remove the extension housing, take out the bolt and retainer holding the speedometer pinion adapter in the housing. Carefully work the adapter and pinion out of the extension housing. Remove the bolts and one nut that holds the extension housing to the transmission case; then slide the extension housing off of the mainshaft. Unwind and slide the yoke seal off the mainshaft.

COVER

1

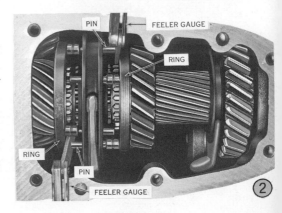

PIN

FEELER GAUGE

RING

RING

PIN

FEELER GAUGE

2

④ To take out the drive pinion, remove the bolts that attach the main drive pinion bearing retainer; then slide the retainer off the pinion. Discard the gasket, grasp the pinion shaft, and pull the assembly partially out of the case.

⑤ Remove the snap ring which locks the drive pinion bearing on the pinion shaft. Remove the pinion bearing washer; and then carefully press the pinion shaft out of the bearing, using an arbor press. Remove the oil slinger. Remove the snap ring and bearing rollers from the cavity in the engine end of the drive pinion.

⑥ Remove the mainshaft bearing outer snap ring, using a hook or flat blade, and then partially remove the mainshaft.

⑦ Tilt the mainshaft, then remove the inner and outer synchronizer cones, and the 2-3 synchronizer sleeve assembly.

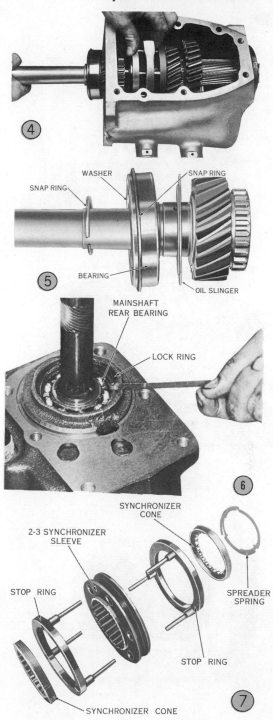

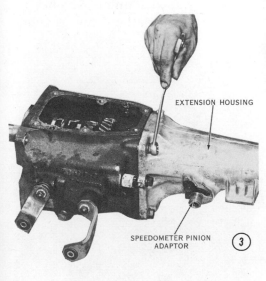

383

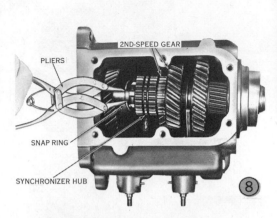

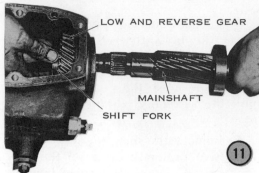

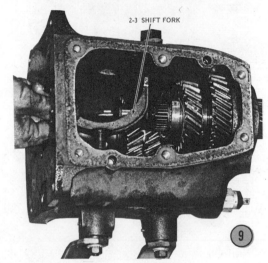

8 Remove the synchronizer hub retaining snap ring, using a pair of snap ring pliers. Slide the hub off the end of the main shaft.

9 Remove the 2-3 shift fork.

10 Slide the second-speed gear, snap ring, and the synchronizer cone and spring off the mainshaft.

11 Remove the low and reverse sliding gear and the shift fork as the mainshaft is withdrawn completely from the rear of the case.

12 Use a feeler gauge to measure the cluster gear end play, which should be 0.0045″–0.0280″. This measurement is necessary to determine whether or not new thrust washers are needed.

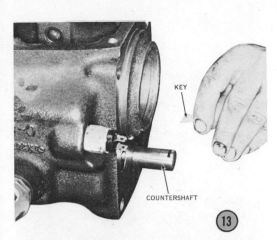

KEY

COUNTERSHAFT

(13)

When synchronizing cones are scored or worn, the gears clash when shifting. Note the grooves in the surface of this cone.

(13) Use a dummy shaft to drive the countershaft toward the rear of the case until the small Woodruff key can be removed. **Caution:** *Hold the dummy shaft tightly against the end of the countershaft to prevent losing the small roller bearings.* Lift out the cluster gear, thrust washers, and the thrust plate from the case. Remove the bearing rollers, washers, and the center spacer from the cluster gear. Use a drift to drive the reverse idler gear shaft toward the rear and out of the case. Remove the Woodruff key from the end of the shaft. Lift out the reverse idler gear, thrust washers, and the 22 roller bearings from the gear.

Cleaning and Inspecting

Clean the case thoroughly with solvent and dry with compressed air. Inspect the case for cracks, stripped threads, and nicks. Dress off any burrs with a fine mill file. Wash the ball bearings in clean solvent and blow them dry with compressed air. **Caution:** *Don't spin the bearings with air pressure, or you will damage them.* Inspect all the needle roller bearings for flat spots or brinelling (pitting). Inspect the

gear teeth on the synchronizer gears and stop rings. Replace any parts that show evidence of chipping or excessively worn teeth. Make sure that the synchronizer sleeve slides easily on the synchronizer hub. Inspect the countershaft gear and all sliding gear teeth for chipping, breakage, or excessive wear; also inspect the teeth on the main drive pinion for the same problems and replace the pinion if necessary. Test the interlock sleeve and pin for free movement in the shift housing. Examine the detent balls for signs of brinelling. Inspect the synchronizer stop ring gear teeth and the threads on the synchronizer inner stop rings for broken teeth or worn threads.

Cluster gear thrust washers wear and must be replaced in order to return the cluster gear end play to specifications. The new thrust washer at the left is for comparison with the worn one.

The internal teeth of this dog clutch, on the end of the clutch shaft, are worn. As a result, the gears will jump out of mesh.

Galled gear teeth. This condition causes noise when the gear is engaged.

Ball bearing defects result in noisy operation. A galled ball bearing (left) indicates that the shaft was turning in the bearing race and must be similarly galled.

Inspect the pins on the synchronizer outer stop ring assembly to be sure that they are straight and securely attached. Inspect the mainshaft gear and bearing mating surfaces. If gear contact surfaces show signs of galling (blistering) or are excessively worn, install a new mainshaft. Inspect the snap ring grooves for burred edges. If rough or burred, use a fine file to correct.

Transmission Principles

Before assembling the parts of the transmission, this is an excellent opportunity to study its operation. Arrange the parts as suggested on the accompanying page, and then follow the instructions alongside the drawings.

To Observe the Operation

Assemble the gears on the bench. If notched wooden supports are available, they will keep the gears from rolling. **Note:** *The illustrated gears are from an unsynchronized transmission which is desirable for study because of its simpler action.* Replace the clutch shaft internal bearing and slide the main shaft into the clutch shaft. Mesh the countergear with the clutch and sliding gears. Shift both sliding gears into neutral. Fig. A.

• Shift the low sliding gear forward (first speed) and turn the clutch shaft, counting the number of turns the main shaft makes for each turn of the clutch shaft. The ratio should be about 2.6/1.0. Fig. B.

• Shift the low sliding gear rearward into mesh with the reverse idler and turn the clutch shaft clockwise, counting the respective number of turns. The ratio should be about 3.5/1.0, but in a reversed direction. Fig. C.

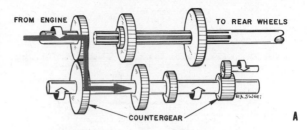

A

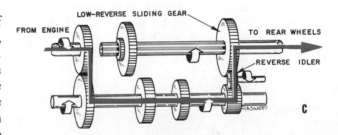

B

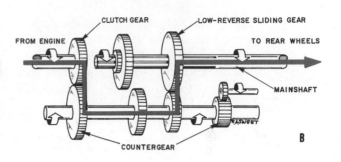

C

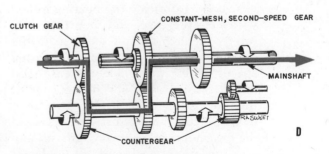

D

• Return the low sliding gear to neutral and shift the second-high sliding gear to the rear (second speed). Turn the clutch shaft clockwise and count the respective number of turns. The ratio should be about 1.6/1.0. Fig. D.

387

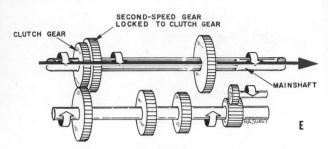

SECOND-SPEED GEAR
LOCKED TO CLUTCH GEAR

CLUTCH GEAR

MAINSHAFT

E

CLUSTER GEAR

14

• Shift the second-high sliding gear forward until the dog clutch engages with the teeth on the clutch shaft. Turn the clutch shaft clockwise and note that it turns at the same speed as the main shaft. Fig. E.

• If the transmission you are using has a synchronizing unit, shift it between second and high to note the synchronizing cone action. The rotating cones make contact first after which spring tension has to be overcome before the teeth can be meshed.

ASSEMBLING

14 Slide the cluster gear bearing roller spacer over the dummy shaft. Coat the bore of the gear with lubricant and slide the tool and spacer into the gear bore. Lubricate the bearing rollers with heavy grease, and then install 22 rollers in each end of the gear in the area around the bore. Coat the bearing spacer rings with heavy grease and install one in each end of the gear. If the cluster gear end play was over 0.028″, install new thrust washers. Coat the washers with heavy grease and position one at each end of the cluster gear. Install the gear and dummy shaft into the case, making sure that the tabs on the thrust washers slide into the grooves in the case. Install the remaining rear thrust washer plate over the dummy shafts at the rear of the gear.

The washer plate must be installed so that the step in the plate engages the ledge inside the rear of the case, thus preventing plate rotation. Install the gear and dummy shaft in the case, making sure that the front thrust washer tabs slide into the grooves and that the rear thrust washer step engages the ledge.

15 Use a soft hammer on the countershaft to drive the dummy shaft forward and out of the cluster gear through the bore in the front of the case. Before driving the countershaft all the way into the case, make sure that the keyway is in line with the key recess in the rear of the case. Insert the shaft key and continue to drive the countershaft back into the case until the key bottoms in the recess.

DUMMY SHAFT

KEY

COUNTERSHAFT

15

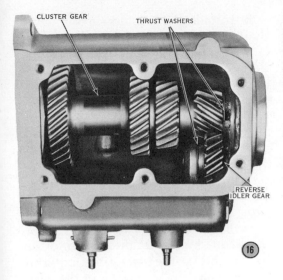

CLUSTER GEAR THRUST WASHERS REVERSE IDLER GEAR

⑯

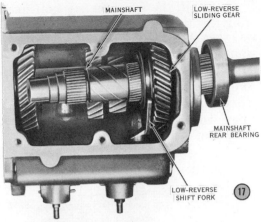

MAINSHAFT LOW-REVERSE SLIDING GEAR MAINSHAFT REAR BEARING LOW-REVERSE SHIFT FORK ⑰

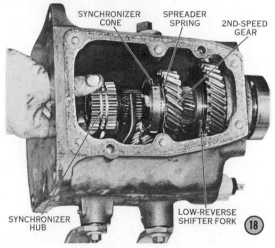

SYNCHRONIZER CONE SPREADER SPRING 2ND-SPEED GEAR SYNCHRONIZER HUB LOW-REVERSE SHIFTER FORK ⑱

⑯ Position the dummy shaft in the reverse idler gear and, using heavy grease, install the 22 roller bearings. Place the front and rear thrust washers at each end of the reverse idler gear, and then position the assembly in the case, with the chamfered end of the gear teeth toward the front. Insert the reverse idler shaft into the bore at the rear of the case, with the keyway to the rear, pushing the dummy shaft toward the front of the transmission. With the keyway aligned with the recess in the case, drive the shaft forward, inserting the key before the keyway is covered. Continue driving the shaft forward until the key seats in the recess.

⑰ While holding the low and reverse sliding gear in position with its fork, insert the mainshaft and bearing assembly through the rear of the case, and through the sliding gear.

⑱ Place the synchronizer spreader spring and the cone on the synchronizer splines of the 2nd-speed gear. Install the 2nd-speed gear on the mainshaft.

If the synchronizer float measurement was over 0.090", install synchronizer shims to reduce the end float to 0.090" or less. Install the shims on the shoulder of the 2nd-speed gear before the spreader spring is installed. If the synchronizer float is below 0.050", an equal amount of material should be removed from the ends of all six synchronizer pins until the end float is over 0.050". Install the synchronizer hub on the mainshaft.

⑲ Install the synchronizer hub snap ring in the mainshaft groove. Make certain that the ring is bottomed all the way around in the groove. Measure the clearance between the synchronizer hub and the 2nd-speed gear, which should be 0.004″-0.014″. Excess end play will cause the transmission to jump out of 2nd-speed gear.

⑳ Install the 2-3 fork in the lever shaft, with the offset toward the rear of the transmission. This illustration shows the relationship of all the shifting parts in case others have been disassembled.

㉑ Hold the synchronizer sleeve and the two outer rings together, with the pins properly entered in the holes in the synchronizer sleeve. Engage the 2-3 shifter fork with the synchronizer sleeve. While holding the synchronizer parts and fork in position, slide the mainshaft forward, entering the synchronizer hub into the synchronizer sleeve and, at the same time, entering the mainshaft rear bearing in the case. **Caution:** *If the synchronizer parts are not assembled as described, it will be impossible to place them in position after the mainshaft is in place, due to interference with the cluster gear.*

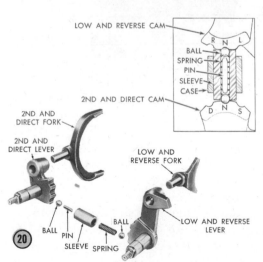

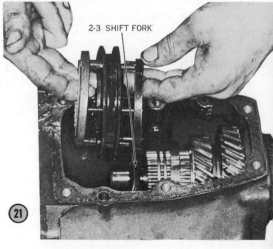

㉒ While holding the synchronizer parts in position, tap the output shaft until the rear bearing bottoms in the case bore. Install the rear bearing snap ring in the groove in the case bore. **Note:** *This snap ring is a select fit.* Unwind and slide the yoke seal front snap ring into place in the mainshaft. Slide the seal onto the shaft, with the lips of the seal toward the rear, and then install the rear snap ring.

㉓ Slide the oil slinger over the pinion shaft and down against the gear. Slide the bearing over the pinion shaft with the snap ring groove away from the gear end, and then use an arbor press to seat it on the shaft. Secure the bearing and washer with the selected thickness snap ring. Four snap rings are available to eliminate all end play. Be sure that the snap ring is properly seated. If the large snap ring around the bearing was removed, install it at this time. Place the pinion shaft in a vise

with soft jaws, and then install the 14 roller bearings in the cavity of the shaft. Coat the roller bearings with heavy grease, and then install the bearing retaining ring in its groove. Install the 3rd-speed inner synchronizer ring in the 3rd-speed outer synchronizer ring. Guide the drive pinion through the front of the case and engage the inner stop ring with the sleeve teeth; then seat the pinion bearing until the snap ring is in full contact with the case.

㉔ Install a new seal in the pinion bearing retainer. Using a new gasket, install the drive pinion retainer against the case. Install and tighten the attaching bolts.

OUTPUT SHAFT

SNAP RING

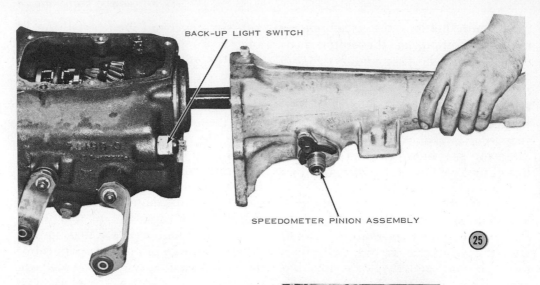

BACK-UP LIGHT SWITCH

SPEEDOMETER PINION ASSEMBLY

(25)

㉕ Using a new gasket, slide the extension housing over the output shaft while guiding the shaft through the bushing and oil seal. Install and tighten the attaching bolts. Install the speedometer pinion and adapter assembly. Install the drain plug and back-up light switch, and tighten them securely.

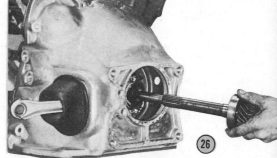

(26)

㉖ Install the gasket and transmission top cover. If the transmission is to be installed in a car or attached to an engine, it is necessary to line up the driven clutch plate with the flywheel pilot bearing. To do this, slip a drive pinion assembly into the clutch plate and apply pressure to the throw-out lever until the pilot end of the drive pinion enters the pilot bushing in the flywheel.

(27)

㉗ Remove the drive pinion, then slide the transmission into place. **Caution:** *Don't touch the clutch throw-out lever after removing the drive pinion; otherwise the clutch plate will slip out of alignment and you will not be able to install the transmission.* **Caution:** *Don't allow the transmission to hang with the drive pinion in the* clutch disc; otherwise you will bend the disc and the clutch will not operate properly. Connect the shift rods to the shift levers. Refill the transmission with Automatic Transmission Fluid, Type AQ-ATF, Suffix "A."

CHECK YOUR KNOWLEDGE

1. Why is a transmission needed?
2. What two types of transmissions are in common use today?
3. How is torque multiplication obtained with gears?
4. What is a dog clutch?
5. How many revolutions of the engine are required for each revolution of the rear wheels when the car is in first gear? Second gear? High gear?
6. How does the second-high synchronizing unit work?
7. What are the five possible gearing combinations using planetary gears?
8. What is a sprag clutch?
9. Of what two parts does the overdrive unit consist?
10. What are the three possible drives through an overdrive unit?
11. Explain how the overrunning clutch operates.
12. Explain what happens in an overdrive unit when the sun gear is held against rotation by engagement of the pawl in the balk ring gear.
13. Trace the power flow through the overdrive unit when it is in overdrive.

Self-Check Tests

TRUE-FALSE

1. The internal combustion engine develops large amounts of power at all engine speeds.
2. A torque multiplier increases car speed.
3. Gears are levers.
4. Reverse gearing requires an idler gear.
5. On a standard transmission a synchronizing device is used on all gear shifts except reverse.
6. Engagement of the planetary gearing unit for overdrive is accomplished by applying power to the ring gear and restraining the sun gear from turning.
7. A forced kickdown results in an overdrive unit when the pawl is pulled out of engagement by the solenoid return spring.
8. A sprag clutch is used in a synchromesh transmission.
9. An overrunning clutch is operated by oil pressure.

MULTIPLE CHOICE

1. Which of the following is *not* a part of a standard shift transmission: a) dog clutch; b) idler; c) synchronizing unit; d) fluid drive?
2. Which of the following is *not* needed with planetary gearing: a) synchronizing cones; b) sun gear; c) planet gears; d) internal gear?
3. Which of the following is *not* part of an overdrive unit: a) overrunning clutch; b) dog clutch; c) solenoid; d) planetary gears?
4. Which of the following is *not* part of an overrunning clutch: a) rollers; b) races; c) sprags?
5. Which of the following is *not* part of a planetary gear set: a) sun gear; b) planet gears; c) internal gear; d) spur gear?

COMPLETION

1. _____ are for the purpose of increasing engine leverage and power.
2. When one of two meshed gears has fewer teeth than the other, the smaller gear will revolve _____.
3. A _____ _____ is an internal gear which can be shifted into mesh with another gear to lock the two shafts together.
4. The _____ _____ brings the two gears to be shifted to the same rotating speed before actual tooth contact is made.
5. _____ _____ results when the entire planetary gearing unit is locked together by means of a clutch.

MATCHING

1. Transmission	a. Power
2. Torque	b. Freewheeling unit
3. Dog clutch	c. Mechanical torque multiplier
4. Synchronizing unit	d. Ring or internal gear
5. Planetary gearing	e. Stepped-up gearing ratio
6. Sprag clutch	f. Second-high gears
7. Overdrive	g. Internal-external gear

Chapter 14

Automatic Transmissions

The past twenty years have seen evolutionary changes in automatic transmission design. Many methods have been developed to provide the needed torque so that internal combustion engine vehicles can start in motion easily and change gears smoothly.

The typical automatic transmission consists of a torque converter and a three-speed, planetary-geared transmission behind the converter.

The converter is a fluid coupling which takes the place of the conventional friction clutch. The planetary gearing units do the work of the helical gears of the synchromesh transmission. The converter provides torque multiplication.

Cross-sectioned view through the Turbo-Hydramatic automatic transmission used with large General Motors engines. Courtesy Buick Motor Division, General Motors Corporation.

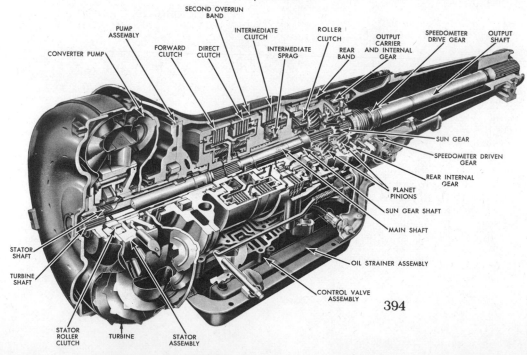

394

DRIVE CHAIN

TRANSMISSION

MANUAL VALVE
SHIFTING LEVER

OUTPUT END

GOVERNOR

The Turbo-Hydramatic transmission is positioned beside the engine in the Cadillac Eldorado and Oldsmobile Toronado. The final drive to the front wheels bolts to the exposed output end of the transmission, and part of the final drive is carried under the engine oil pan to connect to the right front wheel. Courtesy Cadillac Motor Division, General Motors Corporation.

395

FORWARD CLUTCH — DIRECT CLUTCH — SECOND OVERRUN (FRONT) BAND — INTERMEDIATE CLUTCH — INTERMEDIATE SPRAG — REVERSE (REAR) BAND — ROLLER CLUTCH

SELECTOR POSITION	PUMP PRESSURE	FORWARD CLUTCH	DIRECT CLUTCH	2ND OVERRUN BAND	INT. CLUTCH	INT. SPRAG	ROLLER CLUTCH	REV. BAND
PARK—NEUT.	70-150	OFF	OFF	OFF	OFF	OFF	OFF	OFF
DRIVE 1	70-150	ON	OFF	OFF	OFF	OFF	ON	OFF
LEFT 2	70-150	ON	OFF	OFF	ON	ON	OFF	OFF
3	70-150	ON	ON	OFF	ON	OFF	OFF	OFF
DRIVE 1	150	ON	OFF	OFF	OFF	OFF	ON	OFF
RIGHT 2	150	ON	OFF	ON	ON	ON	OFF	OFF
LO 1	150	ON	OFF	OFF	OFF	OFF	ON	ON
2	150	ON	OFF	ON	ON	ON	OFF	OFF
REV.	100-230	OFF	ON	OFF	OFF	OFF	OFF	ON

This diagram of the Turbo-Hydramatic transmission shows which bands and clutches are applied in each driving range. Courtesy Buick Motor Division, General Motors Corporation.

Torque Converters

A torque converter is basically a fluid drive unit with a set of stationary blades *secured to the transmission case*. These blades are arranged so as to change the direction in which the oil flows. They guide the oil into a "path" more nearly parallel to the rotation of the driver unit. This, in effect, speeds up the flow of oil. It should be noted that the power necessary to divert the oil flow is taken from the transmission case and *not from the engine*. In other words, the blades act as a force, simply by remaining stationary while in contact with the flowing oil. This is an application of Newton's Third Law of Motion: *"For every action, there is an equal and opposite reaction."*

To prove that it takes power to change the direction of the oil stream, hold a board against a stream of water from a hose so that the board deflects the

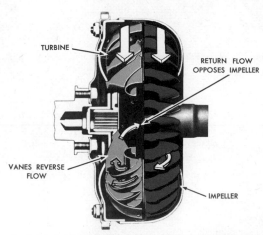

A fluid-drive unit contains an impeller which acts as a centrifugal pump. The vanes accelerate the fluid, and centrifugal force pushes it outward so that it is discharged from the openings around the inner ring. Since the vanes in the turbine are curved opposite to those in the impeller, and the fluid exerts a force that turns the turbine in the same direction as the impeller, there is no torque multiplication in a fluid-drive unit. Courtesy Ford Motor Company.

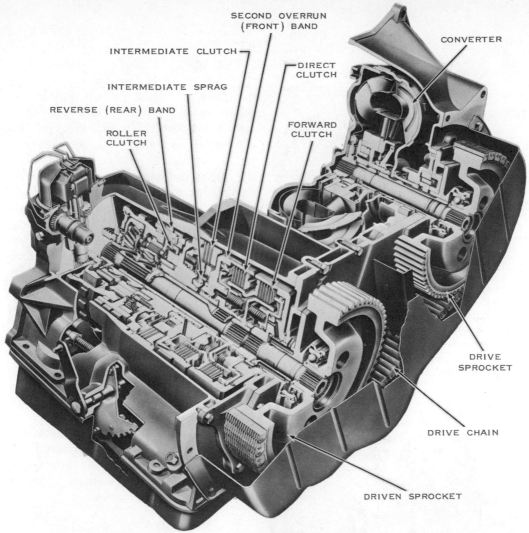

SECOND OVERRUN
(FRONT) BAND

INTERMEDIATE CLUTCH

DIRECT
CLUTCH

INTERMEDIATE SPRAG

CONVERTER

REVERSE (REAR) BAND

FORWARD
CLUTCH

ROLLER
CLUTCH

DRIVE
SPROCKET

DRIVE CHAIN

DRIVEN SPROCKET

This is a sectioned view of the Turbo-Hydramatic transmission, as used on front-wheel drive cars. It shows the chain drive between the converter and the planetary-geared section of the transmission. Courtesy Cadillac Motor Division, General Motors Corporation.

stream. It takes considerable force to hold the board, just as it does to hold the stationary blades against the flowing oil.

The stationary blade assembly *(stator)* is located in the center section between the driver unit *(pump* or *impeller)* and the runner unit *(turbine)*. Oil is directed in a circular path from the pump to the turbine, where the driving power is transmitted, then the oil is returned to the pump in the lower half of the circular path, where its direction and velocity are changed by the stator blades. These changes occur before the oil re-enters the pump. Expressed in slightly different terms, the stator blades force the fluid to make a U-turn and to flow back into the impeller at an angle that helps impeller rotation.

397

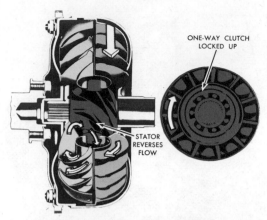

In a torque converter, the stator reverses the fluid flow and returns it to the impeller. The fluid is guided into a "path" that is similar to the direction of impeller rotation. A one-way clutch prevents the force of the fluid from turning the stator. Courtesy Ford Motor Company.

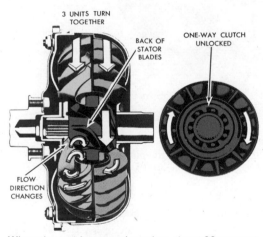

When the turbine speed reaches about 90 percent of the impeller speed, the converter acts as a fluid-drive unit, and no torque multiplication occurs. As the converter approaches the coupling phase, the fluid leaving the turbine strikes the backs of the stator vanes. This unlocks the one-way clutch so that the impeller, turbine, and stator rotate together. Courtesy Ford Motor Company.

The stator is flexibly connected to the transmission case by means of an overrunning clutch so that it is locked when needed, but disengages when speed and power demands change. This change is accomplished automatically by the curvature of the blades. When the oil is directed against the front of the blades, the units are locked in position and perform their torque-converter function. As the speed increases, the oil stream changes direction. The oil strikes the backs of the blades which then freewheel to avoid blocking the returning oil.

Some torque converters have a pitch-changing mechanism in the stator. When extreme acceleration is desired, pushing the throttle to the floorboard actuates a hydraulic mechanism to change the angle of the stator blades.

Torque converters multiply engine power about $2\frac{1}{2}$ times, which is not enough to start a vehicle in motion or to pull it through mud or sand. To achieve higher ratios, a torque-converter transmission includes a three-speed, planetary-geared unit.

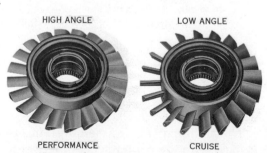

Some stators are designed so that the pitch of the blades can be changed under varying operating conditions. Courtesy Buick Motor Division, General Motors Corporation.

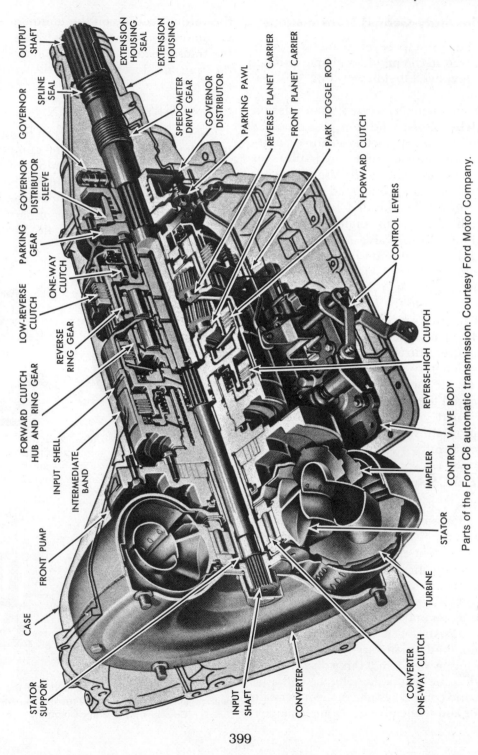

OUTPUT SHAFT

EXTENSION HOUSING SEAL

EXTENSION HOUSING

GOVERNOR

SPLINE SEAL

SPEEDOMETER DRIVE GEAR

GOVERNOR DISTRIBUTOR

PARKING PAWL

REVERSE PLANET CARRIER

FRONT PLANET CARRIER

PARK TOGGLE ROD

FORWARD CLUTCH

CONTROL LEVERS

GOVERNOR DISTRIBUTOR SLEEVE

PARKING GEAR

ONE-WAY CLUTCH

LOW-REVERSE CLUTCH

REVERSE RING GEAR

FORWARD CLUTCH HUB AND RING GEAR

INPUT SHELL

INTERMEDIATE BAND

FRONT PUMP

CASE

STATOR SUPPORT

INPUT SHAFT

CONVERTER

CONVERTER ONE-WAY CLUTCH

TURBINE

STATOR

CONTROL VALVE BODY

IMPELLER

REVERSE-HIGH CLUTCH

Parts of the Ford C6 automatic transmission. Courtesy Ford Motor Company.

399

Planetary-Geared Transmissions

The principles of planetary gears, covered in the previous chapter, should be reviewed before reading this section.

The planetary-geared transmission, which follows the torque converter, consists of planetary-gearing units, lock-out clutches, and a hydraulic control system. The shifts are made hydraulically at specific road speeds. This operation is controlled by a governor which directs oil under pressure to various control valves. The driver can retard the shift point by depressing the throttle. A forced kickdown to second gear occurs when the driver depresses the throttle to the floorboard.

The shifts are made by means of lock-out clutches and bands. When oil pressure is directed to a lock-out clutch, the planetary gearing is forced to rotate as a unit for direct drive. When oil is directed to a piston, a brake band stops one part of a planetary-gearing unit from rotating, and reduction or reverse drive results.

Ford C6 Automatic Transmission

The Ford C6 automatic transmission is representative of the torque-converter types that are widely used today. The student may be familiar with the C4 automatic transmission, which has been used on Ford engines since 1964. The C6 is a heavy-duty version of the C4, larger and with certain refinements. It consists of a torque converter; a compound planetary-gear train controlled by one band, three disc clutches, and a one-way sprag clutch; and a hydraulic control system. A vacuum modulator automatically senses any change in the torque loading on the engine and a vacuum signal is sent through tubing to the transmission valve body; this causes the transmission to shift to the correct gearing range.

PLANETARY-GEAR TRAIN

Because of the complexity of the gear train, it is difficult to show the complete operation of all its parts. Most of the parts are hidden by drums or by the input shell. The best way to see the operation of the units is by means of partially sectioned drawings which do not include all of the parts.

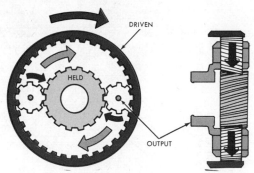

A planetary gearset provides reduction if the sun gear is kept from turning while power is applied to the ring gear. The planetary pinion carrier is the output member. Courtesy Ford Motor Company.

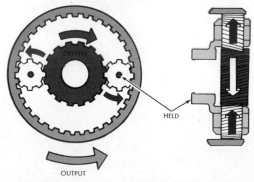

If the planet pinion carrier is held and the sun gear driven, the ring gear will revolve in reverse. Courtesy Ford Motor Company.

HIGH GEAR

In high gear, both the reverse-and-high clutch and the forward clutch are applied; therefore the input shaft is locked to the sun gear and to the ring gear of the forward planetary unit. With these two members locked together, the entire planetary unit turns with the input shaft. Since the planet carrier is splined to the output shaft, this shaft is driven at input shaft speed.

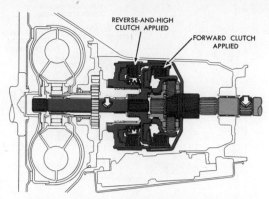

In high gear, both the reverse-and-high clutch and the forward clutch are applied. Courtesy Ford Motor Company.

SECOND GEAR

In second gear, the intermediate band is applied so that the sun gear is held stationary. The forward clutch is also applied so that the input shaft drives the forward planetary unit ring gear; this causes the planetary unit pinions to "walk around" the sun gear and carry the planet pinion carrier around at a speed slower than that of the input shaft. Because the forward unit planet pinion carrier is splined to the output shaft, this shaft is driven in the same direction as the input shaft, but at a reduced speed.

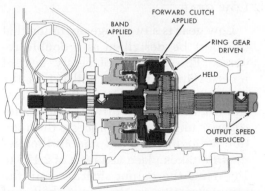

In second gear, the intermediate band is applied so that the sun gear is held stationary. The forward clutch is also applied so that the input shaft drives the forward planetary unit ring gear. Courtesy Ford Motor Company.

In reverse gear, the reverse-and-high clutch and the low-and-reverse clutch are applied. The planet pinion carrier is kept from rotating. Courtesy Ford Motor Company.

REVERSE GEAR

For reverse gear, the low-and-reverse clutch is applied to hold the planet pinion carrier stationary. Also, the reverse-and-high clutch is applied so that the input shaft drives the sun gear. With the carrier held and the sun gear driven clockwise, the planet pinions reverse input rotation and drive the ring gear counterclockwise at a reduced speed. The ring gear turns the output shaft in reverse at a 2.175 to 1.0 reduction of input shaft speed.

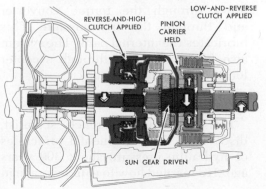

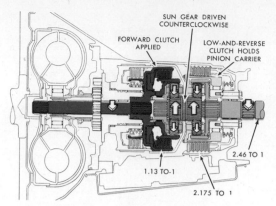

SUN GEAR DRIVEN
COUNTERCLOCKWISE

FORWARD CLUTCH
APPLIED

LOW-AND-REVERSE
CLUTCH HOLDS
PINION CARRIER

2.46 TO 1

1.13 TO-1

2.175 TO 1

In manual low gear, the forward clutch and the low-and-reverse clutch are applied. Courtesy Ford Motor Company.

LOW GEAR

Low gear is a two-stage operation that can best be described as a double reverse. The forward planetary gearset *reverses* input rotation and drives the sun gear with a 1.13 to 1.0 reduction. In turn, the sun gear drives the low-and-reverse unit. In this process, the rotation is *again reversed* and further reduction takes place at a ratio of 2.175 to 1.0. Thus the output shaft turns in the same direction as the input shaft, but with a total reduction of 2.46 to 1.0.

HYDRAULIC-CONTROL SYSTEM

The hydraulic-control system maintains a constant flow of fluid under pressure to control the shifting of the gear train in order to furnish the torque needed at the rear wheels. The fluid flows through the torque converter and through the transmission. This lubricates the internal parts. The system also forces the fluid through a cooler located in the radiator tank.

HYDRAULIC PRINCIPLES

Blaise Pascal, a French scientist, discovered the fundamental principles of hydraulic pressure about 300 years ago. He learned how to gain leverage in

hydraulic applications. Simply stated, Pascal's Law is: "Whenever force is applied to a confined fluid, pressure builds up. This pressure acts equally on equal surfaces, in all directions, and always at right angles to the containing surfaces."

LEVERAGE

Fluid pressure is measured in pounds per square inch (psi). If a force of 1,000 pounds is exerted against a hydraulic piston, with a surface area of 10 square inches, the fluid confined behind the piston will be under a pressure of 100 psi. Thus every square inch of the container will have 100 pounds of force exerted on it.

Assume that one surface of the container is another piston, with an area of 100 square inches, each inch of which is subject to 100 pounds of force. The total force on the larger piston will be equal to the pressure multiplied by the piston area, or 10,000 pounds.
Example:
F = Force in psi
P = Pressure in pounds
A = Area in square inches
Formula $\qquad$ F = P × A
Substituting $\qquad$ F = 100 × 100
Multiplying $\qquad$ F = 10,000 pounds

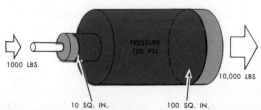

1000 LBS.

PRESSURE
100 PSI

10,000 LBS

10 SQ. IN.   100 SQ. IN.

Here a force of 1,000 pounds is exerted against a piston with a surface area of 10 square inches. The resulting hydraulic pressure against a piston with 100 square inches will be 10,000 pounds. Courtesy Ford Motor Company.

The Ford C6 automatic transmission uses an internal geared pump which is driven by the engine to develop about 100 psi for normal operation. In reverse gear, the pump pressure must be boosted to almost 275 psi. Courtesy Ford Motor Company.

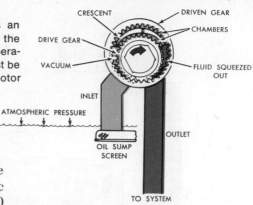

In an automatic transmission, the force required to hold a hydraulic clutch engaged may be as much as 2,000 pounds, depending on the torque being applied and the weight of the vehicle. The source of hydraulic pressure in an automatic transmission is generally an internal-geared pump, driven by the engine. As long as the engine is running, hydraulic pressure is supplied to the system, where it is directed by valves and controlled by governor and throttle pressures. The result is engagement of hydraulic clutches and planetary gearing combinations to provide a smooth flow of power.

MANUAL VALVE

When the driver operates his selector lever, he moves the *manual valve*. On a typical automatic transmission, this on-off valve can be shifted to any one of five positions. This valve directs control pressure to certain systems in order to apply clutches as needed for starting out in each range. The manual valve also furnishes control pressure to the shifting valves for each range, as follows:

RANGE	SYSTEMS BEING CHARGED (FILLED WITH FLUID)	SYSTEMS IN OPERATION
D2	D2 only	First gear lock-out system
D1	D2 & D1	Shift control supply system
D	D2, D1, & L	Forward clutch and governor system
L-R	L & R	Low-and-reverse clutch-apply system and the second-and-high gear lock-out system
R	R only	Reverse pressure booster system and the reverse-and-high clutch-apply system

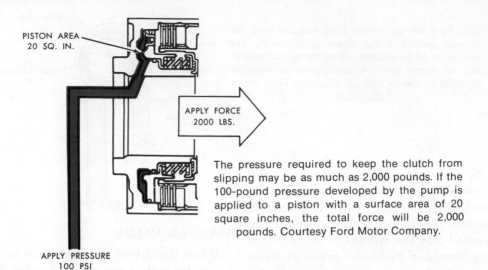

PISTON AREA
20 SQ. IN.

APPLY FORCE
2000 LBS.

The pressure required to keep the clutch from slipping may be as much as 2,000 pounds. If the 100-pound pressure developed by the pump is applied to a piston with a surface area of 20 square inches, the total force will be 2,000 pounds. Courtesy Ford Motor Company.

APPLY PRESSURE
100 PSI

The manual control valve directs control pressure to the holding members and to the shift valves. This diagram shows how the control pressure is directed to two ports at the manual valve, to the primary throttle valve, to the throttle booster valve, and under the 1-2 accumulator valve. Courtesy Ford Motor Company.

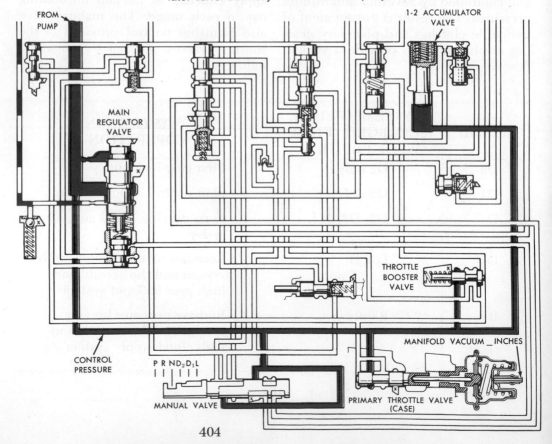

FROM PUMP

1-2 ACCUMULATOR VALVE

MAIN REGULATOR VALVE

THROTTLE BOOSTER VALVE

MANIFOLD VACUUM ___ INCHES

CONTROL PRESSURE

P R ND₂D₁L

MANUAL VALVE

PRIMARY THROTTLE VALVE (CASE)

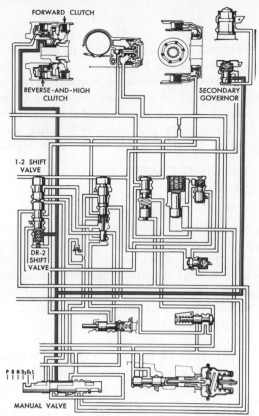

and clutch plates that are used to apply the servo, which is a hydraulically actuated piston.)

LOW-AND-REVERSE CLUTCH-APPLY SYSTEM

When the *manual valve* is shifted to the R position, the low-and-reverse clutch-apply system is charged through the L-R passage in the low-and-reverse ranges. Pressure is transmitted to the clutch piston through the 1–2 shift valve.

The low-and-reverse clutch-apply system is charged through the L-R passage in the low and reverse ranges. Pressure is transmitted to the clutch piston through the 1-2 shift valve. Courtesy Ford Motor Company.

The forward clutch must be applied in all forward ranges. Hydraulic pressure charges the forward clutch and governor when the manual valve is shifted to the D1 range as shown here. (To charge a circuit means to fill it with hydraulic fluid.) Courtesy Ford Motor Company.

FORWARD CLUTCH AND GOVERNOR SYSTEM

The forward clutch must be applied in all forward gears. When the *manual valve* is shifted to the D1 range (also D2 and L ranges), it directs control pressure to the forward clutch and governor as shown. The vehicle is now in low gear. The control pressure is also connected to a passage at the DR2 valve where it will be used to charge the servo-apply system when the DR2 valve shifts. (The servo-apply system includes all the valving, passageways,

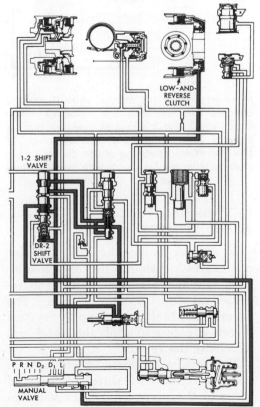

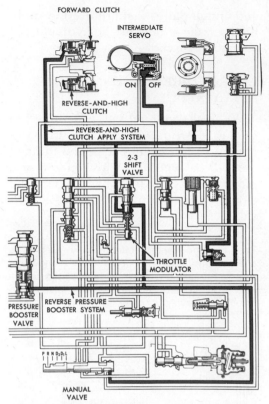

In reverse range, the manual valve R passage charges two systems: the reverse-and-high clutch-apply and the reverse pressure booster systems. High operating pressures—about 275 psi—are needed because of the double torque multiplication required in reverse gear. Courtesy Ford Motor Company.

REVERSE-AND-HIGH CLUTCH-APPLY SYSTEM

In reverse range, the *manual valve* charges two systems: the reverse-and-high clutch-apply system and the reverse pressure booster system. The reverse-and-high clutch-apply system directs pressure to apply the clutch and to release the servo.

The reverse pressure booster system sends full control pressure to differential areas of the pressure booster valve in reverse range only. This is necessary because of the high torque required in reverse. The pressure booster valve is forced up and increases the spring force acting on the regulator valve. It then takes higher pressure to balance the valve so that control pressure rises.

INTERMEDIATE SERVO-APPLY SYSTEM

When the transmission is ready to shift into second speed, the DR2 valve is forced down, and the intermediate servo system is charged by the forward clutch and governor system. Pressure is transmitted between the lands of the DR2 valve, through the 1–2 scheduling accumulator valve and the 2–3 back-out valve. This puts pressure upon the apply side of the servo piston, which moves to apply the band. With the forward clutch also applied, the transmission is in second gear.

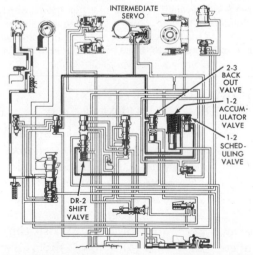

To obtain second gear, the intermediate band must be applied. The intermediate servo-apply system is charged by the forward clutch and governor systems. Courtesy Ford Motor Company.

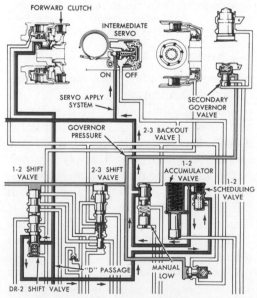

Shift valves have two positions and are controlled by pressure signals from the governor, throttle valve, and downshift valve. When there is no pressure acting on a shift valve, it is held in the downshifted position by a spring. Courtesy Ford Motor Company.

SHIFT VALVES

Shift valves are on-off valves used to change the routing of control pressure. In this way they shift the transmission gear train to a different ratio. The 1–2 shift valve controls the 1–2 and the 2–1 shifts, and the 2–3 shift valve controls the 2–3 and the 3–2 shifts. These valves have two positions and are controlled

Students in the automatic transmission class at Los Angeles Trade-Technical College learn to rebuild a valve body, using the shop manual as a guide. Note the use of safety glasses.

by pressure signals from the governor, throttle valve pressure, and downshift valve.

1–2 SHIFT

To upshift to second gear, the 1–2 shift valve train must apply the servo; which will take over from the one-way sprag clutch. When the governor signals that the transmission is ready to upshift, the pressure on the 1–2 valve forces the valve train down, the DR2 valve blocks the sump passage and routes pressure from the D passage to apply the servo.

Shifting the valve train back up reverses the process. The servo piston spring releases the band so that the one-way sprag clutch takes hold again, and the transmission returns to first gear.

To make a 1-2 upshift, it is necessary to charge the apply side of the intermediate servo. When governor pressure is applied to the top of the 1-2 shift valve, the valve train is forced to move down. The DR2 valve then routes the pressure from the D passage to apply the servo. Courtesy Ford Motor Company.

407

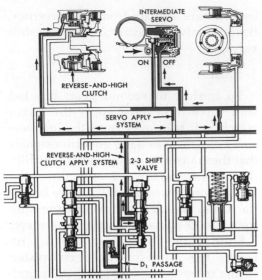

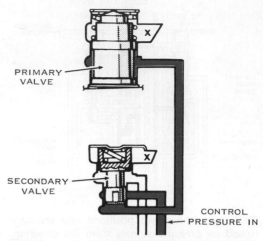

To shift to high gear, the 2-3 valve must release the servo and apply the reverse-and-high clutch. When governor pressure moves the 2-3 shift valve down, control pressure charges the reverse-and-high clutch-apply system. Courtesy Ford Motor Company.

Governor action at vehicle speeds below 10 mph. Control pressure first acts on the face of the secondary valve's large land, pushing the valve in. This opens a connecting passage to the primary valve. Control pressure is then directed to a dead end between the primary valve and lands. The full control pressure is now against the outer end of the secondary valve, holding it in against spring tension. Courtesy Ford Motor Company.

2–3 Shift

To upshift to high gear, the 2–3 valve must release the servo and apply the reverse-and-high clutch. When governor pressure moves the 2–3 shift valve down, control pressure charges the reverse-and-high clutch-apply system. At the same time that the clutch applies, pressure is applied to the release side of the servo piston. The surface area is larger on the release side than on the apply side, so the unbalanced forces release the band.

When the 2–3 shift valve moves back up, the clutch pressure is blocked, and the clutch-apply system is vented to the sump. Spring pressure releases the clutch piston, and apply pressure in the servo puts the band back on so that the transmission downshifts to second gear.

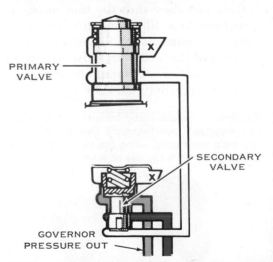

When vehicle speed exceeds 10 mph, centrifugal force is enough to overcome the primary valve spring tension. Thus the valve moves out, relieving the passageway to the sump. The secondary valve can now move out and crack the control pressure line to the governor pressure port. Courtesy Ford Motor Company.

GOVERNOR ACTION

Whenever car speed exceeds 10 mph, centrifugal force overcomes the primary valve spring tension, allowing the valve to move out. This by-passes the hydraulic pressure to the sump so that the secondary valve can move out, slightly opening (cracking) the control pressure line to the governor pressure port. Now, the secondary governor valve becomes a balanced valve; that is, governor pressure acting inward is balanced against the sum of the spring force and centrifugal force acting outward. The governor pressure increases with increased vehicle speed.

Governor pressure is first directed to the ends of the shift valves. When this force becomes great enough to overcome the force holding the valves up, it moves them down to the upshifted position. When the road speed drops below 10 mph, the governor pressure is cut off and both shift valves move up together, causing a 3–1 downshift.

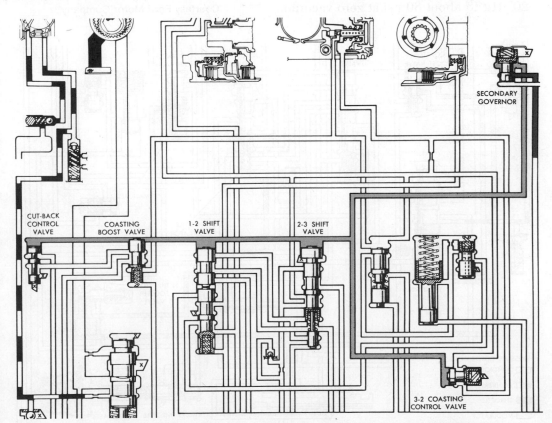

Governor pressure directed to the ends of the shift valves will force them to the upshifted (down) positions. Courtesy Ford Motor Company.

THROTTLE PRESSURE SYSTEM

Throttle pressure is the engine load signal to the hydraulic-control system to delay upshifts and increase the control pressure when the driver wants to accelerate.

Pressure output from the throttle valve rises as engine loading drops. As the engine load increases, this is detected by a spring-loaded, vacuum-diaphragm unit which "senses" the vacuum drop. With the lower vacuum, more throttle pressure is required to balance the diaphragm force against the throttle valve force. Throttle pressure increases steadily from 0 psi at 20″ Hg to about 80 psi at zero vacuum.

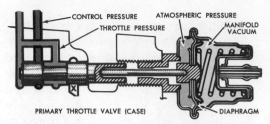

The throttle valve controls throttle pressure which is inversely proportional to the engine vacuum. Courtesy Ford Motor Company.

Throttle pressure system circuit. The primary throttle valve at lower right controls this circuit. Courtesy Ford Motor Company.

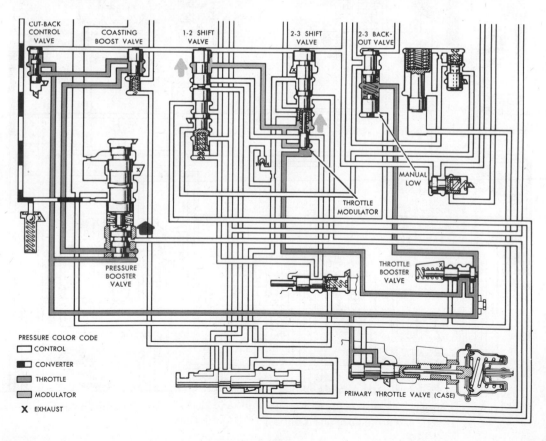

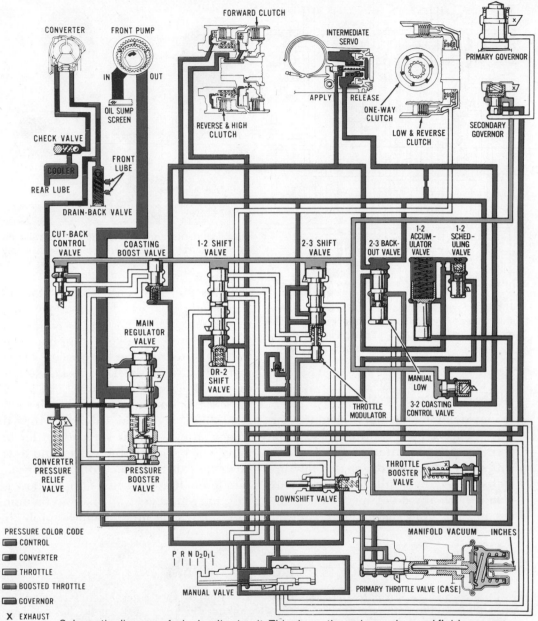

Schematic diagram of a hydraulic circuit. This shows the various valves and fluid passageways when the shift lever is in the D1 position and the transmission is in high gear. When
governor pressure force on the 2-3 shift valve becomes stronger than the combined spring
and modulated throttle pressure forces acting upward at the other end, the 2-3 shift valve
is forced down. Control pressure now flows through the 2-3 shift valve to charge the
reverse-and-high clutch-apply system. When the band is released and both clutches are
applied, the transmission is in high gear. Courtesy Ford Motor Company.

411

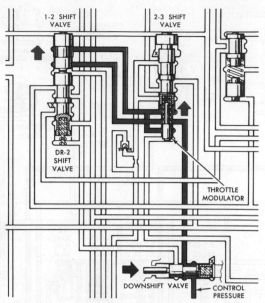

The kickdown system is controlled by the downshift valve. The driver actuates this valve by moving the accelerator pedal past the detent position. Courtesy Ford Motor Company.

These students are learning how to rebuild an automatic transmission. Note the use of safety glasses.

KICKDOWN SYSTEM

The kickdown system is used to override the governor's control of maximum shift speeds in order to force downshifts at higher speeds, or to delay upshifts longer than full-throttle pressure would normally do. A mechanical connection to the accelerator linkage actuates the downshift valve when the accelerator pedal is depressed through the detent.

The downshift valve is supplied control pressure from the D1 passage of the manual valve in the D1 and D2 ranges only. Moving the downshift valve directs this control pressure under the 2–3 shift valve and to a differential area of the 1–2 shift valve in order to move one or both of the valves and thus downshift the transmission. The driver can force the transmisssion to downshift to second gear up to about 65 mph and to low gear up to about 30 mph.

CHECK YOUR KNOWLEDGE

1. Of how many major parts does the modern automatic transmission consist?
2. What part of an automatic transmission does the work of the helical gears in a synchromesh transmission?
3. What part of an automatic transmission does the work of a conventional clutch?
4. What is the purpose of the stator?
5. Where does the stator get its power?
6. Where is the stator located in relationship to the other parts of the torque converter?
7. What is the approximate power multiplication of a torque converter?
8. Of what three main parts does a planetary-geared transmission consist?
9. What is the purpose of the vacuum modulator in the Ford C6 automatic transmission?

10. Which clutches are applied in high gear?

11. Which two parts are applied in second gear?

12. What is the reduction in reverse gear?

13. What is the total reduction in low gear?

14. Who discovered the fundamental principles of hydraulic pressure?

15. What pressure may be required to hold a clutch engaged in an automatic transmission?

16. How is the manual valve shifted?

17. What is the purpose of a shift valve?

Self-Check Tests

TRUE-FALSE

1. The internal combustion engine develops its highest torque at low speeds.

2. The typical automatic transmission uses a converter in combination with a planetary-geared transmission.

3. All of the torque multiplication of an automatic transmission is provided by planetary gearing.

4. The engine drives the stator.

5. Newton's Third Law of Motion is: "For every action, there is an equal and opposite reaction."

6. The stator is kept from rotating by a one-way clutch.

7. Some turbines incorporate a pitch-changing mechanism.

8. The Ford C6 automatic transmission contains a vacuum modulator.

9. Pascal discovered the principle of planetary gearing.

10. The manual valve is shifted by hydraulic-control pressure whenever the transmission shift lever is moved into gear.

MULTIPLE CHOICE

1. Which of the following is *not* part of an automatic transmission: a) planetary-geared unit; b) torque converter; c) synchronizer unit; d) vacuum modulator?

2. The converter: a) is a fluid coupling; b) provides torque multiplication; c) contains a stator; d) all three.

3. The stator is connected to the transmission through a: a) sprag clutch; b) disc clutch; c) lock-out clutch; d) fluid-drive unit.

4. The shift points of an automatic transmission are influenced by: a) throttle pressure; b) vehicle speed; c) engine loading; d) all three.

5. Which of the following does *not* influence the shift points: a) vacuum modulator; b) sprag clutch; c) governor; d) hydraulic control pressures?

COMPLETION

1. Blaise _____, a French scientist, discovered the fundamental principles of hydraulic pressure.

2. The source of hydraulic pressure in an automatic transmission is an internal _____ _____.

3. The _____ valve is shifted by the driver.

4. The _____ is a special type of fluid-drive unit that provides torque multiplication.

5. The _____ forces the fluid to make a U-turn and flow back into the impeller at an angle that helps impeller rotation.

MATCHING

1. Torque converter	a. Mechanical gearset
2. Stator	b. Controls shift points according to engine loading
3. Governor	c. Controls shift points according to vehicle speed
4. Vacuum modulator	d. Fluid-direction-changing member
5. Planetary unit	e. Fluid-drive unit

413

Chapter 15

Drive

Mechanisms

Three drive arrangements are in common use: (1) the conventional front-mounted unit with the drive transmitted to the rear wheels by means of a propeller shaft and a rear axle, (2) a rear-mounted unit with the drive transmitted to the rear wheels through a trans-axle (transmission-differential), and (3) a front-mounted unit which drives the front wheels.

Propeller Shaft

The propeller shaft transmits engine power to the rear drive mechanism where its direction is changed 90° to drive the rear wheels. The propeller

The conventional drive mechanism transfers power from a front-mounted engine, through a propeller shaft (sometimes called a driveshaft), to the rear axle. There a differential unit directs the flow of power to each rear wheel. This illustration shows a torque-tube type of drive in which the shaft is enclosed in a housing to absorb the twisting force set up in the differential unit. Only one universal joint is required. Courtesy Buick Motor Division, General Motors Corporation.

414

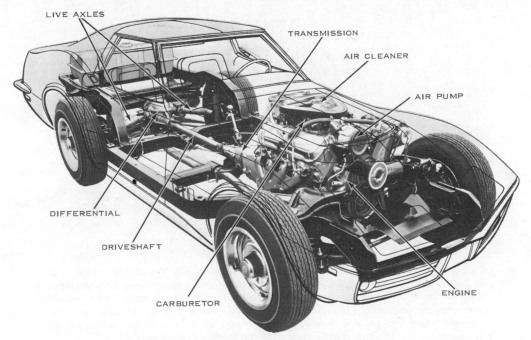

In the Corvette the drive train components are in their traditional locations, but with the addition of a live-axle independent rear suspension. In this system the differential case is fixed.

A rear-mounted engine, with the drive to the rear wheels through a trans-axle and two live-type rear axles. No propeller shaft is required. Courtesy American Iron and Steel Institute.

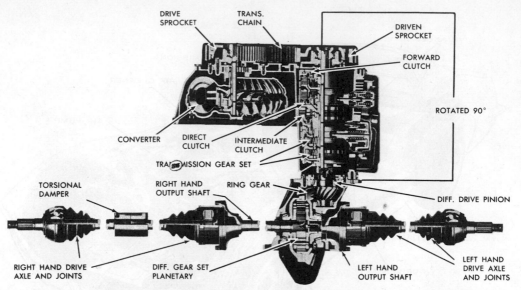

This is the final drive assembly of a front-wheel drive vehicle. It is coupled to the engine in the front through a torque converter and an automatic transmission. This assembly is used on the Oldsmobile Toronado and Cadillac Eldorado. The transmission is mounted alongside the engine, and the flow of power is reversed and directed to the front wheels through live-type axles, one of which passes under the oil pan of the engine. Courtesy Oldsmobile Division, General Motors Corporation.

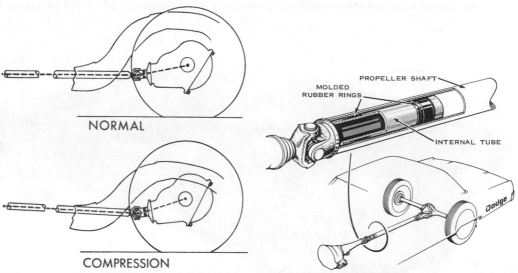

Without a torque tube, the differential unit twists because of the torque being applied to a ring gear. The top view shows the normal relationship between the propeller shaft and the rear axle. The bottom view shows what happens when power is applied. Courtesy Buick Motor Division, General Motors Corporation.

This propeller shaft contains a foot-long steel tube with two molded rubber rings pressed into the main propeller shaft at the front universal joint. This arrangement, which reduces drive-line noise, is used in Dodge cars starting with 1968 models. Courtesy Dodge Division, Chrysler Corporation.

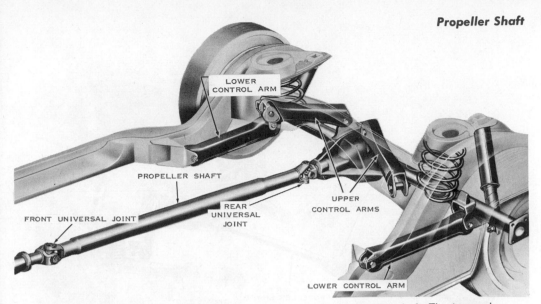

A typical Hotchkiss-type drive assembly, with an exposed propeller shaft. The torque is absorbed by the control arms, which are secured to the body of the vehicle. On cars with leaf-type rear springs, the control arms are not required because the torque is absorbed by the rear springs. Courtesy Buick Motor Division, General Motors Corporation.

shaft must move up and down and *change its effective length* while revolving because of the rear end movements caused by bumps in the road.

The rear end pivots around a shorter arc than does the propeller shaft because it is supported by its spring hanger while the propeller shaft pivots about its front universal joint. To compensate for the difference between the two arcs, a slip joint is installed which allows the shaft to lengthen and shorten in operation.

A unit with an enclosed propeller shaft is called a Torque-Tube Drive. This arrangement is rapidly giving way to the Hotchkiss Drive unit in which the propeller shaft is exposed.

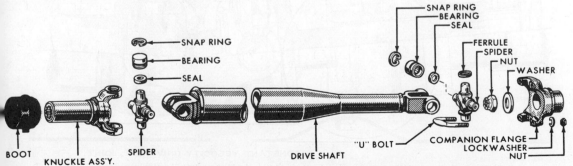

Universal joints allow the propeller shaft to move up and down when the rear axle bounces. At the same time, they transmit engine power to the differential gears smoothly. Courtesy Lincoln-Mercury Division, Ford Motor Company.

417

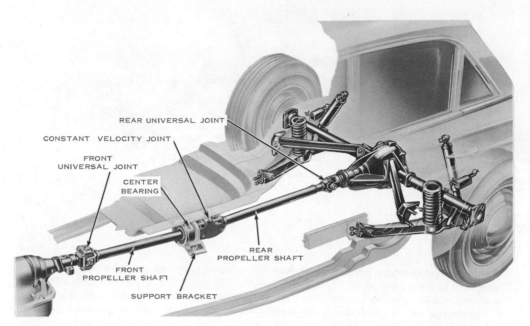

A two-piece propeller shaft, with a constant-velocity universal joint in the center. When the drive is through a universal joint operating at a severe angle, the power flow is erratic. The constant-velocity universal joint compensates for the erratic motion, and the power flow is smoother. Courtesy Buick Motor Division, General Motors Corporation.

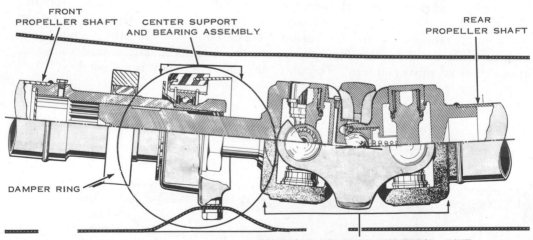

An enlarged view of the constant-velocity universal joint shown in the previous illustration. Courtesy Buick Motor Division, General Motors Corporation.

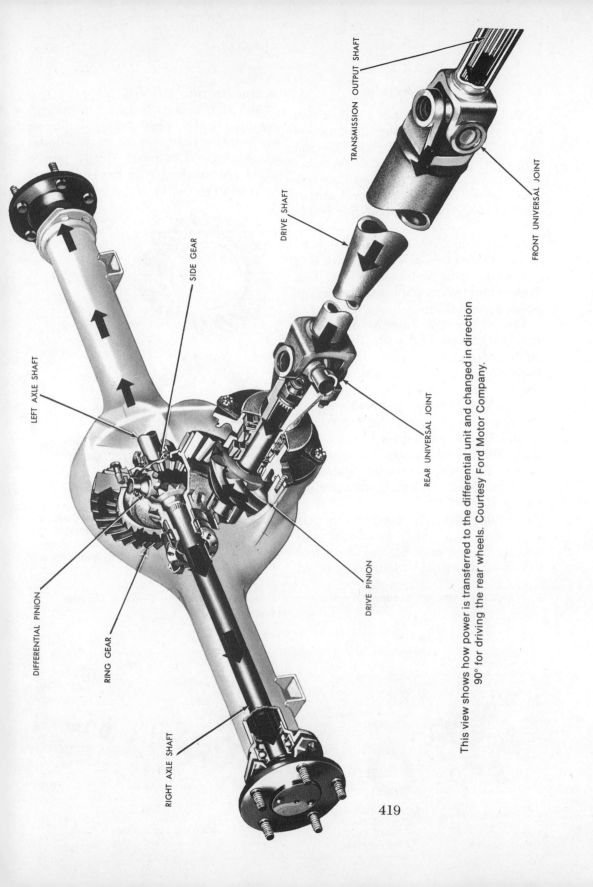

TRANSMISSION OUTPUT SHAFT

FRONT UNIVERSAL JOINT

DRIVE SHAFT

SIDE GEAR

LEFT AXLE SHAFT

REAR UNIVERSAL JOINT

DIFFERENTIAL PINION

RING GEAR

DRIVE PINION

RIGHT AXLE SHAFT

This view shows how power is transferred to the differential unit and changed in direction 90° for driving the rear wheels. Courtesy Ford Motor Company.

Rear Axle

The rear axle contains a differential unit which changes the direction of power flow 90° and permits one rear wheel to speed up more than the other during a turn. This is necessary because the outside wheel must travel farther and, therefore, faster than the inside wheel.

A trans-axle drives the rear wheels by means of two live axles which are connected to it by universal joints. This arrangement allows the rear wheels to move up and down.

The differential consists of a drive pinion gear meshed with a ring gear. Both gears have spirally cut teeth to increase the bearing surface, which reduces the noise level. The drive pinion gear is located below the center line of the ring gear to lower the drive shaft tunnel. Gears which drive below center are called hypoid gears. Their wiping action requires a special high-pressure lubricant to prevent metal-to-metal contact.

A pinion gear has fewer teeth than does the ring gear. Passenger cars usually have a gear ratio of about four to one so that it takes four turns of the engine to turn the rear wheels once.

The ring gear is fastened to the differential case. This drives a pinion shaft on which two or more pinion gears are free to rotate. These pinion gears are meshed with two side gears splined to the axles of the car.

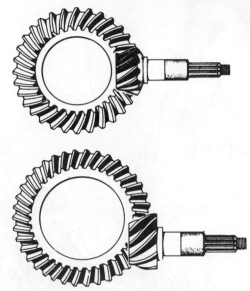

The top view shows a ring and pinion gear set designed to operate on center; the bottom view shows a hypoid gear set which is designed to operate below the centerline so that the drive-shaft can be lowered enough to eliminate the tunnel.

Exploded view of a conventional differential. Courtesy Plymouth Division, Chrysler Corporation.

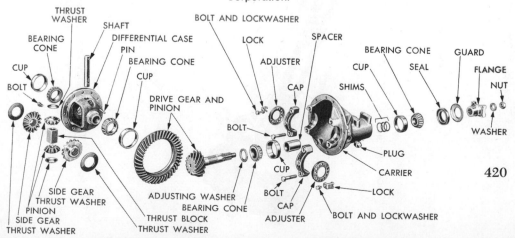

420

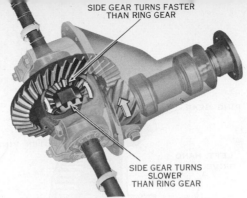

SIDE GEAR TURNS FASTER THAN RING GEAR

SIDE GEAR TURNS SLOWER THAN RING GEAR

During straight-ahead operation, all gears turn together. Courtesy Plymouth Division, Chrysler Corporation.

During a right turn, the right wheel slows up forcing the left wheel to speed up. Courtesy Plymouth Division, Chrysler Corporation.

Theory of Operation

STRAIGHT AHEAD

The differential case is driven by the ring gear, meshed with the drive pinion, which receives its power from the propeller shaft. It is revolving whenever the car is in motion.

The differential case carries the pinion shaft and pinion gears around at the same speed. However, the pinion gears are not revolving on their shafts when the car is moving straight ahead. The differential pinion gears apply equal pressure to both side gears, turning them at the same speed.

Turning

When the car is turning, the outside wheel must move through a longer arc and, consequently, must revolve faster than the inside wheel. To accomplish this, the power applied to the side gears by the pinion gears must be flexible.

Parts of the final drive assembly used on the Oldsmobile Toronado and Cadillac Eldorado front-wheel drive cars. Courtesy Oldsmobile Division, General Motors Corporation.

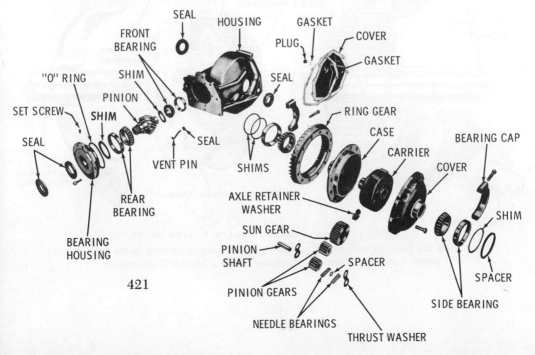

421

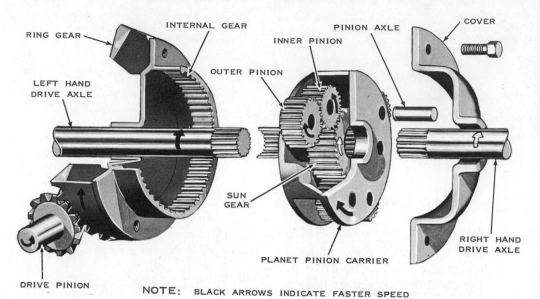

NOTE: BLACK ARROWS INDICATE FASTER SPEED

This shows the action of the gear train of the front-wheel drive unit when the left wheel turns faster than the right wheel. Courtesy Oldsmobile Division, General Motors Corporation.

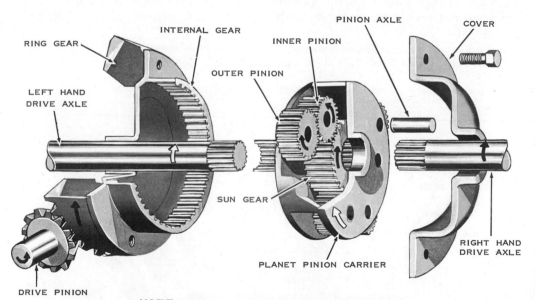

NOTE: BLACK ARROWS INDICATE FASTER SPEED

This shows the gear train in action when the right wheel is turning faster than the left wheel. Courtesy Oldsmobile Division, General Motors Corporation.

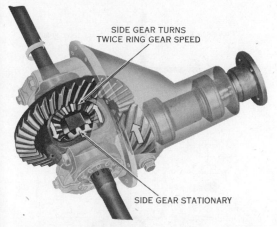

SIDE GEAR TURNS
TWICE RING GEAR SPEED

SIDE GEAR STATIONARY

In the event the left wheel is on ice, it spins because all power is sent to the wheel with the least
traction. Courtesy Plymouth Division, Chrysler
Corporation.

V-GROOVE

CROSS
PIN

CROSS
PIN

That is, as the inside wheel slows up,
it forces the pinions to revolve on the
differential pinion shaft, applying more
turning power to the outside wheel.

Limited-Slip Differential

The limited-slip differential prevents a vehicle from becoming immo-
bile when one wheel loses its traction.
It supplies a higher percentage of torque
to the wheel with better traction. In the
conventional differential, the spinning
wheel (without traction) receives all
the power. Another defect of the conventional differential is swerving on
bumpy roads. When one rear wheel is
bounced into the air by a bump in the
road, that wheel spins. When it returns
to the road, the sudden shock causes
the vehicle to swerve. By limiting the
amount of power applied to the spinning
wheel, the limited-slip differential prevents wheel spinning and the resulting
shock.

The limited-slip differential delivers more power
to the wheel with the better traction. The cross
pins are mounted in V-grooves, which permit
them to move up the sides to apply pressure to
the friction rings. Note that the V-grooves are
inclined planes. Courtesy Chrysler Corporation.

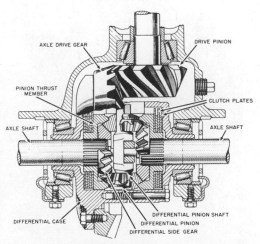

AXLE DRIVE GEAR

DRIVE PINION

PINION THRUST
MEMBER

CLUTCH PLATES

AXLE SHAFT

AXLE SHAFT

DIFFERENTIAL CASE

DIFFERENTIAL PINION SHAFT

DIFFERENTIAL PINION

DIFFERENTIAL SIDE GEAR

Cross-sectioned view through the limited-slip
differential. Courtesy Chrysler Corporation.

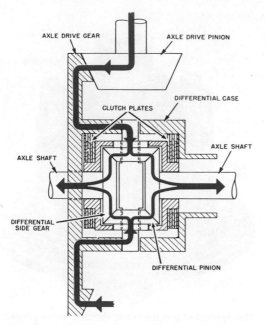

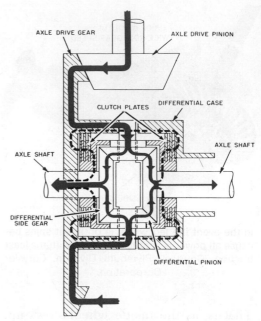

Diagram of the flow of power through the limited-slip differential with both axle shafts turning at the same rate of speed. Courtesy Chrysler Corporation.

Diagram of the flow of power with the axle shafts turning at different rates of speed. Courtesy Chrysler Corporation.

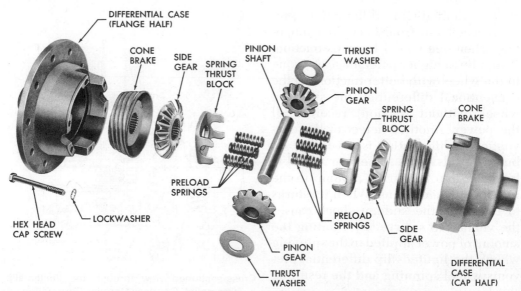

Exploded view of a limited-slip differential unit used on some General Motors vehicles. Courtesy Buick Motor Division, General Motors Corporation.

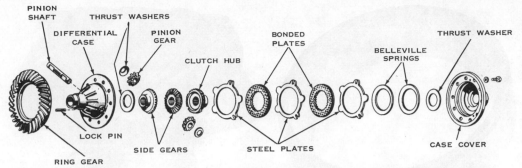

PINION SHAFT · THRUST WASHERS · DIFFERENTIAL CASE · PINION GEAR · CLUTCH HUB · BONDED PLATES · BELLEVILLE SPRINGS · THRUST WASHER · LOCK PIN · RING GEAR · SIDE GEARS · STEEL PLATES · CASE COVER

Exploded view of a limited-slip differential unit used on some Ford vehicles. Courtesy Ford Motor Company.

One type of limited-slip differential assembly consists of two case halves, two cross pins held together by a thrust block, four differential pinions, two bevel side gears, and two sets of clutch rings. The cross pins are made with a flexible joint at the center to permit each one to move independently. The pin ends are machined in the form of a "V," and a similar "V" is machined in each case half to provide a ramped-cam surface. The clutch ring fits over each bevel side gear and mates with a cone surface machined in each half of the differential case.

Driving force moves the cross pins up the ramps of the cam surfaces, applying a load to the clutch rings, which restricts turning of the differential through the friction of the clutch rings with their mating surfaces in the differential case. This provides a torque ratio between the axle shafts based on the amount of friction in the differential and the amount of load power being applied.

When the car turns, this process is partially reversed. The differential gears become a planetary gear set, with the gear on the inside of the curve becoming the fixed gear of the planetary unit.

The outer gear overruns because the outside wheel on the curve has a greater distance to travel. With the outer gear overrunning and the inner gear fixed, the differential pinions are forced to rotate, but, since they are restricted by the fixed gear, they must first move the cross pins back down the cam surface relieving the thrust load of the clutch ring on its mating surface. Thus, when turning, the differential action is similar to that of a conventional differential.

Service Procedures

Backlash and noise are the usual symptoms of trouble in the drive mechanism. Universal joints wear from lack of lubrication causing backlash.

Infrequently, rear ends become noisy from defective bearings, which cause misalignment, necessitating replacement of the bearings and the drive pinion and ring gear set. Both gears must be replaced at the same time because they are lapped together at the factory as a set.

Infrequently, due to improper lubrication, it may be necessary to replace a rear axle bearing.

425

Galled bearings are a source of noise.

Scored teeth are generally caused by inadequate lubrication.

Troubleshooting

If the propeller shaft is out of balance, the entire car may shake at a critical speed. Propeller shaft vibration can be caused by undercoating having been sprayed on the shaft, too much lubricant in the ball-and-trunnion type universal joint, looseness of the transmission flange nuts, looseness of the differential flange nuts, or improper assembly of the splined joint.

Universal joint backlash may be tested by alternately pressing and releasing the accelerator pedal when traveling about 30 mph. Excessive backlash causes a bump each time the accelerator pedal is moved.

Rear end noises are divided into three groups as follows:

• **Gear Noise When Pulling.** If the noise is low pitched and increases in volume as the car is accelerated, it is an indication of scored teeth, incorrect mesh of the teeth, or of the wrong type of lubricant.

• **Gear Noise When Coasting.** If the noise is low pitched and irregular, it is an indication of scored teeth, excessive end play in the pinion bearings, or of incorrect tooth adjustment.

• **Bearing Noise When Pulling or Coasting.** This indicates that the bearings are chipped, scored, or worn; or that the pinion is improperly positioned. Bearings that are badly worn or broken, will make a gravelly, rough grating sound that may change very slightly in volume as the speed is changed.

Repairing a Universal Joint

The power of the engine is applied through small universal joint bearings, which wear quickly when lubrication is inadequate. To lubricate a universal joint, it must be taken apart. This necessitates removing the propeller shaft from the car.

Tools and Equipment

Hydraulic press; $\frac{1}{2}$, $\frac{9}{16}$, $\frac{5}{8}$ and $\frac{11}{16}$ inch combination-end wrenches; two horses; car jack; $\frac{9}{16}$ inch cub socket and "T" handle; plastic hammer; large drift punch.

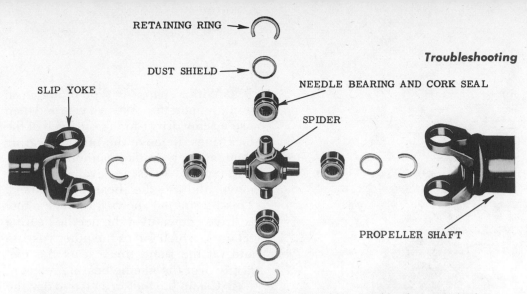

RETAINING RING →

DUST SHIELD →

NEEDLE BEARING AND CORK SEAL

SLIP YOKE

SPIDER

PROPELLER SHAFT

In this type of universal joint, retaining rings are slipped into machined grooves in the bearing housings. Courtesy Oldsmobile Division, General Motors Corporation.

PROCEDURE

① Remove the four flange retaining nuts at each end of the driveshaft, and then lower the entire assembly. Mark the needle bearing retainers and the universal joint yokes so that the parts can be re-assembled in their original positions. Support the yoke in a vise, and then remove the screws and the lock plates. Drive in one of the needle bearing retainers with a blunt punch, which is just slightly smaller in diameter than the retainer. This will drive the spider down against the opposite needle bearing retainer so that it can be removed easily. Take off the other retainers in a similar manner.

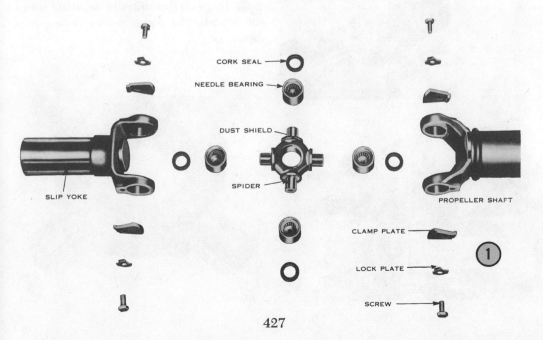

CORK SEAL →

NEEDLE BEARING →

DUST SHIELD

SPIDER

SLIP YOKE

PROPELLER SHAFT

CLAMP PLATE →

①

LOCK PLATE →

SCREW →

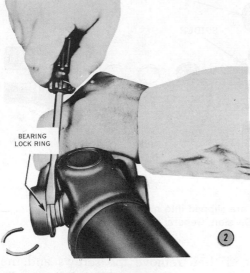

BEARING
LOCK RING

② With a snap-ring type of universal joint, support the yoke in a vise and then use a screwdriver to pry out each of the lock rings. Remove the needle bearing retainers in a similar manner.

③ Special tools are available to remove the needle bearing retainers. This illustration shows how such a tool is driven down over the needle bearing retainer, which forces the other yoke up and, at the same time, seats the tool firmly over the needle bearing retainer.

④ Clamp the tool in a vise so that the pressure closes the slots in the tool. Use a plastic mallet on the bottom part of the yoke in order to free the lower needle bearing retainer, which can then be removed from the tool. The other retainers can be removed in a like manner.

Cleaning and Inspecting

⑤ Clean all parts in solvent. Examine the spider journals for evidence of galling.

⑥ Inspect the needle bearings and the needle bearing retainers for evidence of galling.

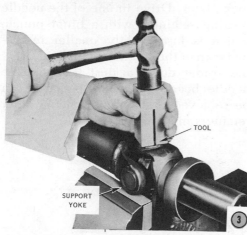

②

TOOL

SUPPORT
YOKE

③

BEARING HELD
IN TOOL

YOKE

SLOT

④

WORN AREA

⑤

WORN AREA

⑥

ASSEMBLING

⑦ Before assembling the universal joint parts, lubricate each of the needle bearing retainers with Multi-Purpose Grease, EP (extreme pressure). Start a needle bearing retainer in the yoke, and the spider with new seals, and then start the opposite needle bearing retainer. Place the assembly in a vise with soft jaws, and then press each needle bearing retainer into place, flush with the yoke. If necessary, use a soft drift punch to seat each of the needle bearing retainers, and then install the lock rings or the lock plates.

Replacing a Rear Axle-Bearing

Strike each of the bearing retainers with a plastic mallet to make sure that the lock rings are securely seated.

Replacing a Rear Axle Bearing

To replace an axle bearing it is necessary to remove the rear brake backing plate so that the axle and bearing assembly can be removed. After repairs are made, the brakes must be bled to remove entrained air.

Tools and Equipment

Rear end assembly with semifloating rear axle; plastic hammer; $\frac{1}{2}$, $\frac{3}{4}$, and $1\frac{1}{4}$ inch sockets; speed handle; slide bar; axle puller; drum puller; pliers; screwdriver; lug wrench; two stands; end play measuring gauge.

PROCEDURE

TAPERED AXLE

① Jack up the rear of the car and install two stands. Pry the wheel cover off with a screwdriver. Remove the wheel nuts and then the wheel. Remove the axle nut, install the drum puller, and then pull the drum.

BEARING
RETAINERS

CROSS

⑦

PULLER

①

SEAL PROTECTING SLEEVE (TOOL)

OIL SEAL

②

TAPERED BEARING SHIMS

④

② Disconnect the hydraulic brake line at the wheel cylinder. Remove the backing plate nuts, and then the backing plate assembly.

③ Install an axle puller, and then remove the axle. Replace the bearing.

④ Install the axle, bearing race, backing plate assembly, and bearing adjustment shims.

⑤ Tighten the backing plate nuts and test the end play, which should be between 0.013 and 0.018 inch. The adjustment is made by adding shims to increase the end play. Because the

measured end play is that of both rear axle bearings, add shims equally to each side to keep the axles and spacer block centralized. Replace the brake drum. Replace the hydraulic brake lines. Bleed the brakes to remove the air. Replace the wheel. Tighten the axle nuts to 145 ft. lbs. torque after the wheels are on the ground. Replace the wheel cover.

PULLER

REAR
AXLE SHAFT

③

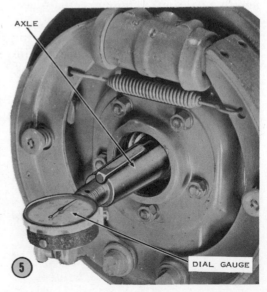

AXLE

DIAL GAUGE

⑤

FLANGED AXLE

⑥ Since 1965, Chrysler products have been using a flanged axle with an adjuster nut behind the right-side axle. This adjustment replaces the shims that were used on the tapered-type axle. To install this type of rear axle, clean the axle housing flange face thoroughly and install a new gasket. Replace the brake support plate assembly on the left side of the axle housing. Apply a thin coat of Multi-Purpose Grease, Grade 2, to the outside diameter of the bearing cup before installing it in the bearing bore. **Caution:** *This lubricant is necessary as a corrosion preventive.* Install the gasket on the studs of the axle housing, carefully slide the axle shaft assembly through the oil seal, and then engage the splines in the differential side gear. Tap the end of the axle shaft lightly with a plastic mallet to seat the axle shaft bearing in its bore. Replace the retainer plate. Install the nuts, and then tighten them to 30–35 ft-lbs. torque. Repeat for the right side of the axle housing. Back off the threaded adjuster of the right axle shaft assembly until the inner face of the adjuster is flush with the inner face of the retainer plate. Carefully slide the axle shaft assembly through the seal and engage the splines in the differential side gear. Tap the end of the axle shaft lightly with a plastic mallet to seat the bearing in the housing bore. Position the retainer plate over the axle housing studs. Install the retainer nuts and tighten them to 30–35 ft-lbs. torque.

⑦ To make the axle shaft end play adjustment, mount a dial indicator on the left brake support as shown. **Caution:** *Both rear wheels must be off the ground; otherwise, a false reading will be obtained.* Turn the adjuster clockwise until both wheel bearings are seated and there is no end play in the axle shafts. Back off the adjuster 4 notches, and then tap the end of the left axle shaft lightly with a plastic mallet in order to seat the right wheel bearing cup against the adjuster. Rotate the axle shaft several times so that a true reading will be indicated, which should be 0.013"–0.023". If necessary, make a correction as required. Install the adjuster lock and tighten the retaining nuts to 30–35 ft-lbs. torque. Remove the dial indicator and install the brake drum, retaining clips, wheel, and wheel cover.

Exploded view of a roller-bearing type assembly which needs no adjusting shims. Courtesy Ford Motor Company.

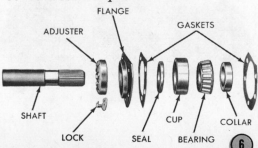

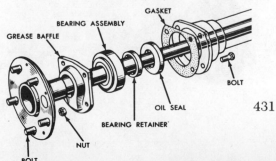

431

Repairing a Differential

Every time the differential gears are removed, either for replacement of gears or bearings, they must be adjusted to operate quietly. The gear teeth must mesh with a full tooth contact so that the driving load is carried over the entire surface.

Tools and Equipment

Ford rear axle assembly; $\frac{1}{2}$, $\frac{9}{16}$, $\frac{11}{16}$, $\frac{3}{4}$ and $1\frac{1}{4}$ inch sockets; ratchets; extension; center punch; ball peen and plastic hammers; wheel puller; torque wrench.

PROCEDURE

DISASSEMBLING

① Jack up the car, drain the rear end of lubricant, remove the axle shafts, and then remove the drive shaft.

② Remove the five nuts that hold the pinion retainer to the carrier and lift out the assembly. Place a piece of rubber hose over the pinion shaft pilot bearing to protect it. Remove the ten nuts that hold the differential carrier and mount it in a holding fixture.

③ Mark both differential bearing caps and bearing supports to ensure proper assembly. Then remove the adjusting nuts locks, bearing caps, and adjusting nuts. Lift the differential assembly from the carrier.

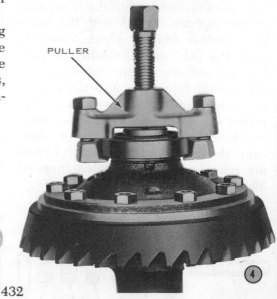

TOOL

INDEX MARK

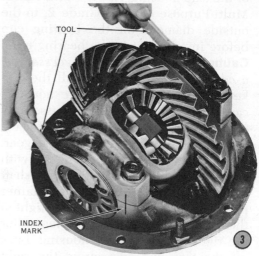

PULLER

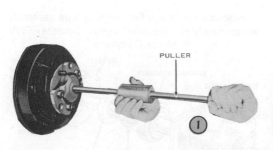

PULLER

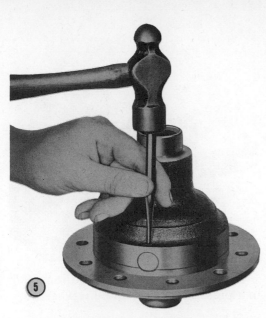

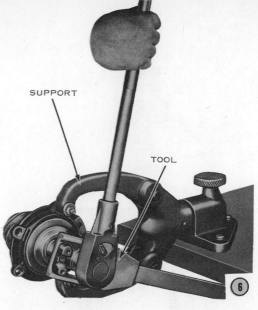

SUPPORT

TOOL

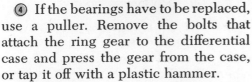

⑤

⑥

TORQUE WRENCH

SUPPORT

TOOL

⑦

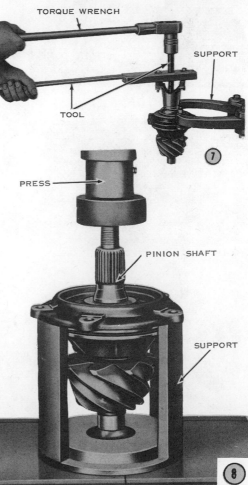

PRESS

PINION SHAFT

SUPPORT

⑧

④ If the bearings have to be replaced, use a puller. Remove the bolts that attach the ring gear to the differential case and press the gear from the case, or tap it off with a plastic hammer.

⑤ Use a drift punch to drive out the differential pinion shaft retainer. Separate the two-piece differential case and drive out the pinion shaft with a brass punch. Remove the gears and thrust washers.

⑥ To disassemble the pinion retainer, remove the O-ring and the pinion-locating shim. Measure its thickness with a micrometer, as you will need this information when assembling the new pinion. **Caution:** *Be careful not to damage the mounting surfaces of the retainer and carrier.* Mount the pinion retainer assembly in a fixture, and then remove the pinion shaft nut and flat washer.

⑦ Remove the universal joint flange and the oil seal. Then remove the slinger.

⑧ Press the pinion shaft out of the pinion front bearing cone and remove the spacer.

433

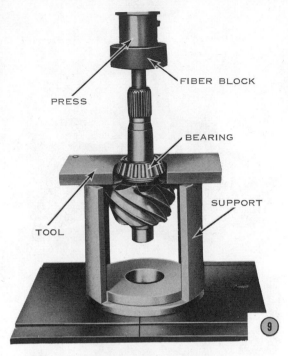

PRESS

FIBER BLOCK

BEARING

TOOL

SUPPORT

⑨

DIAL GAUGE

⑫

⑨ The bearings should be removed in a press if they are to be replaced.

CLEANING AND INSPECTING

⑩ Clean all parts in solvent and inspect for galled teeth, bad bearings, and a groove in the universal joint flange where the oil seal seats.

⑪ Inspect the differential case surfaces for spider gear wear which causes backlash.

⑫ If the gear teeth are broken, pieces may have passed between the closely fitted parts and sprung the case. To check the differential case runout, mount it in the carrier and place a dial gauge against the gear mounting surface. The case must be trued in a lathe if the run out exceeds 0.003 inch.

TO STUDY THE PRINCIPLE OF OPERATION

⑬ Place a side gear and thrust washer into the differential case bore.

⑭ With a plastic hammer, drive the pinion shaft into the case just far enough to retain a pinion thrust washer and pinion gear. Place the second pinion and thrust washer in position and drive the pinion shaft into place. Be careful to line up the pinion shaft retainer holes.

WORN AREA

⑩

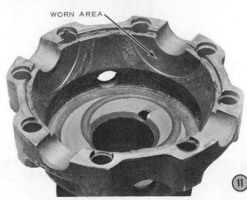

WORN AREA

⑪

THRUST WASHER • PINION SHAFT

13

THRUST WASHER

SIDE GEAR

15

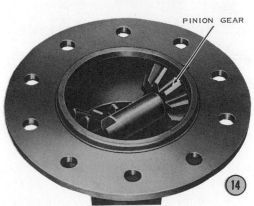

PINION GEAR

14

• To duplicate a turn, rotate the drive pinion gear as before but now hold the upper side gear to simulate the inner wheel on a curve. Note that the lower side gear revolves twice as fast as the ring gear because now the spider gears are revolving on their shafts.

ASSEMBLING

⑯ Remove the ring gear, and then drive in the differential pinion shaft retainer.

⑮ Place the second side gear and thrust washer in position. Temporarily attach the ring gear to the carrier case with the teeth up. Support the drive pinion gear and lay it on the ring gear with the teeth meshing in a normal manner.

• To duplicate the straight-ahead operation, turn the drive pinion gear. Note that the side gears rotate at the same speed but that the spider gears do not turn on their shafts.

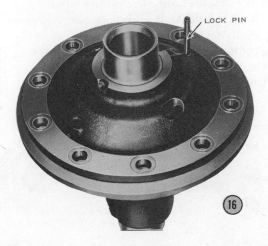

LOCK PIN

16

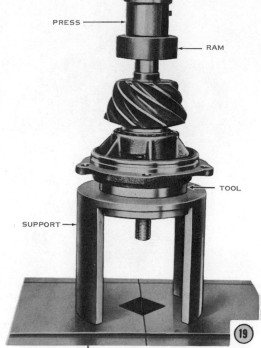

(17) Insert two ⁷⁄₁₆ N.F. bolts, 2 inches long, through the differential flange and thread them three or four turns into the ring gear as a guide in aligning the bolt holes. Press or tap the drive gear into position. Install and tighten the drive gear bolts alternately across the gear to 75–85 ft. lbs. torque. Press the bearings in place using a special driver which fits the inner race.

(18) Group the parts which make up the pinion assembly.

(19) Place a new spacer and the bearing retainer on the pinion shaft, and then install the front bearing cone. Press the cone into position while rocking the pinion carrier. Stop before all play is removed, otherwise the spacer may be compressed too much.

(20) Install the universal joint flange. Place the flat washer over the pinion shaft, and then start the pinion shaft nut. Hold the flange and tighten the pinion shaft nut until the torque required to turn the pinion shaft is 8–12 inch-pounds with used bearings, or 17–27 inch-pounds with new bearings. Rotate the pinion shaft frequently as you tighten the pinion shaft nut to make sure that the bearings are seating properly.

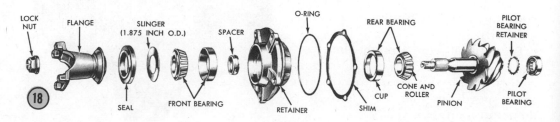

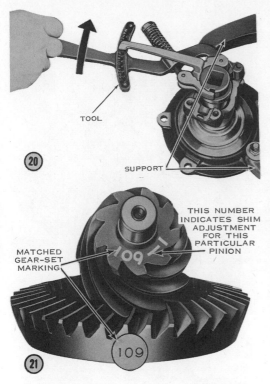

TOOL

20

SUPPORT

THIS NUMBER
INDICATES SHIM
ADJUSTMENT
FOR THIS
PARTICULAR
PINION

MATCHED
GEAR-SET
MARKING

109

21

ADJUSTING

21 Manufacturing tolerances in the pinion bore dimensions make a shim adjustment necessary for proper meshing of the teeth. In the illustrated Ford rear end, the shim is placed between the pinion retainer and the carrier. An increase in thickness moves the pinion away from the drive gear. Many manufacturers place the shim between the pinion gear and the bearing which has an opposite effect on the pinion position.

The standard shim is 0.015 inch. Markings are placed on the end of the pinion gear to indicate variations from standard. A minus one (−1) indicates that a shim 0.001 inch thinner than standard is required; the negative (−) sign indicates that the pinion should be moved closer to the drive gear. A positive sign (+) indicates that the pin-

ion should be moved farther from the drive gear and a thicker shim is required. A pinion marked with a zero (0) is a standard pinion and is assembled with the standard 0.015 inch shim.

To select the proper shim, measure the original shim with a micrometer. Note the dimensional mark on the original pinion. Compare this with the mark on the new pinion to determine how the original shim should be modified. For example: if the original shim was 0.015 inch and the original pinion was marked −1, and the new pinion is marked +1, then the new pinion requires a 0.002 inch thicker shim. Therefore, a shim measuring 0.017 inch should be used. If the new pinion is marked the same as the old pinion, no shim change is required.

22 Lubricate the O-ring and install it in its groove. Be careful not to twist it. Place the correct shim on the carrier, and then install the pinion and retainer assembly. Install the pinion bumper and the retainer bolts. Tighten the bolts to 35–40 ft-lbs. torque.

O-RING

PINION-LOCATING
SHIM

22

TOOL

DIAL GAUGE

RAG

23 Loosen the right-hand nut on the pinion side of the carrier until it loses contact with the bearing cup. Tighten the left-hand nut until the ring gear is just forced into the pinion with zero backlash. Recheck the right-hand nut at this time to make sure that it is still loose, and then tighten it until it just contacts the bearing cup. Now, tighten the right-hand nut two additional notches to preload the bearings while rotating the ring gear several revolutions in each direction to seat the bearings in their cups. **Caution:** *This is important!*

24 Now loosen the right-hand nut to release the bearing preload in order to recheck the backlash. Tighten the left-hand nut just enough to remove any backlash. Tighten the right-hand nut until it just contacts the cup, and then tighten it 2–3 notches more to preload the carrier bearing and to force the ring gear away from the pinion, which will usually result in the correct backlash of from 0.004 to 0.009 inch. Tighten the differential cap bolts to 75–80 ft-lbs. torque. If the backlash is not within

438

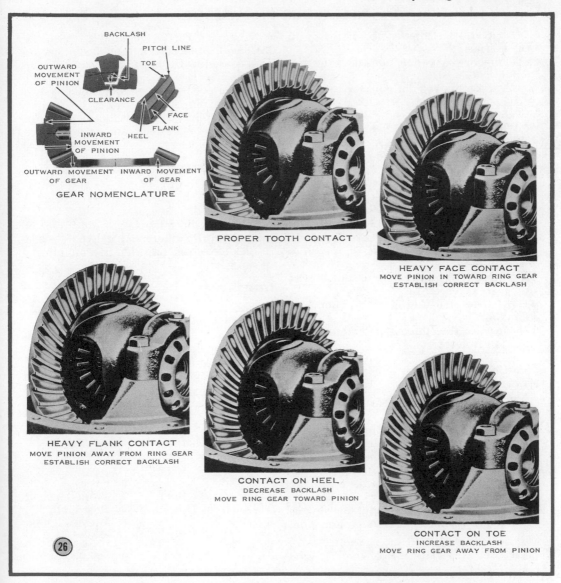

GEAR NOMENCLATURE

PROPER TOOTH CONTACT

HEAVY FACE CONTACT
MOVE PINION IN TOWARD RING GEAR
ESTABLISH CORRECT BACKLASH

HEAVY FLANK CONTACT
MOVE PINION AWAY FROM RING GEAR
ESTABLISH CORRECT BACKLASH

CONTACT ON HEEL
DECREASE BACKLASH
MOVE RING GEAR TOWARD PINION

CONTACT ON TOE
INCREASE BACKLASH
MOVE RING GEAR AWAY FROM PINION

specifications, loosen one adjusting nut and tighten the opposite one an equal amount to move the ring gear away from or toward the pinion.

㉕ Paint the gear teeth with a red lead and oil mixture. Roll a contact pattern by twisting a rag around the pinion shaft to load the gears.

㉖ If the pattern is not correct, make the indicated changes. The pinion need not be disassembled in the Ford rear end to change a shim. If the shim is changed, the backlash will have to be readjusted. When the correct pattern is obtained, clean the marking compound from the teeth.

CHECK YOUR KNOWLEDGE

1. What are the three types of drives in common use?
2. Through what two motions does the propeller shaft move?
3. What are the two duties of the rear end?
4. What is a hypoid gear set? What is its advantage? Disadvantage?
5. What is the usual ratio between the teeth of the rear-end gears?
6. Explain the action of the rear end when going straight ahead. When turning.
7. What is the advantage of the limited-slip differential?
8. Explain the operation of the limited-slip differential when one wheel is on ice. When the car rounds a curve.
9. What are the usual troubles in the drive mechanism?
10. Why is it necessary to replace both rear end gears as a set?
11. What are some causes of propeller shaft vibration?
12. How can the three types of rear end noises be isolated?

Self-Check Tests

TRUE-FALSE

1. The Hotchkiss Drive has an open propeller shaft.
2. The torque tube of the Hotchkiss Drive absorbs the torque of fast starts.
3. The rear end changes the direction of power flow 180°.
4. The pinion gear has fewer teeth than the ring gear.
5. Rotation of the differential housing is continuous whenever the car is in motion.
6. When the car is rounding a curve, the inside wheel must turn through a longer arc and, consequently, must turn faster than the outside wheel.
7. A limited-slip differential contains two sets of differential gears.
8. Some universal joints and propeller shafts contain balance arrows to assure correct alignment.

MULTIPLE CHOICE

1. Which of the following is *not* a part of the rear end: a) idler gear; b) ring gear; c) pinion gear; d) side gear?
2. Which of the following is *not* a part of the limited-slip differential: a) hypoid gears; b) flexible cross pins; c) friction clutch; d) sun gear?

COMPLETION

1. The _____ _____ drive has a single universal joint at the front end.
2. The _____ _____ drive has an enclosed propeller shaft.
3. A drive pinion gear, located below the center line of the ring gear, is called a _____ gear.
4. The _____ _____ differential limits the driving power delivered to a freely spinning wheel.
5. Universal joints wear from lack of lubrication producing _____.

MATCHING

1. Cross and roller
2. Hotchkiss Drive
3. Hypoid

a. Propeller shaft
b. Rear end
c. Universal joint

Chapter 16

Front Axle
and Steering

Steering Gear

The steering-gear mechanism gives the driver the means of turning the front wheels of the vehicle. The mechanism consists of a steering gear box, pitman arm, drag link, tie rod, steering arms, and steering knuckles which carry the front wheels.

Turning the steering wheel turns the steering shaft to which a worm gear is attached within the steering gear box. The worm gear moves a roller through part of an arc. This motion is transmitted to the pitman arm, which moves back and forth across the width of the frame. Several arrangements of rods and levers are in common use but, in general, a drag link, connected to the pitman arm, transmits this movement to two tie rods connected to the two steering arms. Movement of the steering arms turns the steering knuckles and wheels which are pivoted on the front-end support mechanism.

An exploded view of the steering gear mechanism. Note the screw (worm), one of the six simple machines. Courtesy Chrysler Division, Chrysler Corporation.

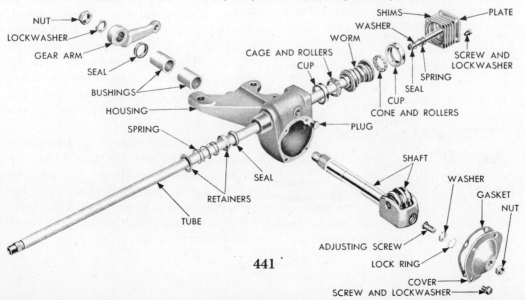

NUT
LOCKWASHER
GEAR ARM
SEAL
BUSHINGS
HOUSING
SPRING
SEAL
RETAINERS
TUBE

CAGE AND ROLLERS
CUP

WORM
WASHER
SHIMS
PLATE
SCREW AND LOCKWASHER
SPRING
SEAL
CUP
CONE AND ROLLERS
PLUG

SHAFT
WASHER
GASKET
NUT

ADJUSTING SCREW
LOCK RING
COVER
SCREW AND LOCKWASHER

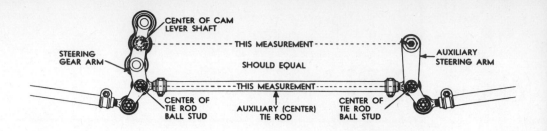

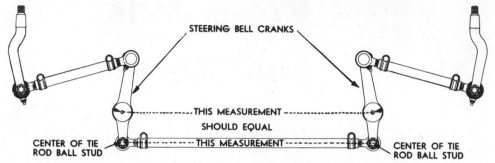

CENTER OF CAM LEVER SHAFT

STEERING GEAR ARM

AUXILIARY STEERING ARM

CENTER OF TIE ROD BALL STUD

AUXILIARY (CENTER) TIE ROD

CENTER OF TIE ROD BALL STUD

THIS MEASUREMENT SHOULD EQUAL THIS MEASUREMENT

STEERING BELL CRANKS

CENTER OF TIE ROD BALL STUD

THIS MEASUREMENT SHOULD EQUAL THIS MEASUREMENT

CENTER OF TIE ROD BALL STUD

Another steering linkage arrangement.

Steering linkage of the Chevrolet. Courtesy Chevrolet Motor Division, General Motors Corporation.

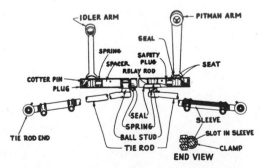

The steering linkage. Courtesy Pontiac Motor Division, General Motors Corporation.

Power Steering

Power steering uses hydraulic pressure built up by an engine-operated pump to assist the driver in turning the front wheels. In all power steering designs, driver "feel" is built into the system by having the driver do some of the work. Two power steering types are in common use: a power-assist tie rod and a power-assist piston within the steering gear box.

In each case, turning the steering wheel moves a valve mechanism which directs oil under pressure to a piston to assist the driver in turning the front wheels. The valve mechanism is designed so that the more force the driver applies to the steering wheel, the more hydraulic pressure is applied to the piston.

The hydraulic valve mechanism is designed to be uni-directional—that is, power assists the driver to turn the front wheels, but road shocks are opposed by hydraulic pressure and, therefore, not transmitted back to the steering wheel.

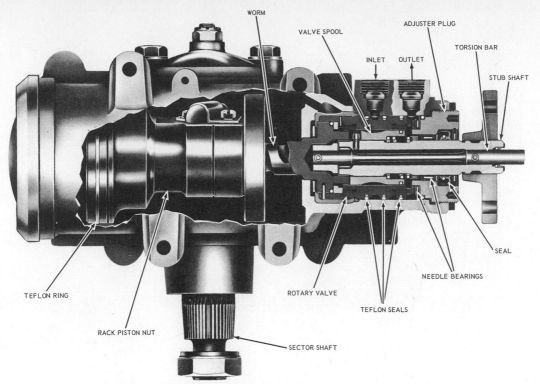

Cutaway view of the General Motors torsion-bar type of power steering gear assembly. Courtesy General Motors Corporation.

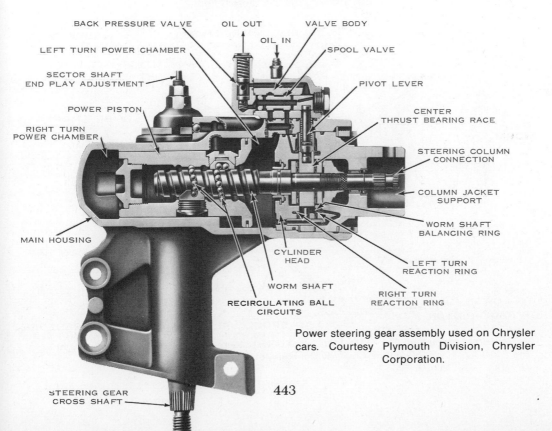

Power steering gear assembly used on Chrysler cars. Courtesy Plymouth Division, Chrysler Corporation.

443

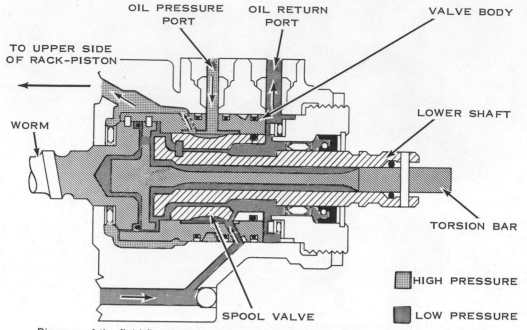

OIL PRESSURE PORT

OIL RETURN PORT

VALVE BODY

TO UPPER SIDE OF RACK-PISTON

WORM

LOWER SHAFT

TORSION BAR

SPOOL VALVE

HIGH PRESSURE

LOW PRESSURE

Diagram of the fluid flow in the torsion-bar power steering gear assembly during a left turn. Courtesy General Motors Corporation.

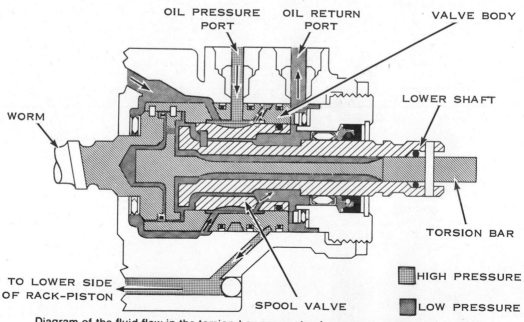

OIL PRESSURE PORT

OIL RETURN PORT

VALVE BODY

WORM

LOWER SHAFT

TORSION BAR

TO LOWER SIDE OF RACK-PISTON

SPOOL VALVE

HIGH PRESSURE

LOW PRESSURE

Diagram of the fluid flow in the torsion-bar power steering gear assembly during a right turn. Courtesy General Motors Corporation.

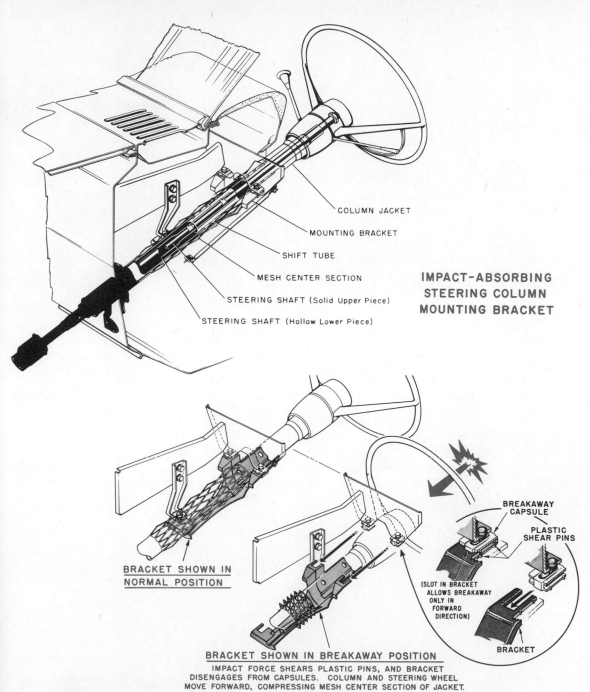

COLUMN JACKET

MOUNTING BRACKET

SHIFT TUBE

MESH CENTER SECTION

STEERING SHAFT (Solid Upper Piece)

STEERING SHAFT (Hollow Lower Piece)

**IMPACT-ABSORBING
STEERING COLUMN
MOUNTING BRACKET**

**BRACKET SHOWN IN
NORMAL POSITION**

BRACKET SHOWN IN BREAKAWAY POSITION

IMPACT FORCE SHEARS PLASTIC PINS, AND BRACKET
DISENGAGES FROM CAPSULES.   COLUMN AND STEERING WHEEL
MOVE FORWARD, COMPRESSING MESH CENTER SECTION OF JACKET.

BREAKAWAY
CAPSULE

PLASTIC
SHEAR PINS

(SLOT IN BRACKET
ALLOWS BREAKAWAY
ONLY IN
FORWARD
DIRECTION)

BRACKET

Details of the impact-absorbing steering column assembly. It is designed to contract at a
controlled rate during a head-on collision in order to minimize injury to the driver. The
assembly consists of four parts: (1) a telescoping steering shaft, (2) a telescoping transmission selector torque tube, (3) a column jacket with a crushable center section, and
(4) a breakaway mounting bracket. Courtesy Dodge Division, Chrysler Corporation.

445

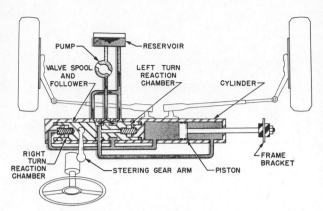

The linkage-type power steering used on Dodge, Ford, and Chevrolet. Courtesy Dodge Division, Chrysler Corporation.

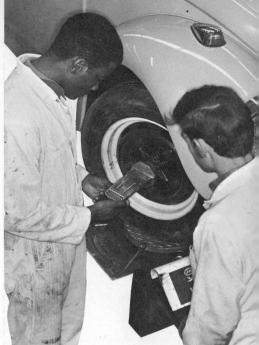

Two students at Los Angeles Trade-Technical College adjust the front-end steering geometry of a vehicle to specifications.

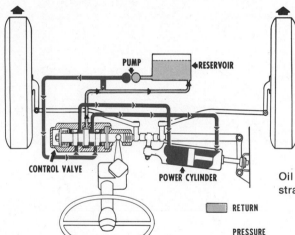

Oil flow in a linkage-type unit, when going straight ahead. Courtesy Lincoln-Mercury Division, Ford Motor Company.

Oil flow during a left turn. Courtesy Dodge Division, Chrysler Corporation.

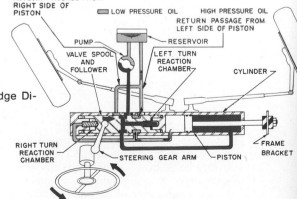

446

Front-end "Geometry"

The front wheels are arranged at various angles to the car frame to provide good steering control and stability. The angles are discussed in the following order: caster, camber, steering axis inclination, toe-in, and turning radius.

Caster is the slant of the knuckle support forward at the bottom. The front wheels, when provided with the proper amount of caster, align themselves in the direction in which the car is moving. Too much caster causes hard steering and shimmy at low speeds. Too little caster causes wander or weave and erratic steering when applying the brakes.

Camber is the angle between a true vertical line drawn through the center of the wheel. The top of the wheel is inclined away from the car, which places the center of the tire under the extended line of the king pin so that the weight of the car is directly over the pivot point, for easier steering.

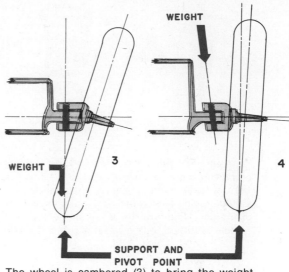

The wheel is cambered (3) to bring the weight directly over the pivot point, but this amount of camber would wear a tire on the outside shoulder. To correct, the wheel is cambered moderately (4) and the king pin is inclined so that the support and pivot point line up.

Steering axis inclination is the outward tilt of the bottom of the knuckle support toward the wheel. Modern engineering practice is to minimize the amount of camber in order to reduce uneven tire wear, and to increase the angular inclination of the steering knuckle support to place its centerline under the pivot point of the tire.

Caster is the tilt of the top of the king pin to the rear. Courtesy Cadillac Motor Division, General Motors Corporation.

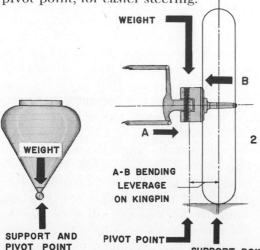

A top spins because its weight is directly over the support and pivot point (1). Without camber (2), the weight of the car is not directly over the pivot point, causing a binding action at A-B.

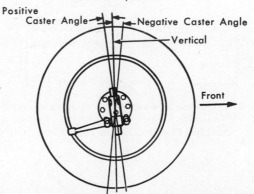

447

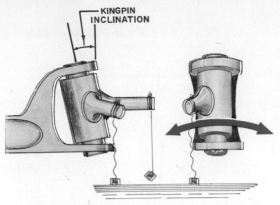

KINGPIN
INCLINATION

A cambered wheel tends to roll away from the center, as does this hoop. To overcome this tendency, the front wheels must be toed-in. The more the camber, the more toe-in is required. Courtesy John Bean Division, Food Machinery and Chemical Corporation.

King pin inclination increases steering stability by raising the axle support on a turn. Thus the front wheels try to maintain a straight-ahead attitude, being kept in this position by the weight of the car. Note how the string shortens as the spindle is turned; with a wheel in place, the axle would lift.

BOTH TRY TO GET AS LOW AS POSSIBLE

WEIGHT OF CAR   WEIGHT OF BALL

This is another way of illustrating that the ball and the car both tend to drop as low as possible. Thus king pin inclination tends to keep the wheels in a straight-ahead position.

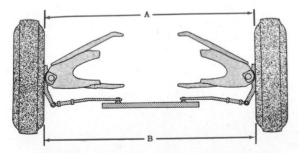

The distance between the rear of the front wheels "B" must be longer than "A" for toe-in. Courtesy Oldsmobile Division, General Motors Corporation.

Steering axis inclination provides steering stability by raising the entire front end of the vehicle during a turn. Gravity causes the spindle ends to tend to return to their straight-out position. This force is not sufficient to cause hard steering, but is enough for excellent directional stability. Steering axis inclination is probably a more important steering-stability factor than caster.

Toe-in is the difference in distance between the front and rear of the front tires measured at spindle height. That is, the wheels are aimed slightly in, as if to cross each other's path. Due to compression of the steering linkage parts, the front wheels tend to turn out or away from each other. To offset this, a small amount of toe-in makes the wheels travel parallel paths and counteracts side scuffing.

Turning radius or toe-out is required on turns. Because the outside wheel on a curve moves on a longer arc than does the inside wheel, the inside wheel must turn at a sharper angle to prevent tire scuffing and wear. To obtain this action, the steering arms are set at an angle to the wheels. Although the tie rod moves each steering arm an equal distance, the angular movement is unequal and the wheels toe-out. The sharper the turning angle, the more toe-out results.

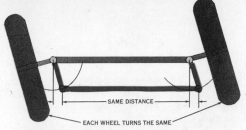

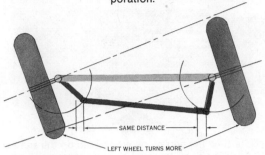

If the steering linkage were arranged about a parallelogram, as in this illustration, both wheels would turn equal amounts. Courtesy John Bean Division, Food Machinery and Chemical Corporation.

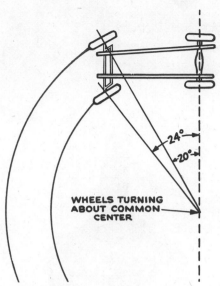

To compensate for the smaller circle traveled by the inside wheel on a turn, it must turn sharper about a shorter radius. Courtesy John Bean Division, Food Machinery and Chemical Corporation.

Service Procedures

Steering stability is an important safety consideration. The car must maintain the straight course set by the driver. It must return to a straight-ahead position after a turn. It must not wander, weave, or dart to one side when the brakes are firmly applied.

Quite frequently, the right front wheel is cramped into the curb when parking. This places an unusual strain which many times leads to bending of the steering linkage, resulting in misalignment.

It is seldom possible, nor desirable, to attempt to adjust one angle of the front end. They are so interrelated that good results can be expected only when the entire front end is analyzed and properly corrected.

Now, although the tie rod moves the same sideward distance, the left steering arm turns the left wheel more sharply because most of its travel is toward the axle. The reverse condition exists on a right turn. Courtesy John Bean Division, Food Machinery and Chemical Corporation.

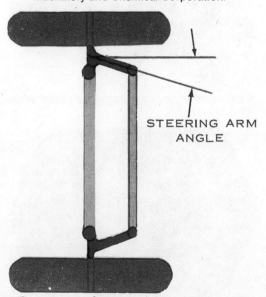

Actually, the steering arms are set at an angle, as shown here. Courtesy John Bean Division, Food Machinery and Chemical Corporation.

449

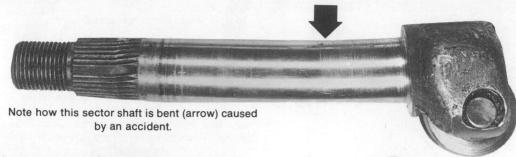

Note how this sector shaft is bent (arrow) caused by an accident.

Note how the serrations are twisted on the same shaft.

Ball joints wear when operated with inadequate lubrication, causing excessive play in the front end.

A galled worm caused by inadequate lubrication.

Troubleshooting

Drive the car on a smooth level road. Release the steering wheel to see if the car continues straight ahead or wanders to either side. (If the road is crowned, it may be necessary to make the test evenly straddled over the centerline. *Make sure there is no traffic.*)

Apply the brakes sharply to test for "diving" or pulling to either side. Diving is caused by loose front-end parts, or by grease or hydraulic brake fluid on the brake lining.

Turn into a side street; then release the steering wheel, which should return to a straight-ahead position by itself; otherwise, the front-end angles are uneven.

WORN AREA

Worn threads inside of this front end nut cause excessive front end looseness and misalignment.

450

Power Steering Troubleshooting

If the steering wheel binds or sticks, or if poor recovery occurs, check the steering gear adjustments. If the power assist fails, check the entire system for damage or broken hoses. Perform a pressure test to determine whether the trouble is in the pump, control valve, or the power cylinder.

If the pressure is low, check the pump drive belt for proper tension. If the tension is correct, the pump may be defective. If the pressure is normal, then the trouble is in the control valve or power cylinder.

If there is excessive free play or lost motion, check the steering gear worm-and-roller mesh adjustment. Check for excessive clearance between the operating linkages.

If the unit is noisy, check the pump belt tension. Too tight an adjustment may cause pump noise, and too loose an adjustment, belt squeal. If the noise cannot be eliminated by a belt adjustment, the pump should be removed for service. A loose pump belt can cause chatter during a sharp turn, or it may

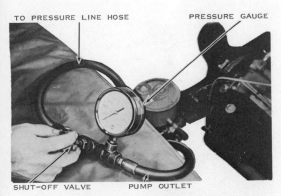

TO PRESSURE LINE HOSE   PRESSURE GAUGE

SHUT-OFF VALVE   PUMP OUTLET

A pressure gauge is necessary to troubleshoot a power steering unit.

also be caused by looseness in the linkage and bushings.

Adjusting a Steering Gear Housing

Steering wheels must turn easily but without excess play which could be the cause of shimmy. Too tight an adjustment results in hard steering.

There are three adjustments on all steering gear mechanisms: (1) the *up-and-down* motion of the worm gear, (2) the *end play* of the sector gear, and (3) the *mesh* of the two gears. The adjustments must always be made in the order above.

Tools and Equipment

Steering gear assembly; $\frac{1}{2}$, $\frac{9}{16}$, and $\frac{5}{8}$ inch box, open-end wrenches; hammer; 10 inch crescent; screwdriver.

PROCEDURE

UP-AND-DOWN PLAY OF THE WORM GEAR

1. Disconnect the drag link from the pitman arm.

2. Test for *up-and-down* play by pulling and pushing on the steering wheel. There must be *no* play, but the bearings must not be tight enough to cause any feelable drag.

3. Adjust by removing shims to take up play. Add shims to loosen the adjustment. Some steering gear housings have an adjustment plug which can be screwed in to remove play and backed out to increase play.

END PLAY OF THE SECTOR SHAFT

4. To test for *end play* of the sector shaft, pull and push on the pitman arm.

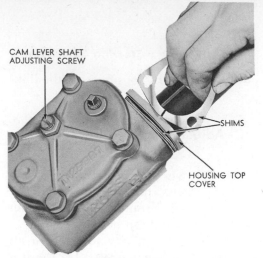

CAM LEVER SHAFT
ADJUSTING SCREW

SHIMS

HOUSING TOP
COVER

Shim-type worm bearing adjustment. Inserting shims increases the end play.

5. To remove any *feelable end play,* loosen the lock nut and turn the adjusting screw in until it seats. Back off the screw the width of the screwdriver slot for clearance. Retighten the lock nut.

Mesh of the Worm and Sector

6. The *mesh adjustment* is made by shifting the position of the sector gear with relation to the worm. In some units the teeth are cut at an angle so that turning the *sector end play adjustment* shifts the sector gear tighter into the worm gear. In some cases shims must be removed from beneath the sector gear to move it closer to the worm. To adjust the *mesh,* turn the steering wheel from one end to its opposite end. Count the number of turns and divide by two to find the *center* position of the steering wheel. Return the steering wheel to this position. This is important because manufacturers always design the worm gear so that a tighter mesh results in the center position and, unless the adjustment is made in this exact position, the gears will bind as the steering wheel is turned through this *high spot.*

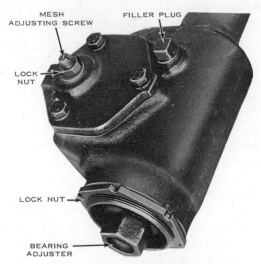

MESH
ADJUSTING SCREW

FILLER PLUG

LOCK
NUT

LOCK NUT

BEARING
ADJUSTER

The large nut at the bottom of this housing is the worm end play adjuster. Courtesy Buick Motor Division, General Motors Corporation.

Making the pitman shaft end play adjustment on a torsion-bar power steering unit, which should be 4 to 8 inch-pounds torque. Courtesy Buick Motor Division, General Motors Corporation.

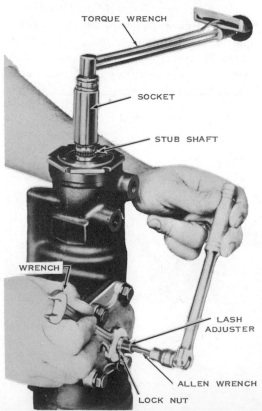

TORQUE WRENCH

SOCKET

STUB SHAFT

WRENCH

LASH
ADJUSTER

ALLEN WRENCH

LOCK NUT

452

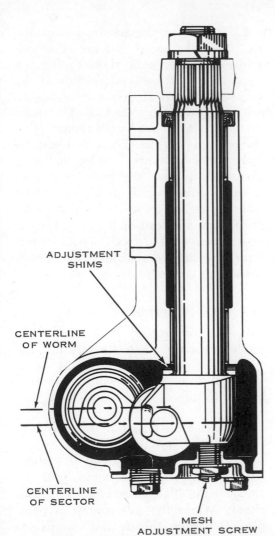

ADJUSTMENT
SHIMS

CENTERLINE
OF WORM

CENTERLINE
OF SECTOR

MESH
ADJUSTMENT SCREW

The mesh adjustment is made by shifting the sector deeper into the worm gear. Note how the centerlines of both gears are offset so that this adjustment can be made by turning the mesh adjustment screw. Some assemblies have adjustment shims which must be removed as needed so as to control the amount that the centerlines of the gears can be moved closer together, to shift the sector deeper into the worm gear.

Making the thrust bearing preload on a torsion-bar power steering unit, which should be 3 to 4 inch-pounds torque. Courtesy Buick Division, General Motors Corporation.

SECTOR SHAFT ADJUSTING SCREW

SECTOR
SHAFT

STEERING SHAFT
AND WORM

OIL
SEAL

WORM
BEARING
ADJUSTER

THRUST
BEARING

GEAR RACK

SECTOR
SHAFT
BUSHINGS

THRUST
BEARING

OIL SEAL

The mesh adjustment is made in this steering gear box by means of the sector shaft adjusting *screw* (top). Courtesy Ford Motor Company.

7. Loosen the lock nut and turn the sector end play screw until all play is removed. Do not tighten too much or the steering wheel will be hard to turn. Test by turning the steering wheel through the *high spot* several times to make sure that you have only a slight drag. Tighten the lock nut.

8. Where shims are provided under the sector shaft, remove one shim at a time and readjust the *sector end play* to make the *mesh* adjustment.

TORQUE WRENCH

SOCKET

STUB SHAFT

ADJUSTING
PLUG

LOCKNUT

ADJUSTABLE
SPANNER WRENCH

Measuring and Adjusting Toe-in

The adjustment for toe-in is to make the tie rod longer or shorter until the setting agrees with the manufacturer's specification. The toe-in adjustment, while the first one checked, is always the last one set because changes in camber and caster affect the toe-in.

Tools and Equipment

Front end to be adjusted; telescopic gauge; Wee-Gee toe-in board; wheel alignment rack; pipe wrench; $\frac{1}{2}$ and $\frac{9}{16}$ inch box, open-end wrenches.

PROCEDURE

TELESCOPIC GAUGE

1. Check the specification chart for the correct toe-in for the car you are going to adjust.

2. Compress the telescopic gauge and install it between the front of the two front tires.

3. Move the points of the gauge up or down on the tire sidewalls until the chain tips just touch the floor. Set the scale adjustment to zero.

4. Pull the car forward from the *center* of the front bumper until the gauge is at the rear of the front wheels and the chain tips just touch the floor. Read the toe-in on the gauge scale.

5. To correct the toe-in, loosen the tie rod end clamps and turn the rods with a pipe wrench. Make the tie rod longer to increase and shorter to decrease the toe-in. Most cars are equipped with two adjustable tie rods. The usual practice is to adjust one of them so that the toe-in is correct. Then turn both tie rods equal amounts, *and in the same direction*, to place the steering gear on its high point which will position the steering wheel correctly for straight-ahead driving. Position the tie rod clamp bosses below the tie rods to avoid interference with the frame, and then tighten the clamp bosses securely.

WEE-GEE BOARD METHOD

1. Pull the car so that one front wheel passes over the plate. Be sure that the front wheels are pointed straight ahead, and pull from the *center* of the bumper. Read the side drag on the scale.

2. Correct the length of the tie rods to eliminate all side drag with the car going over the full length of the plate. After making the adjustment, pull the car over the plate once more for a final check. When the adjustment is completed, tighten the tie rod clamps securely.

Making a toe-in adjustment with a telescopic gauge. The gauge is first installed at the same point on each tire as shown; its position is adjusted until the chain ends just touch the floor, and then the toe-in scale is indexed on the zero mark. Next the car is moved forward until the ends of the chain just touch the floor, with the telescopic gauge at the rear of the tires. The toe-in can now be read directly on the scale. Courtesy John Bean Division, Food Machinery and Chemical Corporation.

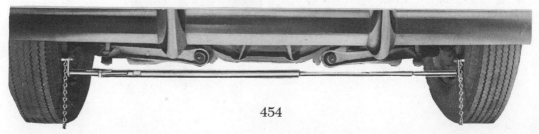

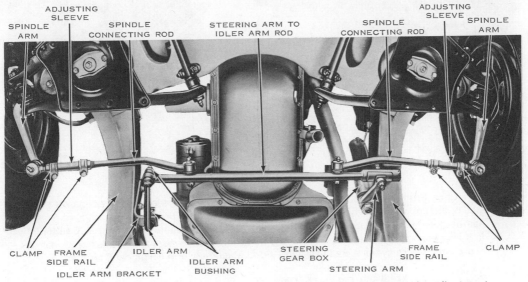

ADJUSTING SLEEVE

SPINDLE ARM

SPINDLE CONNECTING ROD

STEERING ARM TO IDLER ARM ROD

SPINDLE CONNECTING ROD

ADJUSTING SLEEVE

SPINDLE ARM

CLAMP   FRAME SIDE RAIL   IDLER ARM   IDLER ARM BRACKET   IDLER ARM BUSHING   STEERING GEAR BOX   STEERING ARM   FRAME SIDE RAIL   CLAMP

Parts of the steering linkage. The sleeve at each end must be turned for the adjustment in order to correct toe-in. Courtesy Ford Motor Company.

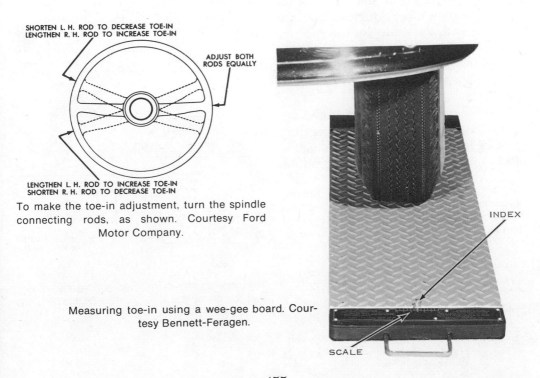

SHORTEN L. H. ROD TO DECREASE TOE-IN
LENGTHEN R. H. ROD TO INCREASE TOE-IN

ADJUST BOTH RODS EQUALLY

LENGTHEN L. H. ROD TO INCREASE TOE-IN
SHORTEN R. H. ROD TO DECREASE TOE-IN

To make the toe-in adjustment, turn the spindle connecting rods, as shown. Courtesy Ford Motor Company.

INDEX

Measuring toe-in using a wee-gee board. Courtesy Bennett-Feragen.

SCALE

455

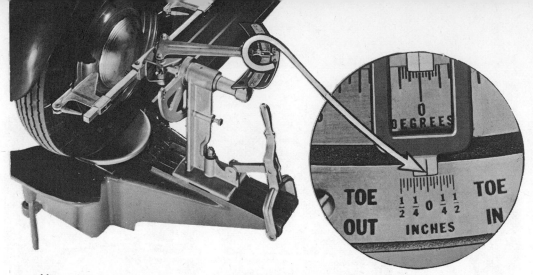

Measuring the toe-in on a front-end alignment rack. The gauge is positioned against the side of the tire, and the wheels are adjusted so that the gauge on one side reads zero. This can be done with either gauge. Then the toe-in can be read on the other gauge. **Caution:** *It is very important that you select a straight section of the wheel and tire for this measurement.* Courtesy John Bean Division, Food Machinery and Chemical Corporation.

MAKING TOE-IN MEASUREMENTS ON A RACK

1. When the toe-in measurement is to be made on a rack, the car must be properly prepared so that the toe-in, caster, and camber angles may be checked with the same set-up.

2. If you are adjusting only toe-in, correct the tie rod length so that the toe-in agrees with the manufacturer's specification.

3. If the caster and camber angles are to be adjusted, the toe-in correction must be left for the last, as any change in either one will affect the toe-in reading.

The height-leveling adjustment on Chrylser Corporation cars with torsion bars must be made before any other front-end angle is checked. Courtesy Plymouth Division, Chrysler Corporation.

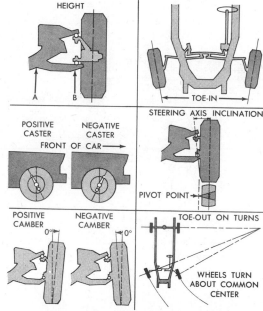

This drawing shows the various front-end angles that you are measuring. Courtesy Dodge Division, Chrysler Corporation.

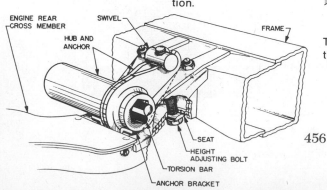

456

Testing and Correcting Front-end Alignment

The alignment of the front wheels is measured in degrees by gauges. To date, three different types of gauges are in common use. The first type takes measurements from the side of the tire or wheel, the second, a spirit-level gauge, is fastened to the spindle, and the third type is in the form of a light beam projected on a wall chart.

All gauges require the car to be level and on some form of turning-radius gauges or turntables so that the front wheels can be turned a measured number of degrees with relative ease.

Tools and Equipment

Car with front end to be aligned; front-end rack or a set of turning-radius gauges; front-end alignment gauges; brake pedal depressor.

PROCEDURE

To Prepare the Car

① Make sure that the car is on a level section of the floor or on a front-end rack. Position the front wheels directly over the center of the turning-radius gauges.

② If you are working on a level floor, it is necessary to place shims under the rear wheels to compensate for the height of the turning-radius gauges.

③ Eliminate all front end looseness before making any alignment measurements or corrections, because play in any of the bearings will cause misalignment. Bounce the front end of the car up and down, and then allow it to settle in its normal running position. Check the front end height against specifications by means of height gauges.

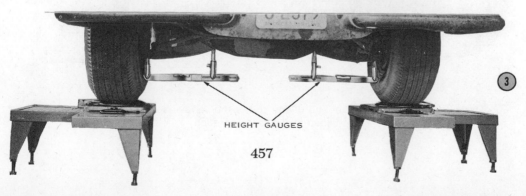

HEIGHT GAUGES

457

Strong magnets will hold the gauges in position while you take a reading on the upright scales. If corrections are necessary, weak front springs can be replaced or shimmed and torsion bars can be adjusted. Apply the brakes by installing the brake pedal depressor.

To Install the Caster-Camber Gauge

④ Remove the wheel cover and the dust cap from both front wheels. Wipe off the machined end of the hub flange. **Note:** *This is the only exposed portion of the hub that is accurately machined.* Check this surface carefully for burrs which could interfere with accurate seating of the gauge. File off any burrs. Position the self-centering plunger in the center hole in the end of the front wheel spindle. The powerful magnet will hold the gauge in place. Twist it a quarter turn in each direction several times in order to secure a positive seat. **Note:** *The self-centering plunger assures that the readings will be taken from the exact center of the spindle.* Repeat for the other wheel.

To Check Camber

⑤ With the gauge securely positioned on the hub, turn the front wheels until the turntable scale reads zero. Level the gauge by twisting it on the wheel hub until the bubble is at zero in the cross vial of the king pin angle gauge, as shown.

⑥ Read the camber scale. The position of the bubble will indicate the camber of the wheel being checked. Record this reading. Repeat for the other front wheel.

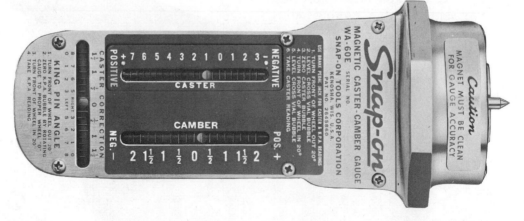

This close-up view of a front-end gauge shows the various scales in detail. Courtesy Snap-on Tools Corporation.

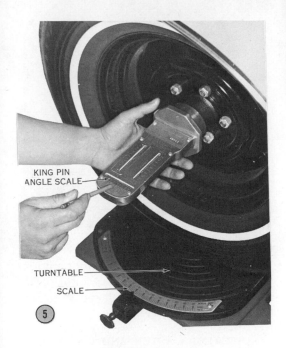

KING PIN
ANGLE SCALE

TURNTABLE

SCALE

⑤

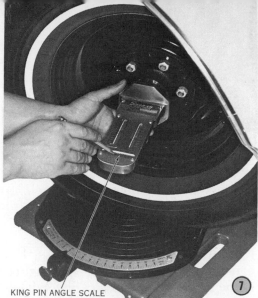

KING PIN ANGLE SCALE

⑦

To Check Caster

⑦ First check that the pointers on both turntables are on zero, and then turn the front of the wheel being checked *out* to 20° on the turntable scale. Level the gauge by twisting it against the hub until the bubble is centered in the cross vial of the king pin angle gauge, as shown.

⑧ Adjust the knurled screw on the bottom of the gauge until the bubble is centered in the caster gauge.

CAMBER
SCALE

⑥

CASTER
SCALE

⑧

459

⑨ Turn the front wheel *in* until the turntable gauge reads 20°. Level the gauge by twisting it on the hub until the bubble is at zero in the cross vial of the king pin angle gauge, as shown.

⑩ Read the caster scale and record it. Repeat for the other front wheel.

CHECKING THE KING PIN INCLINATION

⑪ Because modern cars use ball joints in place of king pins, this angle is sometimes called the steering axis inclination. To check this angle, turn the front of the wheel *out* 20° on the turntable scale. Zero the king pin angle cross vial bubble by twisting the gauge on the hub. Turn the front of the wheel *in* 20°, and then read the king pin inclination angle. Use the calibrations marked "left" for the left wheel and those marked "right" for the right wheel. This angle is not adjustable; therefore, if the readings are not within specifica-

CASTER
SCALE

⑩

tions when the caster and camber angles are correct, this means that some parts are bent and must be replaced in order to restore the correct angles.

CORRECTING CASTER AND CAMBER ANGLES

⑫ For most cars shims or eccentrics are used to change the caster and camber angles. Some cars have upper control arms bolted to slotted holes so that they can be moved. Others have an adjustable strut and eccentric bushing. Still others have serrated upper arm shafts that can be moved for changing the front end geometry. To make these adjustments, first turn the front wheel until the turntable scale is at zero. Install the gauge and center the king pin angle cross vial bubble by twisting the gauge on the hub. The camber scale should now read the same as it did when you recorded it, and any corrections will show directly on this scale. Caster corrections will be shown by movement of the cross vial bubble; the actual change to make is shown on the caster correction scale just above the vial.

KING PIN ANGLE SCALE

⑨

A bent spindle will cause an incorrect camber reading. If the correction is improperly made by bending the spindle support arm, an incorrect wheel lever arm will result. The car will then be hard to steer, with a tendency to wander. Courtesy Weaver Manufacturing Company.

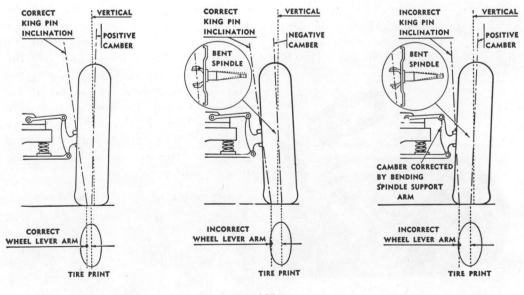

461

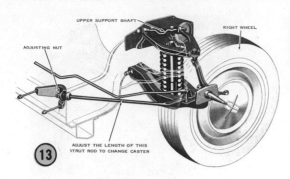

UPPER SUPPORT SHAFT

RIGHT WHEEL

ADJUSTING NUT

ADJUST THE LENGTH OF THIS STRUT ROD TO CHANGE CASTER

13

CASTER-CAMBER CAMS

15

13 In some cases, the upper support shaft can be shifted toward or away from the center of the car as the bolt holes are slotted. The shaft is shifted evenly at both support bolts to make a camber adjustment. If one side is moved out and the other in, then the caster angle will be changed. In some cases, the strut rod can be lengthened or shortened to make a caster adjustment.

14 Shims are positioned between the upper pivot shaft and the frame on some cars. They can be shifted from one side of the upper pivot shaft to the other to change camber. Shifting shims between the front and rear bolts changes the caster angle.

15 To make an adjustment on a front end in which eccentric cams are used, the caster must be adjusted first. Then adjust the camber by moving each cam bolt an equal amount in order to maintain the caster adjustment. **Caution:** *Because both camber and caster are affected by these eccentric cams, it is necessary to recheck the caster after making a camber adjustment.*

CHECKING THE TURNING RADIUS

16 After making the caster, camber, and toe-in corrections, you are ready to check the turning radius. Adjust the front wheels straight ahead and make sure that both turntable scales read zero, *without the pins being in place.* If necessary, jack up the wheel to make an adjustment. Now, turn the front of the left wheel *in* toward the car 20°. The reading on the *right* wheel turntable scale should show more than 20°; the exact amount is dependent upon the wheelbase and must be looked up for each car. Turn the front of the right wheel in toward the car 20° and check the *left* wheel turntable scale. Incorrect or uneven turning radius readings indicate bent steering arms.

SHOCK ABSORBER STUD

SHIMS

FRAME BRACKET

STEEL BUSHING

SHAFT

14

LEFT WHEEL

RIGHT WHEEL

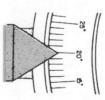

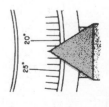

16

CHECK YOUR KNOWLEDGE

1. Through what parts does the steering wheel have to transmit power to turn the front wheels?

2. From where is power-steering hydraulic pressure obtained?

3. What are the two types of power-steering systems in common use?

4. How is driver "feel" built into the system?

5. What is a uni-directional valve?

6. What is caster? What is its function?

7. What is camber? What is its function?

8. What is steering axis inclination? What is its function?

9. What is toe-in? What is its function?

10. What is turning radius? What is its function?

11. What causes the most front-end service problems?

12. Why is it poor practice to attempt to correct one front-end angle?

13. What three suggestions are given to test front-end alignment?

14. What suggestions are given for testing a power-steering unit?

Self-Check Test

TRUE-FALSE

1. The steering worm gear is securely splined to the pitman arm.

2. The drag link is connected to the steering arm.

3. Power steering uses the vacuum obtained from the intake manifold to assist the driver in turning the front wheels.

4. Caster causes the car to steer easier.

5. Camber aligns the front wheels in the direction in which the car is moving.

6. Steering axis inclination is provided to offset the effects of caster.

7. Toe-in is provided to offset the compression of the steering linkage parts.

8. Turning radius is required to offset camber.

MULTIPLE CHOICE

1. Which of the following is *not* a part of the steering gear mechanism: a) pitman arm; b) tie rod; c) connecting rod; d) drag link?

2. Which of the following is *not* an angle of front-end geometry: a) caster; b) steering axis inclination; c) turning radius; d) tie-rod angle?

COMPLETION

1. Turning the steering wheel turns the steering shaft to which a _____ _____ is attached within the steering gear box.

2. A _____ _____, connected to the pitman arm, transmits the steering power to the tie rod.

3. Two power-steering types are in common use: a _____ _____ _____ and a _____ _____ _____ attached to the steering gear box.

4. _____ is a built-in angle which causes the front wheels to align themselves in the direction in which the car is moving.

5. _____ is the angle between a vertical line and a line drawn through the center of the wheel.

6. _____ _____ _____ is the outward tilt of the bottom of the steering knuckle support toward the wheel.

7. _____ is the difference between the front and rear of the front tires measured at spindle height.

8. _____ _____ causes the inside wheel to turn sharper on a curve.

MATCHING

1. Caster
2. Camber
3. Steering axis inclination
4. Toe-in

a. Slant of the wheel outward at the top

b. Slant of the steering knuckle support inward at the top

c. Slant of the wheel inward at the front

d. Slant of the steering knuckle support forward at the bottom

Chapter | **17**

Frame and Wheel Suspension

The frame of the car, which supports the engine, body, and running gear, is made of two hollow "box-like" sections of steel. Cross braces keep the frame from twisting when the car strikes a bump in the road. Since 1960, some cars have been built using the body in place of the conventional frame, calling it "Unibody" construction. This design lowers the body and eliminates many bolts and joints. A short frame supports the engine and front suspension.

In unit construction, the body is built strong enough so that a conventional frame is not needed. Courtesy American Motors Corporation.

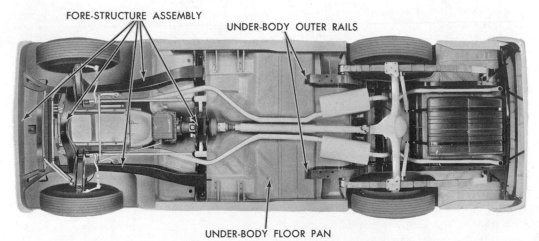

FORE-STRUCTURE ASSEMBLY

UNDER-BODY OUTER RAILS

UNDER-BODY FLOOR PAN

In "Unibody" construction, the body is the structural member and a short frame extends from the front to support the engine. Courtesy Plymouth Division, Chrysler Corporation.

464

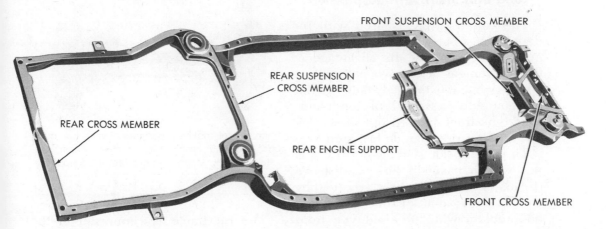

FRONT SUSPENSION CROSS MEMBER

REAR SUSPENSION CROSS MEMBER

REAR CROSS MEMBER

REAR ENGINE SUPPORT

FRONT CROSS MEMBER

The frame is composed of boxlike steel side rails for strength and rigidity. Courtesy Cadillac Motor Division, General Motors Corporation.

Sound control is accomplished in the Maverick, which is of unit construction, by the application of numerous acoustical pads and spray-on sound deadeners. Courtesy Ford Motor Company.

The wheel suspensions are mounted to the frame by springs which absorb road shock. The spring's bounce is snubbed by hydraulically operated shock absorbers. Each front wheel is independently mounted so that either one may move up or down without causing a corresponding body movement. Independent front wheel suspensions cushion road shocks to a considerable degree.

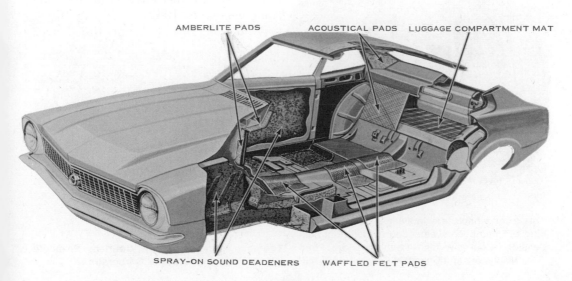

AMBERLITE PADS   ACOUSTICAL PADS   LUGGAGE COMPARTMENT MAT

SPRAY-ON SOUND DEADENERS   WAFFLED FELT PADS

465

Long and Short Arm Suspension

The coiled spring is used with independent front wheel suspension on most passenger cars. Its advantage is that movement of one wheel transfers less movement to the body than did the movement of a wheel of the older, solid-type front axle. Also, coil springs give a softer ride than do leaf springs.

To prevent side scuffing of tires, it is necessary to maintain the same distance (tread) between the tires where they contact the road at all times. This was no problem with the rigid-type front axle of yesteryear because the front wheels were solidly connected. However, with independent front wheel suspension, the tread has to be maintained by tilting the bouncing wheel outward at the bottom. This is done by using a shorter upper control arm, which turns about a shorter radius than does the longer, lower arm.

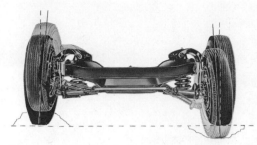

Each wheel moves independently of the other and, therefore, very little shock is transmitted to the body. Courtesy Ford Motor Company.

Springs

The car frame is connected to the axles by springs to absorb road shocks. Two basic types of springs are in common use: leaf and coil. Torsion bars and air-suspension systems replace springs in some cars.

The *leaf spring* is composed of strips of spring steel held together by means of a center bolt. The main leaf has an eye rolled in each end through which the bolts are inserted to attach the spring ends to the frame of the car. The spring is called *semi-elliptic* due to its shape. Single-leaf springs have been used on some cars since 1962.

Rebound clips prevent the leaves

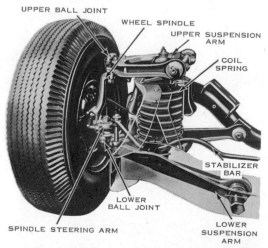

The front wheels are individually sprung. The king pin has been superseded by ball-joint suspension. Courtesy John Bean Division, Food Machinery and Chemical Corporation.

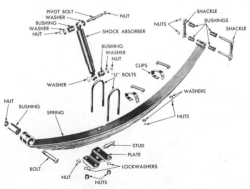

The leaf spring assembly. Courtesy Plymouth Division, Chrysler Corporation.

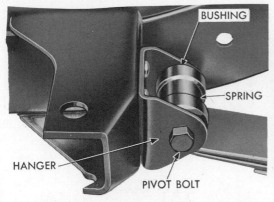

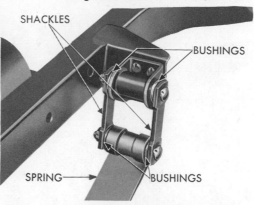

The front of the spring is attached to the frame by a hanger. Courtesy Plymouth Division, Chrysler Corporation.

The rear of the spring is attached by means of a shackle. Courtesy Plymouth Division, Chrysler Corporation.

from separating when the spring rebounds. Usually a metallic sheathing keeps out moisture and dirt while retaining the lubricant. The leaves are separated by pads to minimize noise and hold lubricant.

One end of a leaf spring is attached to the car frame by means of a *hanger,* the other by a *shackle.* The shackle allows the rear end of the spring to move back and forth because its length changes under flexing. Rubber bushings are used between the spring and the hanger to minimize noise.

Coil springs, being longer, provide a softer ride. Coil springs require tracking bars when used to support the rear of a vehicle to prevent the body from sliding sideways. Rubber bumpers prevent the car frame from bottoming on the axle from an unusual bounce.

Torsion bars are replacing springs in many front-end applications. Spring-steel bars, mounted so as to twist under load, return to their original shape when the load is removed. They take up less space than the conventional coil spring and are just as resilient.

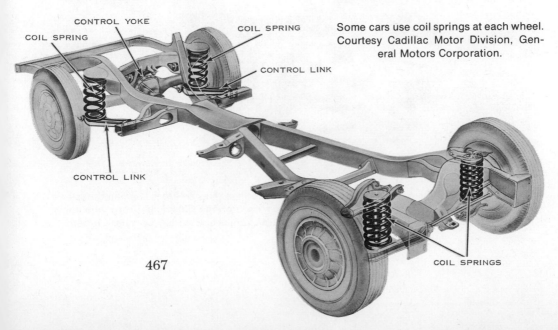

Some cars use coil springs at each wheel. Courtesy Cadillac Motor Division, General Motors Corporation.

467

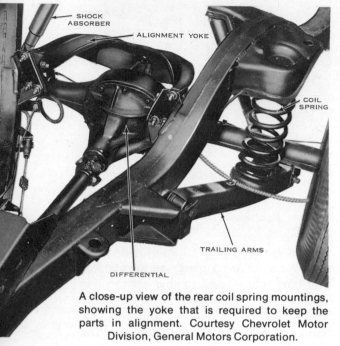

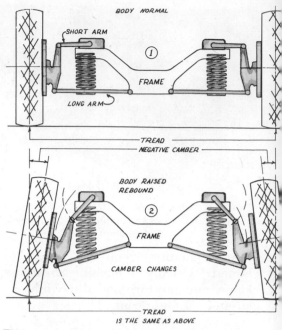

A close-up view of the rear coil spring mountings, showing the yoke that is required to keep the parts in alignment. Courtesy Chevrolet Motor Division, General Motors Corporation.

The same road tread must be maintained even when the wheels are bouncing; otherwise, side scuffing results. The long and short arm suspension provides for a decrease in camber when the body raises so that the tread remains the same.

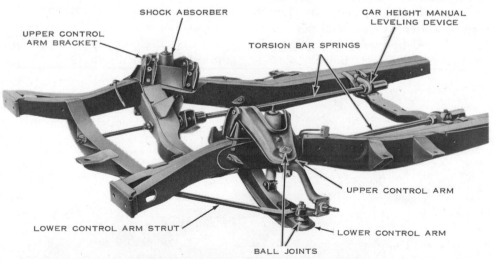

A set of torsion bars takes the place of the front springs. This set-up is used on Chrysler products and is similar to the torsion bar system used on the Oldsmobile Toronado and the Cadillac Eldorado, which are front-wheel drive vehicles. Courtesy Chrysler Corporation.

Shock Absorbers

Shock absorbers are hydraulic restricting devices limiting the speed of spring action. The smoothest ride is obtained with soft springs. However, the rebounce is intensified with them; therefore shock absorbers are needed to restrict the rate of spring action. They do this by moving a piston which forces fluid through a small hole. By varying the hole size in manufacture, the rate of rebound can be closely controlled.

Most shock absorbers are tubular in shape, and have one end fastened to the car frame and the other end to the wheel support. As the wheel moves up, liquid is compressed in a cylinder. It leaves by a small calibrated hole (orifice) which restricts the rate of spring movement. A "pop-off" valve is incorporated to permit large quantities of liquid to be moved quickly from the cylinder under strong impact, as might occur from the wheel striking a deep hole or rut in the road. On the rebound, the pop-off valve closes, so the fluid has to return through the orifice, thus snubbing the rebound more than the bounce.

Stabilizers

To minimize body sway on curves, all modern cars have a stabilizer for linking the two front springs together. Rolling of the car body twists the bar; this applies opposing forces to both springs, tending to prevent too great a difference in spring action. No stabilizer bar is required in the rear because the rear shocks are straddle mounted with the tops angled in toward the center of the car, which tends to oppose body sway on curves.

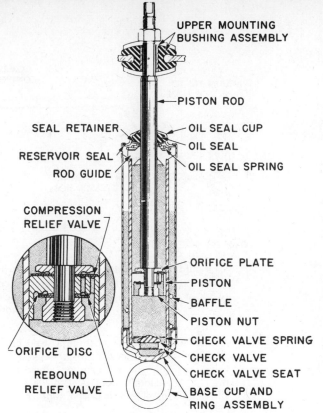

Section through a direct-action type shock absorber. Courtesy Chevrolet Motor Division, General Motors Corporation.

Automatic Level Control System

This system automatically maintains a constant rear vehicle height, regardless of load changes up to 500 lbs. over the rear axle. The system consists of an air compressor, reservoir tank, pressure regulator, height control valve, and two special shock absorbers.

The compressor is a two-stage, vacuum-actuated unit, taking its vacuum supply from the engine. The high-pressure output from the compressor is directed to a reservoir, where it is stored at 125 psi. A height control valve, mounted on the frame, "senses" a change in the attitude (or position) of the rear of the body, and this action opens the intake valve to admit air pressure to the rear shock absorbers. When

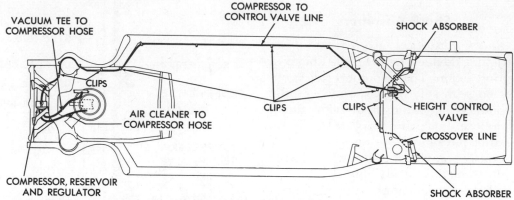

COMPRESSOR TO
CONTROL VALVE LINE

VACUUM TEE TO
COMPRESSOR HOSE

SHOCK ABSORBER

CLIPS

AIR CLEANER TO
COMPRESSOR HOSE

CLIPS

CLIPS

HEIGHT CONTROL
VALVE

CROSSOVER LINE

COMPRESSOR, RESERVOIR
AND REGULATOR

SHOCK ABSORBER

The automatic level control system keeps the rear of the vehicle at a constant height. It does this by means of a vacuum-driven air compressor, and a height control valve, which work in conjunction with two special shock absorbers. Courtesy Buick Motor Division, General Motors Corporation.

The special Superlift shock absorbers used on the rear of the vehicle contain an air chamber which extends the shock absorber when air pressure is directed into it. Courtesy Buick Motor Division, General Motors Corporation.

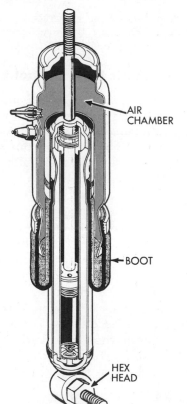

AIR CHAMBER

BOOT

HEX HEAD

the rear of the vehicle reaches its designed level, the intake valve shuts off. When the load is removed, the over-travel lever is forced down, causing the internal arm to open the exhaust valve, which bleeds air from the shock absorbers to lower the rear of the car.

Service Procedures

Shock absorbers are now made in sealed units. If defective, they cannot be repaired; therefore the entire unit must be replaced. Springs seldom require replacement except when a leaf breaks, which is always caused by a defective shock absorber. Spring noises require lubrication or replacement of the leaf pads. Infrequently, coil spring sag requires shimming to re-establish the correct height of the front end.

Troubleshooting

The best test of spring and shock absorber action is to bounce each corner of the car to compare the snubbing action of each shock absorber.

470

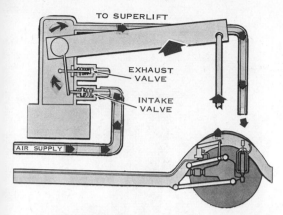

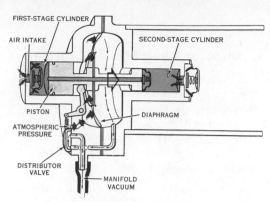

This illustration shows the action of the height-control valve when the rear of the vehicle is depressed. The opened intake valve directs air pressure to the shock absorber, causing it to extend, thus leveling the body. Courtesy Buick Motor Division, General Motors Corporation.

The air pump contains a diaphragm which is actuated by engine vacuum. The diaphragm, in turn, moves a piston back and forth to draw in and compress air. In this drawing, the piston is moving to the right under the influence of engine vacuum, drawing air into the first-stage cylinder. Courtesy Buick Motor Division, General Motors Corporation.

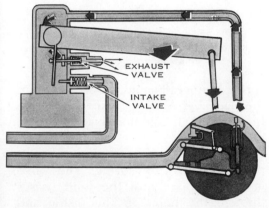

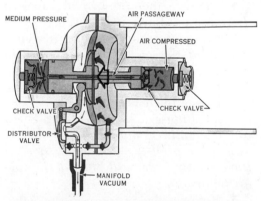

When the weight is removed, the exhaust valve is opened; air is bled from the shock absorber to return the body to the proper height. Courtesy Buick Motor Division, General Motors Corporation.

In this illustration, the piston is moving to the left, compressing the air trapped in the first-stage cylinder and forcing it to move into the second-stage cylinder through the air passageway in the piston. Courtesy Buick Motor Division, General Motors Corporation.

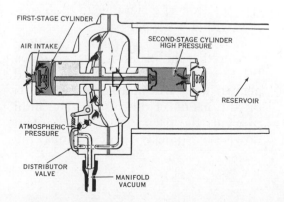

The piston is moving to the right, compressing the air in the second-stage cylinder and forcing it into the reservoir. Courtesy Buick Motor Division, General Motors Corporation.

471

Disassembling Shock Absorbers

Modern shock absorbers cannot be taken apart for service. It is suggested, therefore, that some older models be secured which can be disassembled to study the theory of operation.

Tools and Equipment

Double action, single action, and direct action shock absorber units; ratchet; ¾ inch socket; hinge handle; screwdriver; 10 inch pipe wrench; spanner; shock absorber fluid.

PROCEDURE

SINGLE ACTION

1. Remove the screws and cover to drain the fluid into a clean can.

2. Mount the shock absorber in a vise.

3. Hold the control arm in the *up* position to prevent premature release of the piston.

4. Lower the control arm slowly until the operating cam just releases the piston. **Caution:** *Do not allow the control arm to drop all the way or the heel of the operating cam will bind on the side of the piston.*

5. Remove the piston and the valve from inside of the piston.

6. Remove the spring from the cylinder.

7. Remove the adjustment screw from the side of the housing. Probe the passage from the cylinder to the reservoir with fine copper wire.

8. Inspect for principle of operation:
• Note that the piston is pushed down by the control arm cam and forced against the valve and spring which is on the inside of the piston. The fluid prevents the piston from being driven down too quickly which snubs the

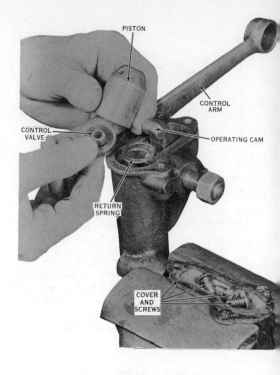

Single-action shock absorber. This type is not in current use, but is ideal for studying the principles of shock absorber operation.

spring bounce. The adjustment valve in the body bypasses the excess pressure from under the piston back into the reservoir.
• When the arm returns, the piston is pushed up by the spring. The valve is sucked open and the fluid passes through the holes in the piston and valve. The upstroke does no snubbing.

9. Replace the spring, valve, and piston assembly.

10. Refill with shock absorber fluid while operating the arm to remove air bubbles.

11. Replace the cover using a new gasket.

12. Close the adjusting screw and open it ½ turn for front springs and ¾ turn for rear springs.

13. Test for resistance to action.

472

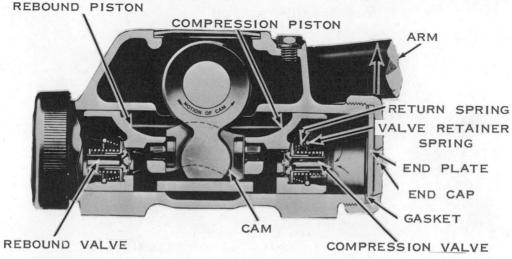

REBOUND PISTON

COMPRESSION PISTON

ARM

RETURN SPRING

VALVE RETAINER SPRING

END PLATE

END CAP

GASKET

CAM

REBOUND VALVE

COMPRESSION VALVE

Double-action shock absorber on compression. Courtesy Oldsmobile Division, General Motors Corporation.

DOUBLE ACTION

1. Remove the filler plug and drain the fluid.

2. Mount the shock absorber in a vise.

3. Pull the shock arm up and remove the left end cap.

4. Remove the valve lock ring and valve.

5. Push the control arm down and remove the right end cap.

6. Remove the valve lock ring and valve.

7. Replace the valve assembly loosely in each piston to note the action:

• COMPRESSION STROKE: The control arm is forced up by the wheel striking a bump. The control arm forces the piston to the right, creating pressure in the cylinder and forcing the intake part of the compression valve to seat tightly. Normal pressures force the fluid through the bleed holes. Excess pressure forces the compression valve open which lets the fluid return to the reservoir. This snubs the action of the spring on the bounce.

• REBOUND STROKE: The control arm is forced down by the returning wheel. The control arm forces the piston to the left, creating pressure in the left cylinder, forcing the intake part of the rebound valve to seat tightly. Pressure on the fluid forces it through the bleed holes. Excessive pressure forces the rebound valve to open and let the fluid return to the reservoir. This snubs the rebound action of the spring.

8. Replace the valves and lock rings.

9. Replace the end caps using new gaskets.

10. Fill the reservoir with shock absorber fluid. Work the arm up and down several times to remove trapped air.

11. Test for resistance to action.

DIRECT ACTION SHOCK ABSORBER

1. Clamp one ring in a vise.

2. Extend the shock absorber and insert a spanner wrench in the dust shield. Unscrew the piston rod guide and then lift off the dust cover.

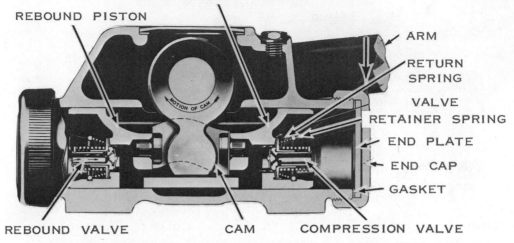

COMPRESSION PISTON

REBOUND PISTON

ARM

RETURN SPRING

VALVE
RETAINER SPRING

END PLATE

END CAP

GASKET

MOTION OF CAM

REBOUND VALVE   CAM   COMPRESSION VALVE

Double-action shock absorber on the rebound. Courtesy Oldsmobile Division, General Motors Corporation.

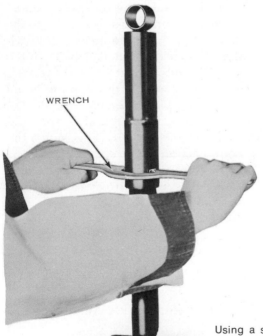

WRENCH

Using a spanner wrench to unscrew the piston rod guide and seal. Courtesy Dodge Division, Chrysler Corporation.

3. Remove the compression valve and cage assembly from the cylinder base.

4. Remove the piston rod nut.

5. Remove the piston and washers. Note the relationship of parts so that you can reassemble them properly.

6. Assemble the parts loosely to note the action:

• COMPRESSION STROKE: The bounce of the wheel compresses the shock absorber, and the valve in the piston permits a small amount of fluid to return to the upper chamber. Most of the fluid is forced through the lower compression valve to the reservoir.

• REBOUND STROKE: The return of the wheel expands the shock absorber, placing compression on top of the piston. The fluid must return through the small holes in the piston which are further restricted by the disc valve being forced against the piston holes. Snubbing action is accomplished on both bounce and rebound.

7. Replace the compression valve and cage assembly.

8. Assemble the piston and valves on the piston rod.

9. Fill the cylinder tube with the correct amount of shock absorber fluid.

10. Add the remaining fluid to the reservoir.

11. Assemble the dust shield and reservoir tube. Tighten the piston rod guide.

12. Test for resistance to action.

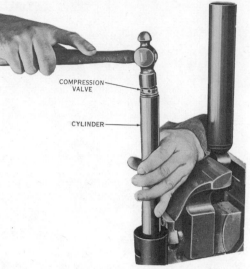

Replacing the compression valve in the cylinder. Courtesy Plymouth Division, Chrysler Corporation.

The rear suspension of this rear-engine race machine is similar in design to the independent front suspension of most automobiles.

475

CHECK YOUR KNOWLEDGE

1. How is a wheel suspended from the frame?
2. What is the advantage of an independently mounted front wheel?
3. How is the tread maintained with an independently mounted front wheel?
4. How is the rear axle suspended from the frame?
5. What is a semi-elliptic spring?
6. What is the difference between a hanger and a shackle?
7. Why have coil springs replaced leaf springs in most modern automobiles?
8. What advantage do torsion bars have over springs?
9. How is a car with air suspension kept level with uneven loading?
10. What is the duty of a shock absorber?
11. On what principle does a shock absorber work?
12. What is the purpose of the pop-off valve?
13. What is the purpose of a stabilizer bar? How does it function?
14. What causes a broken spring?
15. What test is suggested for spring and shock absorber action?

Self-Check Test

TRUE-FALSE

1. The shock absorber absorbs road shocks.
2. The leaf spring is universally used with independent front wheel suspension.
3. Front wheel tread is maintained by using a short upper control arm.
4. Leaf-type springs, being longer, provide a softer ride.
5. The main advantage of a torsion bar is that it provides a softer ride than a spring.
6. The pop-off valve opens on a rebound.
7. On many applications, the stabilizer is fastened to the two shock absorber arms.
8. Shock absorbers cannot be repaired in the field.
9. A broken spring is generally caused by a defective shock absorber.

MULTIPLE CHOICE

1. Which of the following is *not* true of an independent front wheel suspension: a) short and long arm suspension; b) solid-type front axle; c) coil spring; d) shock absorber?
2. Which of the following is *not* a part of a leaf spring mounting: a) semi-elliptic; b) hanger; c) shackle; d) tracking bar?
3. Which of the following is *not* a part of a coil spring mounting: a) stabilizer; b) shock absorber; c) shackle; d) tracking bar?

COMPLETION

1. Wheel suspensions are mounted to the frame by _____ which absorb road shock.
2. With independent front wheel suspension, the _____ has to be maintained by tilting the bouncing wheel outward at the bottom.
3. The leaf-type spring, in common use, is called _____ due to its shape.
4. The _____ allows the rear end of a leaf-type spring to move back and forth as its length changes under flexing.
5. Coil springs require _____ _____ when used to support the rear of a vehicle which prevents the body from sliding sideways.
6. _____ _____ are hydraulic restricting devices which limit the rate of spring action.
7. A _____ _____ is incorporated in a shock absorber so that large quantities of fluid may be moved quickly from the cylinder under a strong impact.

MATCHING

1. Independent front wheel suspension	a. Hydraulic restricting devices
2. Leaf spring	b. Spring-steel rods
3. Torsion bars	c. Semi-elliptic
4. Shock absorber	d. Short and long arm suspension

Chapter 18

Brakes

Brakes are friction devices that convert the *kinetic energy* of car motion into *heat*. The brake lining is made of an asbestos composition which has exceptional friction developing characteristics and is also heat resistant. Pressure on the brake pedal is hydraulically applied to force the brake linings into firm contact with the brake drums.

Power brakes have vacuum-assisting devices which help stop the car. Vacuum is obtained from the engine, and the brake pedal operates a control valve to regulate the amount so that the driver retains the "feel" of stopping the car.

Parking brakes are separate from the regular foot-braking system. They are designed to keep the car from rolling.

This brake testing machine is used to determine the ability of brake lining to withstand heat. Courtesy Raybestos Division, Raybestos-Manhattan, Inc.

This set of brake linings couldn't take it and burst into flame. This is evidence that brakes change kinetic energy into heat. This abuse is the equivalent of one stop of a 5,000 pound car traveling at 100 mph, with all the energy being absorbed by one brake. Courtesy Raybestos Division, Raybestos-Manhattan, Inc.

Fins are used around some brake drums to increase the heat dissipating surface. Courtesy Buick Motor Division, General Motors Corporation.

Should the service brakes fail, the parking brakes may be used to stop the car, but they are not designed for this purpose. Many automatic-transmission-equipped cars contain a notched gear and pawl in the transmission which keeps the car from moving after engagement.

Hydraulic Brake System

Hydraulic brakes transmit pressure of the driver's foot to each brake shoe through tubes containing fluid. The column of fluid moves along tubing to each of the four wheels where it transmits its force to pistons within cylinders at each wheel. Because liquids are not compressible, the force is transmitted equally to each brake shoe.

Liquids follow the law stated by Blaise Pascal (France): "Pressure exerted on any part of a confined liquid is transmitted equally in all directions,

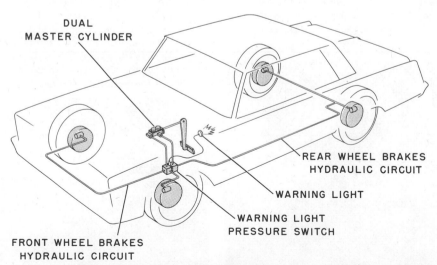

DUAL MASTER CYLINDER

REAR WHEEL BRAKES HYDRAULIC CIRCUIT

WARNING LIGHT

WARNING LIGHT PRESSURE SWITCH

FRONT WHEEL BRAKES HYDRAULIC CIRCUIT

The hydraulic brake system has tubing leading to all four wheels in order to transmit the pressure equally to each brake. For safety, the system is split into two circuits—one for the front wheels and one for the rear. Courtesy Chrysler Corporation.

acts with equal force on equal surfaces, and at right angles to the surfaces." One important phrase of Pascal's law, ". . . acts with equal force on equal surfaces . . ." means that if the area of the surfaces is unequal, the forces will be unequal. Engineers use this fact to apply different pressures to parts of the hydraulic braking system. Because the weight of the car shifts forward on quick stops, larger pistons (with greater area) are used on the front wheels, so that about 55% of the braking effort is applied to the front.

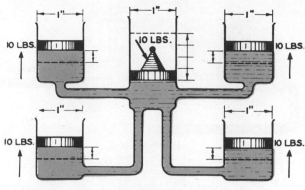

In the automobile hydraulic brake system, the pressure applied to the master cylinder piston is transmitted equally to each wheel cylinder, provided it has the same area. Courtesy Barrett Equipment Company.

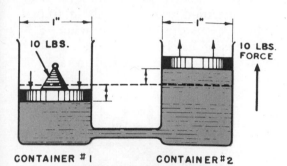

If a pressure of 10 pounds is placed on the piston in container 1, then the piston in container 2 will be able to lift a 10-pound weight a distance equal to the distance moved by the first piston. No change of force or distance is indicated in this drawing—only a change in direction. Courtesy Barrett Equipment Company.

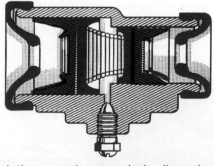

This is the way engineers use hydraulics as *levers*. Notice that the piston at the right is smaller than the one at the left so that unequal forces can be applied to the brake shoes. Courtesy American Brakeblok Division, American Brake Shoes Company.

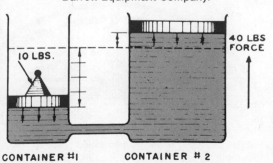

In this drawing, the areas of the containers are unequal, being in the ratio of 4 to 1. If a 10-pound pressure is applied to the piston in container 1, it will be able to push up a 40-pound weight in container 2. But notice that it moves up only one-fourth the distance. Do you see the relationship between hydraulic pressures and mechanical levers, discussed in Chapter 1, Exploring Power Mechanics? Courtesy Barrett Equipment Company.

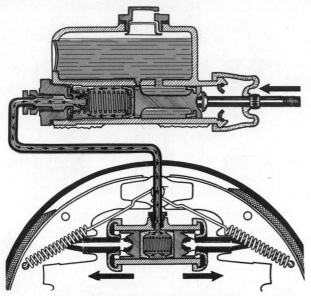

The *master cylinder,* operated by the brake pedal, contains a piston which forces the fluid into the lines. A reservoir is mounted above the master cylinder to furnish fluid lost by leakage or to compensate for changes in quantity due to expansion and contraction from temperature variations.

Releasing pedal pressure allows the return spring to force the piston back to its original position, causing a momentary vacuum ahead of it. Brake fluid is drawn from the reservoir, through holes in the piston, to satisfy the vacuum.

A *check valve* in front of the master cylinder seals the system under a positive sustained pressure of about 10 psi, which keeps the lips of the wheel cylinder cups firmly against the cylinder walls to prevent leakage and entrance of air.

On application of the brake pedal, the master cylinder plunger moves forward, forcing the fluid into the lines. The fluid forces the pistons of each wheel cylinder outward, applying pressure to the brake shoes. Courtesy Pontiac Motor Division, General Motors Corporation.

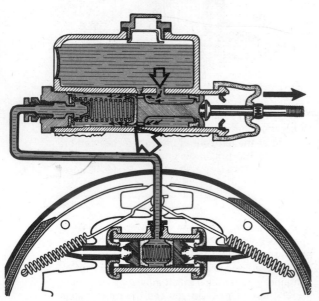

On the return stroke of the piston, fluid enters the system by moving past the lips of the rubber cup. Courtesy Pontiac Motor Division, General Motors Corporation.

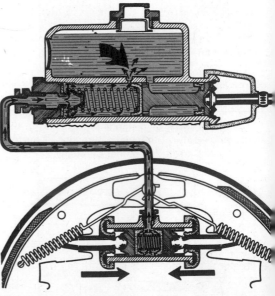

Excess pressure is allowed to bleed back to the reservoir through the compensating port. Courtesy Pontiac Motor Division, General Motors Corporation.

DUAL MASTER CYLINDER

In the interest of safety, a dual master cylinder, in conjunction with a split hydraulic braking system, was introduced on some 1962 models and has been standard equipment since 1967. The master cylinder has two separate units — one piston assembly to actuate the front wheel brakes and the other for the rear wheel brakes. The resulting dual braking system is a safety feature which prevents total brake failure in the event of a hydraulic leak. Also, in the interest of safety, motor vehicle manufacturers have redesigned their stop light systems by removing the usual pressure-sensitive switch from the hydraulic line and replacing it with a mechanical switch, actuated by the brake pedal linkage.

Another change has been in the use of a flexible rubber seal to cover the fluid in the master cylinder reservoir. This keeps dirt and moisture out of the system. The seal is flexible enough to follow the level of the fluid which can flow unrestricted back and forth between the lines and reservoir.

This dual master cylinder is standard equipment on all passenger cars. It contains two separate cylinders — one to actuate the front wheel brakes and the other for the rear wheel brakes. The power piston at the left assists the driver in applying the brakes. Courtesy Oldsmobile Division, General Motors Corporation.

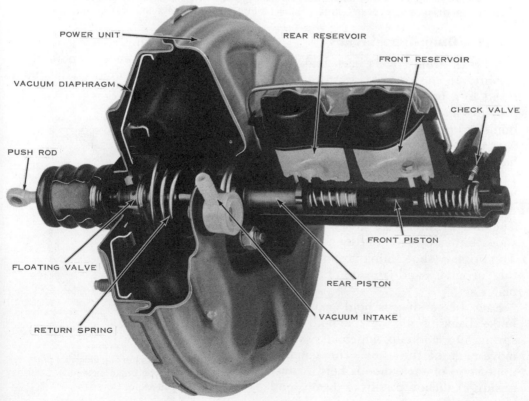

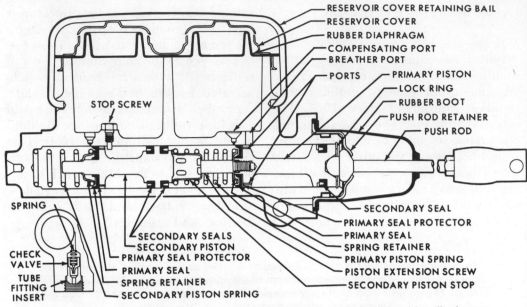

Diagram labels (top illustration):

RESERVOIR COVER RETAINING BAIL
RESERVOIR COVER
RUBBER DIAPHRAGM
COMPENSATING PORT
BREATHER PORT
PORTS
PRIMARY PISTON
LOCK RING
RUBBER BOOT
PUSH ROD RETAINER
PUSH ROD

STOP SCREW

SECONDARY SEAL
PRIMARY SEAL PROTECTOR
PRIMARY SEAL
SPRING RETAINER
PRIMARY PISTON SPRING
PISTON EXTENSION SCREW
SECONDARY PISTON STOP

SPRING

CHECK VALVE
TUBE FITTING INSERT

SECONDARY SEALS
SECONDARY PISTON
PRIMARY SEAL PROTECTOR
PRIMARY SEAL
SPRING RETAINER
SECONDARY PISTON SPRING

This is a sectioned view through a dual master cylinder. Note the flexible rubber diaphragm under the reservoir cover. Courtesy Buick Motor Division, General Motors Corporation.

Drum-Type Brakes

A brake drum covers each brake assembly. It consists of a cast-iron rim fused to a pressed steel disc. The rim provides an ideal braking surface. Some brake drums are made of cast aluminum, with a cast-iron liner; also, some drums have ribs for better heat dissipation.

The brake assembly at each wheel has two shoes: a primary brake shoe for the front and a secondary for the rear. The brake linings are attached to the shoes either by rivets or by adhesives. The primary shoe lining is shorter than the secondary and is made of different material.

Each brake shoe is held against the brake backing plate by a hold-down spring, pin, and cup, which allows free movement of the shoe. The notched upper end of each shoe is held against a single anchor pin by a heavy coil spring. An adjusting screw and spring connect the lower ends of both shoes and provide for a clearance adjustment with the brake drum.

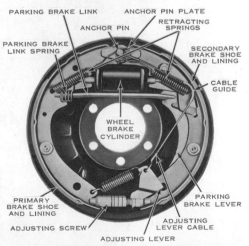

Diagram labels (rear brake assembly):

PARKING BRAKE LINK
ANCHOR PIN PLATE
ANCHOR PIN
RETRACTING SPRINGS
PARKING BRAKE LINK SPRING
SECONDARY BRAKE SHOE AND LINING
CABLE GUIDE
WHEEL BRAKE CYLINDER
PRIMARY BRAKE SHOE AND LINING
PARKING BRAKE LEVER
ADJUSTING SCREW
ADJUSTING LEVER CABLE
ADJUSTING LEVER

This illustration shows the placement of parts of a rear wheel, drum-type brake assembly. Courtesy Ford Motor Company.

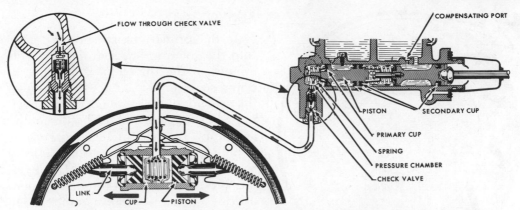

On application of the brake pedal in a dual master cylinder, the front piston moves forward, forcing the fluid into the front wheel lines. The fluid forces each front wheel cylinder piston outward to apply pressure to the brake shoes. The same action takes place at the rear piston, where the hydraulic fluid applies the rear wheel brakes. Courtesy Buick Motor Division, General Motors Corporation.

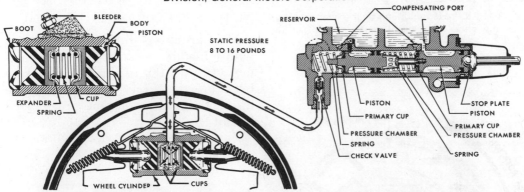

When the brakes are released, the brake shoe return springs force the fluid to return to the master cylinder past the check valve. This valve is designed to maintain a static pressure of 8–16 psi for drum-type brakes, which keeps the lips of the rubber cups tightly against the walls of the cylinders to prevent leaks. The check valve is not used on a master cylinder for disc brakes. Courtesy Buick Motor Division, General Motors Corporation.

SELF-ENERGIZING ACTION

The hydraulic wheel cylinder, mounted on the brake backing plate between the upper ends of the brake shoes, forces the shoes against the brake drum when the service brakes are applied. When the brake shoes contact the rotating drum, they move in the direction of drum rotation until one shoe is stopped by the anchor pin and the other shoe is stopped through the connecting adjusting screw. Frictional force between the drum and the shoe lining would tend to make each shoe rotate outward, around its anchor point, but the drum itself prevents this movement. As a result, the shoes contact the drum with more force than was originally applied. This use of frictional forces, to increase the pressure of the shoes against the drum, is called *self-energizing action*.

483

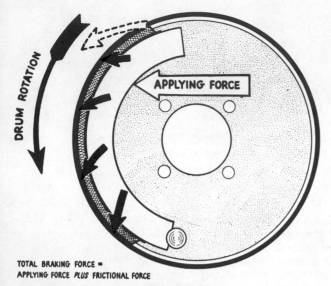

TOTAL BRAKING FORCE =
APPLYING FORCE *PLUS* FRICTIONAL FORCE

Braking force is multiplied by the wrap-in action of the shoe. Courtesy Pontiac Motor Division, General Motors Corporation.

SERVO ACTION

As the primary brake shoe is forced into the rotating brake drum, it travels around in the direction of rotation. In doing so, it applies a force to the end of the secondary shoe through the connecting adjusting screw at the bottom of the assembly. Because the secondary shoe is held firmly at the top end by a fixed anchor pin, it cannot turn. However, the force imparted to it through the connecting adjusting screw forces it to wedge tighter into the drum. Utilization of the force in one shoe to apply pressure to the opposite brake shoe is called *servo action*.

AUTOMATIC BRAKE ADJUSTERS

Most drum-type brakes are equipped with self-adjusting devices, which maintain (1) a constant operating clearance between the brake linings and the drums and (2) a constant brake pedal height.

The self-adjusting devices operate

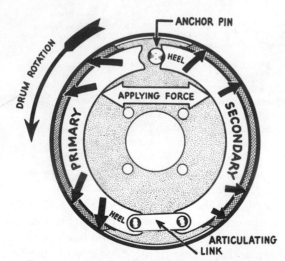

By connecting the primary to the secondary shoe with an articulating link, the wrap-in force generated in the primary shoe is directed to the end of the secondary shoe, forcing it into tighter contact with the brake drum. Courtesy Pontiac Motor Division, General Motors Corporation.

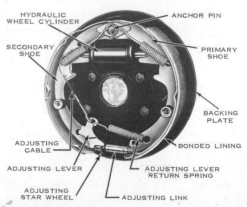

Automatic adjusting devices are standard equipment. They maintain a constant brake pedal height by making an adjustment each time the brakes are applied while the vehicle is moving in reverse. Courtesy Chrysler Corporation.

484

whenever the brakes are applied while the vehicle is moving in reverse. A cable, lever, and return spring arrangement actuates a star wheel on the adjusting screw. During a reverse brake application, the outward movement of the secondary (rear) brake shoe raises the adjusting lever via the attached steel cable. Upon release of the brakes, the cable slackens, and the return spring pulls the adjusting lever against the star wheel to rotate the adjusting screw approximately 15°.

Normally, an adjusting action does not occur until the lining-to-drum clearance is sufficient for the lever to be lifted as described in the previous paragraph. With each reverse brake application, the self-adjuster's ratchet action spreads the lower ends of the brake shoes apart by about 0.0005" (½ thousandth of an inch). Eventually, the lining-to-drum clearance is reduced until there is insufficient movement of the secondary shoe to lift the adjusting lever to the next tooth of the star wheel.

Disc Brakes

Disc brakes have recently been introduced on American cars because they are virtually fadeproof. A typical installation is one with disc brakes on the front wheels and drum-type brakes on the rear. Some sports cars have disc brakes on all four wheels. Because of the difficulties of incorporating a good handbrake mechanism on a disc brake unit, drum type brakes are generally used on the rear wheels.

The disc brake assembly consists of a fixed caliper, a rotating disc, and a splash shield. Most calipers contain four pistons and two shoes and lining assem-

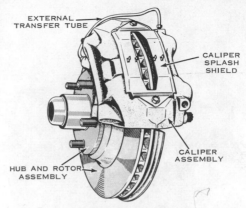

A disc brake caliper assembly is mounted over a rotor on the front wheels of many American automobiles. Courtesy Dodge Division, Chrysler Corporation.

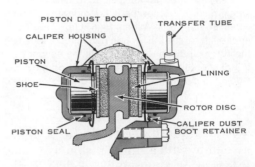

Cross-sectioned view of two pistons, showing how they apply opposing forces to the rotor. Courtesy Dodge Division, Chrysler Corporation.

blies, with the lining integrally molded to the steel shoes. A seal and dust boot are installed on each of the pistons, with a spring behind the piston. Machined surfaces within the caliper hold the shoes and linings in position.

The disc, which is mounted on the front wheel hub, generally has a series of air vent louvers for cooling. The caliper straddles the disc and mounts on a splash shield attached to the steering arm.

485

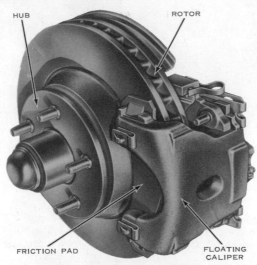

HUB   ROTOR

FRICTION PAD   FLOATING CALIPER

A disc brake assembly used on many late-model cars is designed about a floating caliper and a single piston. Friction pads are mounted on both sides of the rotor. When hydraulic pressure is applied, it forces the friction pad into contact with the rotor, and the reaction pulls the caliper over to apply pressure to the friction pad on the other side of the rotor. Courtesy Ford Division, Ford Motor Company.

A floating-caliper type of disc brake assembly with a single piston first came into use on some 1968 models. Brake linings on both sides of the rotor are actuated by the single piston because of the flexible mounting of the caliper.

A dual master cylinder and a power brake assembly are standard equipment on vehicles with disc brakes. This is because disc brakes are not self-energizing. The dual master cylinder, used on cars with disc brakes on the front wheels, has a large reservoir for fluid. This is because the pistons of these brakes are larger and more numerous than for drum brakes, and thus require more fluid. A residual check valve is required only in the section for the rear wheel brakes. No check valve is used in the section for disc brakes because the residual pressure would hold the brake lining pads against the rotating disc, resulting in excessive wear.

Along with dual hydraulic braking systems and combination disc-drum brake systems, proportioning valves and safety-type warning light switches have come into widespread use. In the event that one part of the hydraulic system fails, the resulting unequal hydraulic pressure at the light switch displaces a piston to turn on a dash warning light.

In some installations, a pressure-restricting valve is incorporated in the hydraulic lines to the rear wheels in order to limit rear wheel line pressure to about $2/3$ of that for the front wheel disc brake assemblies. This prevents premature rear wheel lockup and skidding. Also, a metering valve is sometimes installed in the line to the front

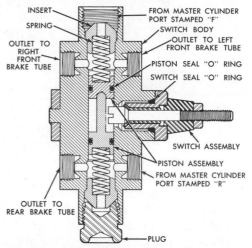

INSERT
SPRING
OUTLET TO RIGHT FRONT BRAKE TUBE
FROM MASTER CYLINDER PORT STAMPED "F"
SWITCH BODY
OUTLET TO LEFT FRONT BRAKE TUBE
PISTON SEAL "O" RING
SWITCH SEAL "O" RING
SWITCH ASSEMBLY
PISTON ASSEMBLY
FROM MASTER CYLINDER PORT STAMPED "R"
OUTLET TO REAR BRAKE TUBE
PLUG

Details of the warning light switch used in dual hydraulic systems. Whenever the pressure in one hydraulic circuit is less than in the other, the piston assembly is displaced toward the low-pressure side, making an electrical contact to light the dash warning lamp. Courtesy Dodge Division, Chrysler Corporation.

486

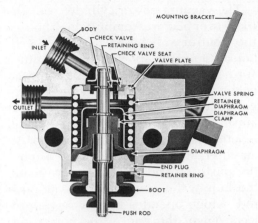

Details of the metering valve that is used on combination disc-drum braking systems. The push rod at the bottom of the unit must be pushed up when bleeding the front wheel brake lines. Courtesy Buick Motor Division, General Motors Corporation.

wheel disc brakes. This is to prevent front wheel brake application until about 125 psi pressure is built up in the hydraulic system. This is done so that the linings in the rear drum-type brakes contact the drums at the same time that the linings in the front disc-type brakes start applying pressure.

One advantage of disc-type brakes is that the braking pressure is toward the center of the caliper, clamping the disc between the linings with equal pressure from both sides. Any heat expansion of the disc is in a direction opposite to brake lining pressure; also, because the linings operate on a relatively small portion of the rotating disc, a greater portion is exposed to the air for more efficient heat dissipation. Therefore disc brakes are virtually fadeproof—that is, they will not fail because of heat.

The linings of disc brakes brush lightly against the rotating disc, even when the brakes are not applied; therefore no brake adjustment is required.

Hub end play is more critical with disc brakes and this must never exceed 0.003″; otherwise, hard cornering will knock back the linings so that the next brake application will require excessive pedal travel.

Power Brakes

Power brakes use engine manifold vacuum to assist the driver in applying the brakes. They consist of three basic elements: (1) a vacuum power cylinder, (2) a conventional hydraulic master cylinder, and (3) a control valve, attached to the brake pedal, which regulates the degree of brake application or release according to the amount of foot pressure. Power brakes are designed to reduce the pedal effort required to stop the vehicle. If failure should occur in the vacuum power system because of a stalled engine, the brakes could still be applied to stop the car, but by a greater effort.

Diaphragm-Type Power Brakes

Early power brakes (up to 1962) were designed to operate by a pressure differential created when atmospheric pressure was evacuated from one side of the power chamber. This forced the piston diaphragm to move and operate the hydraulic master cylinder. A vacuum reservoir was needed to store enough vacuum to allow up to three normal stops, even if the vacuum supply were depleted because of a stalled engine. When the driver depressed the brake pedal, he opened a valve which permitted engine vacuum to enter the front of the power cylinder. The resulting pressure differential moved the power piston forward.

VACUUM-SUSPENDED POWER BRAKES

Since 1963, all power brake units have been completely redesigned to minimize the amount of vacuum needed to operate the unit. In this new design, vacuum is admitted to both sides of the power piston in the released position. The power piston is held in the released position by the piston return spring. When the brake pedal is depressed, the floating valve is designed to admit air to the high-pressure side of the unit to apply the brakes. No vacuum reservoir is needed with the new design.

CONSTRUCTION

The unit is composed of two main sections: the vacuum power cylinder and the hydraulic master cylinder.

The vacuum power cylinder contains the power piston assembly which houses the control valve and reaction mechanism and the power piston return spring. The control valve is composed of the air valve and the floating control valve assembly. The reaction mechanism consists of a hydraulic piston reaction plate and a series of levers. An air filter element is assembled around the push rod and fills the cavity inside the hub of the power piston. The push rod, which operates the air valve, projects out of the end of the power cylinder housing through a boot. A vacuum check valve assembly is mounted in the front housing assembly for connection to the vacuum source.

Two separate fluid reservoirs are integrally cast with the master cylinder.

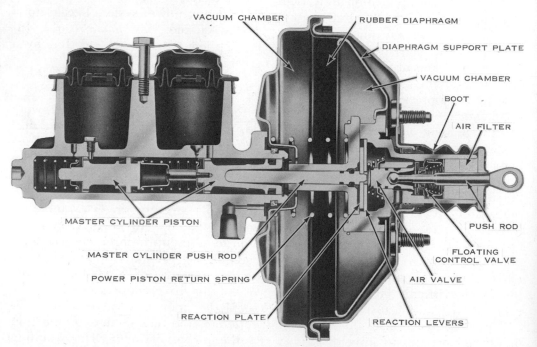

Parts which make up the power brake assembly. Courtesy Buick Motor Division, General Motors Corporation.

They supply fluid to the space between the primary and secondary cups on each hydraulic piston through a hole in the bottom of each reservoir. Connection is made to the wheel cylinders through the hydraulic outlets and a check valve.

PRINCIPLES OF OPERATION
RELEASED POSITION

In the released position, the air valve is seated on the floating control valve. The air, under atmospheric pressure, which enters through the filter element in the tube extension of the power piston, is shut off at the air valve. The floating control valve is held away from the valve seat in the power piston. Vacuum, which is present at all times in the space to the front of the power piston, is free to evacuate any existing air on the rear side of the power piston. This air is drawn through two small passages in the power piston, over the valve seat in the power piston, and then through the piston into the space at the front of the power piston. It is drawn through the check valve and then to the vacuum source.

In this position, there is vacuum on both sides of the power piston, which is held against the rear housing by the power piston return spring. At rest, the hydraulic reaction plate is held against the reaction retainer. The reaction levers are held back against the hydraulic reaction plate by the air-valve spring, which holds back so that its retaining ring rests against the power piston.

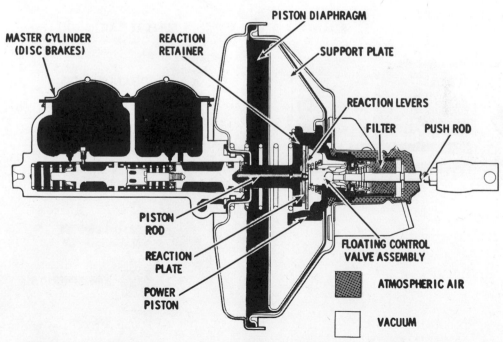

Details of the power brake assembly in the released position. Courtesy Oldsmobile Division, General Motors Corporation.

The floating control valve assembly is held against the air-valve seat by the floating control valve spring. In this position, the by-pass holes in the hydraulic master cylinder are open to the reservoir, and fluid can flow freely in either direction between the hydraulic cylinder and the fluid reservoir.

Residual pressure is maintained in the brake lines by the check valve and its spring.

APPLYING POSITION

As the pedal is depressed, the push rod carries the air valve away from the floating control valve. The floating control valve will follow until it is in contact with the raised seat in the power piston. When this occurs, the vacuum is shut off to the rear side of the power piston, and air, under atmospheric pressure, rushes through the air filter and travels past the seat of the air valve and through two passageways into the housing to the rear of the diaphragm.

Since there is still vacuum to the front side of the diaphragm, the force of the air at atmospheric pressure on the rear of the diaphragm forces the power piston to travel to the front. As the power piston travels to the front, the piston rod carries the master cylinder pistons into the bore of the master cylinder.

After the master cylinder piston primary seals pass the compensating port, hydraulic pressure starts to build up in the hydraulic system. As the pressure builds up on the end of the master cyl-

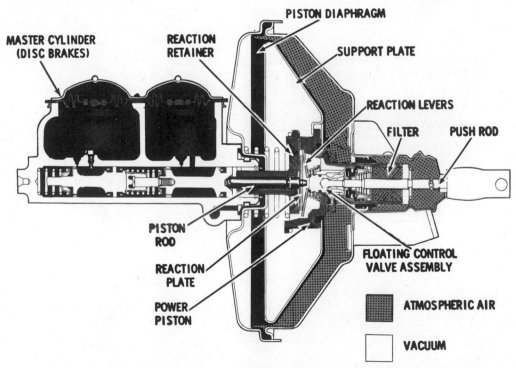

Details of the power brake assembly in the applied position. Courtesy Oldsmobile Division, General Motors Corporation.

inder pistons, the hydraulic reaction plate is moved off its seat on the reaction retainer and presses against the reaction levers. The levers, in turn, swing about their pivots and bear against the end of the air valve-push rod assembly. Since this reaction force is in direct proportion to the hydraulic pressure developed within the brake systems, the driver is able to maintain a "feel" of the degree of brake application attained.

Holding Position

When the desired pedal pressure is reached, the power piston moves to the front until the floating control valve, which is still seated on the power piston, again seats on the air valve. The power

brake will now remain stationary until pressure is either applied or released at the brake pedal.

Releasing Position

As the pressure at the pedal is released, the air-valve spring forces the air valve back until its snap ring rests against the power piston. As it returns, the air valve pushes the floating control valve off its seat on the power piston.

The air valve seating on the floating control valve has shut off the outside air source. When it lifts the floating control valve from its seat on the power piston, it opens the space at the rear of the power piston to the vacuum source.

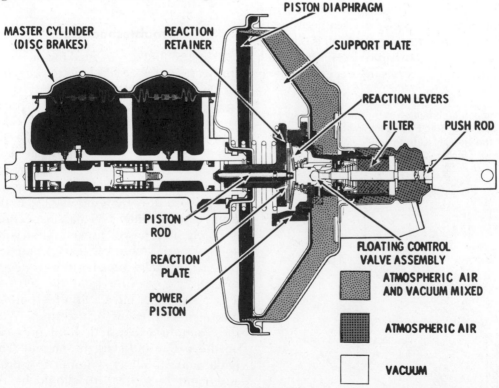

Details of the power brake assembly in the holding position. Courtesy Oldsmobile Division, General Motors Corporation.

491

Since both sides of the power piston are now under vacuum, the power piston return spring will return the piston to its released position against the rear housing. As the power piston is returned, the hydraulic master cylinder pistons move back, and the fluid from the wheel cylinders flows back into the master cylinder through the check valves.

Parking Brakes

Parking brakes must be separate from the foot-operated braking system; this is required by law in most states. They take three forms: (1) driveshaft brakes, (2) a set of cables which moves the rear-wheel brakes mechanically into contact with their drums, and (3) a notched gear and pawl which is engaged within an automatic transmission. Each of these systems has the necessary lever-

In most automatic-transmission-equipped cars, a pawl is shifted into engagement with a ring gear in the transmission for the parking brake. Courtesy Lincoln-Mercury Division, Ford Motor Company.

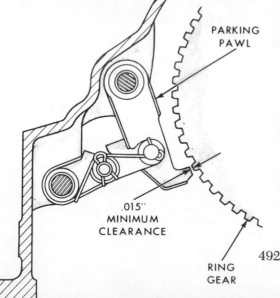

PARKING PAWL

.015"
MINIMUM
CLEARANCE

RING GEAR

age to lock the rear wheels, preventing the car from moving.

Service Procedures

A brake adjustment is required on older models. When the pedal goes to within two inches of the floorboard, the brake shoes should be repositioned. After about 20,000 miles, the brake linings require replacement. If this service is not performed in time, the brake drums will score and must be turned in a brake drum lathe. Occasionally, the hydraulic system will require overhauling. The need for this service is evidenced by leaking hydraulic cylinders, a spongy pedal, or loss of braking power.

Troubleshooting

Test the brakes by making a brake application at about 25 mph to see if the car stops evenly. If the pedal has a spongy feel, air is present in the lines. To check the hydraulic system for leaks, apply pedal pressure and hold it. If the pedal gradually sinks, the system is leaking.

The thickness of the brake lining can be checked only by removing the brake drum and making a visual inspection.

To check a power brake system for a spongy pedal, shut off the engine and pump the brake pedal a few times to exhaust all vacuum from the system. The pedal must have a firm feel; otherwise, air is present in the lines. With the vacuum exhausted, hold pressure on the pedal and start the engine. The pedal should fall away under foot pressure, and less pressure should be required to hold it in the applied position if the unit is operating properly.

Making a Minor Brake Adjustment

The two types of brake systems which can still be found on some of the older cars are: Bendix and Chrysler. Each type is adjusted in a different manner, but both have the same final result of moving the brake shoes closer to the brake drums so that very little pedal movement is required to force the linings into contact with the drums.

Self-adjusting brakes, which are installed on all new American mass-produced vehicles, require a minor adjustment only when new linings are installed. These brakes advance the adjusting screw one notch whenever the linings are worn enough and when the vehicle is stopped during reversing.

Tools and Equipment

Brakes to be adjusted; adjustable wrench; hydraulic brake fluid; jack; brake adjusting tool (Bendix).

PROCEDURE

① Jack up one front wheel and remove the wheel and drum assembly to check if there is enough lining left for safety and no hydraulic leaks. Replace the wheel and drum assembly if the mechanism is in good condition. Add hydraulic fluid to the master cylinder reservoir so that air will not be drawn into the lines during the adjustment.

BENDIX

② Remove the adjusting hole covers from the brake backing plates. Use a brake tool to expand the brake shoes at each wheel until the wheel can just be turned by hand. **Note:** *Moving the end of the tool upward expands the shoes.*

TO SPREAD SHOES ②

The drag must be equal at all four wheels. Back off each adjusting screw 16 notches and check for free operation. It is permissible to back the screw off one or two more notches to eliminate any remaining drag. Replace the adjusting hole covers.

493

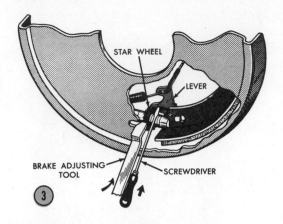

STAR WHEEL

LEVER

BRAKE ADJUSTING TOOL

SCREWDRIVER

③

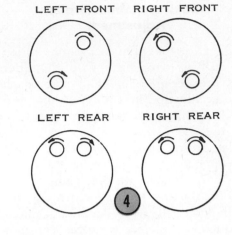

LEFT FRONT   RIGHT FRONT

LEFT REAR   RIGHT REAR

④

BENDIX AUTOMATIC-ADJUSTER TYPE BRAKES

③ These brakes will have to be adjusted only after a reline in order to position the shoes correctly. To do this, hold the adjusting lever away with a thin screwdriver. Tighten the adjusting screw until the wheel drags, and then back off the screw until the wheel turns freely. **Note:** *Moving the end of the tool downward expands the shoes.* **Caution:** *The movement of the adjusting tool is reversed in many 1969 models.* Drive the car on the road and make a few brake applications while in reverse gear which will position the shoes to the correct operating clearance.

CHRYSLER BRAKES THROUGH 1962

④ Since 1963 all Chrysler cars have been equipped with Bendix brakes. However, to service older cars you should be familiar with the older Chrysler brakes.

A cam adjusts the position of each shoe. To make the adjustment, turn the cam in the direction each wheel turns for making both front wheel shoe adjustments and for the front shoes of the rear wheels. Turn the two rear wheel, rear cams as shown. Back off each cam until the wheel is free. Pump the brake pedal several times and check to make sure that all of the wheels are free after adjusting the brakes of all four wheels. Release any dragging brake by backing off the adjustment slightly. Add hydraulic fluid to the master cylinder after each wheel adjustment to compensate for the fluid drawn into the lines.

Repairing a Hydraulic Cylinder

The operating parts of hydraulic cylinders are pistons and rubber cups

A corroded wheel cylinder piston—on the right—and a new one for comparison.

which move every time the brakes are applied, causing wear. Eventually, a fluid leak occurs. Wear is accelerated when a brake adjustment is neglected because the parts must move through longer strokes at each brake application.

Tools and Equipment

$^3/_8$, $^7/_{16}$, $^1/_2$, and $^9/_{16}$ inch combination end wrenches; master cylinder; wheel cylinder; brake fluid; bleeder hose; cylinder repair kits; hone; cleaning solvent; alcohol; 0.003 inch feeler gauge stock.

PROCEDURE

WHEEL CYLINDER

1. Pull the brake drum, and then remove the wheel cylinder from the backing plate. **Caution:** *Use two wrenches on brake lines to avoid twisting them.*

2. Remove the two dust covers, piston, rubber cups, and the spring.

3. Clean all parts in alcohol.

4. Hone the cylinder to remove pits and scores. Clean the cylinder with soap and water to remove abrasive particles and wipe it clean with a rag. A second cleaning in alcohol is required to remove all traces of soap and water. **Caution:** *Wash your hands with soap and water*

to remove all traces of grease and solvent before handling the new rubber parts.

5. Check the fit of the piston in its bore, which should not exceed 0.003 inch.

6. Lubricate the cylinder bore and the new rubber parts with clean hydraulic brake fluid. Slip the spring, rubber cups (cupped sides toward the spring), and pistons (cupped side out) into the cylinder, and install the rubber dust covers to complete the assembly.

7. Install the repaired wheel cylinder on the backing plate. Connect the hydraulic tubing, using new copper gaskets to seal the joint.

8. Bleed the line to remove trapped air. Be sure to fill the master cylinder with fluid before and after bleeding each wheel.

MASTER CYLINDER

1. Remove the master cylinder from the car.

2. To disassemble the cylinder, remove the snap ring, retainer washer, piston, rubber cup, spring, and valve.

Removing the snap ring in the end of the master cylinder which holds the piston assembly in place. Courtesy Lincoln-Mercury Division, Ford Motor Company.

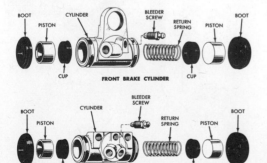

Details of the front and rear wheel cylinders. Courtesy Ford Division, Ford Motor Company.

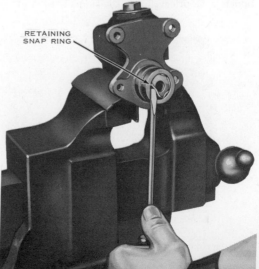

495

WORN GROOVE

After honing a master cylinder, it is very important to remove the sharp edge left at the compensating port; otherwise, the rubber cup will groove as shown and a leak will result.

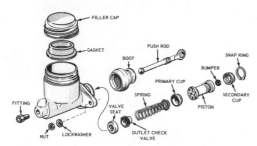

Details of the master cylinder with a standard brake system. Courtesy Ford Division, Ford Motor Company.

Details of the master cylinder used with a power booster. Courtesy Ford Division, Ford Motor Company.

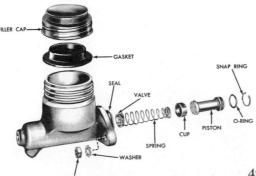

Remove the reservoir cover and the gasket.

3. Clean all parts in alcohol.

4. Hone the cylinder to remove pits and scores. Check the piston fit in the bore, which should not exceed 0.003 inch.

5. Clean the cylinder with soap and water to remove all traces of abrasives. Wipe the cylinder with a rag. A second washing in alcohol is necessary to remove all traces of soap and water. Wash your hands with soap and water before handling new rubber parts.

6. Lubricate the cylinder bore and rubber parts in hydraulic fluid and then install the new valve, spring, rubber cup (cupped end toward the spring), piston assembly (flat end into the cylinder), flat washer, spring retainer, and reservoir cover using a new gasket.

7. Grip the cylinder loosely in a vise and fill the reservoir with hydraulic fluid. Use a screwdriver to push the piston forward until fluid flows from the fitting.

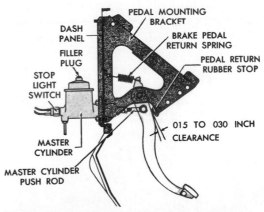

There must be about ¼ inch pedal clearance; otherwise, the compensating port may be covered by the piston. Courtesy Plymouth Division, Chrysler Corporation.

496

8. Install the repaired cylinder on the car. Bleed the air from the pipe joint next to the master cylinder by depressing the piston with the fitting loose, and then tighten it before releasing pressure on the piston. Do this several times to bleed the air from the cylinder. **Caution:** *Be careful not to let the fluid level get too low in the reservoir or air will enter.*

9. Test the pedal free play, which must be ¼ inch. Adjust the push rod length as required.

10. Test the system by holding the brake pedal in the applied position for a few moments. If the pedal holds its position, the system is free of leaks. If the pedal is spongy, the system will have to be bled.

Dual Master Cylinder

DISASSEMBLING

① Before disassembling the master cylinder, clean the outside thoroughly. Use a special tool to remove the tube seats by threading the tool firmly into each seat, and then tapping the tool and seat out of the cylinder body. Remove the two residual pressure valves and springs. **Note:** *No residual check valve is used with disc brakes.* Remove the cover retaining bolt and the clamp, and then take off the cover and the gasket. Empty the brake fluid from the reservoirs.

② Loosen the piston retainer screw, and then press in on the rear piston. Flip the retainer up in order to release the rear piston assembly. Slide the rear piston assembly out of the cylinder bore. Remove the screw and gasket that holds the front piston, and then, upending the master cylinder, tap the open end on a bench to remove the front piston. **Caution:** *If the front piston sticks in the bore, use air pressure to force it out.* Remove the front piston compression spring from the bore. Slide the rubber cups from the pistons. **Note:** *Observe the positions of the cup lips.* **Caution:** *Don't remove the center cup from the rear piston. If the cup is damaged or worn, install a new rear piston assembly.*

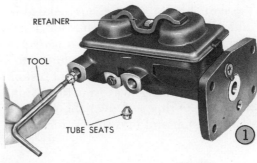

RETAINER

TOOL

TUBE SEATS

①

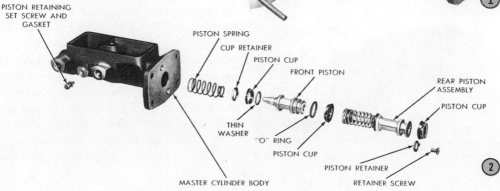

PISTON RETAINING SET SCREW AND GASKET

PISTON SPRING

CUP RETAINER

PISTON CUP

FRONT PISTON

REAR PISTON ASSEMBLY

PISTON CUP

THIN WASHER

"O" RING

PISTON CUP

PISTON RETAINER

RETAINER SCREW

MASTER CYLINDER BODY

②

497

CLEANING AND INSPECTING

Clean the master cylinder thoroughly, using a suitable solvent, and then dry it with compressed air. Wash the cylinder bore with clean brake fluid and inspect the bore for scoring and pitting. Light scratches or corrosion can generally be removed with crocus cloth. Removal of deep scratches or scoring requires honing, provided that the diameter of the bore is not increased more than 0.002″. If it is, the master cylinder must be replaced.

If the master cylinder pistons are scored or corroded, replace them. The piston cups and seals must be replaced whenever a master cylinder is reconditioned. **Caution:** *Always use all of the parts that are furnished in the repair kit. Discard all used rubber parts.*

ASSEMBLING

③ Before assembling the master cylinder, it is most important that all of the parts be dipped in clean brake fluid and placed on a clean paper for draining. **Caution:** *Assembling dry seals can ruin them.* Carefully work the piston cup on the front end of the front piston, with the lip facing away from the piston. Slide the O-ring seal over the rear end of the piston and into the correct land.

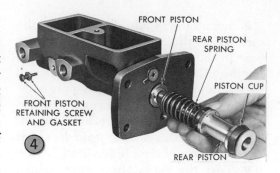

④

Carefully work the rear cup of the front piston into the rear land, with the cup lip facing away from the piston. Slide the cup retainer over the front end of the piston, followed by the piston spring. Slide the piston spring, cup retainer, piston, and cups into the bore. **Caution:** *Keep the parts well lubricated with brake fluid. Also make sure that the lip of each cup enters the bore evenly in order to prevent damaging the sealing qualities of the cups.*

④ Carefully work the piston cup over the rear end of the rear piston, with the lip of the cup facing the piston. Center the spring retainer of the rear piston assembly over the shoulder of the front piston. Push the piston assemblies into the bore, up to the center piston cup. Carefully work the center piston cup into the bore; then push the piston in, up to the rear cup. Carefully work the lip of the rear cup into the bore, and then push in on the piston until it is seated. Holding the piston in this position, move the piston retainer over the piston, and then tighten the screw securely. Install the front piston retaining setscrew and gasket in the cylinder body, and then tighten it securely.

⑤ Install the residual pressure valves and springs in the outlet ports, and then

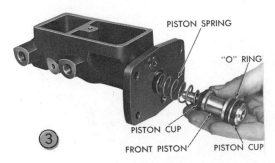

498

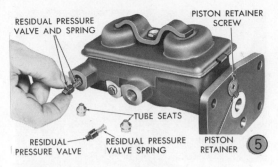

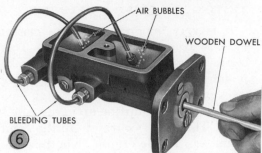

RESIDUAL PRESSURE
VALVE AND SPRING

PISTON RETAINER
SCREW

TUBE SEATS

RESIDUAL
PRESSURE VALVE

RESIDUAL PRESSURE
VALVE SPRING

PISTON
RETAINER ⑤

AIR BUBBLES

WOODEN DOWEL

BLEEDING TUBES ⑥

install the tube seats firmly. Replace the tube nut fittings.

⑥ Before installing the master cylinder on the vehicle, it must be bled to remove the air. To do this, clamp the assembly in a vise, and then attach the bleeding tubes as shown. **Note:** *If the vehicle has disc brakes, be sure that the residual pressure valve is on the end of the tube in the large capacity reservoir in order to keep the brake fluid from being siphoned out.* Fill both reservoirs with brake fluid. Depress the push rod slowly, and then allow the pistons to return under the pressure of the springs. Do this several times until all of the air bubbles are expelled. Remove the

bleeding tubes from the cylinder, and then install the cover and gasket.

⑦ Remove the assembly from the vise and install it on the vehicle by aligning the power brake push rod with the cylinder piston. Slide the assembly over the mounting studs. Install the attaching nuts and tighten them to 9 ft-lbs. torque. Connect the push rod to the brake pedal. Connect the front and rear brake tubes and tighten them securely. Bleed the hydraulic lines at the wheel cylinders as described in the next job sequence (page 500), making sure that the fluid level is maintained.

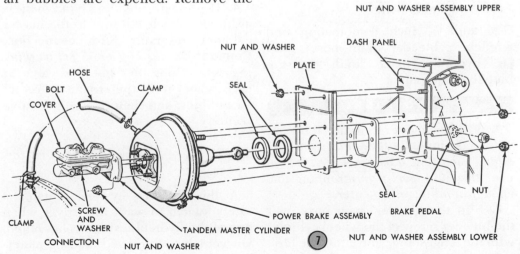

NUT AND WASHER ASSEMBLY UPPER

NUT AND WASHER

DASH PANEL

PLATE

HOSE

BOLT

CLAMP

SEAL

COVER

CLAMP

SCREW
AND
WASHER

CONNECTION

NUT AND WASHER

TANDEM MASTER CYLINDER

POWER BRAKE ASSEMBLY

SEAL

BRAKE PEDAL

NUT

NUT AND WASHER ASSEMBLY LOWER ⑦

499

Testing the Master Cylinder

It is very important that the master cylinder compensates at both ports. This can be checked by applying the brake pedal lightly with the engine running (power brakes), and then watching for a geyser of fluid squirting up in the reservoirs. This may occur only in the front chamber. To determine whether the rear compensating port is open, it is necessary to pump up the brakes rapidly, and then hold the pedal down. Have an observer watch the fluid in the rear reservoir while the pedal is allowed to rise. A disturbance in the fluid indicates that the compensating port is open. If not, it is necessary to adjust the length of the push rod.

Bleeding Hydraulic Brakes

The proper operation of hydraulic brakes requires that the brake lines be free of air. When a line is disconnected, air is admitted into the system and a spongy pedal results. Bleeding the lines removes this air.

Tools and Equipment

³/₈ and ⁷/₁₆ inch combination end wrenches; bleeder drain hose; glass jar; hydraulic brake fluid; pressure bleeding equipment.

PROCEDURE

1. Fill the master cylinder reservoir with brake fluid. **Caution:** *Fluid must be added each time a wheel is bled to prevent the fluid level from dropping low enough to allow air to enter.*

2. Slip the bleeder drain hose over the bleeder screw of the wheel cylinder with the longest line, and allow the hose to hang in a clean container half full of

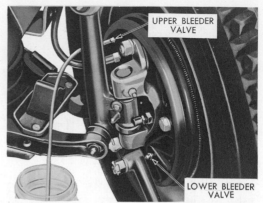

Bleeding the hydraulic brake lines. Courtesy Chrysler-Plymouth Division, Chrysler Corporation.

brake fluid. Loosen the bleeder screw about one turn and depress the brake pedal slowly. Then allow it to return slowly. Repeat this operation at each wheel until the flow of fluid is free of air bubbles.

3. On brakes with two cylinders, the bottom one should be bled first and then the top one. After bleeding the second cylinder, it is desirable to bleed the first one again to make sure of removing all the air.

4. If pressure bleeding equipment is available, attach the unit to the master cylinder reservoir filler connection. **Caution:** *Do not exceed 35 psi working pressure.* Open the bleeder valve at each wheel until the stream is free of air bubbles, and then tighten the valve securely.

BLEEDING A DUAL HYDRAULIC SYSTEM

A dual braking system contains a safety switch to warn the driver when one of the hydraulic systems has failed. On vehicles with disc brakes, a metering valve is sometimes incorporated in the hydraulic lines to the front wheels. This valve is designed to prevent the front brakes from applying until 125 psi pressure is developed in the system. This delaying action is required to keep the front brakes from performing all of the braking action on low-speed stops. Both of these devices require special handling techniques when bleeding the hydraulic lines, and only these special instructions will be discussed here.

HYDRAULIC SYSTEM SAFETY SWITCH

After the brake system has been bled, the dual brake warning light may continue to burn when the ignition switch is turned on. This is due to the pressure

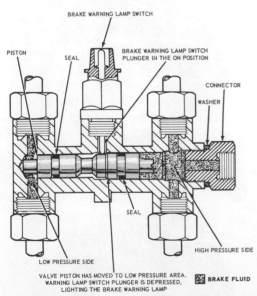

BRAKE WARNING LAMP SWITCH

PISTON

SEAL

BRAKE WARNING LAMP SWITCH PLUNGER IN THE ON POSITION

CONNECTOR

WASHER

SEAL

LOW PRESSURE SIDE

HIGH PRESSURE SIDE

VALVE PISTON HAS MOVED TO LOW PRESSURE AREA. WARNING LAMP SWITCH PLUNGER IS DEPRESSED, LIGHTING THE BRAKE WARNING LAMP

▨ BRAKE FLUID

After bleeding the lines of a dual hydraulic braking system, the piston assembly moves off-center and makes contact with the switch assembly to light the dash warning lamp. It is necessary to crack the bleeder valve in the other brake circuit as explained in the text in order to recenter the piston. Courtesy Ford Division, Ford Motor Company.

differential created during the bleeding operation, which causes the piston to move off-center toward the low-pressure side. This depresses the warning light switch plunger, which closes the contact points and turns the light on.

To centralize the valve, a pressure differential must again be created on the side opposite the system that was bled last. Apply brake pedal pressure and crack one of the wheel cylinder bleeder valves, then tighten it again quickly. This should cause the piston in the hydraulic switch to move toward the center, which will break the warning light circuit.

METERING VALVE

When bleeding the front wheel brakes, it is necessary to depress the bleeder button on the metering valve to allow brake fluid to reach the caliper assemblies. The button can be held in the depressed position with tape, but this must be removed after the bleeding operation is completed.

DISC BRAKES

Because of the greater number and size of the pistons in the calipers, more pumping of the pedal is required to remove the air. Also, it is very important to check the fluid level in the master cylinder reservoir more frequently because of the larger amount of fluid that flows in this circuit. **Caution:** *Before driving a vehicle with disc brakes, be sure that the brake pedal is firm.*

Relining Brakes

Brake lining is cemented or riveted to brake shoes. After about 20,000 miles, the lining usually wears down to the rivet heads and needs to be replaced; otherwise, the drums will score. Bonded lining must be replaced when it is worn down to $3/16''$ thickness.

Relining includes disassembly of the entire braking mechanism, installation of relined shoes, repair of defective hydraulic cylinders, replacement of leaking rear wheel oil seals, assembly of the system, bleeding the lines, and making a brake adjustment.

Tools and Equipment

Brake shoes with new linings; adjustable wrench; brake spring pliers; brake spring removing tool; brake shoe adjusting tool; jack; stands; hydraulic fluid; diagonal pliers; $1\frac{1}{4}$ inch heavy duty socket; sliding "T" handle; rear drum puller.

PROCEDURE

① With the vehicle on a hoist or on suitable stands, remove the plug from the brake adjusting access hole of a front wheel brake assembly. Loosen the brake star adjusting wheel to aid in removing the brake drum. Insert a thin screwdriver into the brake adjusting hole and push the adjusting lever away from the star adjusting wheel. **Caution:** *Care*

must be taken not to bend the adjusting lever. Insert the adjusting tool into the brake adjusting hole, and engage the notches of the brake adjusting star wheel. Release the brake adjustment by prying up with the adjusting tool. Movement of the tool is reversed on some 1969 models.

② Remove the wheel cover, grease cap, cotter pin, locknut, adjusting nut, and the outer wheel bearing. Pull off the wheel and drum assembly. Inspect the linings for wear, shoe alignment, or contamination from grease or brake fluid.

③ Remove the brake shoe return springs with the special tool shown.

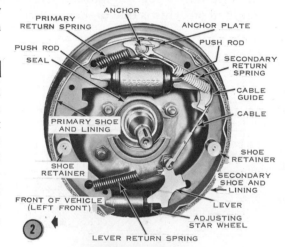

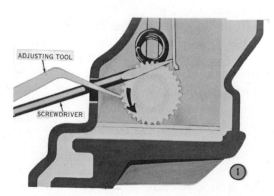

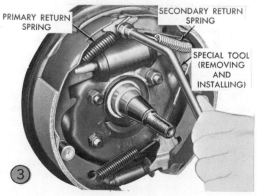

502

④ Remove the brake shoe retainer, spring, and the nails. Slide the eye of the automatic adjuster cable off the anchor and unhook it from the lever. Remove the cable, cable guide, and the anchor plate. Disconnect the lever spring from the lever and disengage it from the shoe web. Remove the spring and the lever. Remove the primary and secondary brake shoe assemblies and the adjusting star wheel from the support.

⑤ Install a wheel cylinder clamp to hold the pistons in the cylinders.

⑥ Remove the plug from the brake adjusting access hole of the rear wheel brakes, and then release the star adjusting wheel. Remove the rear wheel covers, the retaining nuts, and the rear wheel. Take off the clips from the wheel studs that hold the drum to the axle, and then remove the drum. Inspect the brake linings.

This student at Los Angeles Trade-Technical College is disassembling a brake mechanism while the car is on a hoist.

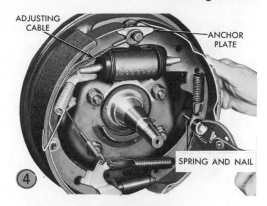

ADJUSTING CABLE
ANCHOR PLATE
SPRING AND NAIL
④

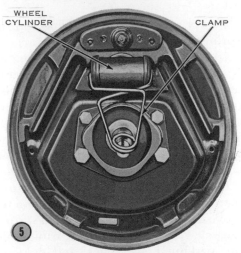

WHEEL CYLINDER
CLAMP
⑤

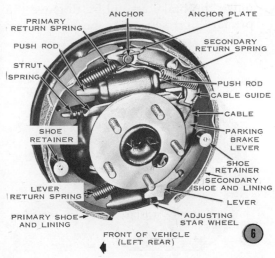

PRIMARY RETURN SPRING
ANCHOR
ANCHOR PLATE
PUSH ROD
SECONDARY RETURN SPRING
STRUT SPRING
PUSH ROD
CABLE GUIDE
CABLE
SHOE RETAINER
PARKING BRAKE LEVER
SHOE RETAINER
SECONDARY SHOE AND LINING
LEVER
LEVER RETURN SPRING
PRIMARY SHOE AND LINING
ADJUSTING STAR WHEEL
FRONT OF VEHICLE (LEFT REAR)
⑥

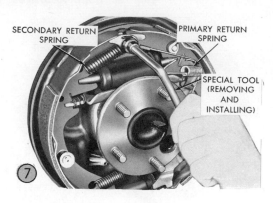

SECONDARY RETURN SPRING

PRIMARY RETURN SPRING

SPECIAL TOOL (REMOVING AND INSTALLING)

⑦

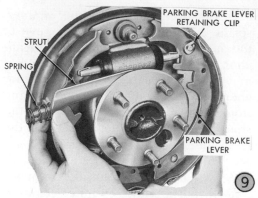

STRUT

SPRING

PARKING BRAKE LEVER RETAINING CLIP

PARKING BRAKE LEVER

⑨

⑦ Pry off the brake shoe return springs.

⑧ Remove the brake shoe retainers, springs, and nails. Slide the automatic adjuster cable off the anchor, and then unhook it from the lever. Remove the cable, cable guide, and the anchor plate. Disconnect the lever spring from the lever, and then disengage it from the shoe web. Remove the spring and lever.

⑨ Spread the anchor ends of the primary and secondary shoes, and then remove the parking brake strut and spring. Disengage the parking brake cable from the parking brake lever, and then remove the brake assembly. Remove the primary and secondary brake shoe as-

semblies and the adjusting star wheel from the support. Install a wheel cylinder clamp tool to hold the pistons in the cylinders.

CLEANING AND INSPECTING

Clean the brake supports, using a suitable solvent, and then inspect for burrs. Clean and lubricate the threads of the adjusting screws.

⑩ Measure the drum run-out with an accurate gauge. The run-out should not exceed 0.006″, or the drum must be turned. Remove only as much material as is necessary to clean it up. **Caution:** *Don't exceed 0.060″ on the diameter over standard drum size.*

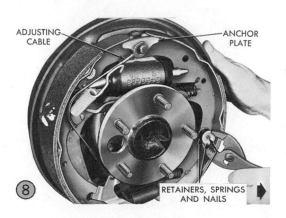

ADJUSTING CABLE

ANCHOR PLATE

⑧

RETAINERS, SPRINGS AND NAILS

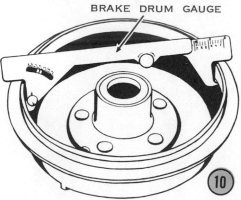

BRAKE DRUM GAUGE

⑩

⑪ New shoe and lining assemblies should be measured and, if necessary, ground to 0.060″–0.080″ under drum diameter.

ASSEMBLING

⑫ Install the front brake shoes by matching a primary shoe with a secondary shoe, and then placing them in their relative positions on a work bench. Lubricate the threads of the adjusting screw and install it between the primary and secondary shoes, with the star wheel next to the secondary shoe. **Note:** *The star adjusting wheels are stamped "R" (right side) and "L" (left side) to indicate their location on the vehicle.* Lubricate the shoe contact area on the support with SylGlyde or an equivalent lubricant. Overlap the anchor ends of the primary and secondary brake shoes, and then install the adjusting spring and lever. Spread the anchor ends of the brake shoes to hold the adjusting lever and spring in position. Position the brake shoes on the support and over the anchor pin. Remove the piston clamp.

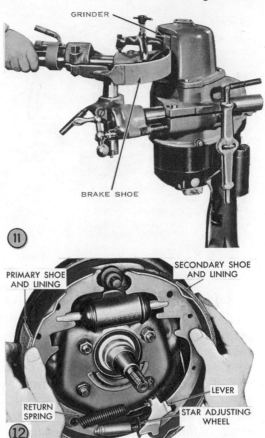

Since 1969, some models are equipped with a new-style Bendix brake mechanism with automatic adjusters. Note the use of an adjuster overload spring, which the other models do not have. The adjusting tool is moved in a direction opposite to the other type of automatic adjusting brake mechanism. Courtesy Chrysler Corporation.

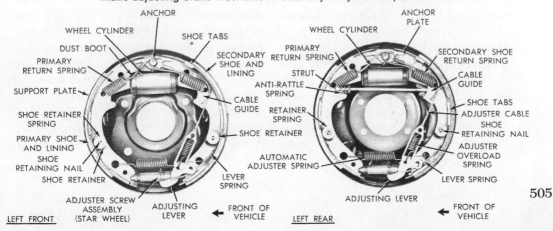

505

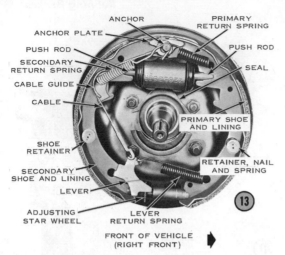

ANCHOR
ANCHOR PLATE
PUSH ROD
SECONDARY RETURN SPRING
CABLE GUIDE
CABLE
PRIMARY RETURN SPRING
PUSH ROD
SEAL
PRIMARY SHOE AND LINING
SHOE RETAINER
SECONDARY SHOE AND LINING
LEVER
RETAINER, NAIL AND SPRING
ADJUSTING STAR WHEEL
LEVER RETURN SPRING

⑬

FRONT OF VEHICLE (RIGHT FRONT) ➤

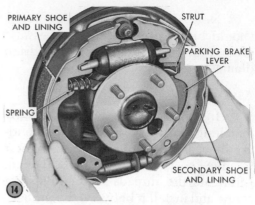

PRIMARY SHOE AND LINING
STRUT
PARKING BRAKE LEVER
SPRING
SECONDARY SHOE AND LINING

⑭

⑬ Install the nails, cups, springs, and retainers. Replace the anchor pin plate. Install the cable guide in the secondary shoe, and then position the eye of the adjusting cable over the anchor pin. Install the retainer spring in the primary shoe. Slide the spring over the anchor. **Caution:** *Make sure that the cable guide remains flat against the shoe web.* Install the return spring in the secondary shoe, and then slide it over the anchor. **Caution:** *Be sure that the secondary spring overlaps the primary spring as shown.* Place the adjusting cable over the guide and then engage the hook of the cable in the adjusting lever. Lubricate the wheel bearings, and then install the brake drum. Adjust the wheel bearings to the proper preload.

⑭ Inspect the platforms of the rear brake supports for nicks or burrs. Apply a thin coat of lubricant to the support platforms at the shoe contact areas. Attach the parking brake lever to the back side of the secondary shoe. Place a secondary and a primary shoe in their relative positions on a work bench. Lubricate the threads of the adjusting screw, and then install it between the primary and secondary shoes, with the star wheel next to the secondary shoe. Overlap the anchor ends of the primary and secondary brake shoes, and then install the adjusting spring and lever. Holding the brake shoes in their relative positions, engage the parking brake cable with the parking brake lever.

⑮ Install the parking brake strut and spring between the parking brake lever and the primary shoes. Remove the piston clamp. Place the brake shoes on the support, and then install the retainer nails, springs, and the retainers. Install the anchor pin plate. Hook the eye of the adjusting cable over the anchor pin. Install the cable guide in the secondary shoe, and then replace the secondary return spring. **Caution:** *Be sure that the secondary spring overlaps the primary spring as shown and that the return spring does not slip between the anchor pin and the eye of the cable.* Place the adjusting cable in the groove of the cable guide, and then engage the

506

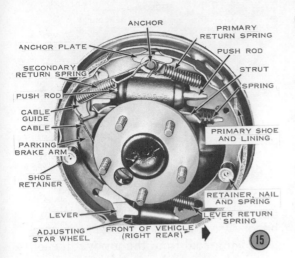

ANCHOR
ANCHOR PLATE
PRIMARY RETURN SPRING
SECONDARY RETURN SPRING
PUSH ROD
PUSH ROD
STRUT
SPRING
CABLE GUIDE
CABLE
PARKING BRAKE ARM
PRIMARY SHOE AND LINING
SHOE RETAINER
LEVER
RETAINER, NAIL AND SPRING
LEVER RETURN SPRING
ADJUSTING STAR WHEEL
FRONT OF VEHICLE (RIGHT REAR)
15

ROTOR   CALIPER

RETAINER

FRICTION PADS

Most disc brakes are designed so that the friction pads can be replaced easily by removing the retainer, and then pulling out the pads.

hook of the cable in the adjusting lever. **Caution:** *Be sure that the cable guide remains flat against the web of the brake shoe.* Install the brake drum and retaining clips. Replace the wheel and tire assembly. Adjust the brakes.

Servicing Disc Brakes

The friction pads can be replaced in most cases by removing a retainer, and then lifting out the pads. In all floating-caliper type disc brakes, it is necessary to remove the caliper in order to be able to replace the friction pads. It is always necessary to remove the caliper from the vehicle in order to service the hydraulic cylinders.

When replacing friction pads, the hydraulic pistons must be pushed back in order to make room for the new, thicker pads. This will displace some fluid and cause it to overflow the master cylinder reservoir unless some of it is drained beforehand. Some mechanics open the bleeder valve before pushing

FRICTION PAD

CALIPER

Some Bendix disc brake assemblies require the caliper to be removed so that the friction pads can be slipped out from the bottom of the caliper assembly.

in the hydraulic pistons, which keeps the displaced fluid from returning to the reservoir. However, it is necessary to bleed the disc brakes if the bleeder valve was opened.

507

① Raise the vehicle and place it on jack stands. Remove the front wheels. **Caution:** *Care must be taken not to interfere with or damage the caliper shoe retainers, the bleeder screw, or the cross-over line.* Disconnect the brake line at the caliper inlet fitting. Remove the two bolts holding the caliper assembly to the steering knuckle, and then remove the caliper assembly by sliding it up and away from the disc. Remove the cross-over line by disconnecting the fittings from the inboard and outboard caliper halves. Remove the two screws holding the caliper shoe retainers to the caliper bridge, and then remove the retainer assembly. Remove the shoe and lining assemblies.

② Position a piece of soft wood inside the caliper bridge area, between the pistons, as shown. Seal the cross-over outlet on the inboard half of the caliper with your thumb. Use an air hose to apply pressure to the fluid inlet hole in order to force one piston out of the inboard half of the caliper. Position a seal plate over the bore of the piston previously removed, retaining it with a C-clamp as shown, and then force the remaining pistons out with air pressure.

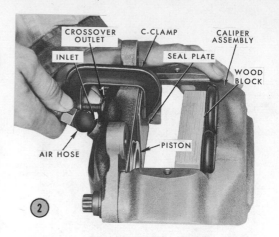

② Remove and discard the piston dust boots. Use a piece of plastic to remove the piston seal from the groove in each piston bore of the caliper housings. **Caution:** *Don't use a metallic device to remove the seals, or you will scratch the bores.*

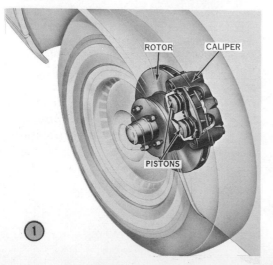

CLEANING AND INSPECTING

Clean all parts with brake fluid and wipe them dry, using a clean, lint-free cloth. Use an air hose to blow out all passageways.

Inspect the piston bores in the caliper housings for corrosion, scoring, pitting, or other damage. Bores with minor imperfections can generally be cleaned with crocus cloth. Units with deep scores require replacement. **Note:** *Black stains on the walls of the bore are caused by the piston seals and are not harmful.*

Check the piston seal and dust boot grooves in the bores for damage. Check each piston for pitting and scoring, and to see whether the chrome plating is worn off.

ASSEMBLING

③ Position the caliper assembly in a vise, clamping it on the inboard housing, with the bores facing up. Install the

508

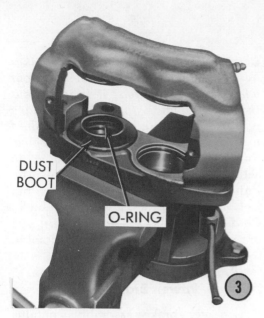

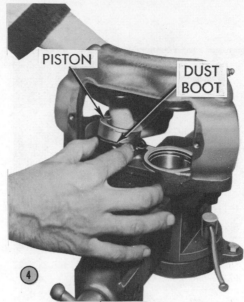

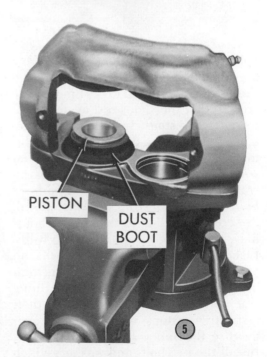

bleeder fitting in the outboard caliper housing. **Note:** *In the following operations use the lubricant supplied with the kit of parts. Brake fluid is not recommended as an assembly lubricant.* Lubricate the bores in the inboard housing. Lubricate the piston O-ring seal, then install the seal in the second groove in the housing bore. Lubricate the lips of the dust boot, then install the dust boot in the upper groove of the housing bore, making sure that the dust boot is properly seated in the groove.

④ Lubricate the piston, and then start it inside of the dust boot.

⑤ With your thumb and forefinger, compress the dust boot against the piston and work the boot around until the piston is installed in it. Reposition the piston as necessary and slowly force it into the caliper bore. As the piston moves down, the dust boot lip will seat in the groove on the piston. **Note:** *When the piston is fully seated, trapped air under the dust boot may cause the dust boot lip to disengage from the piston groove.* If this occurs, re-install the lip in the groove, using your thumb nail as a guide. Repeat for the second piston in the inboard housing. Invert the caliper in the vise, and repeat the piston installation for the outboard half.

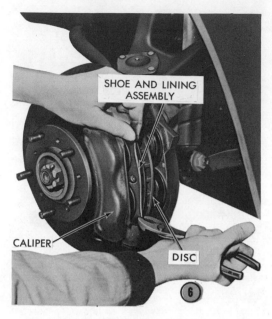

SHOE AND LINING ASSEMBLY

CALIPER

DISC

⑥

Caution: *When bleeding disc brakes having a metering valve in the front wheel hydraulic lines, it is important that you depress the metering valve push rod to assure that the brake fluid will pass through the metering valve.* Pump the brake pedal several times to actuate the piston seals and to seat the linings. Install the wheels, remove the jack stands, and then lower the vehicle. **Caution:** *Don't move the car until you are sure that the brake pedal is solid.*

Repairing a Diaphragm-Type Power Brake Unit

A power brake assembly contains three basic elements combined into a single unit: (1) a vacuum power cylinder, (2) a hydraulic master cylinder, and (3) a mechanically actuated valve to control the degree of brake application.

Tools and Equipment

Moraine vacuum-suspended, diaphragm-type power brake unit; $7/16$, $1/2$, and $9/16$ inch combination-end wrenches; torque wrench; screwdriver; pliers; Truarc pliers; Tool J-21601; push rod height gauge; brake fluid; Declene; Dow Corning silicone grease.

DISASSEMBLING

① Remove the reservoir cover and the diaphragm to avoid damaging them. Place the power brake assembly in a vise, with the push rod end up. Clamp the unit firmly on the sides of the master cylinder reservoir. **Note:** *Scribe a mark on the bottom of the front and the rear housings to facilitate assembly.* Remove the boot and place two adjustable wrenches so that each grips a mounting bracket. Rotate the rear housing counter-

⑥ Remove the caliper assembly from the vise, and then install the shoe and lining assemblies into the caliper bridge area so that the shoes rest against their respective pistons. Install the shoe retainers and tighten the screws to 8 ft-lbs. torque. **Note:** *The linings can be installed at this time, or they can be installed after the caliper assembly is bolted to the steering knuckle.* Install the cross-over line to the caliper housings, tightening the fitting to 25 ft-lbs. Install the caliper. Make certain that all of the pistons are fully seated in their bores and that the shoe and lining assemblies are positioned against their respective pistons; when installed over the disc, the linings should face the disc. Install the two bolts and washers which secure the caliper assembly to the steering knuckle; tighten the bolts to 95 ft-lbs. torque. Connect the brake pipe to the inlet fitting on the caliper, tightening it to 25 ft-lbs. torque. Bleed the brakes.

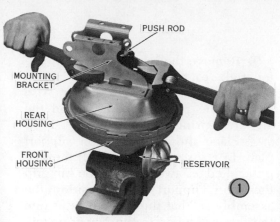

PUSH ROD

MOUNTING
BRACKET

REAR
HOUSING

FRONT
HOUSING

RESERVOIR

①

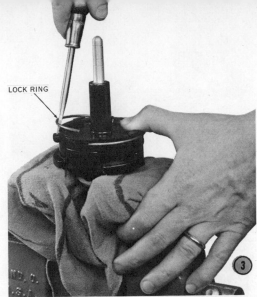

LOCK RING

③

clockwise to the unlocked position.
Caution: *The housing is spring-loaded.*

② Lift the rear housing and the power
piston assembly from the unit, and then
remove the return spring. Remove the
clevis and jam nut from the push rod.
Remove the retaining ring on the push
rod, and then remove the silencer. Reposition the master cylinder assembly
in a vise to facilitate removal of the front
housing from the master cylinder. Remove the seal and the vacuum check
valve from the front housing. Remove
the power piston assembly from the

rear housing. **Caution:** *Handle the
power diaphragm carefully.* Guard
against grease, oil, foreign material,
nicks, or cuts.

③ Remove the silencer from the neck
of the power piston tube, and then pry
the lock ring from the power piston by
lifting one end out from under the large
divided locking lug.

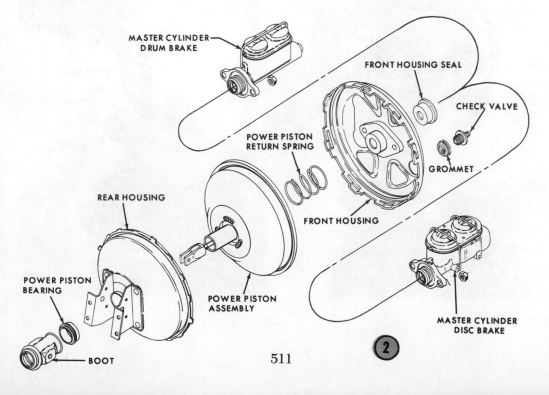

MASTER CYLINDER
DRUM BRAKE

FRONT HOUSING SEAL

CHECK VALVE

POWER PISTON
RETURN SPRING

GROMMET

REAR HOUSING

FRONT HOUSING

POWER PISTON
BEARING

POWER PISTON
ASSEMBLY

MASTER CYLINDER
DISC BRAKE

BOOT

②

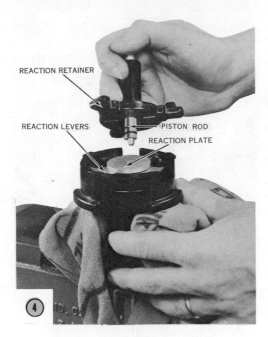

REACTION RETAINER

REACTION LEVERS

PISTON ROD

REACTION PLATE

④ Remove the reaction retainer, piston rod, reaction plate, three reaction levers, and the air-valve spring. Also remove the reaction bumper and the air-valve spring retainer.

⑤ Place the power piston support plate in a vise as shown. Pull the diaphragm edges away so that you can grip the steel support plate. Position the assembly so that the three lugs fit into the three notches in the power piston. Press down on the support plate and rotate it counterclockwise until it separates from the power piston. Remove the diaphragm from the support plate and lay both parts aside.

⑥ Position the power piston in a vise which is padded with a shop towel. **Caution:** *Don't clamp on the tube because the outside acts as a bearing surface.* Use Truarc pliers to remove the snap ring on the air valve.

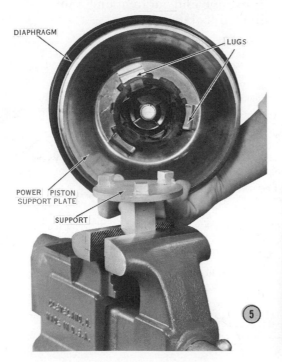

DIAPHRAGM

LUGS

POWER PISTON SUPPORT PLATE

SUPPORT

SNAP RING

AIR VALVE

POWER PISTON

512

⑦ Insert the power piston in a press, and then remove the air-valve assembly, using a $3/8''$ drive extension as a tool.

⑧ Remove the air-valve push rod assembly to release the following parts from the power piston: control valve, retainer, push rod limiter washer, and the air filter. Remove the floating control valve assembly from the push rod as it must be replaced with a new assembly. The master cylinder push rod can now be pressed from the center of the reaction retainer. Remove the O-ring seal from the groove in the master cylinder piston rod.

CLEANING AND INSPECTING

Use Declene or denatured alcohol to clean all metal parts thoroughly. Blow out all passages, orifices, and valve holes. Place the cleaned parts on paper to dry.

If rust is found inside either of the housings, polish it with crocus cloth, washing afterwards with cleaning fluid. **Caution:** *The use of gasoline, kerosene, or any solvent with the slightest trace of mineral oil will damage the rubber parts.* **Caution:** *Dirt is the major cause of trouble in service.*

Always replace all rubber parts because they are the key to controlling the flow of fluid and air.

PRESS

TOOL

To remove the air-valve assembly, support the power piston in a press. **Caution:** *Make sure that the power piston casting is fully supported to keep it from breaking.*

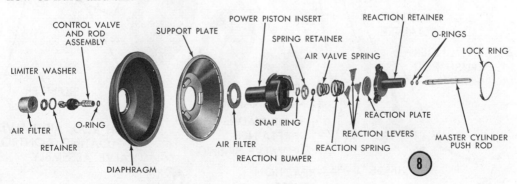

CONTROL VALVE AND ROD ASSEMBLY
SUPPORT PLATE
POWER PISTON INSERT
REACTION RETAINER
SPRING RETAINER
O-RINGS
LOCK RING
AIR VALVE SPRING
LIMITER WASHER
O-RING
SNAP RING
REACTION PLATE
AIR FILTER
RETAINER
AIR FILTER
REACTION LEVERS
MASTER CYLINDER PUSH ROD
REACTION SPRING
DIAPHRAGM
REACTION BUMPER

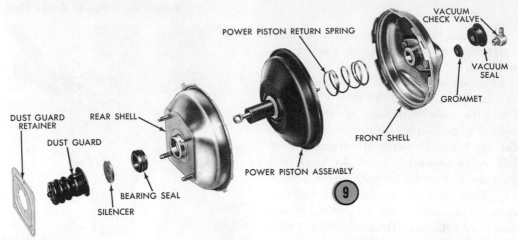

POWER PISTON RETURN SPRING

VACUUM CHECK VALVE

VACUUM SEAL

GROMMET

FRONT SHELL

POWER PISTON ASSEMBLY

REAR SHELL

DUST GUARD RETAINER

DUST GUARD

SILENCER

BEARING SEAL

⑨

ASSEMBLING

⑨ Replace the vacuum check valve in the front housing, using a new grommet. Position a new seal in the front housing so that the flat surface lies against the bottom of the depression. Install the master cylinder on the front housing, but do not tighten the retaining nuts as the cylinder must be removed later for gauging.

⑩ Place a new lubricated O-ring seal in the groove on the master cylinder piston rod. Insert the rod through the re-

action retainer so that the round end protrudes from the reaction retainer tube. Position a new O-ring seal on the air valve in the second groove from the push rod end. The floating control valve assembly must be replaced, since the force required to remove it distorts the parts. Place the new valve on the air-valve assembly so that the face of the valve is against the seat on the air valve. Wipe a thin film of power brake lubricant on the floating control valve at the large OD (outside diameter) and on the O-ring seal on the air valve.

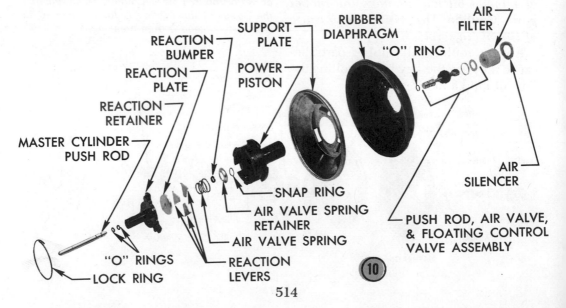

SUPPORT PLATE

RUBBER DIAPHRAGM

AIR FILTER

REACTION BUMPER

"O" RING

REACTION PLATE

POWER PISTON

REACTION RETAINER

MASTER CYLINDER PUSH ROD

SNAP RING

AIR VALVE SPRING RETAINER

AIR VALVE SPRING

AIR SILENCER

"O" RINGS

LOCK RING

REACTION LEVERS

PUSH ROD, AIR VALVE, & FLOATING CONTROL VALVE ASSEMBLY

⑩

514

INSTALLER
J-21601

POWER
PISTON

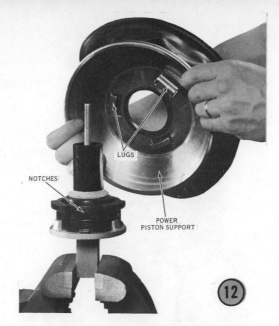

NOTCHES

LUGS

POWER
PISTON SUPPORT

⑫

⑪

⑪ Press the air valve-push rod assembly (air valve first) onto its seat in the tube of the power piston. Place the valve retainer over the push rod so that the side seats on the floating control valve. Start the floating control valve and its retainer into the power piston tube. Press the valve into its seat in the tube by placing the installer (Tool J-21601) on the top of the retainer and pushing it down by hand. After the floating control valve is seated, position the push rod limiter washer over the push rod and down onto the floating control valve. Stretch the air filter element over the end of the push rod, and then press it into the power piston tube.

⑫ Place the power piston support in a vise. Position the power piston on the support so that the three lugs fit into the notches.

⑬ Assemble the power piston diaphragm support plate from the side opposite the locking tangs. The raised flange of the diaphragm must be pressed through the hole in the center of the support plate. Be sure that the edge of

the center hole fits into the groove in the flange of the diaphragm. Pull the diaphragm away from the OD of the support plate so that it can be gripped with your hands. Lubricate the bead of the diaphragm where it contacts the power piston. Hold the support plate with the locking tangs down, and then place the diaphragm assembly over the tube of the power piston. The flange of the diaphragm must fit into the groove on the power piston. Press down and rotate the support plate clockwise until the lugs on the power piston come against the stops. **Note:** *The assembly can now be turned over and placed in a padded vise, with the tube facing down.* **Caution:** *Don't clamp it tightly.*

DIAPHRAGM

SUPPORT
PLATE

⑬

515

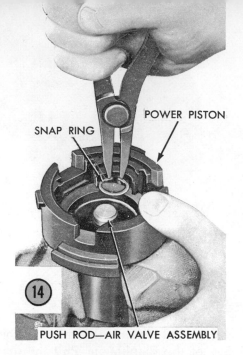

SNAP RING

POWER PISTON

PUSH ROD—AIR VALVE ASSEMBLY

⑭

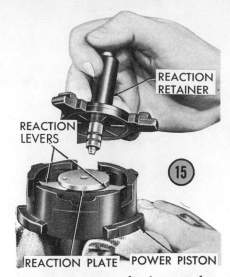

REACTION RETAINER

REACTION LEVERS

⑮

REACTION PLATE   POWER PISTON

⑭ Use a pair of Truarc pliers to install the snap ring in the groove of the air valve. Place the air valve spring retainer on the snap ring. Assemble the reaction bumper into the groove in the end of the air valve. Position the air-valve return spring on the retainer with the large end down.

⑮ Place the three reaction levers in position, with the ears on the wide end in the slots of the power piston. The narrow ends will rest on top of the air-valve return spring. Position the reaction plate, with the numbered side facing up, on top of the reaction levers. Press on the plate until the large ends of the reaction levers pop up so that the plate rests flat on the levers and the plate is centered.

⑯ Assemble the master cylinder piston rod and the reaction retainer assembly to the power piston. With the round end of the piston rod up, and with the reaction retainer held toward the top of the piston rod, place the small end of the rod in the hole in the center of the reaction plate. Line up the ears on the

reaction retainer with the notches in the power piston. Then push the reaction retainer down until the ears seat in the notches. Maintain pressure on the reaction retainer, and then position the large lock ring over the master cylinder push rod. One end of the lock ring goes under the lug on the power piston which has a raised divider in the center. As you work the lock ring around the power piston, it should slip over an ear of the reaction retainer, under a lug on the power piston, and continue alternately over and under until the other end of the lock ring seats under the lug with the raised divider. **Caution:** *Make sure that both ends of the lock ring are secured under the large lug.*

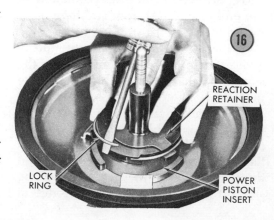

⑯

REACTION RETAINER

LOCK RING

POWER PISTON INSERT

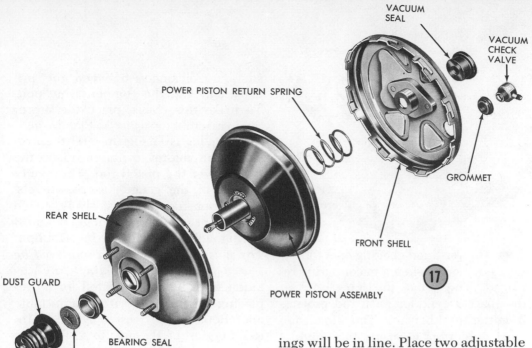

VACUUM SEAL

VACUUM CHECK VALVE

POWER PISTON RETURN SPRING

GROMMET

REAR SHELL

FRONT SHELL

DUST GUARD

(17)

BEARING SEAL

POWER PISTON ASSEMBLY

SILENCER

(17) Place a new power piston bearing in the center of the rear shell so that the flange on the center hole of the housing fits into the groove of the bearing with the large flange on the stud side of the housing. Lubricate the inside of the bearing. Position the air silencer over the holes on the tube of the power piston. Lubricate the tube. Assemble the power piston to the rear shell. Lubricate the tube of the reaction retainer, and then lay the assembly aside.

(18) Place the front housing in a vise, with the master cylinder down. Position the power piston return spring over the inset in the front housing. Lubricate the ID (inside diameter) of the support plate seal and the beaded edge of the diaphragm. Hold the rear housing and the power piston assembly over the front housing, with the master cylinder push rod down. Position the rear housing so that, when rotated into its locked position, the scribe marks on the hous-

ings will be in line. Place two adjustable wrenches on opposite brackets. Press down and rotate the housings clockwise into the locked position. **Caution:** *Be extremely careful not to break the studs loose in the rear housing. Also be careful not to put pressure on the power piston tube when locking the housings.* Push the felt silencer over the push rod in order to seat it against the end of the power piston tube. Place the snap ring retainer on the push rod so that it holds the silencer against the power piston tube. Push the plastic boot on until it seats against the rear housing. The raised tabs on the side of the boot should locate in the holes in the center of the brackets. Assemble the jam nut and clevis to the push rod.

(18)

517

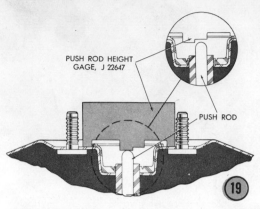

PUSH ROD HEIGHT GAGE, J 22647

PUSH ROD

(19)

(19) The push rod gauging operation is necessary only when a major part is replaced. The gauge measures how far the master cylinder push rod projects from the front housing. This dimension must be correct to insure that there is adequate clearance between the primary cup and the compensating port. To make this check, place the power brake assembly in a vise so that the master cylinder is facing up, and then remove the master cylinder. Place the gauge over the piston rod. The center section of the gauge has two levels. The piston rod end must always touch the lower section of the gauge, but must never touch the shorter section. **Caution:** *The master cylinder push rod must be seated firmly before gauging.* Any variation must be compensated for by replacing the push rod with an adjustable one. Replace the master cylinder. Install and torque the nuts to 25 ft-lbs.

CHECK YOUR KNOWLEDGE

1. What do brakes do to the kinetic energy of car motion?
2. Of what material are brake linings made?
3. Where does a power brake unit obtain its source of power?
4. Why are parking brakes always separate from the regular braking system?
5. What is the great advantage of hydraulic brakes?
6. What is the purpose of the check valve in the master cylinder?
7. What is the purpose of the dual master cylinder?
8. What is the advantage of using a flexible rubber seal to cover the hydraulic fluid in the master cylinder reservoir?
9. How are brake linings fastened to the brake shoes?
10. What is meant by the self-energizing action of brakes?
11. What is servo action?
12. When do automatic adjusters operate?
13. What is the great advantage of disc brakes?
14. Why is a power booster needed with disc brakes?

15. Why are proportioning valves required with combination braking systems?
16. Explain the action of a power brake under the four headings: released position, applying position, holding position, and releasing position.
17. When is a brake adjustment required?
18. How can you tell if air is present in the hydraulic lines?

Self-Check Tests

TRUE-FALSE

1. Brakes change kinetic energy into heat.
2. Many automatic-transmission equipped cars contain a notched gear and pawl arrangement in addition to the usual parking brake.
3. Some Bendix-type brakes are self adjusting.
4. In some states parking brakes are required by law to be separate from the foot-operated braking system.
5. The brakes need not be adjusted until the brake pedal can be pressed to the floorboard.
6. If air is present in the hydraulic lines, the cylinders will leak fluid.

MULTIPLE CHOICE

1. Which of the following does *not* apply to brake lining: a) generates heat; b) asbestos; c) high frictional characteristics; d) good hydraulic fluid absorbing characteristics?

2. Which of the following is *not* a part of the master cylinder: a) bleeder valve; b) piston; c) reservoir; d) check valve?

3. Which of the following is *not* a part of a power-brake system: a) vacuum-reserve tank; b) control valve; c) combination vacuum-fuel pump; d) vacuum-power cylinder?

COMPLETION

1. _____ are friction devices used to stop the car.

2. Power brakes require _____ to assist in stopping the car.

3. A notched gear and _____ is used as a parking brake in some automatic-transmission equipped cars.

4. The _____ cylinder is operated by the brake pedal.

5. Most cars are designed so that about _____ per cent of the braking pressure is applied to the front wheels.

6. When the brake pedal goes to within _____ inches of the floorboard, the brake shoes should be repositioned.

MATCHING

1. Brakes
2. Master cylinder
3. Power brakes
4. Notched gear and pawl

a. Vacuum actuated
b. Friction device
c. Hydraulic pump
d. Emergency brakes

Chapter 19

Wheels and Tires

Tire Construction

There are three basic elements in a tire: cord, tread, and bead. The cord is the container or body, which has the ability to flex. The strength of a tire is based upon the strength of the cord. The tread is the wearing surface which protects the cord; it might be called the sole of the tire. The bead is composed of wires which become the anchors for the cord of the tire. They are also the means by which the tire is held to the rim. Rim dimensions are a critical factor in the design of the basic tire elements.

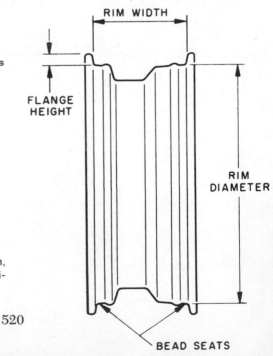

Details of the wheel rim, showing how the measurements are determined. Courtesy Dodge Division, Chrysler Corporation.

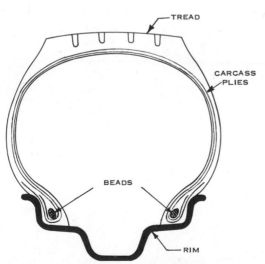

Cross-sectioned view through a tire and rim, showing the various parts. Courtesy Dodge Division, Chrysler Motors Corporation.

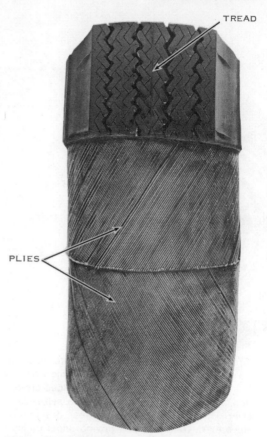

TREAD

PLIES

This cutaway tire shows the relationship between the cord plies and the tread. Courtesy Dodge Division, Chrysler Corporation.

Tire tread patterns are designed to minimize road noises and at the same time develop the best traction possible. Slitting the tread into many small blocks is effective in minimizing skidding. The small blocks scrape the pavement dry and maintain traction under braking pressures. Special tread designs are available for driving in snow or soft mud. They have extra large cleats which are self-cleaning.

Cord Plies

Tires are built up of layers of cord, called plies; they are encased in rubber, cemented together, then covered with more rubber to form the tread and sidewalls. Until a few years ago, most passenger car tires contained four cord plies. The normal flexing of a tire as it rolls along the roadway generates heat between the plies — the more plies, the more heat. Furthermore, tires having more plies tend to dissipate (lose) this heat more slowly, since rubber is a good insulator. Heat is an enemy of the materials used in tire construction. It weakens the cords and rubber and thus increases the chance of failure. In the past, the heat problem was overcome by specifying higher inflation pressures to reduce flexing, but higher pressures do not lead to a comfortable ride.

Now, two-ply tires are being used to replace the older, four-ply tires. These newer tires have load ratings and wear characteristics equal to the four-ply tires of the same size. Although there are fewer layers of cord, the amount of cord in a two-ply tire remains the same as in its four-ply predecessor. Extensive testing has proven the fact that two-ply tires can carry the same loads as equivalent four-ply tires.

Cord Materials

The plies of a tire carcass are usually made from fabric (cloth). Cotton, long the most widely used material, has almost completely given way to rayon, which is stronger. Tires with rayon plies can withstand heavier loads and measure up to the demands of high-speed freeway driving.

Nylon, which made its appearance sometime later, is even stronger than rayon but, being a thermoplastic, it is prone to take a "set" when left standing overnight. Tires with nylon plies

521

ASYMETRICAL TREAD DESIGN

SELF-SEALING PLY

POLYESTER
CORD PLY

RAYON
CORD PLY

STEEL-REINFORCED
PLY

Tires with polyester plies in addition to the usual rayon plies have added strength. This Uniroyal tire has a steel-reinforced belt for added protection against nail penetration and a self-sealant layer. This unusual rear wheel tread design provides extra traction when driving under difficult conditions. It is quieter than snow tires because the deep-lug tread is mounted to the inside of the vehicle so that the noise is dissipated underneath the car. Courtesy Uniroyal, Inc.

thump until they warm up. Recent improvements in nylon fibers have minimized this problem, but rayon remains the most widely used type of cord for original equipment tires.

All 1970 passenger car tires will contain plies of polyester in addition to the usual two rayon plies. These tires are so much stronger than conventional tires that the manufacturers are doubling the usual mileage warranty.

Cord Angles

The cord layers that form the plies of a tire are usually placed at an angle of 32°–38° to the centerline of the tire. A low-cord-angle tire has better lateral stability—that is, it tends to roll under less in a turn—and thus it provides better handling. It also has high-speed durability. Unfortunately, along with these desirable characteristics come added stiffness and resistance to flexing, which result in a rougher ride.

Radial-Ply Tires

A radial-ply tire is quite different from a conventional tire. The main difference is that the tire cords are placed from bead to bead at right angles to the tire centerline, rather than at the conventional angle of 32°–38°. As a result, the sidewalls are much softer than those of a conventional tire, and they flex independently of the tread. The sidewalls alone take the flexing of cornering, which allows more of the tread to stay on the roadway during turns. Conventional tire sidewalls, on the other hand,

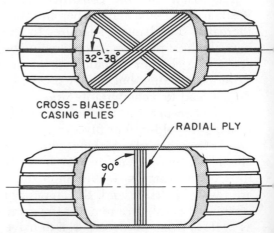

32°-38°

CROSS-BIASED
CASING PLIES

RADIAL PLY

90°

This drawing shows the comparison between the cord angles of conventional and radial-ply tires. Courtesy Dodge Division, Chrysler Corporation.

ROAD CONTACT
CONVENTIONAL

ROAD CONTACT
RADIAL

This illustration shows the difference between a radial-ply tire and a conventional tire during a turn. Note how the softer sidewalls of the radial-ply tire allow more of the tread to remain on the road for better cornering. Courtesy Dodge Division, Chrysler Corporation.

have very little flexibility. In a turn, the whole tire must flex, which distorts the tread and raises part of it off the roadway.

There are some very important things to remember about the use and maintenance of radial-ply tires. Recommended air pressure must be maintained. The flexibility of these tires makes them appear soft even when properly inflated. However, as explained, it is this softness which provides better cornering. Over-inflation takes away this advantage. Also, because of the difference in operating characteristics, radial-ply tires must not be used in combination with conventional tires. Under no circumstances should they be used on the front wheels only; otherwise dangerous oversteer will result.

Because the metric system is used to designate the size of a radial-ply tire, the sizes differ from conventional tire sizes. If a conventional tire size is 6.50 × 13, its radial-ply replacement size would be 175 R14. For a 6.95 × 14, the replacement would also be 175 R14. Because radial-ply tires do not provide as much vehicle ground clearance, they cannot be used on some models without changing the wheel size. Note that in the first example mentioned above, it

This worm's eye view under glass shows how the tread of a conventional tire is distorted by the stiffer sidewalls during a turn at 25 mph. Courtesy B. F. Goodrich Company.

was necessary to go from a 13″ wheel to a 14″ wheel when installing radial-ply tires.

Wide-Oval Tires

The wide-oval tire is nearly two inches wider than a conventional tire. Nylon cord is used in its construction. The extra two-inch width results in a tire with an exceptionally wide cross-section in relation to its height, and a larger "footprint" on the road. The advantages of wide-oval tires are that they

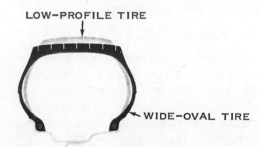

LOW-PROFILE TIRE

WIDE-OVAL TIRE

This superimposed view shows the difference in shape between a low-profile tire and a wide-oval tire. Courtesy Dodge Division, Chrysler Corporation.

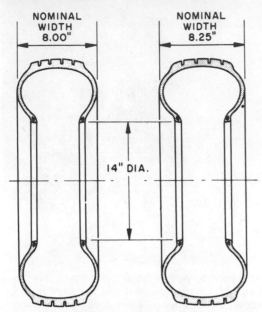

"CONVENTIONAL"

NOMINAL
WIDTH
8.00"

LOW-PROFILE

NOMINAL
WIDTH
8.25"

14" DIA.

Comparison between the dimensions of a conventional and a low-profile tire wheel. Courtesy Dodge Division, Chrysler Corporation.

grip the road better, corner better, and start and stop quicker. Even on wet pavement, they stop in 25% less distance than conventional tires. The extra width gives these tires a low, sporty appearance.

Wide-oval tires carry a new type of designation, such as G70 × 15. The figure 70 means that the profile height is 70% of the width. The 15 indicates the the tire is designed to be mounted on a 15" diameter wheel.

Tire Ratings

To compare different kinds of tires it is necessary to have a rating scale. Tires that are specified for a new vehicle are commonly referred to as original equipment tires. They have been exhaustively tested to make certain they are right for the car. (Obviously, tires that are adequate for one car may be substandard for a higher-performance vehicle.)

More technically, these tires are referred to as 100-line tires, meaning that they meet the vehicle's tire requirements 100%. This is the standard rating scale; replacement tires are measured in terms of this original, 100-line tire.

Replacement tires are manufactured in various grades, some of which are superior to the original equipment tires, and others inferior. A superior tire may be rated 150-line, meaning it has a quality level that is 50% better than the 100-line tire. Inferior tires may be rated as 80-line—a quality level that is 80% of the 100-line tire.

Ply Rating

Two-ply tires are as strong and safe as those with four plies. Some people have found this hard to believe, but it is accepted in the automotive industry.

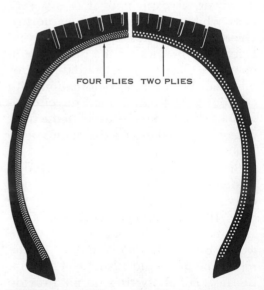

FOUR PLIES   TWO PLIES

This drawing shows a comparison between the cord plies of a two-ply and a four-ply tire. Note that the thicker plies of the two-ply tire equal the thickness of the four-ply tire. Courtesy Dodge Division, Chrysler Corporation.

The term *ply rating* is the industry yardstick for comparing load ratings of tires. A two-ply tire having the same load-bearing capability as a four-ply tire is given a four-ply rating.

It has been conclusively proven, in many miles of test track driving, that a two-ply tire is cooler running and softer riding than a comparable four-ply. In comparing the two types of tires, the two-ply has the following advantages: On the average it (1) runs 4.4% cooler, (2) provides superior riding and handling qualities, (3) produces 1.7% improvement in fuel economy, (4) results in better traction and skid resistance, and (5) is of equivalent strength to a comparable four-ply tire.

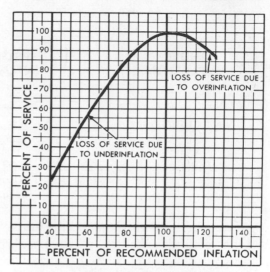

Graph showing the effect of inflation on tire life. Courtesy Lincoln-Mercury Division, Ford Motor Company.

Inflation Pressure

Three factors influence the load rating of tires: the volume of air contained in the tire, the number of plies used in its construction, and the inflation pressure. Increasing any of these factors increases the load rating of a tire and, conversely, decreasing it reduces the load rating.

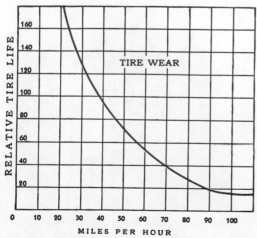

Graph showing the effect of speed on tire life.

Because of the importance of correct inflation, and the fact that this is to be maintained by the owner, the inflation pressure information appears in the owner's manual and is also displayed prominently on a sticker, either on the underside of the deck (trunk) lid or on the face of the left front door latch pillar.

Increasing the pressure in a tire *above its rating*, increases its load-carrying capability *up to a certain point*. Pressures beyond the critical point have only harmful effects. An increase of 6-8 psi *above normal* is about the limit for a two-ply, passenger car tire. A tire which should be inflated to 24 psi for normal service may be inflated to 30-32 psi for higher-than-normal loads, but even higher pressures cannot compensate for excessive overloads.

Higher-than-normal pressures distort the tire and make the tread wear abnormally fast in the center. They reduce the tire's ability to envelop rocks and road

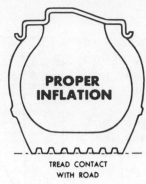

| UNDER-INFLATION | PROPER INFLATION | OVER-INFLATION |

TREAD CONTACT
WITH ROAD

TREAD CONTACT
WITH ROAD

TREAD CONTACT
WITH ROAD

Underinflation causes the shoulders to wear excessively, while overinflation causes the center of the tread to wear excessively. Courtesy Lincoln-Mercury Division, Ford Motor Company.

protrusions, and this increases the probability of bruise damage. Higher pressures also increase shock loadings on the car's suspension system and structure, because a hard tire transmits more road shocks to the wheels.

Tread-Wear Indicators

Since 1968, tread-wear indicators are being built into all standard type tires. These indicators are molded as part of the tread rubber compound. When a normal new tire tread of $^{11}/_{32}''$ wears down to $^{1}/_{16}''$, several smooth spots will appear around the circumference. These smooth areas are to alert the driver to the fact that it is time to replace the tire. Once a tire has worn down to less than $^{1}/_{16}''$ of tread, traction and skid characteristics rapidly approach an unsatisfactory condition.

Service Procedures

Front wheel bearing lubrication is required at 5,000 mile intervals. Self-sealing tubeless tires have reduced, but not eliminated altogether, the need for repairing flat tires. With smaller wheels, higher rotational speeds have resulted in problems of wheel bounce and vibra-

tion. Tire trueing and wheel balancing are required to restore a smooth ride.

Troubleshooting

Incorrect inflation or misalignment causes characteristic wear patterns on front tires. The illustrations will assist in determining the cause. Wheel bounce and vibration can be tested by driving the car on a smooth road and holding the steering wheel lightly to determine whether or not it jiggles.

IRREGULAR DEPRESSIONS

Irregular depressions result from loose front end parts. Courtesy Oldsmobile Division, General Motors Corporation.

Underinflation and excessive camber cause this shoulder wear. Courtesy Plymouth Division, Chrysler Corporation.

Overinflation causes this type of wear. Courtesy The Rubber Manufacturer's Association.

FEATHERED EDGES

Feathered edges are caused by improper toe-in, which causes scuffing. Courtesy Oldsmobile Division, General Motors Corporation.

OUTSIDE OF TREAD WORN

Excessive camber caused this characteristic wear. Courtesy Oldsmobile Division, General Motors Corporation.

527

Exploded view of a front wheel assembly: (1) bearing nut, (2) thrust washer, (3) outer bearing cup, (4) hub, (5) inner bearing cone and rollers, (6) dust seal, (7) wheel cover, (8) grease cap, (9) cotter pin, (10) outer bearing cone and rollers, (11) steering knuckle, (12) inner bearing cup. Courtesy Dodge Division, Chrysler Corporation.

Lubricating and Adjusting a Front Wheel Bearing

The front wheel is mounted on two ball or roller bearings. After the bearings have been removed, either for lubrication or replacement, it is necessary to adjust them so they are not too tight, which would burn them up; or too loose which would cause the outer edges of the rollers to chip.

Tools and Equipment

Front wheel assembly; 10 inch adjustable wrench; diagonal pliers; wheel bearing lubricant; $\frac{1}{8} \times 2$ inch cotter key; jack; hammer; brass punch; screwdriver.

PROCEDURE

1. Jack up the car and remove the wheel cover.

2. Remove the dust cover.

3. Remove the cotter key and nut.

4. Pull the wheel out about 1 inch, and then push it back to expose the outer bearing.

5. Remove the washer and outer bearing assembly.

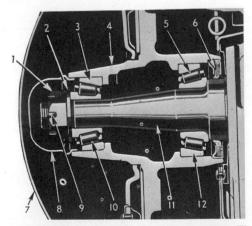

Sectioned view of a front wheel assembly. The numbers are the same as for the previous illustration. Courtesy Dodge Division, Chrysler Corporation.

6. Remove the wheel and drum assembly.

7. Tap out the rear bearing and grease retainer.

8. To replace the bearing race if chipped or galled:

• Punch the old race out by using a brass punch and hammer, tapping evenly around the race.

• Drive the new race in place by tapping evenly around it.

9. Lubricate the bearing with wheel bearing grease. Use no other kind; otherwise, it will melt and work into the brake lining.

10. Place the large bearing into the wheel, taper end in.

11. Install a new grease retainer by tapping evenly all around.

12. Replace the wheel on the spindle.

13. Install the small bearing after lubricating, with the taper end in.

14. Replace the washer and nut.

15. Tighten the nut until the wheel has a slight drag. Loosen the nut one cotter key notch for running clearance, which is about 0.002 inch. Shake the wheel to check for side play; there must be none.

BEARING

Lubricating a wheel bearing. Courtesy Bennett-Feragen.

16. Install a new cotter key to lock the adjusting nut.

17. Install the dust cap.

18. Install the wheel cover.

19. Lower and remove the jack.

Mounting a Tire

The drop-center wheel has two ledges to support the inflated tire and a groove in the center of the rim to hold the compressed beads when the tire is being removed. The safety ridges keep the beads on the ledges in the event of a blowout.

Tools and Equipment

Tire and wheel assembly; two tire irons; tire mallet; bead-breaking machine; tire-testing tank; tubeless tire repair kit.

A loose bearing race causes erratic wheel action.

Tire Repair

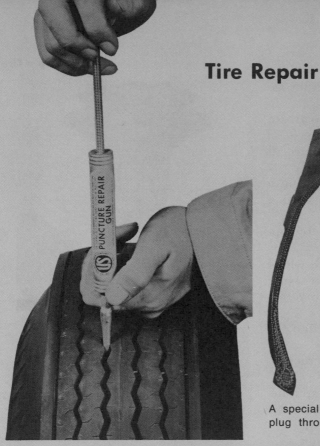

Small holes in tubeless tires can be repaired by injecting a sealing compound. Courtesy United States Rubber Company.

A special needle is used to force the rubber plug through the carcass. Courtesy Goodyear Tire & Rubber Company.

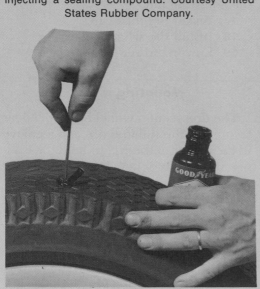

A rubber plug can be used to repair larger holes. Courtesy Goodyear Tire & Rubber Company.

Larger cuts can be repaired by inserting a rubber plug with a head on it. Courtesy The B. F. Goodrich Company.

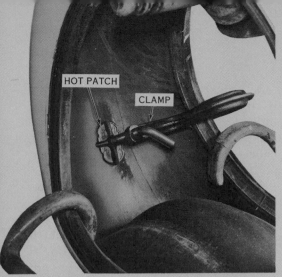

HOT PATCH

CLAMP

A hot patch can be applied from the inside of the tire. Courtesy Oldsmobile Division, General Motors Corporation.

A band is used to seat the beads of a tubeless tire so that it can be inflated. In the absence of such a tool, a rope can be drawn around the tire in order to place pressure on it. Courtesy United States Rubber Company.

These are the steps required to mount a tire properly. Courtesy Rubber Manufacturer's Association.

1 Be certain that rim flanges and bead ledge (especially hump and radius) areas are smooth and clean. Remove any oxidized rubber, dried soap solution, rust, heavy paint, etc., with a wire brush or a file.

2 Lubricate tire beads, rim flanges, and bead ledge areas with a liberal amount of thin vegetable oil soap solution, or with an approved rubber lubricant.

3 Make certain that valve core is inserted in valve stem prior to inflating.

4 Be sure assembly is securely locked down on mounting machine.

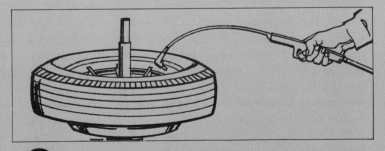

5 Do not allow air-pressure to exceed 40 pounds during the bead seating process. If beads have not seated by the time pressure reaches 40 pounds, deflate the assembly, reposition the tire on the rim, re-lubricate and re-inflate it.

6 Use an extension gauge with clip-on chuck so air-pressure build-up can be closely watched and so that you can stand well back from the assembly during the seating process.

531

1. Remove all air from the tire.

2. Loosen the edge of the beads from the rim. Be careful not to damage the sealing surfaces, otherwise the tire will leak.

3. Compress one portion of the top side of the tire, about ¼ turn from the valve, and drop it into the center groove.

4. Insert a tire iron between the top part of the bead and the rim on the side where the tire is the loosest, and then pry the edge of the tire over the rim. Be careful not to damage the bead and sealing areas.

5. Insert a second tire iron between the bead and rim about 6 inches farther along the rim, and then pry the bead over the rim. Remove the first iron and insert it 6 inches farther on in order to continue the prying process. Repeat the alternate use of tire irons until one side of the tire is over the rim.

6. Remove the other side of the tire by dropping one side of the bead into the well, and then prying the loosest section over the edge of the rim. Use both irons alternately as before. Be careful not to damage the bead and sealing areas.

To Replace the Tire

1. Lubricate the beads with soapy water or a rubber lubricant and start one portion over the rim. Hold this portion in place with your feet while you pry the bead over the rim edge with the tire irons. **Caution:** *Be careful not to injure the sealing areas.*

2. Drop the "worked" portion of the bead into the groove and continue around the rim.

3. Adjust the tire so that the red dot is aligned with the valve stem. The dot indicates the light side of the tire and should be adjusted to line up with the valve stem, which is the heavy part of the wheel, for balance.

4. Pry the second bead of the tire into place as before. Hold the "worked" portion in position with your feet.

5. Inflate the tire. Make sure that it centers itself properly on the rim. It may be necessary to use a band or cord around the tire to press the sealing rings into contact with the rim during inflation. **Caution:** *Release the band before pressure is built up. This is an important safety precaution.*

Balancing a Wheel

Out-of-balance wheels cause wheel tramp and shimmy at high speed. The constant vibration wears out the moving parts of the front end. Wheels must be balanced both statically and dynamically. Static balance is balance at rest, while dynamic balance is balance in motion.

Dynamic balancers are divided into two types: mechanical and electronic. Mechanical balancers contain rotating parts in which weights are shifted until the wheel is in perfect balance. The machine is stopped, and proper weights substituted for the machine weights.

Electronic balancers pick up vibration impulses from the wheel support to trigger a strobe light which is pointed at a rotating wheel, making it appear to stand still so that the operator will know where to place the weight.

In all cases, the wheel must be statically balanced before it can be balanced dynamically.

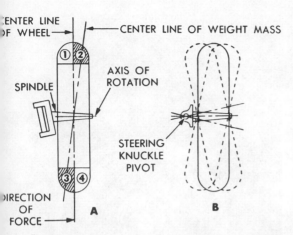

Dynamic unbalance causes sideway thrusts which destroys riding comfort. Courtesy Alemite Division, Stewart-Warner Corporation.

Tools and Equipment

Wheel and tire assembly to be balanced; Alemite wheel balancer; hammer; weights; weight-removing pliers.

PROCEDURE

PRELIMINARY CONSIDERATIONS

① Each front wheel must run true; otherwise, wheel tramp will be evident even after the wheel is balanced. A wheel which has excessive runout should be changed with the spare tire or changed to the rear of the car, which is not quite as sensitive. To check for lateral runout, rest your hand on the spinner motor and hold a piece of chalk about $\frac{1}{8}$ inch from the side of the tire. Turn the wheel by hand and, if the space varies more than $\frac{1}{8}$ inch, the runout is excessive.

② To check for radial runout, place the spinner in front of the tire so that the pulley is about $\frac{1}{8}$ inch from the tread. Turn the wheel slowly by hand; again, if the space varies more than $\frac{1}{8}$ inch, the runout is excessive.

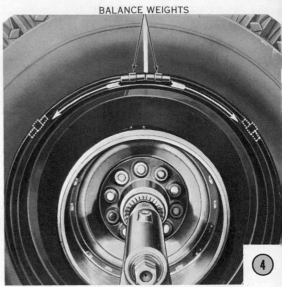

③ The runout can be corrected by equipment that is designed to true up the tread by grinding rubber from the high spots. This operation improves the riding quality of the vehicle greatly. Before starting to work on the tire, remove all old balance weights, stones, and pieces of glass.

Static Balance

④ There are several types of static balancers on the market. Some of them mount the wheel vertically, allowing the heavy part to turn to the bottom. Others mount the wheel horizontally, and the heavy part tilts the wheel on the vertical arbor. It is also possible to correct the static balance with the wheel mounted on the front hub of the car. However, the drag of the lubricant makes this testing method less sensitive than the others. If the grease is removed from the hub and light oil substituted, a good job can be performed in this manner. When you have located the heavy part, install a static balance weight on the rim. If the required weight is over 2 oz., apply two weights, one inside and one outside the rim. In some instances, it will be necessary to substitute two weights for a heavy one and

spread them apart as shown in order to obtain a better static balance. **Caution:** *Securely fasten the weights to keep them from flying off when you spin the wheel for dynamic balance.*

Electronic Equipment—Static Balance

⑤ If the wheels are to be balanced on electronic equipment, jack up the center of the car so that the wheels are about two inches off the floor. Move the balancer opposite the wheel, and aim

the strobe light at the hub cap. Turn the wheel outward about 20° and slide the pickup under the axle. Raise the magnet so that it contacts the lower control arm at a *cleaned surface,* as close to the wheel as possible. Chalk a reference mark on the wheel at any position. Some mechanics use the tire valve as a reference mark.

⑥ Switch the balancer to No. 1 position for standard wheel balancing, or to No. 2 position for supersensitive balancing. Tap the top of the wheel. If the pickup is contacting the front end support properly, the strobe light will flash. Check to be sure that the wheel revolves freely. If the brakes are dragging, back off the adjustment. On vehicles with disc brakes, it is necessary to pry the discs away from the rotor to make the wheel free-spinning. Start the wheel spinning by hand, and snap on the motor switch. Push the spinner pulley against the tire tread to speed up the wheel. When the meter reaches its highest point, pull the spinner away and look quickly at the wheel to notice the position of the reference mark. Stop the wheel by placing the spinner pulley against the tire tread and pulling up on the brake lever. Turn the wheel by hand until the reference mark is in the same position as it appeared when the meter needle showed the highest reading. Now apply a weight to the top of the wheel on the outside of the rim. Use about ½ oz. weight per meter graduation.

⑦ Spin the wheel again and watch the meter. If the needle stays in the green area, the wheel is balanced statically. If not, note the position of the reference mark at the highest meter reading. Stop the wheel. Turn it by

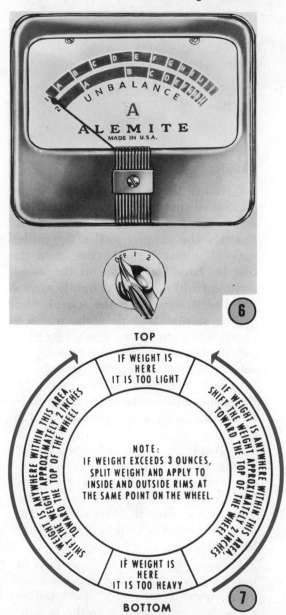

TOP

IF WEIGHT IS HERE IT IS TOO LIGHT

IF WEIGHT IS ANYWHERE WITHIN THIS AREA, SHIFT THE WEIGHT APPROXIMATELY 2 INCHES TOWARD THE TOP OF THE WHEEL

NOTE:
IF WEIGHT EXCEEDS 3 OUNCES, SPLIT WEIGHT AND APPLY TO INSIDE AND OUTSIDE RIMS AT THE SAME POINT ON THE WHEEL.

IF WEIGHT IS ANYWHERE WITHIN THIS AREA, SHIFT THE WEIGHT APPROXIMATELY 2 INCHES TOWARD THE TOP OF THE WHEEL

IF WEIGHT IS HERE IT IS TOO HEAVY

BOTTOM

hand so that the reference mark is at the same position as it appeared to be when the needle was at the highest meter reading. Check the position of the weight, and change or shift it as illustrated. Recheck after each adjustment.

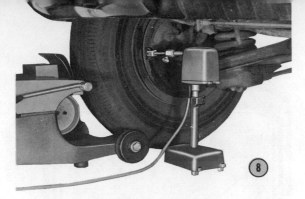

(8)

Electronic Equipment—Dynamic Balance

(8) Turn the wheel out. Place the pickup so that the magnet contacts the front center of the brake backing plate. Position the spinner so that the pulley makes contact with the tire, turn the tire by hand, and snap on the motor switch. Hold the spinner lightly against the tire to speed up the wheel. Shut off the spinner and allow the wheel to coast. When the meter reaches its highest reading, note the position of the reference mark. Stop the wheel, and turn it so that the reference mark is in the same position as it appeared to be when the meter reading was at its highest point.

(9) Apply ½ of the indicated weight to the inside front of the wheel near the pickup magnet. Apply the other half to the outside of the wheel, half way around from the first weight. This second weight is required to maintain static balance.

(10) Spin the wheel again and, if the pointer stays in the green area, the wheel is balanced dynamically. If the pointer rises to the red area, note the position of the reference mark at the highest meter reading. Stop the wheel and turn it to this position. Mark the location of the *outside* weight, and then change or shift both weights as illustrated.

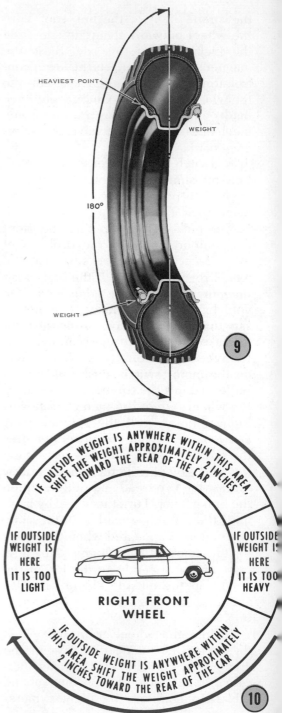

HEAVIEST POINT

WEIGHT

180°

WEIGHT

(9)

IF OUTSIDE WEIGHT IS ANYWHERE WITHIN THIS AREA, SHIFT THE WEIGHT APPROXIMATELY 2 INCHES TOWARD THE REAR OF THE CAR

IF OUTSIDE WEIGHT IS HERE IT IS TOO LIGHT

IF OUTSIDE WEIGHT IS HERE IT IS TOO HEAVY

RIGHT FRONT WHEEL

IF OUTSIDE WEIGHT IS ANYWHERE WITHIN THIS AREA, SHIFT THE WEIGHT APPROXIMATELY 2 INCHES TOWARD THE REAR OF THE CAR

(10)

On-the-Car Mechanical Equipment

① Remove the wheel cover and all of the wheel weights from both sides of the wheel rim. Clean the outside of the wheel rim to assure correct positioning of the mounting ring. Select the proper size mounting ring, and then place it on the wheel rim, with the "V" marker positioned over the tire valve. Secure the ring with the locking levers. **Caution:** *Turn the levers all the way against the ring. Any lever not locked will show red.* **Caution:** *Pull firmly on the mounting ring to be sure that it is locked securely in place.*

② Place the balancing head on the mounting ring, with the fasteners in position over the sockets, and then snap the head in place with a light push. **Caution:** *Pull firmly on the balancing head to be sure that it is securely in place.* **Note:** *A slight outward movement is normal.*

③ Place a jack under the front crossmember, and then raise both wheels about two inches. Roll the wheel spinner up to the tire so that the spinner con-

BALANCING HEAD

②

tacts the tire tread firmly in the center. Spin the wheel, using the foot control. **Note:** *If the wheel does not spin freely, check the wheel bearings, dragging brakes, or the positioning of the spinner.* With the wheel spinning slowly, grasp the *small* knob and move it in or out until you see a continuous red streak appear in the window on the balance head face. Now, spin the wheel to its maximum speed. Grasp the *large* knob and move it in or out until the wheel vibration is reduced. Again grasp the *small* knob and move it in or out until the vibration is further reduced. **Note:** *A firm pull or thrust is important.* Work both knobs until the vibration is eliminated entirely. Stop the wheel by pushing down on the brake handle.

①

③

SCALE

ARROW

④

④ Read the amount of weight needed on the proper scale. **Caution:** *Remember that there is a separate scale for each wheel size.* Use chalk to mark the position of the weight needed, as indicated by the red arrow. Remove the balance head and the mounting ring.

⑤ Place the required weight on the rim at the chalk mark. When the amount of weight to be added is more than three ounces, divide it in half and place half of it on each side of the wheel. **Caution:** *The weights must be placed directly opposite each other as shown.*

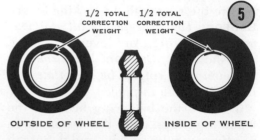

1/2 TOTAL CORRECTION WEIGHT   1/2 TOTAL CORRECTION WEIGHT   ⑤

OUTSIDE OF WHEEL   INSIDE OF WHEEL

This collapsible tire has been developed to fit the small luggage space of sportscars. When the spare tire is needed, it can be inflated easily with the compressed gas cylinder attached to the tire hold-down clamp. Courtesy Ford Division, Ford Motor Company.

CHECK YOUR KNOWLEDGE

1. What are the three basic elements of a tire?
2. How is a tire made?
3. How is a tire tread made?
4. What two problems must be considered when designing a tire tread pattern?
5. What advantage does a wider tire have?
6. What two engineering problems have smaller tires caused?
7. What problems have smaller tires caused the serviceman?
8. Why does a tire wear more at high speeds?
9. What is the advantage of a drop-center rim?
10. What is the advantage of radial-ply tires? Disadvantage?
11. How often is front wheel bearing lubrication required?
12. How can you tell whether the front wheels are out of alignment or the tires incorrectly inflated?
13. How can you tell whether the front wheels are out of balance?

Self-Check Tests

TRUE-FALSE

1. The duty of the tire is to pass all the road shock to the spring where it is absorbed.
2. Tire plies are made of rubber.
3. Rayon cords are used in quality tires because of their strength.
4. Cutting the tire tread into large diamond blocks is effective in minimizing skidding in wet weather.
5. Tubeless tires have intensified tire balance problems.
6. Tire wear increases rapidly with speed.
7. Out-of-balance wheels cause a characteristic tire wear pattern.

MULTIPLE CHOICE

1. Which of the following is *not* part of a tire: a) tube; b) casing; c) ply; d) tread?
2. Which of the following is *not* a part of modern tire design: a) decreased pressure; b) higher rotating speeds; c) wider tires; d) decreased wheel tramp?
3. Front wheel bearing lubrication is required every: a) 1,000 miles; b) 5,000 miles; c) 10,000 miles; d) 25,000 miles.

COMPLETION

1. _____ _____ are made of layers of cord impregnated with rubber.
2. Older passenger car tires contained _____ layers or plies; new ones two.
3. _____ _____ are designed to minimize road noises and, at the same time, present the best traction possible.
4. Slitting the tread into many _____ _____ is effective in minimizing skidding in wet weather.
5. _____ _____ depends on the tire width and weight of the car.
6. A safety ridge around the rim prevents _____ the tire from the wheel in the event of a blowout.

MATCHING

1. Ply	a. Rayon
2. Tread	b. Wheel
3. Drop center	c. Pattern
4. Cord	d. Layer

INDEX

A

Additives, 86
Adhesion, 82
Adsorption-regeneration system (of evaporative
    emission control), 344–346
Afterburners, 340
Air
    cleaners, 161, 162
    guard system, 340
    injection reactor system, 336, 341
    pollution, 327–358
    system tuning and troubleshooting, 355–358
    valve type carburetors, 157–159
Alcohol, 69
Alternators
    general discussion, 257, 258
    repairs, 272–277
Aluminum cylinder block, 36
Ammeter, 230
Amperage, 202
Amperes
    formula, 206
    turns, 203
Anti-foam agents (in oil), 86
Antifreeze, 69
Automatic brake adjusters, 484
Automatic level control system, 469–471
Axle
    flanged, 431
    rear, 420

B

Backfire-suppressor, 341
Backlash, 425
Base (transistor), 260
Batteries
    capacity, 224
    general discussion, 201
Bearings
    general discussion, 127
    insert installation, main, 140, 141
    Plastigage (clearance), 141
    shim stock (clearance), 140
    tri-metal, 127
Bernoulli, Daniel, 151
Blow-by, 57
Boring bar, 133
Brakes
    adjusters, automatic, 484
    bleeding hydraulic, 500, 501
    disc, 485–487
    drum-type, 482

Brakes (*cont'd*)
    minor adjustment, 493, 494
    parking, 492
    power, 487–492
    relining, 501–507
    servicing, 507–510
By-pass
    oil filter, 88
    valve repair, 97

C

Caliper, 507
Camber, 447, 461
Cam-ground piston, 123
Camshaft, 103
Capacitor-discharge ignition, 292
Carbon removal, 55
Carburetor
    Carter BBS & BBD (overhauling), 177–185
    Ford single-barrel (overhauling), 168–177
    general discussion, 150–156
    mixture calibration (graph), 336
    Rochester 4MV/4MC (overhauling), 186–196
Caster
    adjusting, 461
    camber gauge, 458
    general discussion, 447
Charging system, 264
Charts (See *Diagrams*)
Chisels, 19
Circuit
    breaker, 205
    breaker points, 308
    electrical, parallel, series, 202
    testing for open, 246
    testing for shorted, 247
Cleaner Air System (CAS)
    general discussion, 337
    tuning, 349, 350
Climate Combustion Control (CCC), 339
Clutch
    alignment tool, 370
    definition, 361
    operation, 363
    overrunning, 377
    pedal adjustment, 364–366
    rebuilding, 366–370
Cohesion, 82
Coil springs, 467
Collector, 260
Combustion
    chamber design, 335

540